CMP

SECOND INTERNATIONAL CONFERENCE
ON
MANOEUVRING AND CONTROL OF MARINE CRAFT
MCMC, 92

INTERNATIONAL COMMITTEE

LOCAL ORGANISING COMMITTEE

Acknowledgement is made to the Royal National Lifeboat Institution for the use of the figure which appears on the front cover of this book.

Manoeuvring and Control of Marine Craft

Proceedings of the Second International Conference, held in Southampton, UK, 14-17 July 1992.

Editor: P.A. Wilson, Department of Ship Science,
University of Southampton

Computational Mechanics Publications
Southampton Boston

P.A. Wilson
Department of Ship Science
University of Southampton
Highfield
Southampton
UK

British Library Cataloguing-in-Publication Data

A Catalogue record for this book is available
from the British Library

ISBN 1-85312-180-0 Computational Mechanics Publications, Southampton
ISBN 1-56252-109-8 Computational Mechanics Publications, Boston, USA

Library of Congress Catalog Card Number 92-70439

Printed and Bound by Bookcraft Ltd, Bath

PREFACE

The very successful International Conference on Modelling and Control of Marine Craft held in April 1990 at Exeter University caused great interest and required a second conference to be organised to follow up the enthusiasm that had been generated. The second conference, MCMC, 92 was held at the University of Southampton, in July 1992.

The title of the conference, whilst still retaining the same acronym, has changed to encompass Manoeuvring. This was carefully chosen since the essence of the design process is to produce a marine craft, be it ship, submarine, ROV or sail-board that is manoeuvrable and also controllable.

The conference covered three main subject areas;

- Ship Simulation

- Control

- Mathematical Techniques

The papers that have been submitted have come from more than ten countries. There are forty-two papers in the proceedings, and many new and innovative ideas are presented.

The Conference organisers would like to thank all participants to the Conference and in particular the following:

1. To all the authors for meeting the deadlines for submission of the papers.

2. The session chairmen.

3. The following organisations:

> a) The Office of Naval Research (European Office)
> b) Institute of Marine Engineers
> c) M.T.D. Ltd
> d) University of Southampton

4. Dr. M.M.A. Pourzanjani and Dr. G.N. Roberts for providing the first conference and being guiding lights and such great help in organising this second conference.

5. Computational Mechanics Publications for their patience.

P.A. Wilson
Department of Ship Science
University of Southampton

CONTENTS

SECTION 3: DIRECTIONAL CONTROL

SECTION 4: UNCONVENTIONAL VEHICLES

SECTION 5: ADVANCED TECHNIQUES

SECTION 1: DESIGN AND TRAINING

Ship Handling Training Using Physical Simulators

L. Kobyliński, J. Nowicki, L. Balcer
Faculty of Ocean Engineering and Ship Technology, Technical University of Gdańsk, Majakowskiego 11/12, 80-952 Gdańsk-Wrzeszcz, Poland

ABSTRACT

During recent years particular attention has been paid to safe handling of ships. In order to increase safety, a system approach has to be applied, and one element of the system is human efficiency. This could be increased by appropriate training, for which electronic full bridge simulators became operational since late sixties and at present some thirty five simulators are available. Apart from electronic simulators, physical model — handling simulator was developed in Grenoble in 1967 and is still being used for training. A similar idea has been pursued in Iława, Poland since 1980 and is at present a fully developed simulator facility where large manned models are being used for training, described in detail, as well as models used for training and research purposes. More than ten years of experience during which more than 600 masters and pilots were trained showed that there are advantages of using these kinds of simulators for training. The best training would be achieved using both methods of training at the same time, and a unique opportunity of such training is now available with the joint courses held by Maritime School in Kotka, Finland on the new electronic simulator and in Iława on physical models.

INTRODUCTION

During the last years particular attention of ship operators and shipbuilders has been focused on safe handling of ships. Diminishing the risk of collisions falls within the scope of the safe handling. Several serious casualties involving collisions which led to disastrous results stirred public opinion and stimulated maritime administrations to take actions. The International Maritime Organization started development of requirements on maneuverability of ships and eventually recommendation on the provision and the display of maneuvering information on board ships was adopted by the

IMO Assembly in 1987. Work on the preparation of the maneuverability standards for ships is well in progress at IMO, and respective recommendation is expected to be adopted in 1993.

On the other hand, Resolution 17 of the International Conference on Training and Certification of Seafarers, 1978, recommends that before assuming command, masters of large ships or ships of unusual maneuvering characteristics should attend ship handling courses on installations capable of simulating the maneuvering characteristics of ships. This resolution stimulated development of electronic maneuvering simulators, many of them being installed in several countries. Also, a few installations where large self-propelled models of ships are used for maneuvering exercises are available. There were numerous papers on electronic simulators published, but only few refer to physical simulators. The paper presented concentrates on physical simulators.

HUMAN FACTOR IN THE SYSTEM OF SAFETY AGAINST COLLISIONS

Safety against collisions, where under collisions we understand collisions with other ships, grounding and collisions with fixed objects like piers, quays, off-shore installations etc., depends on several factors. Those factors are diagrammatically shown in Fig. 1 which is a version of Venn's diagram, including technical means such as waterways marking, improving steering devices, anticollision radars etc., legislative actions e.g. IMO recommendations, national regulations, separated traffic schemes etc., traffic control systems and finally human factor. The above factors are strongly interconnected, therefore the system approach to the safety is appropriate (see ref. [1]).

Analysis of causes of casualties reveals that human factor plays an important part in most of them. Therefore any improvement of this factor significantly increases the safety, although it is difficult to attach any numerical values to this effect. There are five basic groups of features which influence the action of the man: physical predispositions, psychical predispositions, character, morale and integrity, knowledge and experience and finally training degree [2].

Increasing safety requires improvement of all the above features of the man in control, however the dynamics of the three first features is not great, although it might be influenced by training. Knowledge and experience, and most of all, training degree may be seriously influenced by training. The main purpose of developing electronic and physical simulators is training.

DEVELOPMENT IN THE APPLICATION OF MANOEUVRING SIMULATORS

The application of simulators for improving training in handling various hazardous operations has quite a long history. The use of the maneuvering simulators dates to the mid sixties when an early electronic full bridge simulator became operational in 1966 at Yokohama University and in 1967 a physical maneuvering simulator was built in Port Revel in France. The extensive history of development and present state of art of maneuvering simulators was published by Puglisi [3] in 1987, who provided the list of about 40 full bridge shiphandling simulators being operational at that time. Since then at least 3–4 new simulators have been installed.

Common to all electronic full-bridge simulators is a wheelhouse fitted with controls and equipment identical to the real ship and visual screen out of the bridge windows covering up to 360° view. The appropriate mathematical model represents maneuvering characteristics of the ship and features of the environment. Different mathematical models and different methods of simulation of visual environment were used in simulators.

There are only three ship handling training centres using large manned self propelled models to simulate various maneuvers. The first was already mentioned as installations in Port Revel in France, the others are in Iława in Poland and in Southampton in Britain. Several models are used in each training center, representing various types of ships, built in large scale (1:24 to 1:14). There are attempts to simulate marine environment, port approaches, narrow passages, canals and locks etc., including currents and waves, shallow water and bank effects. Various maneuvering games could be arranged in such an environment.

HISTORICAL DEVELOPMENT OF THE IŁAWA CENTER

Considering the need for training of ship masters on simulators, the Ship Research Institute in Gdańsk decided in 1975 to start construction of the physical simulator installation. At that time plans for a large installation of this kind on the shore of lake Silm near Iława were prepared, however due to lack of resources the construction was not started. Model experiments with free running models aimed at estimation of maneuvering characteristics of ships were, however, performed at the Experimental Center of the Ship Research Institute in Iława on lake Jeziorak since 1958 and a great deal of experience has been gained. Therefore, in 1980 in order to satisfy demands for training ship masters in handling large tankers it was decided to build the large model of a tanker, to mark some exercise areas on lake Jeziorak and to start training. These first attempts were successful and during the following years two further models were constructed, more exercise areas demarcated and training became joint enterprise with Maritime Academy in Gdynia.

In 1986, old plans of building the Ship Handling Center on lake Silm were revived and in mid 1991 the new center became operational with further models added to the fleet of models. Interest in the training was growing and up to the end of 1991 almost 600 masters were trained. The center is now operated by the separate organization acting under the name: The Foundation for Ship's Safety and Marine Environment Protection.

LAY-OUT OF THE CENTER AND WATER AREAS

The present site of the Ship Handling Training and Research Center is on the shore of the lake Silm near Iława-town, which is situated on the railway line Warsaw–Gdańsk, about 120 kilometers from Gdańsk. On the shore site of about 100 x 70 meters there are two hangars for storing 8 large training models and several smaller models for research purposes, slipways, and the building which provides lecture and computer rooms, a room for the porter, lounge and pantry for trainees, electronic workshop and a few guest rooms. There are some other auxiliary facilities including trafo-station, well, battery station and maintenance station. Several piers, quays and docks are also provided, and a simulating harbor.

The choice of the site of the center was made taking into account the following aspects.

1° the extension of water areas should be large enough to enable the performance of maneuvering games with large models,

2° the exercise areas should be sheltered from strong wind,

3° there should be available deep and shallow water areas,

4° the exercise areas should be remote from any traffic.

The Lake Silm meets the above requirements.

Various exercise and testing areas are demarcated on the lake. They are shown in Fig. 3. Four main sections of these areas could be separated.

— Iława port and its approach, consisting of piers and quays forming basins, shallow water area and anchorage,

— main training area including straight line and curvilinear passages, sharp turns, turning areas, bank effect area, ferry terminals, piers, and current maker. All seamarks are fitted with navigation lights for night exercises,

— open sea training areas which include curvilinear paths (captains canal), sea berths, anchorage buoy, SPM and turning circles area,

— testing area for testing maneuvering characteristics of models (turning circle tests, models-zag tests, spiral maneuvers, etc).

Almost all the sections mentioned are covered by the tracking system, with a record of the model track available on the shore station. Fig. 3 shows points where special bearing receivers of this system are installed.

The distances in training areas are in the same linear scale as the models i.e. 1:24 or, partly, 1:16 for the ferry model. The areas are not mock-ups of some real harbors or approaches. They include the set of basic essential maneuvering problems which most frequently require solutions based on a good knowledge of ship maneuvering. Fig. 2 shows an example of the training area (problem of sharp turn on the waterway) superimposed on its prototype full scale area. Fig. 6 shows an example of the port maneuver executed by models during maneuvering course. The lay-out of water areas and the navigation marks construction were prepared taking into account the specifics of the water reservoir and the fact that the master of the model carries only a pilot/visual navigation.

The important, new part of water areas for models is the specially designed artificial canal together with the mock-up lock. The canal is now in the construction stage and it is planned to be completed in 1993. The entrance to it is situated just above 'Ferry Quay' in the east part of 'The water areas for models' — Fig. 3.

MODELS USED FOR TRAINING PURPOSES

When designing a model being used for training as the simulator of the full scale ship, the following aspects have to be taken into account:

— main assignment: training, research or both,

— proper choice of the ship type,

— systems and mechanisms to be simulated,

— model scale,

— systems of control of the model.

The ship types modelled were chosen primarily with the view to fulfilling the STCW 1978 Convention. At the same time they were supposed to be useful for research purposes. Bearing this in mind the following models were constructed: (Fig. 5).

1   145.000 tdw tanker
2   52.000 tdw bulk carrier
3   21.000 tdw ro-ro vessel
4   25.000 gt twinsrew carpassenger ferry

Linear scale of the first three models is 1:24, that of the ferry model is 1:16. The choice of the scale poses some difficulties because the size of the model has to be sufficiently large in order to provide space for two to three people. On the other hand technical possibilities and cost effectiveness have to be taken into account.

The models are handled most frequently by two crew men. One person plays the part of master by giving adequate orders and the other person plays the part of helmsmen and engineer, (Fig. 4). Operational parameters of the following systems and equipment are simulated on the models:

— propeller, its thrust and change of revolution in time and pitch control parameters for both propellers in ferry model,

— rudder, rudder angle and time of rudder movement hard to port to hard to starboard according to rudder angular velocity,

— thrusters or tugs and their trust,

— windlasses, pulling force, anchor, anchor chain hauling speed, anchor chain length,

— ship navigation lights system for training and research activities at night,

— sensors and recording system for research measurements,

— necessary navigation devices.

The main model equipment is shown Fig. 7. The parts of the models situated above the water surface, especially superstructures, are not strictly the same as on the real ship, but their dimensions, typical shape and distribution of areas are modelled to scale adequately. The ferry model has only framework construction instead of full superstructure in order to diminish the effect of wind, which is not scaled down otherwise. This construction can be filled in by flat plates. This the way wind sensitivity of the ferry model is regulated.

The basic modeling laws for models and consequently the majority of their mechanisms are determined by Froude law of similitude which gives the known relations for representation of forces, times and speeds. Naturally some "scale effect" is observed in the models behavior, but because of the rather considerable measurements of the model it is not very large.

IDEAS BEHIND THE TRAINING PROGRAMS

The analysis of casualties on the sea was the starting point for the development of the training program. As is well known, in about 1/3 of all ship collisions, the casualties involved human error. The same amount of

CRG casualties is attributed to the poor controllability of ships. The poor controllability firstly influences the following maneuvers:

1. maneuvers executed in wind and current,

2. maneuvers in which slowing down or stopping of a ship is required,

3. maneuvers in which fast sheering or sharp turning is required,

4. maneuvers executed in restricted water or in the proximity of other ships.

With these four items as the background, the program of the practical training, and the configuration of exercise area were elaborated. The vital influence of a wind maneuvering motion, stressed in many papers, is present because not all exercise areas are isolated from the action of a wind. However, in most places the wind velocity is slowed down by the configuration of shores or by specially erected protecting screens.

The second important natural factor is a current which plays an important part in maneuver in harbours situated on rivers. A transverse current also poses additional difficulties for ships sailing in narrow waterways. The current generator used in our Training Center satisfies all demands for practical training. The main goal of training in shiphandling in our Training Center is to familiarize with maneuvering characteristics of ships whose behaviour is qualified as unusual. The program of practical training is prepared in such a manner that as time elapses, the level of difficulty of exercises will increase.

The practical shiphandling training starts with standard maneuvering testes on "open sea" (unrestricted area), during which the participant will have the possibility to verify the maneuvering characteristics of a given type of ship. At the same time the adaptation of participants to the model scale takes place.

Then they execute a set of rescue maneuvers, after which they begin to solve the problem of navigation on leading beacons and lights.

The next day is dedicated to problems related with approaches to the ports. During the following four days the participants practice harbour maneuver, maneuver in the proximity of a bank wall and in other types of restricted waters. They see in practice the hydrodynamic interaction between ships meeting and passing in narrow waterways, as well as ship-to-ship maneuver under way. They try also to execute different maneuvers using anchors.

An ocean towing of a ship by ship completes the training program. The participants are not forced to execute properly all maneuvers included in the program. To some extent the execution of maneuvers depends on personal skill, and some people need more time to adapt to specific model conditions. More important is to appreciate all the problems of a given maneuver in given conditions. The ship models illustrate the immediate consequences of given orders.

Of course, each maneuver can be repeated a number of times, and instructors prompt the participants towards the correct decision, if necessary.

APPRAISAL OF THE PHYSICAL SIMULATORS

The advantages and disadvantages of electronic and physical simulators are well known and are fully listed in the brochure provided by Port Revel, therefore no attempt is made to repeat them again. The point, however, must be stressed, that any comparison of these two types of simulation technique is in the authors' opinion inappropriate. Each method meets other requirements and provides different possibilities. More than ten years of experience and opinions of masters, many of them having completed courses on both electronic and physical simulators, leads to the conclusion that combination of both methods is most desirable. That is why an agreement was reached with Kotka Maritime College (Finland), where the new electronic full-bridge simulator was installed, to organize combined two-week courses in Kotka and in Iława using both methods. This will provide a unique opportunity to take advantage of the best features of electronic simulator and of maneuvering exercises on models.

In the program of practical training on ship models the most important parts are maneuvers in restricted water areas, in entrances to port basins and in the presence of other ships, piers and quays and current and other maneuvers where complex hydrodynamic phenomena occur.

In such cases the important factor is that the trainee visualizes the real danger of the particular situation. The navigation aids (ARPA, positioning system) are not of great value in such cases and are rather replaced by personal estimation of the situation. A 360° vision from the bridge of the model is very useful in such situations. In addition, the masters eyes are situated almost at the same level as on the real ship. As a result, a very realistic perspective is obtained which makes if possible the proper execution of all delicate maneuvers like berthing and overtaking in canals and other narrow waterways.

Many other special maneuvers like anchoring, ocean towing or ship to ship maneuvers are also possible owing to realistic representation of hydrodynamic forces involved.

The general opinion of trainees is that training using models is very efficient for pilots and masters who operate up to the phase of berthing. They feel that for them the anticipation of ship behavior in different situations under action of hydrodynamic and aerodynamic forces is very important, in order to undertake proper action. The whole atmosphere and psychological reaction when the master is at the controls on the bridge of the model is correctly simulated, which makes the use of models a very efficient method in training.

REFERENCES

1. Kobyliński, L. 'Safety against capsizing.' *Schiffbauforschung,* Sonderheft, 1987, Bd1.

2. Balcer, L., Kobyliński, L. 'Human aspects of ship maneuverability.' *IMAEM '87 IV Congress.* 25–30 May 1987, Varna, Bulgaria.

3. Puglisi, J.J. 'History and future development in the application of marine simulators.' *MARSIM '87, Proceedings,* Trondheim, p. 5–29

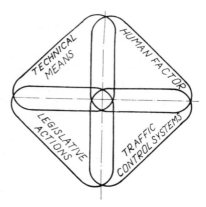

Figure 1: Diagram of safety against collisions factors.

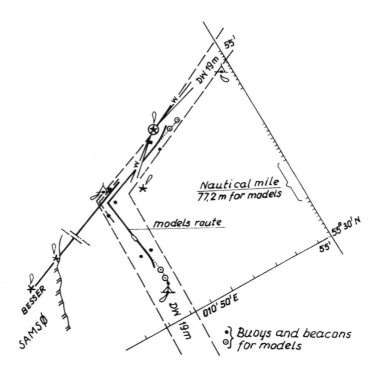

Figure 2: Comparison of the training route for the models with a real route for ships.

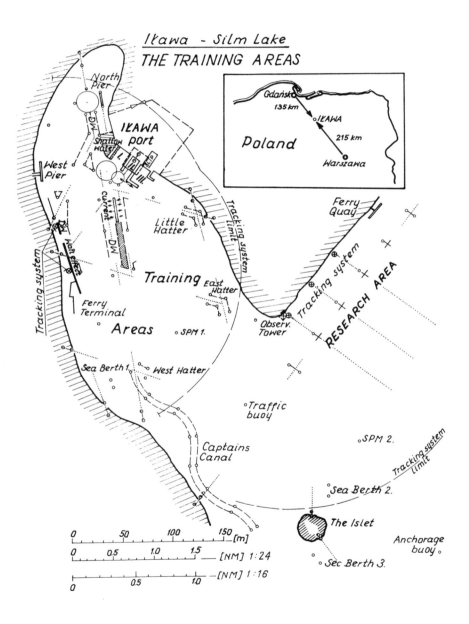

Figure 3: The water areas for models.

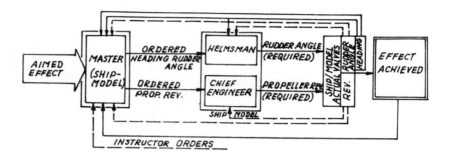

Figure 4: Control system for ship and model.

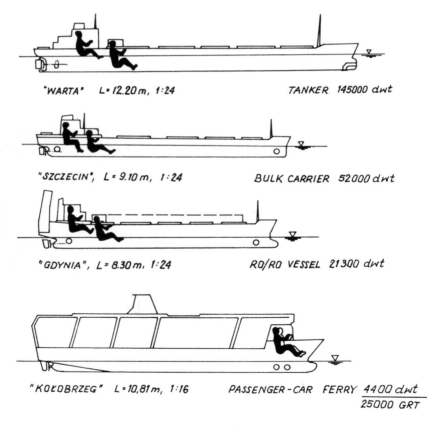

Figure 5: The training models.

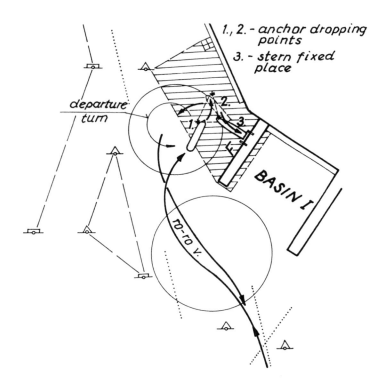

Figure 6: Model-ship manoeuver in Iława Port, (example of instruction for trainees).

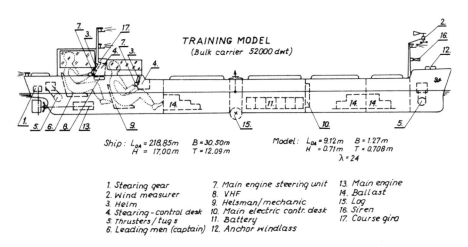

Figure 7: Main model equipment.

Aiding Port Design Using Ship Manoeuvring Computer Simulation

I.J. Lowry

MacGregor-Navire Transmarine Consultants Ltd, 86/90 Front Street, Whitley Bay, Tyne and Wear NE25 8DN, UK

ABSTRACT

The design of a port has to reflect the limitations of a vessel's piloted controllability. If the port imposes limitations on a vessel's controllability then the probability of a maritime collision, ramming or grounding occurring must increase. Surface ship manoeuvring mathematical models have steadily increased in sophistication in recent years, becoming more accurate over wider ranges of application as more efficient algorithms are combined with faster digital computers. In common with other fields of engineering, ship simulation is application orientated and should not be studied in isolation of its end usage. This paper focuses on the applicability of ship manoeuvring computer simulation in aiding port design. A case study demonstrates the effectiveness of simulation techniques to solve critical port design problems where proposals could impinge upon the ships' dynamic operations.

INTRODUCTION

Advances in digital computers have brought computers a new era of applicability. Within the maritime industry, ship manoeuvring computer simulation can aid the port designer to determine the optimal waterway configuration and/or port layout, where a vessel's imposed controllability can be of critical importance for a proposed design.

Statistical data attributes a considerable percentage of maritime casualties to poor ship controllability. In 1981, Miller et al [1] analysed the collisions, rammings and groundings (CRGs) of 835 tankers greater than 10 000 grt in US navigable waters. They concluded that one third of these casualties were attributed to poor ship controllability. In the International Chamber of Shipping statistics [2], 75 per cent of marine CRGs occur in restricted waters. Restricted waters place the greatest demands on the vessel/mariner to manoeuvre safely since a number of externalities have to be taken into consideration.

The concept of ship controllability is important when discussing port designs which impose limitations on a vessel's manoeuvring performance. Ship controllability is elegantly defined by Saunders [3] as *'an expression of the certainty and dependability with which a desired manoeuvre can be executed'.* By definition ship controllability is dichotomous in nature; adequate control is not only constrained by the dynamics of the vessel itself but also the effectiveness of the mariner in initiating safe control.

Piloted controllability is defined as the relative ability of a piloted vessel to change position and orientation at desired rates [4]. Under this definition the piloted vessel is considered to be under the control of a skilled shiphandler.

In terms of manoeuvrability and controllability, port configuration is an important parameter. In critical areas port designers must develop an appreciation of a vessel's likely controllability. In open waters a vessel's controllability is unhindered. When externalties such as channel depth and alignment; current streams and so on are introduced the term imposed controllability is used since limitations on the vessel's dynamic performance are imposed by the local environment.

The use of computer simulation techniques to ascertain vessel performance in a port environment has been investigated. The SNAME H-10 panel developed the "ABC Design Harbour" to assess simulation in relation to ship control [4]. Eda et al [5] performed a simulation study of a vessel's behaviour during its transit through Staten/Bayonne Island straits, comparing the results with the actual vessel's passage. The results produced were comparable. Khattab [6] performed an analysis on the safe wind limit for a ferry to berth safely without tug assistance. This study involved the simulation of a ferry under various environmental conditions. This study also provided the master with additional experience in the handling of this vessel within the proposed port design/modifications.

The simulation methodology discussed within varies from other methods since a modular ship manoeuvring model is introduced into the simulator. This model is different in structure to the traditional hydrodynamic derivative approach to ship modelling. A modular model is used to enable quick formulation from known quantitative sub-system input/outputs. This approach is important during the validation stages where the pilot's qualitative comments on an aspect of the model's behaviour can be interpreted into a quantitative form allowing the model to be modified quickly and effectively.

This paper focuses on a case study which highlights the importance and effectiveness of ship manoeuvring simulation in ascertaining the imposed controllability placed on four vessels whilst trying to navigate a proposed breakwater development. An appreciation of the vessel's controllability is conveyed to the port designer through the pilot and the hydrodynamist, thereby bringing together professionals from different disciplines to identify and thereafter, rectify possible design faults that impinge on the vessel's safe control.

PORT OPERATIONAL CONSIDERATIONS

In terms of ship manoeuvrability and controllability, port configuration is an important parameter. The introduction of the human factor to the ship control system has led researchers to make distinctions between the vessel's controllability without human involvement, known as inherent controllability and with human involvement, referred to as piloted controllability.

The difference between a vessel's inherent manoeuvring characteristics and piloted controllability is defined by Landsburg et al [7] as the 'piloting margin'. Under most conditions the SNAME H-10 Panel on Ship Controllability postulate that a shiphandler will demand less controllability from a vessel than it inherently possesses. Of more interest to port designers is the manoeuvring margin defined by SNAME [4] as the difference between the performance of a piloted vessel and its manoeuvring constraints. In restricted waters the manoeuvring margin diminishes with reductions in the amount of water available. A vessel, in manoeuvring along a channel, develops a swept path as she alters course along that channel. For safe control the manoeuvring margin must be positive. Hence, channel width must be greater that the vessel's swept path. The swept path is mathematically defined by Cook [8] as;

$$\text{Swept Path} = L^2 + B^2 \, \text{Sin}[\text{atan}(B/L) + a]$$

where;

B = Vessel's Beam
L = Vessel's Length
a = $Xa + 2Sa$
Xa = Mean observed drift angle
Sa = Standard deviation of sample drift angles.

The mean observed drift angle of any vessel type varies according to the depth of underkeel clearance and loading conditions. A vessel proceeding along a channel will not necessarily produce a linear track, indeed researchers [8-11] have demonstrated that ship manoeuvring control in channels produces an oscillatory track because of the frequent application of small amounts of helm to check yaw and maintain a steady course. In applying statistical techniques to this deviation off track, port designers have stipulated minimum channel widths for vessels in the range 4-10 beam widths as presented in table 1 [11].

The port/waterways configuration must also depend upon local marine geography, buoy positioning and the prevailing environmental conditions. In Atkins and Bertsche [12] the importance of the vessel's manoeuvring characteristics with respect to optimal port/waterway design is highlighted since a pilot under varying environmental conditions may steer his vessel at a drift angle to maintain a steady course.

Table 1: Differences in recommended channel widths

Researcher	Recommended Width	Remarks
PIANC 2nd IOTC	4B	for oil tankers
PIANC Working Group	5B	general criterion
Maquet	10B 8-9B	Probability Simulation
Wagenningen Simulator	8B	Human Pilot Simulation
EASAMS Ltd	6-7.5B	Maximum Deviation Method
Japanese General Guidelines	0.5L 3-6B	Guidelines

Whilst approaching the confined waters of a berth/port, the vessel has to reduce speed. With constant environmental forces and reduced controlled ship forces (rudder, hull) the manoeuvring margin has begun diminishing. The port designer must allow for an additional margin of safety. Augmentation of the manoeuvring margin is commonly observed in any port with the use of tugs and bow/stern thrusters to maintain control.

Designing channels for safe navigation must reflect the needs of the vessel for safe passage. Channel width is a function of; vessels' beams, envisaged swept paths, bank suction, vessel interaction and dredging constraints. Channel depth is related to the above factors and the phenomena of squat. With changes in a vessel's speed and underkeel clearance the rate of squat or sinkage can seriously affect a vessel's handling characteristics. The term bank suction is basically squat in a lateral form, as a vessel approaches the bank, an asymmetric flow is generated around the hull which creates a turning moment increasing in intensity as the proximity of the bank draws closer. These additional turning moments are counteracted by the helmsman. However, on occasion these moments have become so large that vessel control is lost. A definitive criterion for the safe distance off a bank along a channel would be difficult to formulate due to a number of externalities, such as; bank gradient, the channel's alignment, the controllability of vessels using the channels (further complications may exist if vessels have to pass in the channel). Squat is well documented in the literature and is one of the prime determinants of channel dimensions. In summary squat increases;

  o with decreasing under keel clearance,
  o as channels become more restrictive,

Squat varies indirectly with

- ship length,
- hull form, greater for a tanker than finer form ships
- the square of the vessel's forward speed.

The ability of vessels to turn and stop within the port or waterway environment is of paramount importance. This problem has been highlighted in the Suez Canal [13] where 3rd generation container vessels have run aground on various bends in the canal. The controllability constraints imposed on these vessels by the canal were greater than the allowable manoeuvring margin at those bends.

PORT DESIGN SIMULATION

The structure of the port design simulator is given in figure 1. The key parameters which need to interact to produce meaningful results are the;

- Type of ship controller (real or fast time)
- Ship manoeuvring mathematical model
- Port/waterway database
- Simulation scenario

The integration of these validated parameters can be employed to assist in the design and the planning of waterways, ports and oil terminals.

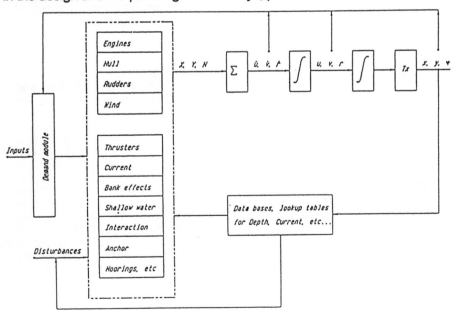

Figure 1: Schematic of a port design simulator

SHIP MANOEUVRING MATHEMATICAL MODELLING

The development of mathematical modelling techniques in the evaluation of a ship's manoeuvring characteristic has gained greater impetus in recent years with the technological advances in digital computers. The mathematical model adopted for this study was the McCallum direct force model [14]. This model considers the forces and moments generated to be analogous to the pressure lift and drag situation when fluid flow is passed across a foil. The angle of attack is substituted for the vessel's drift angle. This model is best suited to studies of this nature where, in terms of assessing port design with respect to vessel dynamics, a vessel is controllable if the controlled forces generated by the vessel are greater than the uncontrolled hydrodynamic and effector forces acting on the vessel. The force model approach allows direct force and moment comparisons to be made without the added complications of nondimensionalisation as with the traditional hydrodynamic derivative approach to ship modelling.

The ship is considered to have three degrees of freedom; surge, sway and yaw. The application of a further 3 degrees of freedom to cater for heave, pitch and roll is regarded as cosmetic since it is assumed that the vessel is operating in calm waters.

The conventional Newtonian based equations of motion for a vessel operating with 3 degrees of freedom, developed by Davison and Schiff [15] and modified by Nomoto [16], to take account of the added virtual mass and inertia phenomena, are the fundamental equations of this model. The model is modular in structure to take account of the sub-systems which operate within the overall manoeuvring function of the vessel. The model is developed and discussed in McCallum [14] and enhanced further in Pourzanjani [17,18] and Lowry [19].

The forces in the X (fore-aft direction) and Y (athwartship) direction and moment N about the yaw axis are;

o Surge equation : $m_1 \dot{u} + m_2 vr$ = $X = X_h + X_r + X_p + X_e$
o Sway equation : $m_2 \dot{v} - m_1 ur$ = $Y = Y_h + Y_r + Y_p + Y_e$
o Yaw equation : $I_z \dot{r}$ = $N = N_h + N_r + N_p + N_e$

Where u and v are the surge and sway velocities respectively, I_z is the moment of inertia about the yaw axis and r is the yaw rate. The subscripts h,r,p and e represent the hull, rudder, propeller and external forces respectively. The ship's mass in the surge and sway directions are denoted m_1 and m_2 respectively. Given the fundamental structure of the model there are 43 model coefficients to be evaluated and integrated into the model before a representative model of the vessel's manoeuvring dynamics can be achieved. Once the coefficients have been evaluated the model is tested to ensure validity across the spectrum of manoeuvring regimes (see table 2).

Table 2: Ship manoeuvring regimes

Regime	Ship motion	Engine command
Manoeuvring forward	Ahead	Ahead
Stopping	Ahead	Astern
Backing	Astern	Astern
Checking sternway	Astern	Ahead

Validation of the model structure is of paramount importance to the whole concept of aiding port design through ship manoeuvring simulation. In port design studies, one method adopted, as with the case study presented, is to validate the models with pilots from the port in question or pilots with experience with the ship type that has been modelled. This approach ensures the vessel is tested through all regimes by experienced mariners who can make qualitative assessments on the model's performance. Using existing ship trials data to perform this task is difficult since a majority of manoeuvring data is restricted to full and half ahead turns and a crash stop. In ship controllability terms this data is subjective since it is the lower speed transient response of the ship to the helm that is of utmost importance.   When the model is validated to an acceptable standard, the model is introduced to the port database for its validation procedure.

PORT DATABASE
The port or waterway configuration is modelled via the port database. This database is managed to contain the following data;

    o   Water depths
    o   Tide streams
    o   Civil structure coordinates
    o   Buoy/navigational aids position

The adopted method of holding port data gives the spatial and, if necessary temporal, relationships of the current and depth over the whole port/waterway area.

The effect of the current on the dynamics of the vessel is calculated in the ship model such that the current vector velocities are read off for each iteration according to the relative position of the ship's bow and stern. It is essential that the spatial relationships of the currents are produced in this manner, so that for example, if the bow enters a lock or an indent where there is little current, the current acting on the stern will begin to swing the vessel as would be expected.

The presence of shallow water is equally vital as this influences the vessel's behaviour. Throughout the run the mariner can determine his underkeel clearance at the bow and stern to ascertain any affects on his perceived ship control strategy. The Doppler log and echo sounder instrumentation indicate the effects of current and depth to the user. The bottom stabilised Doppler log, by indicating the surge and sway velocities relative to the ground, is particularly useful in berthing manoeuvres.

The wind parameter is input at the start of each run. The problem of windage on high sided vessels is a major limitation to their controllability and must therefore be reflected in a sophisticated wind model. The wind model adopted calculates the lift and drag effects of the relative wind on the ship. The "sailing" effect of ships can thus be demonstrated, which is of particular interest for failure studies. The port database must be constructed with valid data. The siting of breakwaters, buoys and modified structures is easily achieved by alteration of the relative x-y coordinates.

SIMULATION SCENARIO

The simulation scenario is based upon a selection of runs to be carried out which concentrate on the worst case. A perceived worst case is determined from elementary examination of the manoeuvring situation and the environmental data. A matrix of runs around this worst case is performed. This technique enables an examination of a number of variables to be carried out with a minimum number of runs, as those situations where there is no perceived difficulty in manoeuvring, such as zero wind condition, receive little attention.

AN ORIGINAL PORT DESIGN CASE STUDY USING SHIP SIMULATION

This case study is presented to demonstrate that a vessel's controllability could be investigated at the port concept design stage. This study brought together practising maritime pilots, hydrodynamists and consulting civil engineers to ascertain the siting of an additional breakwater at an existing port. The aim of this study was to find a compromise to the limitations that a cost effective breakwater design would impose on the controllability of vessels frequently using the existing port.

THE DESIGN BRIEF

The civil engineers were faced with the problem of designing a breakwater into a 5 knot cross current that would be cost effective, protect the existing port, satisfy specification requirements and not restrict vessel movements through the port.

THE SHIPS TO USE THE PORT

This problem was solved using real-time simulation techniques. Initially, four vessels that regularly visited the port and reflected the typical sizes of vessels using the port were modelled. The validation procedure was completed by two pilots from the port, to a high degree of dynamic fidelity. The four vessels used in the study are given as;

o   FERRY1: 130m x 22.6m x 5.1m, Rudders > 2, Screw > 2 x CPP, Bow Thruster

o   FERRY2: 108m x 20.4m x 4.9m, Rudders > 1, Screw > 2 x CPP, Bow Thruster

o   LPG: 71m x 12.8m x 5.4m, Rudders > 1, Screw > 1 x CPP, Bow Thruster

o   CARGO: 90m x 15.0m x 5.0m, Rudders > 1, Screw > 1 x rhp, Bow Thruster

The problems posed are quite interesting, the design of the breakwaters has to be economically viable, satisfying the needs of the port and the dynamics of the vessels that have been using the port or are expected to use the port.

Another area of validation apart from the ships' models is the port database. High fidelity representation of currents and depth are important if the results of the study are to be meaningful to the civil engineers and alike.

PORT CURRENTS AND DEPTHS
Strong currents can have a detrimental effect on a vessel's controllability. In confined waters these effects are more noticeable due to the imposed controllability limitations. The port extension is to be constructed into a current stream which is almost perpendicular to the breakwater entrance, reaching a speed of 5 knots (see figure 2). The current velocity field was supplied by the civil engineers following a physical model study. The depth across the database was deep and modelled accordingly.

The currents in this study relative to the size of the vessels that use the port are quite strong. As the vessel approaches the port entrance there will be an instance where the vessel's bow is protected from the current stream by the proposed breakwater whilst the stern is not. A turning moment will develop influencing the vessel's handling characteristics.

WIND
For this study the worst case wind was given as a 30 knots South Easterly (Force 7). The LPG and cargo vessels had aft accommodation whereas the ferries had high superstructure decks. All vessels during the validation procedure had no problem navigating the port entrance in slack water with no wind.

INITIALLY PROPOSED DESIGN - "A"
The initially proposed design for the breakwater, after analysis of the physical model results, is denoted "A" (see figure 2). This design was the most cost effective, based upon protection of the inner port to local wave action and currents. The inner breakwater spur is virtually perpendicular to the outer breakwater extension which is quite short. Initial interpretation of the proposed design suggests that the entrance is quite tight, requiring all vessels to make a 90 degree turn to starboard once they are just inside the breakwater.

SIMULATION RESULTS - DESIGN "A"   The four vessels are presented
as approaching the port under a 30 knot South Easterly wind and a 5 knot current in the direction indicated.

FERRY1 and FERRY2 were successful in negotiating the breakwater entrance. The twin CPP/twin rudder arrangement of FERRY1 was easier to control than FERRY2 in these adverse conditions resulting in a greater margin of safety through the port. FERRY1 had greater shaft separation than FERRY2.

The pilots controlling LPG and CARGO were unable to control the vessels; the LPG vessel's bow thruster was found ineffective against the

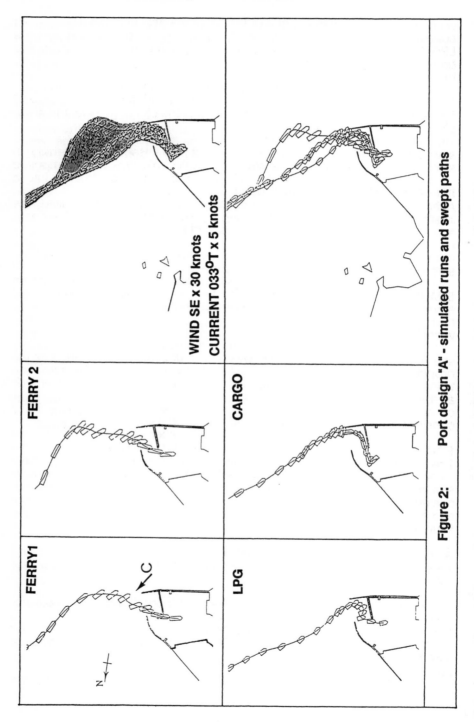

FERRY 2

FERRY1

CARGO

LPG

WIND SE x 30 knots
CURRENT 033°T x 5 knots

Figure 2: Port design "A" – simulated runs and swept paths

wind as the pilot tried to turn the vessel to starboard, she drifted downwind colliding with the breakwater spur. The CARGO, 19 metres longer than LPG, found great difficulty in negotiating the acute starboard turn inside the breakwater mouth where the vessel has to reduce speed and use its bow thruster to bring her bow to wind.

The swept paths of the vessels (excluding FERRY2) are presented in figure 2. The shaded area given in the design elucidates the point that the pilots attempted various control strategies to safely navigate all the vessels into the port. The basic problem with the initial design is the acute starboard turn and the lack of protection from the current stream as the ship reduces speed to make the turn.

INTERMEDIATE PORT DESIGN - "B"
After consultation between the civil engineers and the port pilots an intermediate design was proposed and implemented on the simulator. The acute starboard turn was to be reduced by setting the inner spur back at an angle giving the illusion of a wider port entrance. To protect the vessel from the current during the final approach phase the breakwater arm was extended as given in figure 3.

SIMULATION RESULTS - DESIGN "B"
The widening of the port entrance gave the pilots an easier approach. The swept path of the vessels is narrower which symbolises a direct controlling strategy for all of the vessels. Three of the four vessels were successful in reaching the inner port. The LPG vessel is relatively small compared with the ferries, however, she exhibits a classic manoeuvring quality with right handed CPP propellers, that in going astern the stern swings to starboard. The LPG has to lose way before making the turn which results in the bow canting to port as the astern movement is applied which, when coupled with the bow cant caused by the current turning moment at the mouth, results in a considerable swing to port that the bow thruster is unable to counteract.

FINAL PORT DESIGN - "C"
The final port design was a compromise of both designs "A" and "B". The inner spur remained unchanged. The outer breakwater arm was straightened and extended further into the seaway than initially proposed in design "A". These changes were necessary to reduce cost over design "B" and to protect the port from wave action from an easterly direction (see figure 4).

SIMULATION RESULTS - DESIGN "C"
All the vessels, except the LPG, were successful in navigating the proposed design. LPG is known to the pilots as possessing poor manoeuvring characteristics and is regarded by them as being underpowered. The subject of poor ship controllability is not proportional to ship size. In this case study the LPG vessel was the smallest vessel.

The swept path for this port design shows a greater increase in area than for design "B", but less than "A"; a result expected in compromising between designs.

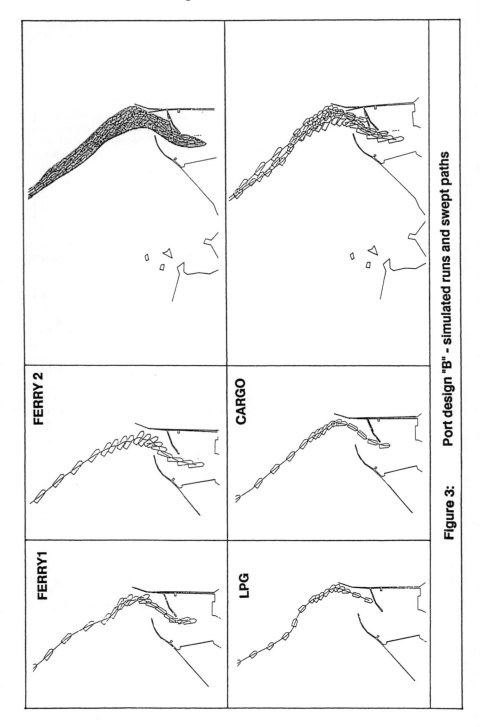

Figure 3: Port design "B" - simulated runs and swept paths

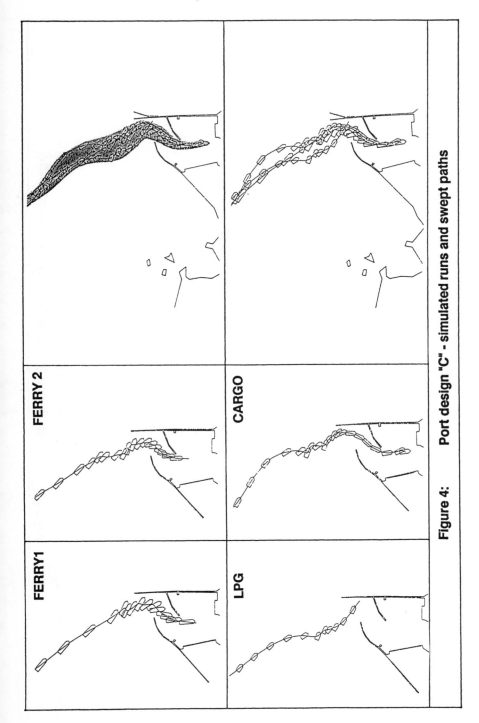

Figure 4:   Port design "C" - simulated runs and swept paths

CONCLUSIONS

This paper presents a method of assessing proposed port designs through real time ship simulation techniques. The methodology described is applicable to any port design problem. The effective use of professionals from differing fields to ascertain an optimal port design is fundamental to the whole concept of aiding port design using computer simulation techniques.

This case study presents an appreciation of the manoeuvring problems vessels can face in navigating confined waters requiring a high degree of vessel control. Ship manoeuvring studies can be used to assess effectively;

       o   Optimal Channel Alignments
       o   Primary Dredging Areas
       o   Buoy/Navigational Mark Positioning
       o   The Siting of Civil Structures

Additionally, if pilots from the port in question are used to perform the simulated runs, then they, themselves have begun training in controlling vessels, in complete safety, within the proposed development.

The approach adopted within to solve the problem posed to the port designers proved economically viable in terms of a percentage of total cost of constructing breakwater "C" as opposed to a costly palliative approach should breakwater "A" have been constructed.

With further developments in simulation technology inevitable, the use of ship manoeuvring models to aid the port designer will be enhanced further. The optimal approach for port design studies in critical areas of imposed controllability limitations must, as adopted within, take a multi-disciplinary format bringing together professionals from the fields of port design, ship handling and ship hydrodynamics.

ACKNOWLEDGEMENTS

I would like to express my gratitude to Messrs I.R. McCallum and R Body of Maritime Dynamics Ltd, the pilots who took part in this study and the Department of Maritime Studies, University of Wales College of Cardiff.

REFERENCES

1. Miller E, Ankudinov V, et al, 'Evaluation of Concepts for Improved Controllability of Tank Vessels', *Marine Technology*, Vol 18, No.4, pp 365-381, October 1981.

2. International Chamber of Shipping, 'Marine Casualty Report Scheme', Report I-50, London, October 1972.

3. Saunders H.F, *Hydrodynamics in Ship Design*, Vol II, SNAME, New York, 1957.

4. Sname H-10 Panel, 'Proposed Procedures for Determining Ship Controllability Requirements and Capabilities', *First Ship Technology and Research (STAR) Symposium*, Washington D.C, August 26-29, 1975.

5. Eda H, Falls R, Walden D, 'Ship Manoeuvring Safety Studies', *SNAME*, Vol 87, pp 229-250, 1979.

6. Khattab O, 'Ship Handling in Harbours Using Real Time Simulation', *Second International Conference on Ship Manoeuvrability and Control*, London, May 1987.

7. Landsburg A.C, Card J.C, et al, 'Design and Verification for Adequate Ship Manoeuvrability', *SNAME*, Vol 91, pp 351-401, 1983.

8. Cook R.C, 'Evaluation of Deep Draught Coastal Port Designs', CAORF, Kings Point, New York, no date.

9. Witt F.G.J, 'Analysis of Simulated Manoeuvres', *Proceedings 2nd International Conference on Marine Simulation*, MARSIM'81, Kings Point, New York, 1-5 June, 1981.

10. Hwang W.Y, 'The Validation of a Navigator Model for Use in Computer Aided Channel Design', *Proceedings 6th CAORF Symposium on Harbours and Waterways Development*, Kings Point, New York, 29-30 May 1985.

11. Kim W.S, 'Port Design and Simulation: Validity of Microprocessor Aided Port Design Simulation and its Application', PhD Thesis, University of Wales, Cardiff, November 1990.

12. Atkins D.A, Bertsche W.R, 'Evaluation of the Safety of Ship Navigation Harbours', *Spring Meeting STAR Symposium*, Coronada, California, 4-6 June 1980.

13. *Marine Week*, 'Containership Manoeuvrability', pp30-32, May 1978.

14. McCallum I.R, 'A New Approach to Ship Manoeuvring Simulation', PhD Thesis, The City University, May 1976.

15. Davison K.S.M, Schiff L.I, 'Turning and Course Keeping Qualities of Ships', *SNAME*, Vol 54, pp 152-200, 1949.

16. Nomoto K, 'Problems and Requirements of Directional Stability and Control of Surface Ships, *Journal of Mech. Eng Sci.*, Vol 14, No.7, pp 1-5, 1972.

17. Pourzanjani M.M.A, Zienkiewicz H.K, et al 'A Hybrid Method of Estimating Hydrodynamically Generated Forces for use in Ship Manoeuvring Simulation', *International Shipbuilding Progress,* Vol 34, No.399, pp 207-216, 1987.

18. Pourzanjani M.M.A, 'Formulation of the Force Mathematical Model of Ship Manoeuvring', *International Shipbuilding Progress*, Vol 37, No.409, pp 5-32, 1990.

19. Lowry I.J, 'Ship Controllability: An Industrial Perspective', PhD Thesis, University of Wales, Cardiff, January 1991.

SECTION 2: SHIP SIMULATION

The Role of Ship Manoeuvring Prediction and Simulation Techniques in Ship Projects - Case Study of a Baltic Cruise Ferry

K. Larjo (*), M. Heikkilä (**)

(*) Silja Line, Helsinki, Finland

(**) VTT Ship Laboratory, Espoo, Finland

ABSTRACT

A new class of cruise ferries has been taken into use by Silja Line for the traffic between Helsinki and Stockholm in the Baltic. The two new sister ships are larger than their predecessors. The route of these vessels consists of narrow and restricted fairways with many turns through large archipelago areas. In the project the manoeuvring capabilities of the newbuildings were important from the beginning and these capabilities were finally evaluated by simulations in the shiphandling simulator of Technical Research Centre of Finland (VTT).

The different stages of the simulation project are described in the paper. The topics dealt with are: background information of the project, the ship and the fairway modelling, the assessment of preliminary operational limits, training of crew teams before ship delivery, the model verification by full-scale trials and on-job feedback from the traffic, the training for the second ship and plans for continuation, the lessions learned and the needs for further development.

The role of a simulation program developed to run on microcomputer and to be used as an aid for navigational passage planning is discussed. This is a follow-up development that combines the whole earlier experience together and forms the simulation of ship manoeuvring as part of the daily operation.

INTRODUCTION

During the last twenty years, there has been a tendency to design both the fairway and the ship as a functional unit. The situation has changed because the fairway is nowadays often protected by environment policy. This puts the pressure on the ship manoeuvrability and position accuracy. It has resulted in rapid development with manoeuvring devices, remote controls and simulator training.

Significant advances have been made in recent years in ship manoeuvring prediction especially regarding operations in restricted waters as well as in simulation and simulator techniques to present these manoeuvres realistically.

With these developments of the state-of-the-art, it has become possible to adjust early in the project the manoeuvring capabilities of a ship - its hydrodynamics, equipment and the people who operate it - to the fairways and the harbours used in the actual traffic. This model for the design and subsequent training approaches the one used in the aviation industry.

A full-bridge shiphandling simulator is an ideal system for the provision of training and practice in exceptional shiphandling and navigational situations. These situations require special shiphandling skills, but they occur too seldom to allow the accumulation of adequate experience. The skills can not be trained or practised with real ships because the situations are often either too difficult or dangerous. When a newbuilding or fairway is taken into use or a new port of call is chosen, there are good reasons to consider the use of a shiphandling simulator. Thus the necessary experience can be acquired and it is also possible to define the preliminary operational limits.

Silja Line ordered two new ferries in 1987 for the route between Helsinki and Stockholm. The dimensions exceeded those of the existing ferries and great care had to be paid on the manoeuvrability. The main dimensions of the newbuildings, ms SILJA SERENADE and ms SILJA SYMPHONY, and their two predecessors are shown in table 1. The side view of the ships is presented also in figure 1. The cruise-passenger ferries accommodate 2500 passengers, have a length of 203.5 m and most important for their handling point of view have a lateral windage area of 6562 m^2. This wind area is very large compared to the underwater lateral area.

TABLE 1

Main dimensions of the ships

		ms FINLANDIA ms SILVIA REGINA	ms SILJA SERENADE ms SILJA SYMPHONY
Length; oa	[m]	160.0	203.5
Length; pp	[m]	150.0	180.6
Breadth	[m]	24.8	31.5
Draught	[m]	6.1	6.8
Nr of propellers	[-]	2	2
Nr of rudders	[-]	2	2
Lat. wind area / LT	[-]	4.39	4.24
Mov. rudder area / LT	[-]	0.0306	0.0358

The route of these vessels consists of narrow and restricted fairways with many turns through large archipelago areas. The approaches to Helsinki, Kustaanmiekka Sound, presented the greatest difficulty to operate the larger ferries. The fairway at Kustaanmiekka goes amid old fortified islands that are historically invaluable and the width of the channel cannot be increased. The fairway width is 100 meters at Kustaanmiekka and the ship has to turn 15 or 20 degrees at the inlet. If the margin between the ship's side and the channel bank is kept at least as 15 meters then the steering accuracy has to be ± 14 meters in the sound even in calm weather.

In the project the manoeuvring capabilities of the newbuildings were significant from the beginning and especially manoeuvrability in wind was considered crucial. The manoeuvrability was assessed on four levels:
- initial studies by Silja Line
- model test program by the shipyard
- evaluations and training using the shiphandling simulator
- on-board simulation facility

These different stages of the project are discussed in this paper.

BACKGROUND TO THE SIMULATOR USAGE

The initial study by the Silja Line

The first preliminary study was ordered by Silja Line and conducted by SSPA Marine Consulting AB in Göteborg 1987. The study was made using the main dimensions of the ships and relying partly on experience from other Silja Line vessels. The report predicted slight dynamic instability and the turning ability to be better than existing company vessels.

Official concern

General considerations and actions The Port Authority of Helsinki and The Finnish Board of Navigation initiated by the end of 1988 a research work to assess the need for the improvement of the approach fairways to Helsinki. To accommodate future traffic using the narrow fairway through the Sound of Kustaanmiekka, hydraulic model tests and simulator runs have been carried out by VTT, described by Heikkilä [5]. Although no changes were made to the fairway as a result, the detail knowledge about its hydrodynamic effects was greatly improved.

The Swedish Board of Navigation has guidelines to limit ship size in certain fairways. If the limit is exceeded, special precaution has to be taken to trade the fairway. A meeting was held three years before the delivery of the vessels between the representatives from the Silja Line and the Swedish Board of Navigation to decide the requirements for maintaining the same level of safety as with the earlier ship size.

Solutions selected A concensus was reached about the following actions:
- Model tests had to be performed.
- The manoeuvrability had to reach the Norrbin P-index 0.3.
- Slow speed manoeuvring had to be improved by Schilling or Jastram rudders and an Integrated Remote Control System (joystick control) should be installed.
- A local weather report should be ordered to help the master to choose the safe fairway for the weather condition.
- An accurate position fixing system should be used. (Differential GPS system was set up three months after the traffic started.)
- The Integrated Navigation System should be developed with special emphasis to carry out the turns using constant radius autopilot. It was to present the Passage Plan and the shallow water areas on the radar as well.
- Wind and speed limits should be defined in the manoeuvring simulator.
- The officers should have simulator training.

Shipyard manoeuvring model test series

The manoeuvring model test series was made by the MARINTEK laboratory in Trondheim in 1988 on behalf of the builder, Wärtsilä Marine Turku Shipyard. The model tests were carried out using radio-controlled free running model. The test series consisted of turning and zig-zag tests. In the tests the rudder area was slightly larger in proportion to vessel size than usual. The results indicated better steady turning and yaw checking ability than the existing company vessels and the requirement for Norrbin P-index greater than 0.3 was fullfilled. Powering and resistance tests revealed that although the displacement was 50% larger than on their predecessors, the power required was only 15% higher.

Wind tunnel tests were conducted by the VTT Ship Laboratory to determine the wind forces. Some crabbing tests were also conducted by the VTT for the Wärtsilä Marine in 1988. Different rudder profiles (NACA and IfS) were tested. Conventional NACA rudders with Jastram rotors were chosen for the ships. An interesting decision was made about the maximum rudder angles as a result of the crabbing tests. The rudders were to turn 55 deg. inwards and 35 deg. outwards to get the best possible crabbing conditions with conventional rudder engines.

The main parameters affecting the manoeuvrability of the ships had thus been fixed based on the evaluations described above. The next step was to assess the manoeuvrability in the fairways using the shiphandling simulator.

SIMULATOR AND SIMULATION MODELS

Simulator

General description The full-bridge ship handling simulator used in this project has been operated by the VTT Ship Laboratory for ship related research from the beginning of 1986. The simulator, which is also used for training of pilots and deck officers, is situated in Espoo, Finland. A description of the evolvement of the VTT simulator has been given by Haapio and Heikkilä [2].

The visual system The visual system is of a computer-generated-imagery (CGI) type. Depending on the degree of realism i.e. amount of details in the visual model, the simulations can be carried out in day, dusk and night conditions. The nominal dimensions of view observed from the bridge are 240 and 30 degrees horizontally and vertically respectively. The information content of the visual scenes consist of land masses, quays, prominent buildings, navigational marks an other ships. Nocturnally, lights are shown with characteristic colours, flashing periods and sectors.

The wide view is necessary when the narrow fairways with frequent bends of up to and over 90 degrees such as leading through the Finnish archipelago or manoeuvring in harbours are simulated. For this kind of shiphandling, the frequent use of visual information, also abeam of the ship, is typical. The fairways in the archipelago are often rather narrow - only a hundred meters wide - so that the vertical angle of view of 30 degrees, divided 21 degrees below and 9 above horizon allows viewing the natural passing distances.

The bridge The equipment of the simulator bridge consists of the normal shiphandling facilities such as controls for machinery, rudders and transverse thrusters, radars, autopilot, indicators for control systems, log, echo sounder and anemometer. The radar simulator of the system uses ARPA radars, which are real ship equipment.

The Silja Line ships are equipped with integrated bridge featuring advanced constant radius autopilot, differential GPS, joystick control for harbour manoeuvres etc. The simulator did not have such an advanced autopilot. It was decided to provide the helmsman and the pilot with information to facilitate hand steering in the same way as the autopilot is used. This additional information provided is described later in the paper with simulator runs.

The simulator models

Ownship mathematical model structure The ship manoeuvring simulation model of the VTT ship handling simulator has been developed by the British National Maritime Institute (NMI, nowadays British Maritime Technology BMT) and its main features have been described by Dand [1].

The characteristic features of this simulation model are its modular form and its wide applicability in a speed range from full astern to full ahead including harbour manoeuvres with large drift angles. The modular structure means that the model is composed of different modules such as ship's hull, propellers, rudders, main engines, transverse thrusters, tugs, wind effects, hydrodynamic interactions with other ships and the fairway. In principle in this kind of a model any hull can be combined with any rudder, propeller, superstructure or engine for sailing in any fairway configuration and traffic situation.

The methods used for developing ownship and fairway models for the simulator have been described by Heikkilä [3]. The ship model construction for the simulator consists of hydrodynamic and aerodynamic model tests and incorporating properly scaled features already resident in the simulator. Models of main engines such as medium or slow speed diesel engines or steam turbines, transverse thrusters, fixed or controllable pitch propellers with correct time constants or wind force coefficients are normally taken from the simulator database.

The modular approach in the modelling of manoeuvrability brings along some special requirements for both the Planar Motion Mechanism (PMM) measurements and the subsequent analysis of the results. To clarify the interference effects between the hull, propeller and rudder modules, the model in the measurements is equipped with both propeller and rudder dynamometres.

It is preferable in the PMM tests to have the model equipped with propellers and rudders due to the interactions and the changes to the flow pattern around the hull due to these appendages.

The complete PMM model test series covers several operating regions:
- *Cruising speed and acceleration* measurements include variations in the rudder and drift angles and some speed reduction with full forward thrust as well as speed reduction to zero with full forward thrust and variations in the rudder angles.

-   *Forward motion with deceleration and stopping* are measured at one speed varying propeller thrust from full ahead to full astern and with the rudder angle as a parameter.
-   *Astern motion with deceleration and stopping* are measured at one speed varying propeller thrust from full ahead to full astern and with the rudder angle as a parameter.
-   *Harbour manoeuvres* are covered with slow speed and large drift angles (0 - 180 degrees) propeller stopped

The ship model   The task of modelling the SILJA SERENADE and SILJA SYMPHONY into the simulator was of the most demanding type - that of a particular ship in the exact fairway the ship is intended for. The modelling was made using results from the free-running model tests and wind tunnel measurements, described above, and from VTT's own PMM test results.

PMM tests in the extent required for a simulator model had been carried out at the VTT for a ferry model with almost identical hull form and dimensions. This simulation model was scaled to represent the new ship and adjusted to reproduce the results of standard manoeuvres from free-running model tests. The wind force coefficients had been measured at the VTT wind tunnel for this ship.

The fairway model including ship-bank interactions   The simulator models for the fairways consist of the depth information including bank effects, the radar image and the visual image as seen from the bridge. The latter include all the navmarks and other details that are needed for navigation.

Helsinki with its harbours had been modelled to the simulator in the earlier project mentioned above. The Kustaanmiekka sound is abt 100 metres wide, the depth in the middle is 20 metres and the islands are situated so that the bank effects are unsymmetrical. Especially this unsymmetry required validation of the simulator model against the hydraulic model test results.

In the model tests, the behaviour of the ships in the fairway due to the sea bottom topography was assessed in a series of free-running model tests. The models were steered into the strait at three lateral positions - right side, middle and left side - and with three speeds corresponding to 5, 10 and 15 knots. The controls were centered and held fixed in the actual measurement.

The simulated effects on the ship were adjusted to correspond the results of these model tests. Example results of comparable model test run and simulation are shown in figure 2. As can be seen from the figure, the bank suctions are considerable at the speed of 15 knots of the test. The condition depicted in this figure accentuates the problems of Kustaanmiekka Sound. The first bank on port turns the ship towards the island on the starboard which again turns the ship towards the next island on the port side. This figure also effectively shows why model tests and simulator runs should be carried out parallell when modelling difficult hydraulic conditions in fairways.

THE EVALUATIONS USING SIMULATION

The initial evaluation of wind effects

As the effect of wind on the ship manoeuvrability was of special concern, an initial evaluation of these effects was made in the form of extensive calculations early in the simulation project. Both the steady state conditions, i.e. the drift angle and required amount of rudder application, and dynamic turning ability under different wind speeds and directions were calculated. The results of this evaluation were used as input to the assessment of operational limits in the simulator.

A comparison with another Silja Line ship ms WELLAMO was included in the calculations. The calculation model for this ship was not as sophisticated as that of the newbuildings due to the lack of PMM test data, although wind tunnel measurements had been carried out for the ship and results from free-running model tests as well as sea trial measurements were available. The calculations for ms WELLAMO formed a basis to consider the effects of the evaluation results on operational limits, because its handling characteristics using autopilot steering within archipelago fairways were well known to the project group.

The steady state calculations were made using three wind directions relative to the ship heading, 45, 90 and 135 degrees from the bow. Four values, 2.0, 2.9, 4.0 and 6.7, of the important ratio of wind speed to ship speed were used in the calculations with all the wind directions by varying ship speed with constant wind speed of 20 m/s. The speed ratio 6.7, ship speed 5.8 knots together with wind speed of 20 m/s, proved to be critical for shiphandling, because with two wind directions the rudder control alone was not sufficient for maintaining steady ship attitude. From the point of view of the passage thorough Kustaanmiekka the ship sweep width due to the drift angle was important. A drift angle of 10 degrees produces a sweep width of abt. 65 metres in a passage, which is 100 metres wide. The steady state drift angle of 10 degrees is reached at a ship speed from 10 to 12 knots with wind speed of 20 m/s depending on the wind direction.

The dynamic evaluation of the wind effect on the turning ability was made by simulating turning circles with different wind conditions. As in the steady state calculations, the influence of the ratio of wind speed to ship speed was significant with the speed ratio values greater than three but depending on the wind direction. An example of the simulated turning circles with wind is presented in figure 3a. In this figure three turning circles to port are shown - one without wind and the other two with side winds alternatively from port and starboard. The initial ship speed in these three simulations was 8.7 knots and the wind speed was 15 m/s, i.e. the wind speed to ship speed ratio as 3.35. Although the results of ms WELLAMO are not presented here, in principle the behaviour of that ship resembles that of the newbuildings.

When a turn is executed using a constant radius of turn autopilot, the effect of the wind is not as drastic as in turns with constant rudder angle. This can be seen in figure 3b, where simulated turns with a turning radius of 0.3 nm are shown. The ratio of wind speed to ship speed is the same 3.35 as in figure 3a. The turning radius of 0.3 nm corresponds to approximately a turn with constant rudder angle of 20 degrees and the autopilot has a margin of 15 degrees available to compensate wind effects. It was concluded that the newbuildings with the constant radius autopilot would be adequately manoeuvrable in wind.

The simulator runs

The simulator runs were carried out in three phases. In the first phase, started in parallel with the Kustaanmiekka fairway study, the masters and the chief mates of the newbuildings carried out runs in different external conditions   to familiarize themselves with the vessel. In these runs the optimal path through Kustaanmiekka was found.   During the second phase the same persons methodically defined the operational limits for the vessel. In the third phase before delivery of each of the two ships, the actual crew teams were trained.

The Silja Line ships are equipped with integrated bridge featuring advanced control functions. Technically the navigation system is nearly as advanced as the present development of electronic devices allows. The radars are Rasterscan ARPA radars capable to display symbolic charts of the shallow water boundaries and ship's programmed track. The autopilot can steer along the preprogrammed track automatically using Differential GPS, Doppler and gyros corrected to true north.

The speciality of the autopilot is to display the next turn and the next course on the radar screen. The turn is presented as a geometrical curve defined by the turning radius and the next course. The system helps the navigator to decide when the vessel has reached the line of turn. This type of an autopilot combined with the radar is described by Larjo [6].

The integrated navigation system on the vessel is capable of displaying navigation information more effectively than was possible in the simulator without autopilot and as the turns or tracks could not displayed on the radar. During the familiarization phase, the first runs with the simulator were not satisfactory because the navigational data was insufficient compared to the precision required.   The simulator was simply old fashioned compared with the vessel. The first solution to cope with this discrepancy was an installation of separate display to provide the navigator with numerical information about the drift angle, the turning radius and the cross track error. The trial results improved at once.

For the later simulation phases it was decided to provide the helmsman and the pilot with information to facilitate hand steering in the same way as the autopilot is used. This additional information was in the form of a graphics display showing a digital chart of the fairway including shoreline and the optimal track. On this chart, the position of the vessel was plotted once per second in real time in the form of a correctly scaled ship shape. In addition to this present position information, also the time history of the positions and a prediction of the future track of the center of gravity as a constant radius curved "heading line" was shown. The constant radius autopilot was succesfully imitated during the simulations with this curved path prediction display.

Familiarization with ship manoeuvrability capabilities Simulator runs started in the summer 1989 with a group of captains. The first task was to specify the maximum speed in the sound of Kustaanmiekka. It was clearly defined after few runs that the maximum safe speed was 12 knots. The bank effects became disturbing at 13 knots, stranding was probable with 14 knots and there was no chance to navigate the sound with 15 knots. The passage out from the harbour proved to be more difficult than the opposite direction. This result is due to the short approach line to the sound after a 60 degree turn.

Assessment of preliminary operational limits The second task, in winter 1990, was to define the maximum wind velocity. According to the statistics from the Finnish Meteorological Institute the wind speeds at Helsinki approaches have been ≥ 15 m/s in 1.41 percent of the observations and ≥ 19 m/s in 0.14 percent. The test group learned from the model tests that the worst wind direction was from the quarter. When the wind velocity was 20 m/s it became difficult to control the turns with the wind 45 degrees from the bow or on the quarter. The wind limit was set to 20m/s. Only head on winds up to 20 degrees from the bow were safe above 20 m/s. It was decided to train the officers with ship speeds below 12 knots and wind forces below 20 m/s.

Training of crew teams The first training for the Silja Line bridge teams took place late in the summer 1990 about two months before the delivery of ms SILJA SERENADE. The second, similar training for ms SILJA SYMPHONY was carried out in the spring 1991. The training for the crew of the first ship was carried out using the simulation model developed from the model test results only, whereas the crew of SILJA SYMPHONY had the advantage of drawing from the experience of the first vessel, too. Altogether the number of the simulator runs in the training before the ship deliveries exceeds 300.

The graphical and alphanumerical outputs from the runs were considered by the navigators more helpful than the conventional manoeuvring test diagrams. The reports were studied later when facing difficult weather conditions. It was clearly shown, that the simulator training improved the navigation performance.

The simulator results were used to define the navigation accuracy margins. The fairway width is 100 meters at Kustaanmiekka and the ship has to turn 15 or 20 degrees at the inlet. The vessel length is 203 meters and the beam is 32 meters. In calm weather the drift is 3.5 degrees in the turn and it widens the sweep area by abt. 10 meters. If the margin between the ship's side and the channel bank is kept at least as 15 meters then the steering accuracy has to be ± 14 meters. This is easily done with a good conventional radar. The situation is different in strong wind. The drift angle is 10 degrees and the total sweep area is 62 meters. The margin to the channel bank should be 14 meters. The navigation accuracy has to be ± 5 meters. The conventional radar can not meet this accuracy and an accurate position fixing method is essential.

Differential GPS beacons were set up by the authorities in Sweden and Finland to meet the accuracy of 5 meters. The satellite pseudorange corrections are sent from standard marine Non Directional beacons. In the end of 1991, the DGPS 2 sigma accuracy was from 5 to 10 metres. It has degraded occasionally to 15 meters. Improvements with the system and dynamical tests are now proceeding and we believe that the accuracy requirement will be met.

The model verification in full scale

As the simulation task at hand was most demanding, special emphasis was laid on the verification of the model behaviour. A comprehensive manoeuvring test program was carried out on the sea trials of the first vessel, ms SILJA

SERENADE by the builders Masa-Yards New Turku Shipyard. The VTT Ship Laboratory was responsible for both the speed and manoeuvring test measurements. The portable measuring system for ship trials developed at the laboratory was used for the measurements. This system consists of an accurate microwave positioning system coupled to a microcomputer for the measurement of ship's control variables as well as recording the whole measurement. The system has been described by Heikkilä & Tuovinen [4]. The manoeuvring test program consisted of turning circles with two different rudder angles, two different zig-zag tests, pull-out tests, accelerating, decelerating and stopping tests as well as thruster manoeuvres.

The general agreement between the identically made test results calculated with the simulator model and those recorded during the ship trials was most satisfactory, as can be seen from the figures 4a, 4b and 4c. In the simulations, the same wind speed and direction was used as was recorded during the trial manoeuvre. In the turning tests the agreement in the magnitude of the drift angle can especially be noted. Also in those manoeuvres, for which no model tests were available, such as accelerating, decelerating and stopping tests, the agreement was good. Thus the model was deemed to be valid for the wide operation range it was intended for. This, naturally, was a great relief for those responsible for the simulations both at the SiljaLine and at the simulator, because the crew team simulation training for the first vessel had already been carried out. The validity of the bank suction effects at Kustaanmiekka and wind effects have been assessed in the traffic by the crew of the ship. The possible changes needed to the simulator model was taken up for discussion when the training for the crew of the second ship was in preparation. As a result of these discussions no changes were made to the model.

A FOLLOW-UP PROJECT - THE ON-BOARD SIMULATION FACILITY

A simulation program developed to run on a microcomputer combines the whole earlier experience together and forms the simulation of ship manoeuvring as part of the daily operation. Screen view from the program is reproduced in figure 5. With an on-site simulation model it is also possible to verify easily the model, discuss its improvement and further development.

The desktop simulator is used daily. The model is run on the same graphic chart and the track line that is used on the radar. The desktop simulator (DTS) is used for various tasks:
-    to choose a safe fairway in different weather conditions
-    to lay the track geographically correct on the synthetic map
-    to train for pilotage certificate
-    to test difficult turns in severe weather conditions before reaching the hazardous area, special attention is paid on wind from the quarter
-    to study incidents
-    to continuously verify the model

The desktop simulator is an effictive way to present the manoeuvring information to the navigator as recommended by IMO.

CONCLUSIONS AND FUTURE DEVELOPMENTS

The total ship handling safety assessment

With the developments of the state-of-the-art in manoeuvring prediction and simulation, it has become possible to adjust early in the project the manoeuvring capabilities of a ship - its hydrodynamics, control equipment and the people who operate it - to the fairways and the harbours used in the actual traffic. A simulation project like this one combines the development of the manoeuvrability of the ship and the training of her crew into a total ship handling safety assessment. It can also become a continuous part of the operations.

This model for the design and subsequent training approaches the one used in the aviation industry and in the future even more so when the training for the advanced bridge equipment is added to the agenda. With the on-board simulation facility, the maritime operations are perhaps even ahead of the aviation because the simulation training and simulation usage is part of the daily passage planning.

The development of a simulator model should not be looked at as a one time investment. This particular project has had continuity after the deliveries of the ships: refreshment training of the crew before winter conditions and training for new officers. New control methods can also be evaluated in a simulator instead of practising them for the first time in real life. The results here were successful to such extent that the authorities included simulator runs in the general pilot licence examination for passenger ships.

The role of simulator equipment

It was quite obvious from early of this project, that the control system on the bridge of the simulator had to resemble that of the real ship at least in the information content of certain key elements. The most important of these for the steering of the ships through Kustaanmiekka are the positioning accuracy and the capability of constant radius turns.

The role of the advanced on-board control systems is strengthening and the modelling of them is becoming more important also in the simulators. Ships like the new Silja Line ferries, that operate round the year in very restricted waters, are in this operation dependent on the advanced control systems. It is logical that their simulator modelling will in the future require exactly the same control functions.

Some future developments

The desktop simulator will soon present recorded tracks simultaneously with the simulated track. A black box function will be integrated with the desktop simulator. The position, the ground speed and the course over ground will be recorded from the Differential GPS receiver. The recording will be displayed on the Graphical Map Editor and the simulated tracks can be verified with the recorded tracks. This will be an easy way to study and document incidents.

The Integrated Navigation System will include the mathematical model in the future. The present Integrated Navigation System does not use any hydrodynamical data. It controls the turns by the longitudal and the transverse speed, the heading, the rate of turn and the cross track error. Therefore the system does not know when the vessel is not able to steer along the preprogrammed track when the wind is too strong. A mathematical model that simulates the autopilot commands on the radar screen should be a natural addition to the system. With the aid of the prediction the navigator can filter and reduce his errors and misjudgments.

The slow speed navigation is mainly a crabbing problem. The crabbing philosophy will be part of the slow speed navigation in narrow fairways. A Remote Control that integrates the thrusters, the rudders and the main propellers is very effective to reduce the speed and to control the drift angle simultaneously. The Integrated Remote Control will be added to the Integrated Navigation System in the future. It will promote the full use of the navigation system and the mathematical model. This crabbing facility will also be integrated with the desktop simulator.

REFERENCES

1.   Dand, I.W. 'On Modular Manoeuvring Models.' *RINA International Conference on Ship Manoeuvrability - Prediction and Achievement*, Gatwick, April 29th -30th and May 1st 1987.

2.   Haapio, A. & Heikkilä, M. 'A Shiphandling Simulator for Training and Research - The evolution of a project from buyer's specification to completition.' *Nordic Ship Technical Meeting NSTM-85*, Lyngby, Denmark, 1985.

3.   Heikkilä, M. 'On the Development of fairway and Ship Models to Shiphandling Simulator.' *The 5th Marine Technology Symposium - Noise & Vibration, Winter Navigation, Hydrodynamics. VTT Symposium 92*, Espoo, Finland, January 11th-12th 1988.

4.   Heikkilä, M. & Tuovinen, J. 'Speed and Manoeuvring Trial Measurements.' *The 4th Marine Technology Symposium - Ship Vibration, Noise & Hydrodynamics. VTT Symposium 68*, Espoo, Finland, January 13th-14th, 1986.

5.   Heikkilä, M. 'The Evaluation of Manoeuvrability through a Narrow Strait using Full-Bridge Shiphandling Simulator.' *Joint International Conference on Marine Simulation and Ship Manoeuvrability MARSIM & ICSM 90*, Tokyo, Japan, June 4th - 7th 1990.

6.   Larjo, K. 'Advanced Bridge Systems for Rational Navigation in restricted Waters.' *Third International conference on Bridge design and Ship Operations*, organised by The Nautical Institute and Det Norske Veritas, Oslo, Norway, October 21st - 22nd 1987.

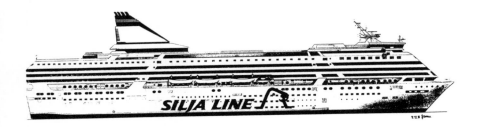

Figure 1: The side view of ms SILJA SERENADE and ms SILJA SYMPHONY

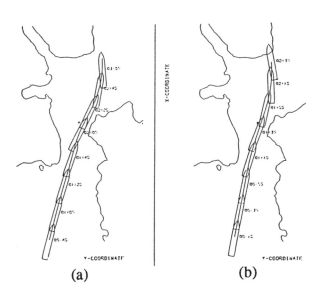

(a)   (b)

Figure 2: The comparison of bank effect in a) model test and b) simulation
Ship speed 15 knots.

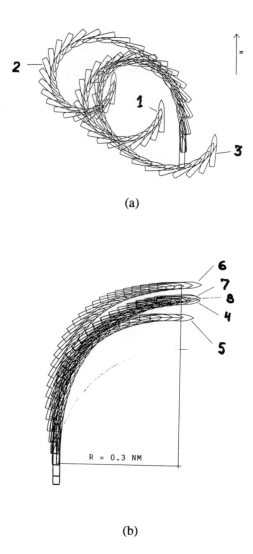

Figure 3: The simulated turns in wind. Wind speed 15m/s. Ship speed 8.7knots
a) Constan rudder angle setting 35 degrees. 1 = without wind,
    wind directions: 2 = 90deg, 3 = 270deg
b) Autopilot constant radius setting 0.3 nm. 4 = without wind,
    wind directions: 5 = 360deg, 6 = 90deg, 7 = 180deg, 8 = 270deg

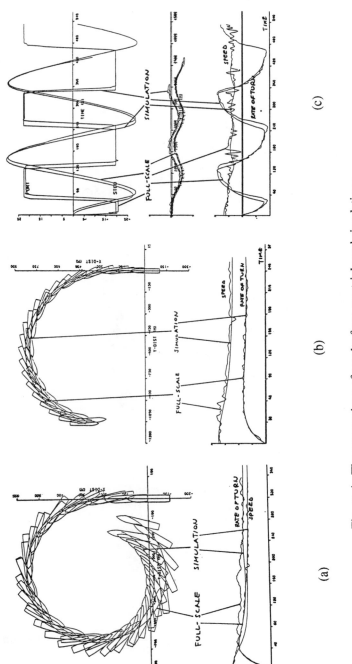

Figure 4: The comparison of results from sea trials and simulations.
Ship speed 16.5knots
a) Turning circle with 35 degrees of rudder
b) Initial turn with 15 degrees of rudder
c) 20/20 zig-zag test

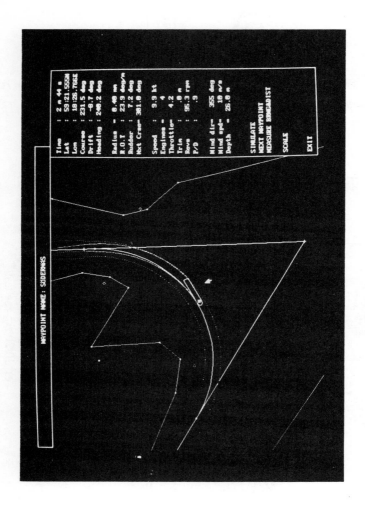

Figure 5: A simulated turn on the screen of the on-board simulation facility

Practical Ship Manoeuvring Models for Real Ship Manoeuvring Problems

I.R. McCallum

Department of Maritime Studies and International Transport, University of Wales, College of Cardiff, Cardiff, UK and

HR Mardyn Ltd, Llantrisant House, Mid Glamorgan CF7 8BS, UK

ABSTRACT

The use of ship simulators is becoming routine for the solution of a wide range of port design and ship operational problems. Many of these tasks demand a ship manoeuvring model which can be developed in a short time using very limited data. There is however a need for ship manoeuvring models used in simulators, particularly those used for close quarters manoeuvring, to be valid in all manoeuvring regimes and at slow speeds.

This paper examines the structure of models used for representing hull forces and moments in three degrees of freedom, from the point of view of their ease of use, their validity over all manoeuvring regimes, and their applicability. A number of case studies is presented which illustrate the type of studies which are common for ship simulators, and for which there are particular modelling constraints imposed by the circumstances of the study.

INTRODUCTION

The ship manoeuvring simulator has now become a routine tool for many training and research or development applications, with the range of possible applications widening as the true cost of simulation decreases. There are now about forty ship simulators worldwide which are of sufficient capability to provide a wide range of training. Of these, less than half may be thought of as having the necessary flexibility and comprehensiveness of software to be able to carry out port design work.

The main requirements of a ship simulator which is to be used wholly or in part for the design of ports, or the evaluation of operational strategies for ships may be summarised as being:

- The ability to represent a new sea area or harbour quickly and flexibly

- The ability to produce a new or modified mathematical model quickly and flexibly, and of sufficient range of validity, from sparse data.

- An ability to respond to market forces, in terms of cost and time, in such a manner as to be able to attract clients.

- An ability to record and print out the results of a number of runs in a meaningful manner, and to analyse the results of runs statistically.

This paper is concerned with the second of these requirements. The others are however of equal importance, as the results of a port design study are unlikely to be of commercial use if all the requirements mentioned are not met.

Because a number of simulators are now able to fulfil these roles, it has become commonplace for ship simulators to be used for a wide range of port design and operational studies, and the range of applicability is increasing. Such studies place an increasing stress on the ability of the simulator staff to provide new mathematical ship models, usually to severe constraints of time and cost. Maritime Dynamics operate two small simulators which have been increasingly used for a range of such studies in the past few years. This work is carried out under a Joint Venture arrangement with Hydraulics Research Ltd, called HR Mardyn. Studies undertaken have included:

- Studies to investigate whether a proposed charter vessel will be suitable for entering a particular port, usually where there are tight manoeuvring constraints. This type of study usually needs the ship model to be produced in a few days, from little data apart from that obtainable from such publications as Lloyds Register.

- Investigations on the dredging needs for a port when operating a new ferry. This work is becoming increasingly common as ferry companies operate new, large ferries, usually with large windage. Again models have to be produced which are able to represent the behaviour of the ferry within close tolerances, with a minimum of data. In one of these studies, the ferry was not out of drydock after lengthening when the study was performed, and so no ship trials were available.

- A number of studies involving the possible consequences to ship operations after a barrage is built. This involves less emphasis being placed on the ship model, as the barrage has to

deal with a range of ship types.   A model needs therefore only
to be representative of a type of ship, rather than being a good
simulation of a particular vessel.

Model Scope
The ship mathematical model used for these studies has to be able
to operate in all manouevring regimes, (Fig 1), particularly with the
ship at zero or slow speed, and respond realistically to all the ship
effectors, such as thrusters, propellers and rudders.   Models also
need to be able to respond to a wide range of environmental
conditions, including:

- Shallow water effects
- Bank effects
- Wind effects
- Current, including space varying current
- Waves

    Other effects, such as tugs, anchoring, mooring, fendering,
collision forces, lock blockage etc, may be simulated where the
demands of the task require it.

    For nearly all applications, it is adequate for the mathematical
model to operate in three degrees of freedom only, (surge, sway and
yaw).   Environmental effects which would normally cause motion in
other degrees of freedom, such as waves, can still be represented,
by simulating the effect in the three degrees of freedom of the
waves.   Waves will predominantly cause the ship to respond in
heave roll and pitch, but there will also be a motion in surge, sway
and yaw, and it is this motion which is calculated.   Exceptions are
those applications where the motion in roll, pitch and heave are of
prime importance to the topic being studied or the training being
carried out. Applications would include offshore supply vessels,
where the need is to keep a vessel alongside a rig in high waves,
or for submersible operations.

BASIC MODULAR MODEL FORMAT

    It is by now standard methodology to use a modular model,
where the forces of each of the environmental effects and
hydrodynamic forces are represented in separate modules, and the
resulting forces added together, Fig 2.   Accelerations can then be
obtained directly, integrations of which with respect to time will
yield velocities.   These velocities will conventionally be in ship
axes, with the usual convention of using body centred axis systems.
    Further integration and transformation will yield the ship position
in earth centred coordinates, which is what is usually required.
For those environmental effects which are position varying, such
as currents and depths, environmental databases are conventionally
used to produce the local values of current and depth.

    The method of writing the hydrodynamic equations for ship
motion in three degrees of freedom, taking into account the
variation of added mass with direction of motion, is classically and

elegantly written by Nomoto[1], as follows:

$$(m + m_x)u - (m + m_y)vr = X$$
$$(m + m_y)v + (m + m_x)ur = Y$$
$$I_z + J_z = N$$

Eq. 1

where m_x and m_y are the added masses in surge and sway respectively and J_z is the added inertia, and X, Y and N are the sum of the forces and moments in the three body centred axes.

Using a modular model, equations of motion for effector and environmental forces are able to be produced relatively straightforwardly, and most models encountered use similar equations for these purposes.   There is however still a large variation in the types and scale of the terms used to mode the hull hydrodynamic forces, and it is in this area that this paper concentrates.

REPRESENTATION OF HULL FORCES AND MOMENTS.

Hydrodynamic Derivative Method
The conventional manner of representing the hull hydrodynamic forces has, for at least the past quarter century, been to use a Taylor expansion of the velocities in surge and sway, u and v, the yaw rate r and the rudder angle, with the terms non-dimensionalised, usually with respect to either a nominal velocity or the actual ship total velocity.   Many examples of this type of model exist, and Fig. 3 shows a representation used with great effect for many years in the Marad Computer Aided Operations Research Center CAORF for many years, (2).   As is usual with this type of model, the hull hydrodynamic forces and moments are represented by a series of terms, each non-dimensionalised as indicated at the bottom of the Figure.

Although this type of model has been used in many applications, and is still used regularly, for example recently by Martinussen, (3), Kouishi (4), and many others, for the type of work for which simulators are increasingly being used in modern applications, it suffers form a number of limitations.   These may be summarised as:

   - Where models are non-dimensionalised with respect to the ship speed, they cannot be expected to function at zero speed.   As it is precisely near this speed that most critical ship manoeuvres are undertaken, methods have to be found to overcome this problem.   One such is to use a separate model for low speed work, merging the models at some design speed of perhaps one metre per second.   This method is used by Kouishi, (4).   This leads to a large expense in producing a comprehensive model, as two must be made.

- The relationship between the model coefficients and the physical behaviour of the ship is at least indirect in many instances. This is evidenced by the wide disparity between the terms used by different researchers. Although a very good model/ship fit can be obtained for any given trajectory by optimising the derivatives for that run, it is often found necessary to alter the derivatives as a function of speed, or indeed rudder angle. If this is found to be necessary, it must be that the model structure is incorrect for the whole range of manoeuvres.

- The determination of coefficients can be long-winded and expensive, often requiring extensive tank test data. This is again incompatible with the needs of many port design applications, where a model must often be produced in a few days from minimal data. Derivatives of ships which fall between two existing ships in size or shape can usually be interpolated from existing results, and this can save some time and expense. Other methods for obtaining derivative values have included full scale manoeuvring trials, often associated with system identification techniques, (2). The results of these techniques have not however stood the test of time, and they do not appear to be regularly used at present for the production of simulator mathematical models.

It must be re-iterated however that this type of representation of the hull forces and moments is regularly used, with a great deal of success.

The Force Model

This model has now been used for over a decade, being first introduced by McCallum in 1980, (5), and extended by Pourzanjani, (6), (7). It was made to overcome the perceived problems outlined above, by modelling directly the forces and moments on the hull by treating the hull as an inclined foil surface. Environmental and effector forces are introduced in precisely the same manner as in the hydrodynamic derivative form of model, so that the basic modular structure of the model is retained.

The approaches of McCallum and Pourzanjani differ in detail in that the latter introduces a more theoretical viewpoint in evaluating the forces, leading to somewhat more complex equations for hull forces and moments, while the former's expressions are rather more empirical in nature, using a simple curve fitting technique. Both approaches however yield good fits for hull lift and drag forces over the whole range of angles of incidence of the hull. Fig. 4 shows a match obtained by Pourzanjani for a Container Ship, using the equations of (6), and Fig. 5 the fit obtained by the author on a model of a submersible vessel, matched to towing tank results. In each case both the shape of the lift and drag forces and the magnitudes are correctly modelled over the whole range of

drift angles.   Because the Force model is direct in its conception,
it does not use any non-dimensionalising, and so will operate at all
speeds.   Because the formulation of the equations is similarly
direct, the coefficients can be obtained from very little data.   An
empirical coefficient estimation process has been devised which will
predict the coefficients of the model for the physical dimensions
and hull shape of the ship, and a knowledge of its basic turning
behaviour.   Once a preliminary model has been formulated, it may
be optimised to any available ship trial data by adjustment of
coefficients in a straightforward and logical manner.

This has led to the situation where a new ship model can be
obtained in a few days from very limited ship data, and this is
regularly done.

Of particular interest in the formulation of the Force model is
the way in which the centre of pressure of the hull forces moves
as a function of drift angle. Early investigations with wind tunnels
on hull forms, Fig. 6, (taken from McCallum, (5)), indicated that for
full form ships the centre of pressure could be very far forward in
the hull.   Experimental work carried out on a long, narrow hull
form enabled the variation of the centre of pressure to be more
accurately plotted, Fig. 7.   It will be seen that for angles of
incidence up to 10 degrees, the centre of pressure lies totally
outside the hull. It is found that the major differences between the
unstable manoeuvring behaviour of bluff hulls, which are generally
directionally unstable, and more slender hulls, which are frequently
marginally stable or stable, is directly related to the shape of the
Migration of Centre of Pressure, (MCP) curve.   Hulls of higher
block coefficient will generally tend to have their CP further
forward over a larger angle of incidence than will more slender hull
forms.

Heuristic Model
A frequent occurrence is for a model to be required, very quickly,
for a ship designed to move in a restricted waterway, where there
is little or no data for the ship other than that obtainable from
Lloyds Register, but where those responsible for operating the ship
need to be fully satisfied that the model is capable of performing
in all circumstances.   An important element in the validation of
such a model will be the subjective assessment of the masters or
pilots with whom the estimation will be performed, it is essential
that the model be structured so that not only can the
manoeuvring data be matched to any ship trials, but that the
qualitative opinions of the pilots can be translated into relevant
changes to the model so that the "feel" of the ship is deemed to be
correct.

This need to be able to adjust the behaviour of the model
within minutes, in a predictable manner, while retaining the
necessary basic Modular Model structure has led to the formulation
of a method of modelling the hull hydrodynamics which has been
found to be simple and effective.   The methodology is to predict
the steady state values of the surge and sway velocities which

would obtain if the present operating circumstances were to be continued for a long time. The actual instantaneous values of the surge, sway and yaw accelerations are then obtained by using a simple first order lag to relate the instantaneous values to the steady state values. Provided the basic model structure is retained, and the appropriate cross coupling terms in ur and vr of eq. 1 used, the degree of fit obtainable is of high order. As the nature of a hull becomes more complex, for example by having more thrusters and rudders, terms may simply be added until the dynamic behaviour is adequately predicted.

The basic modelling philosophy may thus be simply stated as being that which is modelled is what the user will experience, in the three degrees of freedom. Each term in the model is thus directly related to specific aspects of hull behaviour, and so the optimisation process referred to above is simple and direct. A hull form can be optimised so as to satisfy the most demanding pilot in a few hours. The model works in all manoeuvring regimes, and at all speeds, with no non-dimensionalising.

Two other features of this model format are of direct applicability to the needs of port operational studies:

The model can be produced from little data. Often the level of data obtainable from Lloyds Register is all that is available, and occasionally models have had to be produced using data of the type that the ship is a "225m long bulker". In the latter case, use is made of the concept of pseudodata, whereby a set of manoeuvring data is produced either from a similar ship type, from a knowledge of how such a ship might behave, or from running a previously validated mathematical model.

A very wide range of marine vehicles models can be produced. Models have been made of ferries, hydrofoils, jetfoils, frigates and a whole range of conventional ship types, of all sizes and manoeuvring performances.

Shallow water effects are catered for in a similarly direct manner, by evaluating what effects are produced in each of the three degrees of freedom by the onset of shallow water. Appropriate changes are then made to the model coefficients, as a function of the water depth. As the effect of each coefficient in the model is entirely predictable, this method has been found to be effective in producing all the necessary changes in ship behaviour with the onset of shallow water.

All the other environmental and effector forces are predicted in the same manner as in the other models.

APPLICABILITY AND FUTURE TRENDS

Examples of the use of the models are contained in Annexes 2-4. It will be be seen that the use of the simpler manoeuvring models need not be confined to simpler applications. Ten years' use of the heuristic model has given the users of it a great deal of confidence in its ability to predict manoeuvres with at least an accuracy comparable with any other form of modelling in common use.

The range of applicability of the Force and Heuristic models has been found to be large.   The ability of both methods to operate in all manoeuvring regimes, to be able to be made quickly from limited data, and to be able to be partially generated automatically, has proved of great use in commercial applications where speed of development and price are of importance. Experience has shown that the models are able to be used where pilots need to be satisfied that ships are operating satisfactorily over all manoeuvring regimes.   The models have been found to be rugged, in that additional effector and environmental forces can be added at will.

The Force Model will tend to be used where the actual forces experienced by the hull are of prime importance.   Such applications will include the evaluation of mooring forces, and the determination of causes of ship instability in manoeuvring. Otherwise, for a large range of uses, the Heuristic model has been found to be fully adequate for investigations, and for a very wide range of training uses.

All three forms of model discussed here are rather crude approximations of the hydrodynamic behaviour of hull forms.   The very rapid increase in computing power over the past few years has now made it fully feasible to implement modelling methods based on more valid theoretical grounds.   One of the most potentially promising is to use simple flow representation methods, using a fine mesh over the hull form.   This method was suggested by Rizzi and Purcell, (8), as an application of a Super-Computer.   Now that it is feasible to get the computing power of a supercomputer on the researcher's desk, this method may become more widely used.

ANNEX 1 - HULL MODELLING IN THE FORCE AND HEURISTIC MODELS

A1.1.   Force Model.

Hull hydrodynamic forces and moments are modelled by Pourzanjani as follows, (taken with permission from (7)):

$$Cd_{90} = Cdl_{90} + [(Cd2_{90} - Cdl_{90})\sin^{0.5}al]$$

$$Cl_p = 0.5.K.pi.AR.\sin (2al)|\cos(al)|$$

$$Cl_c = 0.5.Cd_{90}.\sin(2al)|\sin(al)|$$

$$Cl_t = Cl_p = Cl_c$$

$$Lift_h = 0.5.U^2LDCl_t$$

$$Cd_p = 0.5.K.pi.AR.\sin (2al)|\sin(al)|$$

$$Cd_c = Cd_{90}.\sin^3(al)$$

$$Cd_0 = 0.5.AR.pi.\cos^2(al)$$

$$Cd_t = Cd_p = Cd_c$$

$$Drag_h = 0.5.U^2LDCd_t$$

$$N_v = k(13) \ r|r|$$

with the following nomenclature:

al	Drift angle
Cd_{90}	Cross flow drag coefficient
Cdl_{90}	Cross flow drag coefficient at small incidence
$Cd2_{90}$	Cross flow drag coefficient at 90 deg. incidence
Cl_c	Cross-flow lift coefficient
Cl_p	Potential flow lift coefficient
Cl_t	Total lift coefficient
Cd_0	Drag coefficient at zero incidence
Cd_c	Cross-flow drag coefficient
Cd_p	Potential flow drag coefficient
Cd_t	Total drag coefficient
D	Draft
$Drag_h$	Hull drag force
L	Length between perpendiculars
$Lift_h$	Hull lift force
k(13)	Constant
N_v	Viscous drag moment
U	Fluid velocity or ship speed

Equivalent equations used by the author are:

$$LH = k(7) \sin(2.al) - k(15) \sin(4.al).ubrsq$$

$$DH = (k(8) + k(9) \sin^2(al).ubrsq$$

$$Nv = k(13).r|r|$$

with the following nomenclature

al	Drift angle
DH	Hull drag
k(..)	Coefficients
LH	Hull lift
Nv	Hull viscous drag.
ubrsq	Fluid velocity or ship speed

It is found that both sets of equations yield similar results.

Both authors determine the position of the centre of pressure by either experimental results or by analytical expressions to represent analytical results.

A.1.2.   Heuristic Model

Hull forces and moments are represented by the following expressions, for a small, single screwed vessel of moderate block coefficient going ahead.   Similar expressions are used for other types of ship and other manoeuvring regimes:

a. Steady State Velocities:

$ur = |u/k(9)|$
$Uss = k(4).ns - k(5).u.r^2$
$Vss = k(7).ur.r$
$Rss = k(2).(del)^{k(26)}.ur.sign(del).ur$

b.   Accelerations:

$du = (Uss-u)/k(6)$
$dv = (Vss - v)/k(19)$
$dr = (Rss + k(3).(u - k(4).ns) - r)/k(1)$

with the following nomenclature:

del	rudder angle
dr	yaw acceleration
du	surge acceleration
dv	sway acceleration
k(..)	Coefficients
ns	Shaft speed
r	Yaw rate
Rss	Steady state yaw rate
u	Surge velocity
ur	Speed multiplier
Uss	Steady state surge vlocity
v	Sway velocity
Vss	Steady state sway velocity

ANNEX 2 - SOME CASE STUDIES

A2.1.   Ferry Operations at Portsmouth

In order to cater for a new large vessel at the relatively congested ferry port at Portsmouth, it was necessary to lengthen the jetty, and to determine the extent of any changes in the dredging patterns or any other changes in the layout of the port necessary to operate the ship.   Many modern ferries are characterised by having a very large lateral wind area and a shallow draught, with the result that wind is frequently the determining factor for manoeuvring.   In this port, it was necessary to determine whether it was necessary to move a training vessel in the possible path of the ship, to find the extent of any dredging and to find out if it was necessary to resite a power cable.   The main constraints on the ship modelling were a tight timescale, and a relative lack of manoeuvring data on the ship.   As the manoeuvres are ship-critical, it was important to get a model which behaves realistically in all manoeuvring regimes, and could be produced quickly using the small amount of ship data available.

The ship was modelled using the heuristic model, and validated by the port's pilots and those of the ferry company, to ensure that the ship behaved realistically throughout the manoeuvring regimes, and particularly in response to wind forces.

Over 80 runs were carried out in the simulator, the results showing that only a limited amount of dredging was needed, that operations were feasible in the limited space available, and that an extension to the jetty did not compromise manoeuvres.   A typical result of a manoeuvre is shown in Fig A1, in which the limited manoeuvring space, limited by the presence of a number of warships, is well shown.

The value of such a study, when it is possible that substantial capital works could be required if the manoeuvring behaviour of a ship does not permit an adequate safety level, is evident.

The cooperation of Portsmouth City Council is gratefully acknowledged.

A2.2.   Manoeuvres into Great Yarmouth

This port is characterised by having a strong cross current at the entrance, a very narrow channel and a sharp 90 degree bend just inside the channel.   Ships have to enter at a reasonable speed to be able to counter the cross current, but once inside the breakwaters, with no cross current, need to slow to be able to negotiate the bend.   The radius of the bend is less than the turning radius of some ships using the port, and so it is in general necessary to slow to the speed at which either differential engine thrust or bow thrusters are able to be used to assist the turning.
  It is not possible to turn larger ships at the berth, as the river is too narrow, and so ships leaving have to back down the channel, negotiating the bend using their thrusters for controlling ship direction.   RoRos have a large windage, and so tend to be blown onto the bank if adequate control cannot be maintained.

  A study was undertaken to determine the suitability of a particular ship to negotiate the port, and in particular to check that the effectors were adequate to enable operations to be carried out in a range of environmental conditions.   A severe constraint on producing the ship model was that the amount of data was limited to a set of drawings and limited trial data, and the time available for producing an initial set of conclusions was one week. Operations had to be equally valid in all manoeuvring regimes, as many of the operations were conducted at slow speeds and going astern.   In these circumstances the Heuristic Model was able to be used, as the model could be produced in a few days from the limited trial data available.   The model dynamic performance was checked by pilots with experience in similar vessels, to an agreed set of characteristics.

  It was concluded that the effectors would be able to manoeuvre the ship into the port, in winds up to gale force, despite the relatively high windage.   A typical entry manoeuvre is shown in Fig A2, in which the set of the tidal stream is clearly shown in the approach manoeuvre.   Once the ship is inside the port, it slows, and negotiates the bend using the thruster.   The wind set is shown after the bend has been negotiated.   It will be seen too that large drift angles, of up to 40 degrees, are present during the passage of the bend and the difficulty of negotiating the bend is illustrated.

A2.3.   Prediction of Submersible Performance

This task was different from the previous ones, in that extensive model tank tests were available, and it was necessary to produce a manoeuvring model which could be used as a design tool for very low speed manoeuvring under external power.   In this case, the hull performance at slow speeds and large drift angles is required. As the vessel was to be undowered during manoeuvres, there was no need to model the engine performance.

As in this case the values of the lift and drag on the hull were of prime importance, as these determined the necessary control forces required, it was appropriate to use the Force Model. The experimental results were matched using the terms of Annex A1, and a very extensive set of trial manoeuvres was carried out to examine the manoeuvrability of the vessel in all regimes, with external towing forces and in wind and current conditions.

In this case a comparison was carried out with the results of a number of models based on hydrodynamic derivatives.   A conclusion was made that the use of derivative based models can be of limited validity for slow speed manoeuvres.   This is entirely consistent with the author's previous experience, as it was for precisely this reason that the Force Model was developed.

The cooperation of Vosper Thorneycroft (UK) is gratefully acknowledged.

REFERENCES

1.   Nomoto, K.   'Problems and Requirements of Directional
Stability and Control of Surface Ships'.   J. Mech. Eng. Sci., Vol. 14
No. 7, 1972, pp1-3.

2.   NMRC.   'A System for Estimation of Hydrodynamic Coeffcieints
for Full Scale Ship Tests'.   NMRC Kings Point, NY, 11024, Appendix
A.

3.   Martinussen, K and Linnerud, I.   'Techniques for Predicting
Manoeuvring Characteristics of Ships at the Design Stage'.   proc.
Int. Comf. on Ship Manouevrability, RINA, Gatwick, 29Apr. - 1 May
1987, Paper 18.

4.   Kouichi Shouji et al. 'Hydrodynamic Forces by Propeller and
Rudder Interaction at Low Speed.'   Proc. MARSIM & ICSM 90, Soc.
Nav. Arch. of Japan, Tokyo 4-7 June 1990, pp 369-376.

5.   McCallum, IR.   'A New Approach to Manoeuvring Ship
Simulation'.   PhD Thesis, The City University, London, 1976.

6.   Pourzanjani M et al.   'A Hybrid Method of Estimating
Hydrodynamcally Generated Forces for use in Ship Manoeuvring
Simulation.   Int. Shipbuilding Progress, Vol 34, No 399, (1987).

7.   Pouzanjani M.   'Formulation of the Force Mathematical Model
of Ship Manoeuvring'.   Int. Shipbuilding Progress, Vol 37 No 409,
(1990), pp 5-32.

8.   Rizzi, A and Purcell CF.   'Large Scale CYBER 205 simulation of
Vortex Flowfields Arond Submarines'.   Proc, First Int. Symp. on
Maritime Simulation, Springer Verlag 1985, ISBN 0-387-15630-8, 1985,
pp 114-124.

MANOEUVRING REGIMES

	Ship Moving	Engines Going
Normal Manoeuvring	Ahead	Ahead
Stopping	Ahead	Astern
Backing	Astern	Astern
Checking Sternway	Astern	Ahead

Figure 1: Manoeuvring Regimes

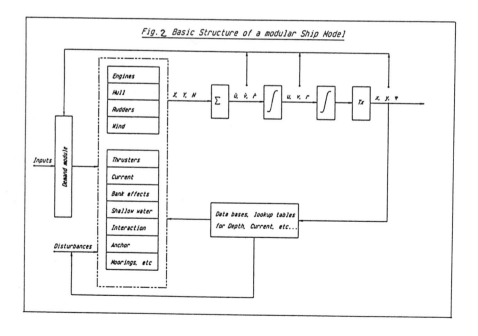

Figure 2: The Modular Model

Equations of Motion. The nonlinear differential equations of motion can be expressed as:

$$M \begin{bmatrix} \dot{u} \\ \dot{v} \\ \dot{r} \end{bmatrix} = \frac{1}{2}\rho U^2 \ell^2 \begin{bmatrix} C_X \\ C_Y \\ \ell\, C_N \end{bmatrix} + \begin{bmatrix} F_{xp} \\ F_{yp} \\ M_{zp} \end{bmatrix} + \begin{bmatrix} mvr \\ -mur \\ 0 \end{bmatrix} + \begin{bmatrix} \Gamma\underline{w} \end{bmatrix}$$

$$\begin{array}{cccc} \text{hydrodynamic} & \text{propulsion} & \text{inertial} & \text{environmental} \\ \text{terms} & \text{terms} & \text{terms} & \text{disturbances} \end{array}$$

and

$$\dot{\psi} = r$$

$$\dot{x} = u\cos\psi - v\sin\psi$$

$$\dot{y} = v\cos\psi + u\sin\psi$$

Where the nondimensional hydrodynamic terms are expanded as:

$$C_X = X_\bullet + X_{vr}(v')(r') + X_{vv}(v')^2 + X_{\delta\delta}\, K_r(\delta)^2$$

$$C_Y = Y_\bullet + Y_v(v') + Y_r(r') + Y_{vvr}(v')^2(r') + Y_{vrr}(v')(r')^2 + Y_{vvv}(v')^3 + Y_{rrr}(r')^3 + Y_{\delta\delta\delta}\, K_r(\delta)^3$$
$$+ Y_\delta\, K_r(\delta)$$

$$C_N = N_\bullet + N_v(v') + N_r(r') + N_{vvr}(v')^2(r') + N_{vrr}(v')(r')^2 + N_{vvv}(v')^3 + N_{rrr}(r')^3 + N_{\delta\delta\delta}\, K_r(\delta)^3$$
$$+ N_\delta\, K_r(\delta)$$

where,

$$v' \equiv \frac{(v-v_c)}{U}, \quad r' \equiv \frac{(r-r_c)\ell}{U}, \quad \text{and} \quad U = \left\{(u-u_c)^2 + (v-v_c)^2\right\}^{\frac{1}{2}}$$

Figure 3: The Hydrodynamic Derivative Type of Model (Source: MARAD)

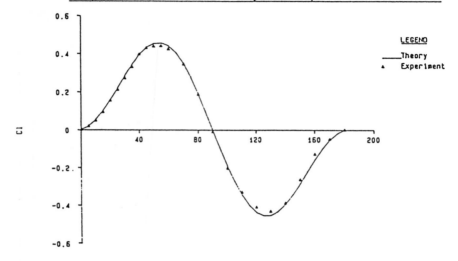

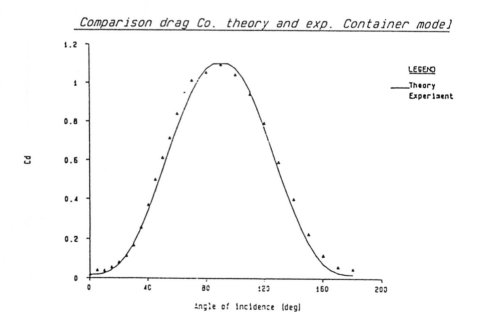

Figure 4: Comparison of Model and Ship Data, by Pourzanjani

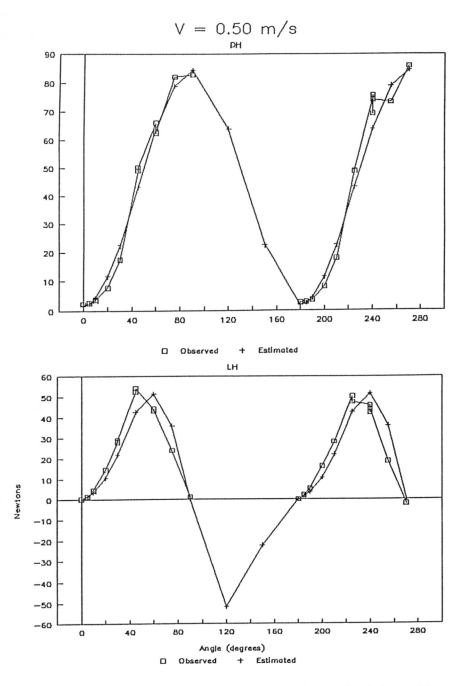

Figure 5: Comparison of Model and Experimental Data for Submersible (Experimental Data Courtesy Vosper Thorneycroft (UK))

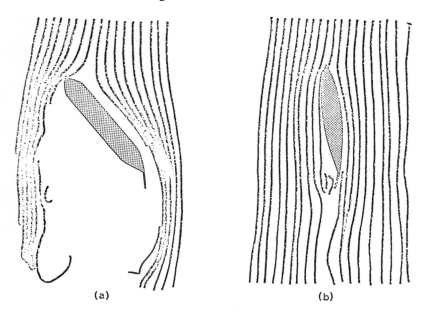

Figure 6: Streamline Flow on Hull Forms. a. VLCC, b. MARINER

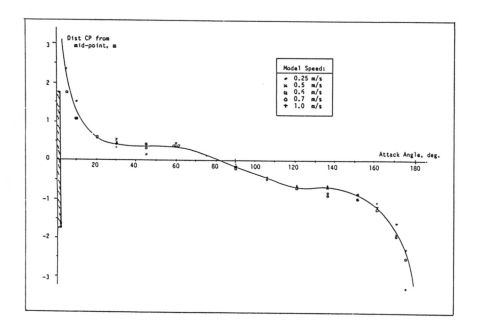

Figure 7: Distance of Centre of Pressure from Midpoint as Function of Angle of Attack

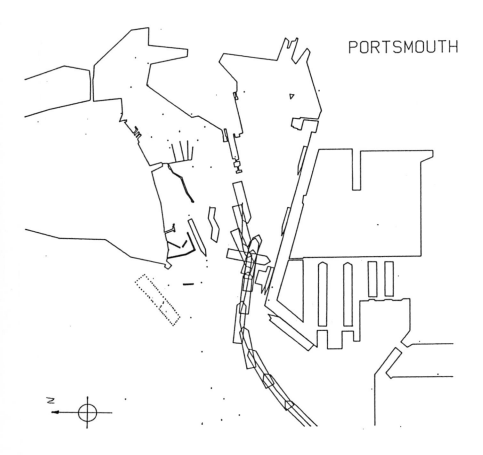

PORTSMOUTH

Figure A1: Manoeuvres in Portsmouth

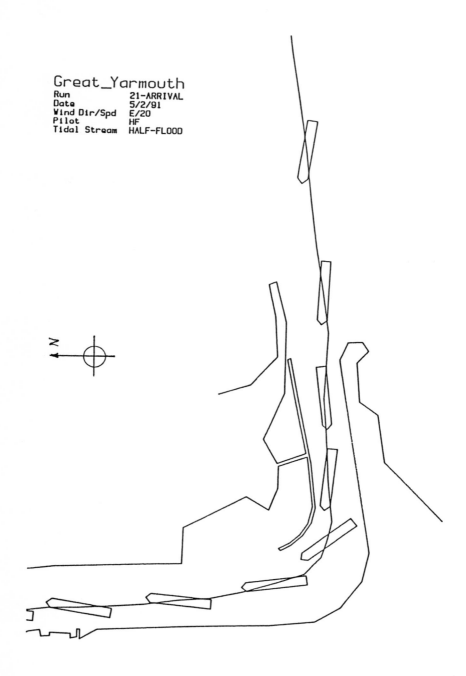

Figure A2: Manoeuvres in Yarmouth

Manoeuvring Characteristics of a Ship in Deep and Shallow Waters as a Function of Loading Condition

K. Kijima (*), S. Tanaka (*), M. Matsunaga (**), T. Hori (***)

(*) Department of Naval Architecture, Kyushu University, Hakozaki, Higashi-ku, Fukuoka 812, Japan

(**) Research Institute, Nippon Kaiji Kyokai, Mitaka, Tokyo 181, Japan

(***) Oshima Shipbuilding Co., Ltd., Oshima, Nagasaki 857-24, Japan

ABSTRACT

It is considered that a loading condition and water depth are important parameters for the prediction of ship manoeuvrability at the initial design stage. For the prediction of ship manoeuvrability with high accuracy, it will be required to estimate the hydrodynamic forces acting on ship accurately in any conditions. At the first, the hydrodynamic forces acting on ship in deep and shallow waters with parameter of loading condition are shown by use of the proposed prediction method from viewpoint of practical design. In the second, the manoeuvring performances of full scale ship are discussed and compared with the sea trial results in deep water. Lastly, the manoeuvring characteristics of a ship in any loading condition are discussed with the effect of water depth.

1. INTRODUCTION

From the view point of marine safety, it is of importance to evaluate the ship manoeuvring performance at initial design stage. The manoeuvring performance of ship, in general, will be estimated in fully loaded condition, when it is required to get the information of the manoeuvrability. IMO has been discussed on the establishment of ship manoeuvring performance standard, and the recent preliminary results of discussion have pointed out that fully loaded condition in deep water should be dealt with as first step. The discussion of ship manoeuvring performance standard should be basically considered on fully loaded condition in deep water as fundamental condition expressing her inherent performance.

On the other hand, the ship generally is operated not always only in fully loaded condition, but also in half loaded condition or trimmed condition. The manoeuvring characteristics are influenced considerably by the effects of loading condition depending on ship's form. Furthermore, the sea trial tests of newly built ships are mostly executed in ballast condition for dry cargo ships. From these points, one of the authors has proposed the practical prediction method for manoeuvrability in any loading condition such as half loaded, ballast loaded and trim by stern condition[1]. However, since this method has only been investigated about model ships, the discussion on the prediction of manoeuvrability of full scale ship should be done in much more detail.

The other importance to be considered in ship design and also included in the manoeuvring booklet which IMO has adopted as resolution A.601(15) is the performance in shallow water. One of the authors has already proposed the estimation method of hydrodynamic forces acting on ship in shallow water in fully loaded condition[2]. But it is considered that the manoeuvring characteristics in shallow water may be affected remarkably by the effects of loading condition as well as the water depth.

In this paper, at first, the hydrodynamic forces acting on ship in deep and shallow waters with parameter of loading condition are shown by using of the simplified estimation method from viewpoint of practical design. Secondly, the practical method is applied to the prediction of full scale ship at the design stage, and compared with the sea trial results in deep water. Lastly, the manoeuvring characteristics of a ship in any loading condition are discussed with the effect of water depth.

2. BASIC MATHEMATICAL MODEL

The mathematical model for prediction of ship manoeuvrability used in this paper has been already proposed by one of the authors as shown in reference [1], that are as follows.

$$
\left.
\begin{aligned}
(m' + m'_x)\left(\frac{L}{U}\right)\left(\frac{\dot{U}}{U}\cos\beta - \dot{\beta}\sin\beta\right) + (m' + m'_y)r'\sin\beta &= X' \\
-(m' + m'_y)\left(\frac{L}{U}\right)\left(\frac{\dot{U}}{U}\sin\beta + \dot{\beta}\cos\beta\right) + (m' + m'_x)r'\cos\beta &= Y' \\
(I'_{zz} + i'_{zz})\left(\frac{L}{U}\right)^2\left(\frac{\dot{U}}{L}r' + \frac{U}{L}\dot{r}'\right) &= N'
\end{aligned}
\right\} \quad (1)
$$

The superscript " ′ " refers to the non-dimensionalized quantities as follows.

$$m', m'_x, m'_y = m, m_x, m_y/\frac{1}{2}\rho L^2 d_m, \quad I'_{zz}, i'_{zz} = I_{zz}, i_{zz}/\frac{1}{2}\rho L^4 d_m$$

$$X', Y' = X, Y/\frac{1}{2}\rho L d_m U^2, \quad N' = N/\frac{1}{2}\rho L^2 d_m U^2$$

$$r' = rL/U$$

where m, m_x, m_y : ship's mass, added mass of x, y axis of ship respectively, L : ship length, β : drift angle, d_m : mean draft, U : ship speed, r : angular velocity, X, Y, N : external force of x, y axis and yaw moment about the center of gravity of ship respectively.

The external forces shown in the right hand side of the equation (1) are assumed as follows.

$$\left.\begin{array}{l} X' = X'_H + X'_P + X'_R \\ Y' = Y'_H + Y'_P + Y'_R \\ N' = N'_H + N'_P + N'_R \end{array}\right\} \tag{2}$$

In the equation (2), the subscript " H " symbolizes ship hull, " P " propeller and " R " rudder. Y'_P and N'_P in equation (2) express the term of lateral force and yaw moment acting on propeller respectively. But these terms are very small compared with the other terms such as Y'_H, Y'_R etc. during forward speed. Then the terms of Y'_P and N'_P are assumed as negligible small in this paper.

For the longitudinal component of the forces, the following expressions are assumed.

$$\left.\begin{array}{l} X'_H = X'_{\beta r} r' \sin\beta + X'_{uu}\cos^2\beta \\ X'_P = C_{tp}\left(1 - t_{P0}\right) n^2 D_P^4 K_T\left(J_P\right)/\frac{1}{2}L d_m U^2 \\ K_T\left(J_P\right) = C_1 + C_2 J_P + C_3 J_P^2 \\ J_P = U\cos\beta\left(1 - w_P\right)/\left(n D_P\right) \end{array}\right\} \tag{3}$$

where t_{P0} : thrust reduction coefficient in straight forward moving, C_{tp} : constant, n : propeller revolution, D_P : propeller diameter, w_P : effective wake fraction coefficient at propeller location, J_P : advance coefficient, C_1, C_2, C_3 : constant, $X_{\beta r} = \partial^2 X/\partial\beta\partial r$, etc.

The lateral force and yaw moment acting on ship hull are expressed as follows.

$$\left.\begin{array}{l} Y'_H = Y'_\beta\beta + Y'_r r' + Y'_{\beta\beta}\beta|\beta| + Y'_{rr}r'|r'| \\ \qquad\qquad\qquad + \left(Y'_{\beta\beta r}\beta + Y'_{\beta rr}r'\right)\beta r' \\ N'_H = N'_\beta\beta + N'_r r' + N'_{\beta\beta}\beta|\beta| + N'_{rr}r'|r'| \\ \qquad\qquad\qquad + \left(N'_{\beta\beta r}\beta + N'_{\beta rr}r'\right)\beta r' \end{array}\right\} \tag{4}$$

The terms on rudder force are assumed as follows.

$$\left.\begin{array}{l} X'_R = -\left(1 - t_R\right) F'_N \sin\delta \\ Y'_R = -\left(1 + a_H\right) F'_N \cos\delta \\ N'_R = -\left(x'_R + a_H x'_H\right) F'_N \cos\delta \end{array}\right\} \tag{5}$$

where t_R : coefficient for additional drag, a_H : ratio of additional lateral force, x'_R : nondimensional distance between the center of gravity of ship and center of lateral force $(x'_R = x_R/L)$, x'_H : nondimensional distance between the center of gravity of ship and center of additional lateral force $(x'_H = x_H/L)$, δ : rudder angle.
The normal force acting on rudder " F'_N " is assumed as the following expressions.

$$\left.\begin{array}{l} F'_N = (A_R/Ld)\,C_N U_R^2 \sin \alpha_R \\ C_N = 6.13 K_R/(K_R + 2.25), \quad U_R^2 = (1 - w_R)^2 \{1 + C\,g(s)\} \\ g(s) = \eta K \{2 - (2 - K)\,s\} s/(1 - s)^2 \\ K = 0.6\,(1 - w_P)\,/\,(1 - w_R), \quad w_R = w_{R0} \cdot w_P/w_{P0} \\ \alpha_R = \delta - \gamma \cdot \beta'_R, \quad \eta = D_P/h_R, \quad \beta'_R = \beta - 2 x'_R \cdot r' \ , \quad x'_R \simeq -0.5 \\ s = 1.0 - (1 - w_P)\,U \cos \beta/nP \end{array}\right\} \quad (6)$$

where K_R : aspect ratio of rudder, A_R : rudder area, C : constant for starboard and port rudder, w_{P0}, w_{R0} : effective wake fraction coefficient at propeller, rudder location in straight forward moving respectively, γ : flow straightening coefficient, h_R : rudder height, U_R : effective rudder inflow speed, α_R : effective rudder inflow angle.

3. HYDRODYNAMIC FORCE IN DEEP WATER

The above mentioned mathematical model will be available for estimation of the manoeuvring performance of a ship. The performance can be predicted if the hydrodynamic force acting on hull, propeller and rudder are estimated by some methods. These hydrodynamic forces such as the lateral force and yaw moment coefficients in even keel condition and trimmed condition, longitudinal component of the forces, rudder force and its interaction forces, in general, have been obtained by the model test or the data base .
In this paper, the approximate formulae to estimate the forces, which are such Y'_β, $Y'_r \cdots$ etc., acting on ship with her principal particulars in deep water are used as shown in reference[1].

4. HYDRODYNAMIC FORCE IN SHALLOW WATER

The approximate formulae for estimating the hydrodynamic force acting on a ship in shallow water are proposed[2]. These formulae are obtained semi-empirically from the results of numerical calculations based on lifting surface theory, and model tests in full load condition. Basically, the above formulae for full load condition can be applied to the case of shallow water by correcting the hydrodynamic derivatives and coefficients which have been originally obtained for deep water.
In this paper, to estimate the hydrodynamic force acting on a ship

in shallow water with function of loading condition, the above method is developed to the case of ballast and half load conditions as follows.

$$D_{shw} = f(h) \times D_{dep} \tag{7}$$

where D_{shw} : derivatives in shallow water including ballast and half load conditions, D_{dep} : derivatives in deep water, including ballast and half load conditions, $f(h)$: correcting factor, $h = d_m/H$ (d_m: mean draft, H: water depth).

The correcting factor $f(h)$ for the effect of water depth is assumed as follows. For $Y_\beta', Y_{\beta\beta}', Y_{\beta rr}', N_\beta'$ and N_r';

$$f(h) = 1/(1-h)^n - h \tag{8}$$

For the other derivatives, the following factors are assumed.

$$f(h) = 1 + a_1 h + a_2 h^2 + a_3 h^3 \tag{9}$$

where, for instance

$$Y_\beta'; \quad n = 0.40 C_B B/d_m$$

for $Y_r' - (m' + m_x')$;

$$a_1 = -5.5(C_B B/d_m)^2 + 26 C_B B/d_m - 31.5$$
$$a_2 = 37(C_B B/d_m)^2 - 185 C_B B/d_m + 230$$
$$a_3 = -38(C_B B/d_m)^2 + 197 C_B B/d_m - 250$$

where C_B : block coefficient, B : ship breadth.

For the interaction force coefficient among hull, propeller and rudder, wake fraction w_{P0}, w_{R0} at propeller, rudder location respectively, and flow straightening coefficient γ have the most dominant effect on manoeuvring motion especially in shallow water[3]. Therefore, these interaction force coefficients in shallow water are assumed as follows.

(a) The wake fraction ratio $\varepsilon = (1 - w_{R0})/(1 - w_{P0})$ is assumed to be independent of water depth.

(b) The wake fraction coefficient w_{P0} at propeller location in shallow water is estimated by correcting the coefficient for deep water as shown in reference[4], that is as follows.

$$\frac{(1 - w_{P0})_{shw}}{(1 - w_{P0})_{dep}} = \cos\ (C_{wp0} \cdot d_m/H) \tag{10}$$

where $(1 - w_{P0})_{shw}$: wake factor at propeller location in shallow water, $(1 - w_{P0})_{dep}$: wake factor at propeller location in deep water, C_{wp0} : constant for each type of ship.

(c) The flow straightening coefficient γ for shallow water is defined on basis of measurements as shown in reference[5].

5. NUMERICAL SIMULATION AND DISCUSSION

The numerical calculation on hydrodynamic force and simulation on manoeuvring motion of a ship in deep and shallow waters with function of loading condition are carried out by using the above mentioned approximate formulae.

The model ships used for this investigation are VLCC(Ship A), high speed container ship(Ship B), and bulk carrier(Ship C) shown in Table 1 .

Table 1: Main particulars of model ships

Name of Ship		A	B	C
Type of Ship		VLCC	Cont.	Bulk
FULL	$L_{(m)}$	2.50	3.00	2.50
	$B_{(m)}$	0.436	0.435	0.443
	$d_{m(m)}$	0.157	0.163	0.156
	C_B	0.802	0.572	0.803
HALF	$d_{m(m)}$	0.117	—	0.125
	C_B	0.782	—	0.790
BALLAST	$d_{m(m)}$	0.084	0.094	0.074
	C_B	0.766	0.518	0.758

As the example, the results on non-dimensionalized lateral force ($Y'_H = Y_H/\frac{1}{2}\rho L d_m U^2$) and yawing moment ($N'_H = N_H/\frac{1}{2}\rho L^2 d_m U^2$) about midship acting on bare hull for oblique motion by using the above mentioned method are shown in Figure 1 on Ship A.

In this figure, the plotted symbols such as circle, rhombus, square, triangle and cross shapes show the measured results with every loading conditions which are full load, half load, ballast with even keel and ballast with trimmed(1 % and 2 % to ship length in trim by stern) conditions in deep and shallow waters. The estimated values on Y'_H and N'_H agree well with the measured results of the model ship in deep water($H/d_m = 6.0$)and shallow water ($H/d_m = 1.3$) with every loading condition, as though the model tests are carried out at only one case of full load condition in shallow water. As a result, these estimated data will be practically useful to predict ship manoeuvrability in deep and shallow waters including the effect of loading condition at design stage.

At the next, the numerical simulations on turning motion of a model ship are carried out by applying these hydrodynamic forces acting on ships and the estimated results are compared with the measured ones.

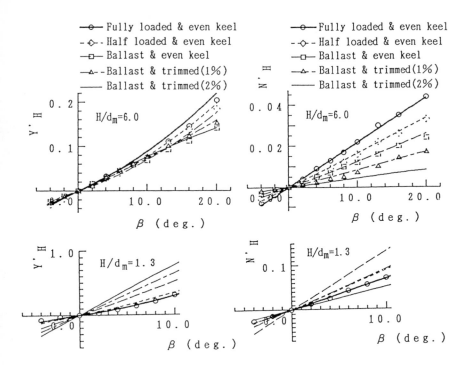

Figure 1. Hydrodynamic forces acting on a ship as function of loading condition in deep and shallow waters.

Figure 2 shows the turning trajectories and time histories of ship speed (U/U_0, where U_0 : initial speed) , drift angle (β) , angular velocity (r') and heading angle (ψ)on Ship A due to the rudder angle of 35 degrees in full load condition with even keel and in ballast with trimmed condition in deep water.

From these comparisons, the simulation results based on the proposed formulae for estimating the hydrodynamic forces acting on ship agree well with the measured results of free running model test. It may be considered that the above mentioned method will be useful for prediction of manoeuvrability of model ships including ballast with trimmed condition in deep water.

5.1. Prediction for the manoeuvrability of full scale ship

The above mentioned methods are investigated about only model ships. Our final aim is to predict the manoeuvring performance of full scale ship. Furthermore, the sea trial tests of newly built ships are mostly carried out in ballast condition for dry cargo ships, even though fundamental condition expressing her inherent performance for the assessment is a fully loaded condition. Therefore, this approach is applied for the prediction of full scale ships in deep water.

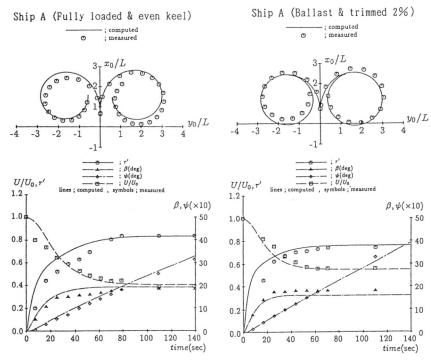

Figure 2. Turning characteristics on Ship A due to the rudder angle 35 degrees in deep water.

The full scale ships used for the prediction are an oil tanker(Ship D), a bulk carrier(Ship E) and a VLCC(Ship F) shown in Table 2 .

Figure 3 shows the turning trajectories on Ship D due to the rudder angle of 35 degrees. Figure 3-(a) and 3-(b) on Ship D show the results in fully loaded & even keel condition and ballast & trimmed condition respectively. Figure 4 shows the time histories of ship speed (U/U_0, where U_0 : initial speed), propeller shaft revolution (n/n_0, n_0 : initial revolution of propeller shaft) and heading angle (ψ) during starboard turning motion after rudder execution. Figure 5 shows the time histories of rudder angle(δ) and heading angle(ψ) during 10°–5° modified zig-zag manoeuvring motion on Ship E in ballast & trimmed condition.

In these figures, the plotted circles show the sea trial results of full scale ship. The scale effects are left out of consideration in these calculations. Besides, a main engine of ship is actually regulated by a governor to control

Table 2: Main particulars of full scale ships

Name of Ship		D	E	F
Type of Ship		Tanker	Bulk	VLCC
FULL	$L_{(m)}$	219.6	172.0	307.0
	$B_{(m)}$	32.2	30.5	54.0
	$d_{m(m)}$	11.7	10.7	19.5
	C_B	0.802	0.803	0.813
BALLAST	$d_{m(m)}$	6.5	5.2	8.1
	C_B	0.799	0.758	0.765

the revolution of propeller during turning motion. But propeller revolution is assumed to be constant during manoeuvring motion.

From these comparisons, the simulation results in ballast & trimmed condition have a little differences from the sea trial test results.

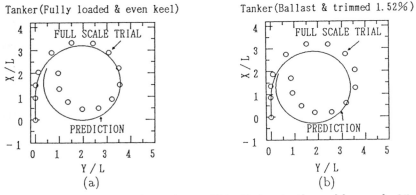

Figure 3. Turning trajectories on Ship D due to the rudder angle 35 degrees in deep water.

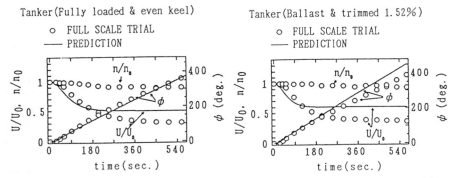

Figure 4. Time histories of U/U_0, n/n_0 and ψ on Ship D due to the rudder angle 35 degrees in deep water.

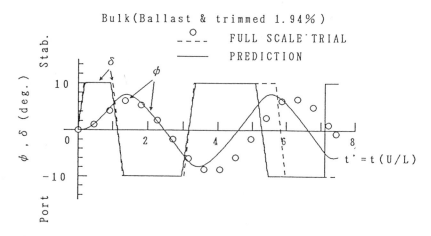

Figure 5. 10°-5° modified zig-zag manoeuvre of Ship E in deep water.

The scale effects will be an important factor to predict the performance of full scale ship by means of the method based on model ship. According to the past studies[3][6], the interaction forces between hull, propeller and rudder are pointed out as the significant parameter as well as the forces acting on bare hull. Hence, the scale effects are considered in difference of effective rudder inflow speed between full scale ship and model ship in this section. The scale effects are taken into the parameters of effective wake and flow straighting factor.

By using these factors, the numerical simulation of full scale ship are carried out. Figure 6 and Figure 7 show the trajectories of turning motion of Ship F with rudder angle 35 degrees in fully loaded condition and ballast condition respectively. Figure 6-(a) and 7-(a) show the simulated results when the value of the wake fraction ratio $\varepsilon = (1 - w_{R0})/(1 - w_{P0})$ and flow straighting coefficient γ are obtained by the approximate formula[1] for model ships.

From these figures, the predicted results in the correlation factor being $\varepsilon = 1.2$ agree well with the the measured results than in $\varepsilon \approx 1.0$ which are obtained by the approximated method. In ballast condition, the predicted results in the flow straighting coefficient being $\gamma = 0.4$ agree well with the measured results than that in the estimated coefficient γ for model ship.

In general, the sea trial results of full scale ship include the effects of main engine control and external disturbances such as wind, wave and current. Needless to say, those effects must be considered in the prediction. However, in fact the sea trial results of full scale ships also include measurement error such as error due to measurement method or measurement process.

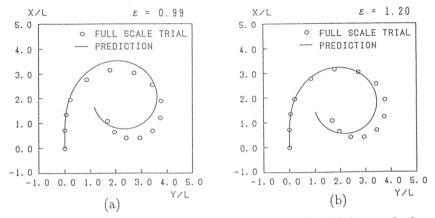

Figure 6. Turning trajectories on Ship F in fully loaded & even keel condition.

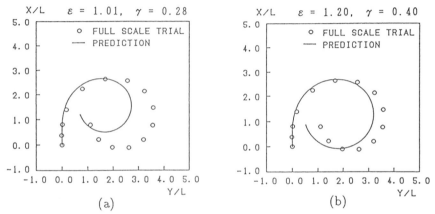

Figure 7. Turning trajectories on Ship F in ballast & trimmed condition.

From these discussions, it is not too much to say that the present method can predict ship manoeuvrability including the effects of loading condition at the design stage.

5.2. Manoeuvring characteristics in deep and shallow waters

The ship is generally operated not always only in fully loaded condition in deep water, but also in half loaded condition or trimmed condition in shallow water, such as the berth approach manoeuvres of VLCC. But it will be very difficult to predict the manoeuvring performance in shallow water including ballast and half load condition by means of model test at the early stage of design. Hence, the simulation study using the hydrodynamic force model can be said to be useful for ship design or ship operation at present.

Figure 8 to 10 show the results, for example, of numerical simulation on the effects of loading condition in turning motion and 10°–10°zig-zag manoeuvring motion in the case of Ship A(VLCC). The above simplified method for estimating the hydrodynamic force acting on a ship in any condition are used. The squat of ship will be an important factor in predicting the performance in shallow water. However, in this paper, the settled draft and trim of ship are assumed to be constant during manoeuvring motion, because her speed is comparatively small in this calculation.

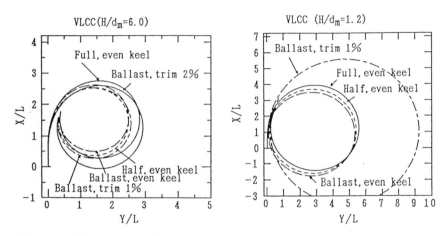

Figure 8. The effects of loading condition on turning trajectory of Ship A in deep and shallow waters.

Figure 8 shows the turning trajectories in deep water($H/d_m = 6.0$) and shallow water ($H/d_m = 1.2$) due to the rudder angle of 35 degrees with every loading condition which are fully loaded, half loaded and ballast, in even keel and trimmed condition.

Figure 9 shows the time histories of heading angle(ψ) during 10°–10°zig-zag manoeuvring motion in deep water and in shallow water with function of loading condition.

Steady turning ability can be evaluated by means of the non-dimensional advance (A_d/L, A_d; advance, L; ship length) and non-dimensional tactical diameter (D_t/L) in turning motion. The first overshoot angle in 10°–10°zig-zag manoeuvre will be one of the most important criteria for course keeping ability as well as yaw checking ability. Then Figure 10-(a) and 10-(b) shows A_d/L, D_t/L in turning motion which are full loaded, half load, ballast load with even keel and ballast with trimmed (1 % and 2 % to ship length) conditions. The parameter "d_m" and "H" describe the mean draft of ship and water depth respectively in these figures. Figure 10-(c) shows the results of the first overshoot angle (ψ_1) in 10°–10°zig-zag manoeuvre. According to these results, the criteria such as A_d/L, D_t/L and ψ_1 will be remarkably affected by the loading condition, especially in shallow water.

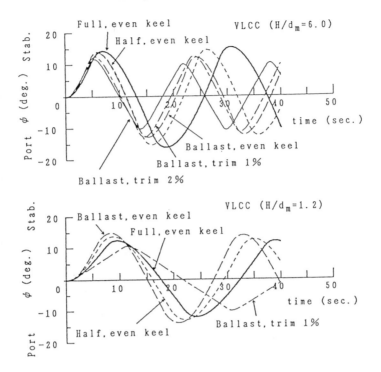

Figure 9. The effects of loading condition on 10°–10° zig-zag manoeuvring motion of Ship A in deep and shallow waters.

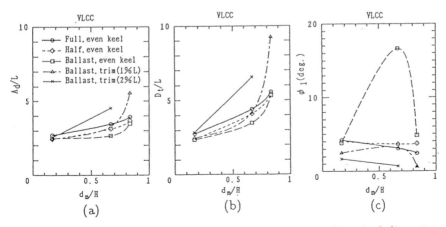

Figure 10. Non-dimensional advance, non-dimensional tactical diameter and the 1st overshoot angle in 10°–10° zig-zag manoeuvre as function of loaded condition.

6. CONCLUDING REMARKS

As the above, this paper proposed the estimation method for hydrodynamic forces acting on hull, propeller and rudder in deep water and shallow
water including the effects of loading condition from the view point of the
practical design. For predicting ship manoeuvring performance, the numerical simulations are carried out by using these estimated forces. These
approach is applied to the prediction of full scale ship. Furthermore, the
manoeuvring characteristics of a ship in any loading condition are discussed
with the effect of water depth. The major concluding remarks can be summarized as follows.

(1) The above mentioned method is based on model ships, but it will
be able to predict the manoeuvring performance of full scale ship if the
interaction coefficients such as the wake fraction and the flow straightening
coefficients are fully considered with high accuracy.

(2) Advance, tactical diameter in turning motion and the first overshoot angle in 10°–10°zig-zag manoeuvre will be remarkably affected by the
loading condition, especially in shallow water.

There still remain some problems to be solved. However, this approach
will be useful for prediction of ship manoeuvrability at the design stage.

The authors would like to thank Mr. T. Katsuno and Mr. Y. Nakiri
for their assistance in carrying out the experiments and computations.

REFERENCES

[1] Kijima, K., Katsuno, T., Nakiri, Y. and Furukawa, Y. 'On the Manoeu-
vring Performance of a Ship with the Parameter of Loading Condition'.
Journal of the The Society of Naval Architects of Japan, Vol. 168, pp.141 -
148, 1990.
[2] Kijima, K. , Nakiri, Y. , Tsutsui, Y. and Matsunaga, M. ' Prediction
Method of Ship Manoeuvrability in Deep and Shallow Waters '. *Proceedings
MARSIM & ICSM 90*, pp.311 - 318, 1990.
[3] Kijima, K., Murakami, M., Katsuno, T. and Nakiri, Y. 'A Study on the
Ship Manoeuvring Characteristics in Shallow Water'. *Trans. of The West-
Japan Society of Naval Architects*, No.69, pp.111 - 122, 1985.(in Japanese)
[4] Kijima, K. , Yoshimura, Y. and Takashina, J. 'Mathematical model for
ship manoeuvring in shallow water'. *Bull. of The Society of Naval Architects
of Japan*, No. 718, pp.13 - 26, 1989. (in Japanese)
[5] Hirano, M. , Yumuro, A. , Nonaka, K. and Kobayashi, H. 'Prediction
of Ship Manoeuvrability in Shallow water'. *Bull. of The Society of Naval
Architects of Japan*, No. 668, pp.45 - 57, 1985. (in Japanese)
[6] Kijima, K. , Asai, S. and Yamagami, M. 'Prediction of Ship Manoeuvrability in Deep water'. *Bull. of The Society of Naval Architects of Japan*,
No. 668, pp.27 - 45, 1985. (in Japanese)

Realistic Simulation of Tug Forces on a Manoeuvring Vessel

M.R. Renilson, P.A. Brandner, R.L. Tasker

Australian Maritime College, Newnham Drive, Launceston, Tasmania, Australia

ABSTRACT

Realistic simulation of shiphandling manoeuvres requires not only a reliable hydrodynamic model of the ship, but also an accurate representation of the forces available from the assisting tugs. When a ship is underway the latter requires careful consideration of the hydrodynamic forces on the tug hull and the propeller forces available.

A series of physical model tests have been performed to determine the hydrodynamic forces and moment on a typical omnidirectional stern drive tug over the full 360 degrees of heading angles. This has been combined with published propeller curves, Oosterveld[1], to enable the tug to be modelled at any orientation to the flow possible during the ship handling manoeuvre.

Using this mathematical model, existing operating procedures are investigated to identify the techniques which give the maximum possible force from the tug for given ship velocities. The results are compared with the so called 'indirect towing' favoured by the conventional tractor tug.

1 INTRODUCTION

The shiphandling simulator at the Australian Maritime College is regularly called upon to investigate new port designs and to train marine pilots to handle large ships in confined water. Both these applications involve considerable use of shiphandling tugs, and the reliability of the results from the simulator depends heavily on the accuracy of the modelling of the tug forces.

The effectiveness of a shiphandling tug is often measured by bollard pull at zero forward speed. Although this is a quick and simple measure of its usefulness it is often questioned as it is well known that it decreases with speed in a conventional towing situation.

By setting up a mathematical model to represent the forces on the tug, the maximum force available from the tug in different situations is investigated. This can be used as an input to the shiphandling simulator to ensure more realistic representation of the tug forces, and hence more accurate simulation of the shiphandling manoeuvre.

2 MATHEMATICAL MODEL

2.1 General

In order to investigate the forces available for shiphandling, a force balance was carried out on a tug applying a constant force to a ship. The forces and moments acting on the tug are the result of the following three factors:

* The reaction force from the ship acting either at the point of contact, or at the towline position;

* The hydrodynamic forces and moment on the tug hull in oblique flow; and

* The hydrodynamic forces on the propellers operating at known revs and angle of rotation.

The influence of interactions, such as between the ship and the tug, and between the tug propellers and hull, have been neglected at this stage.

The force systems and sign convention are shown in Figure.1:

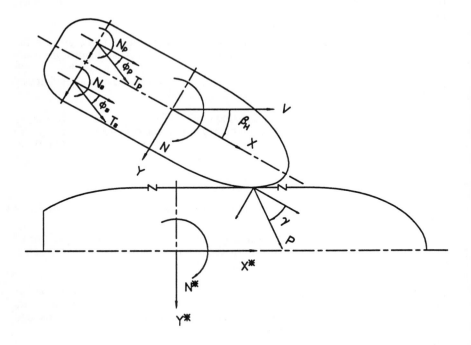

Figure.1 Force systems and sign conventions

The (X,Y,N) coordinate system is fixed in the tug and the (X,Y,N)* coordinate system is fixed in the ship.

2.2 Tug equilibrium
For equilibrium in the horizontal plane the following equations must be satisfied:

$$X_H + X_P + X_S = 0 \qquad (1)$$

$$Y_H + Y_P + Y_S = 0 \qquad (2)$$

$$N_H + N_P + N_S = 0 \qquad (3)$$

For each condition the required ship reaction force, P, and its direction, γ, are specified. From this, together with the geometry of the tug, the forces and moment from the ship, $(X,Y,N)_S$, can be calculated. The hydrodynamic forces, $(X,Y,N)_H$, acting on the tug at the desired drift angle and velocity are known from model experiments, and hence the forces required from the propellers for equilibrium can be found using equations (1), (2) and (3).

2.3 Reaction forces from the ship
The reaction force from the ship, which balances that from the tug, may act at either the position of the towing point, if the tug is operating in the pulling mode, or at the point of contact on the bow of the tug if operating in the pushing mode as shown in Figure.2. Although the former position remains fixed the latter is a function of the angle between the tug and ship centrelines. This also depends on the tugs bow fender profile.

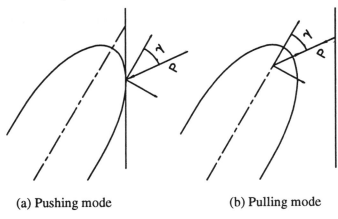

(a) Pushing mode   (b) Pulling mode

Figure.2 Reaction force representation

2.4 Hydrodynamic forces on the tug hull
The hydrodynamic forces have been determined from a series of tank tests carried out in the 60m towing tank in the Ship Hydrodynamics Centre at the Australian Maritime College. The model used was 1: 25 scale, particulars of the full scale tug are listed in Appendix-A. Tests were carried out on the bare hull only, forces measured were those in the horizontal plane with the model free in pitch, heave and roll. The model was tested at velocities ranging between 3 - 10 knots full scale and drift angles ranging between 0 - 360 degrees. An example of the results is shown in Figure.3 for a full scale speed of 5 knots (Fn = 0.144).

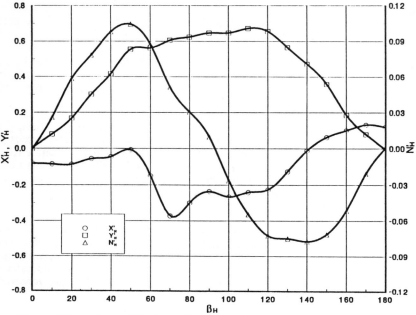

Figure.3 Experimentally determined hydrodynamic forces on tug hull

2.5 Tug propeller forces

The propeller forces, $(X,Y,N)_P$ required for equilibrium are calculated from equations (1) - (3) as $(X,Y,N)_H$ and $(X,Y,N)_S$ are known. The transformation of these to the actual propeller locations, $(T,\phi)_P$ and $(T,\phi)_S$ is statically indeterminate to the first degree. However a fourth equation may be formulated using the condition that (T_P+T_S) = minimum, resulting in the lowest total thrust, hence the following transformations:

$$\text{for } \left|\frac{X_M}{X_P}\right| < 1$$

$$T_P = \frac{1}{2}\left|\frac{X_M}{X_P} + 1\right|\sqrt{Y_P^2 + X_P^2}, \qquad \phi_P = \arctan\frac{Y_P}{X_P} \qquad (4)$$

$$T_S = \frac{1}{2}\left|\frac{X_M}{X_P} - 1\right|\sqrt{Y_P^2 + X_P^2}, \qquad \phi_S = \arctan\frac{Y_P}{X_P}$$

$$\text{for } \left|\frac{X_M}{X_P}\right| > 1$$

$$T_P = \frac{1}{2}\left|1 + \frac{X_M}{X_P}\right|\sqrt{Y_P^2 + X_M^2}, \qquad \phi_P = \arctan\frac{Y_P}{X_M} \qquad (5)$$

$$T_S = \frac{1}{2}\left|1 - \frac{X_M}{X_P}\right|\sqrt{Y_P^2 + X_M^2}, \qquad \phi_S = \arctan -\frac{Y_P}{X_M}$$

where

$$X_M = \frac{N_P + x_P Y_P}{y_P} \tag{6}$$

The force term X_M, represents the force in the X direction required by each propeller to balance $(Y,N)_P$ and depending on the magnitude of $|X_M/X_P|$ the forces will be configured in one of the two modes as shown in Figure.4.

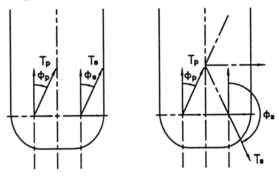

(a) Mode 1, $\left|\dfrac{X_M}{X_P}\right| < 1$, $\phi_p = \phi_s$ (b) Mode 2, $\left|\dfrac{X_M}{X_P}\right| > 1$, $\phi_s = 180 - \phi_p$

Figure.4 Configurations of propeller forces

The moments, Np and Ns, which occur on each of the propellers as shown in Figure.5, have been found to have a negligible effect and are ignored.

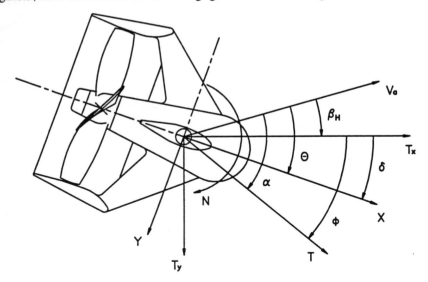

Figure.5 Propeller forces and sign convention

As $(T,\phi)_p$ and $(T,\phi)_s$ are known the required propeller rps, n, torque, Q, and angle of rotation, δ, are calculated using a model developed from published open water test results, carried out at MARIN, Oosterveld[1]. The results are for a MARIN Ka 4-70 series screw with P/D=1 in nozzle no. 19A. Curves of C_T - β_P, α - β_P, C_Q - β_P and C_M - β_P, for θ varying between $0-180$ degrees are shown in Figure.6.

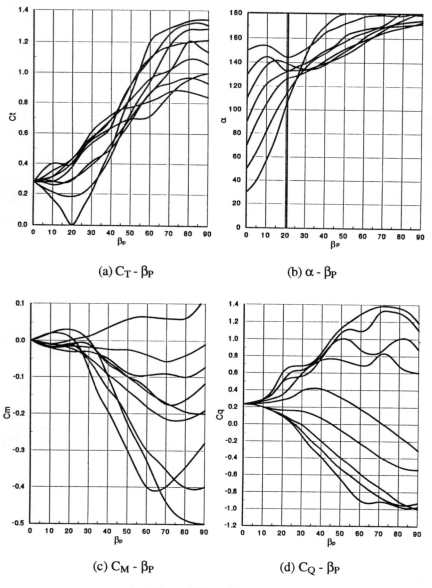

(a) C_T - β_P (b) α - β_P

(c) C_M - β_P (d) C_Q - β_P

Figure.6 Propeller curves

Simultaneous solution of the following equations for β_P then enables the calculation of n, Q and M:

$$C_T(\beta_P,\theta)\, V_A^2 - \frac{T}{^1\!/_2\rho A_0}\, \text{Sin}^2\beta_P = 0 \tag{7}$$

$$(\phi + \beta_H) - \alpha(\beta_P,\theta) = 0 \tag{8}$$

$$\beta_P(C_T) - \beta_P(\alpha) = 0 \tag{9}$$

The values of n and Q can then be compared with the engine characteristics to determine if the equilibrium position is possible.

3 RESULTS AND DISCUSSION

3.1 Tug performance in the pushing mode
When operating in the pushing mode the tug is generally made fast on a short line. This enables the tug to pull if required to do so and in certain circumstances some force may be induced in the line to aid the tug in maintaining position.

For this example of the application of the method to the pushing mode, the situation where a transverse force only is required, with no longitudinal component, as shown in Figure.7 is presented. It is assumed that the ship is neither swaying or yawing, and the effect of forward speed on the maximum force available from the tug is investigated.

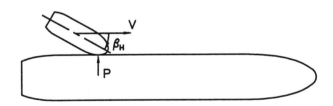

Figure.7 Tug and ship arrangement for pushing investigation

For a fixed velocity and drift angle, Figure.8 shows a plot of the required thrust and its direction for each propeller against transverse force applied to the ship. The two modes of operation of the thrusters defined above can be clearly seen. It is important to note that the length of time it takes to rotate these thrusters makes mode 2 an impracticable operating condition.

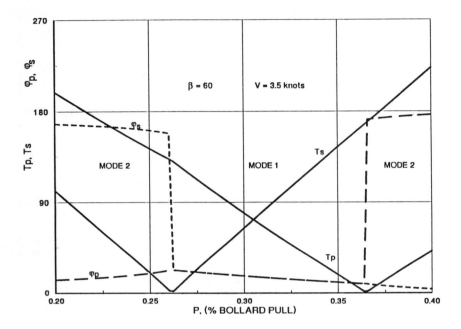

Figure.8 Variation of required thrust and direction for each propeller with P

By varying the speed the operating envelope for a fixed drift angle can be obtained as shown in Figure.9. The boundaries of the two modes of operation can also be seen.

The maximum force available at a drift angle of 60 degrees can be seen to occur at about 5.6 knots. In this condition the thrusters are both operating at maximum revolutions in mode 1.

The results for a range of drift angles are presented in Figure.10 where the maximum force possible as a function of speed can be seen. The lines for each drift angle indicate the condition where the thrust and revolutions from both thrusters are equal.

As can be seen the maximum thrust available does not fall off dramatically with increasing speed as may have been expected. This is because, as the speed increases the hydrodynamic force increases to compensate for the loss of direct thrust from the thrusters. A larger portion of this can be transferred to the ship because as the speed increases the drift angle is decreased and the lateral centre of pressure moves forward.

This only occurs if the drift angle, β_H, of the tug is decreased as the speed increases. If the tug remains at 90 degrees there is a dramatic reduction in thrust available with increasing speed as shown.

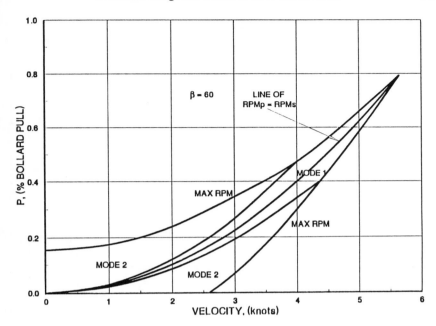

Figure.9 Operating envelope for a fixed drift angle

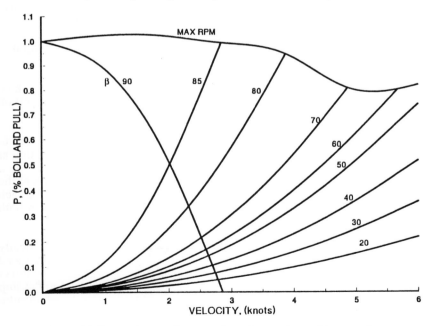

Figure.10 General operating envelope for tug in pushing mode

3.2 Tug performance in the pulling mode

When pulling, this type of tug operates with a long line over the bow. Two cases are considered here, where the tug is required to impart a pure sway force to steer the ship and where it is required to impart steering and braking forces.

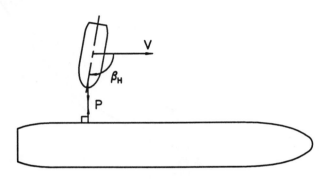

(a) steering case

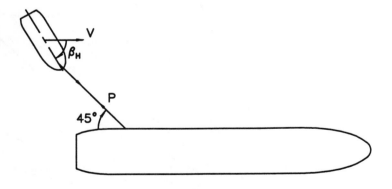

(b) steering and braking case

Figure.11 Tug and ship arrangement

3.2.1 Steering case For this investigation the tug and ship are arranged as shown in Figure.11(a) with the line lead athwartships.

Using the same technique as described above, the operating envelope for this condition can be obtained as shown in figure.12. Here it can be seen that forces of the order of the bollard pull can be developed at speeds up to about 4 knots. Again this is achieved by variation of the drift angle of the tug and utilising the hydrodynamic force generated by the hull.

3.2.2 Steering and braking case For this investigation it is assumed that equal steering and braking forces are required so that the line is at 45 degrees to the ships centreline as shown in Figure.11(b).

The general operating envelope for the braking and steering case is shown in Figure.13. The results indicate that in this case forces in excess of the bollard pull are achievable with increasing velocity.

For purposes of comparison the tug was located at a drift angle of −45 degrees where the line is athwartships on the tug, in the so called indirect towing position used by the tractor tug, Baer[2]. As shown in Figure.13 this type of tug is not particularly effective in this position.

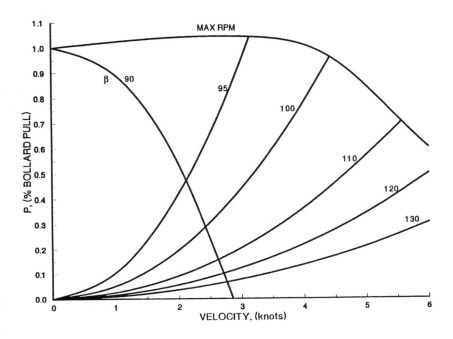

Figure.12 General operating envelope for steering case

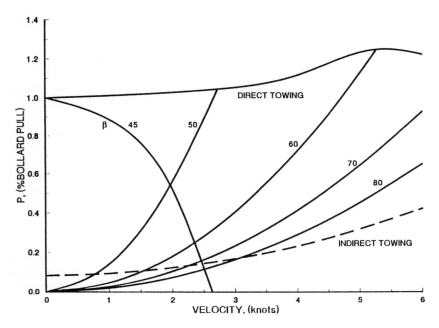

Figure.13 General operating envelope for steering and braking case

4 CONCLUSIONS

By making use of the mathematical model developed it has been shown that the omnidirectional stern drive tug is capable of imposing forces on a ship of the order of its bollard pull across the entire range of shiphandling velocities if used in a way such that hull forces supplement the propeller forces.

It has also been possible to show that the indirect towing mode favoured by the tractor tug is not suitable for this type of tug, because of increased difficulty in handling and the forces induced are significantly less than the bollard pull.

5 FUTURE

The next step in the study is to verify the performance predicted by the mathematical model in consultation with tug operators and marine pilots.

Further refinements are planned in the mathematical model before it is used in the shiphandling simulator. Tank tests will be conducted to estimate the interaction forces between the tug and ship in deep and shallow water. Estimations will be made of propeller and hull interaction and the influence of propeller wash on the ship in confined waters. For realistic simulation it will also be necessary to determine the time it takes for the tug to manoeuvre into position to apply a required force on the ship, and to take into account the fact that the tug operator may not be able to achieve the optimum configuration in each case.

NOMENCLATURE

A_0 propeller disk area, $A_0 = \dfrac{\pi D^2}{4}$

B tug beam on waterline

C_M propeller moment coefficient, $C_M = \dfrac{M}{{}^1\!/_2 \rho A_0 D(V_A^2 + (0.7\pi nD)^2)}$

C_Q propeller torque coefficient, $C_Q = \dfrac{Q}{{}^1\!/_2 \rho A_0 D(V_A^2 + (0.7\pi nD)^2)}$

C_T propeller thrust coefficient, $C_T = \dfrac{T}{{}^1\!/_2 \rho A_0 (V_A^2 + (0.7\pi nD)^2)}$

D propeller diameter
L tug length on waterline
n propeller revolutions per second
P tug/ship force
T propeller thrust, draft of tug
$\left.\begin{array}{l} X \\ Y \\ N \end{array}\right\}$ forces in tug fixed coordinate system

$X_H' = \dfrac{X}{{}^1\!/_2 \rho V_A^2 BT}$, $Y_H' = \dfrac{Y}{{}^1\!/_2 \rho V_A^2 TL}$, $N_H' = \dfrac{N}{{}^1\!/_2 \rho V_A^2 TL^2}$

$\left.\begin{array}{l} X^* \\ Y^* \\ N^* \end{array}\right\}$ forces in ship fixed coordinate system

V_A advance velocity of propeller
V velocity of tug/ship
$\left.\begin{array}{l} x \\ y \end{array}\right\}$ distances in tug fixed coordinate system

Greek symbols

α angle of rotation of propeller thrust vector from velocity vector
β_H drift angle of tug hull
β_P advance angle of propeller blade, $\beta_P = \arctan \dfrac{V_A}{0.7\pi nD}$

δ angle of rotation of thruster
ϕ angle of rotation of thrust vector
γ angle of rotation of tug/ship force vector
θ thruster angle of incidence

subscripts

H hydrodynamic
P propeller
S ship
p port
s starboard

REFERENCES

1.Oosterveld, M.W.C. 'Ducted Propeller Characteristics.', Paper No.4, R.I.N.A, *Proceedings of the Symposium on ducted Propellers*, London, 1973.

2.Baer, W. 'Safety in Towing.', Paper No.4, *Proceedings of the 1st North American Tug Convention,*.

3.Kosi, K., Hirao, S., Yoshikawa, K. and Nagagawa, Y. 'Study of Abilities of Harbour Tugboats.' No. 162,*Papers of the Autumn Lectures of the Japanese Shipbuilding Institute,* 1987.

APPENDIX-A TUG PARTICULARS

The body plan and particulars of the tug on which the study has been based are as follows:

length overall	33.00 m
beam overall	11.65 m
length on waterline	30.50 m
beam on waterline	10.25 m
draft to baseline	4.25 m
propeller diameter	2.20 m
engine power x 2	2650 KW
bollard pull	50 tonnes
designer	Barnes and Fleck, Newcastle, Australia

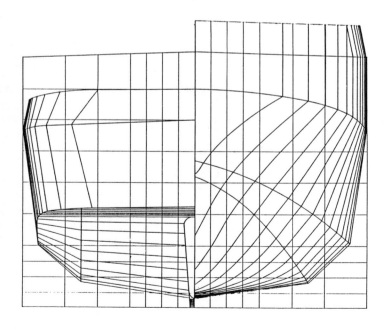

body plan

Prediction of Stopping Manoeuvres of a Ship in Shallow Water

M. Fujino, H. Kagemoto, Y. Ishii, T. Kato
Department of Naval Architecture and Ocean Engineering, University of Tokyo, 7-3-1 Hongo, Bunkyo-ku, Tokyo 113, Japan

ABSTRACT

Methods for the prediction of stopping manoeuvres of a ship in shallow water area are discussed. Stopping due to propeller reversing is dealt with and the emphasis is on the shallow water effects because stoppings are usually required in shallow water area such as in ports. Two kinds of attempt are made for the prediction of stopping manoeuvres. One is the numerical simulation in which all the hydrodynamic forces acting on a ship in its stopping manoeuvres are determined experimentally. The other one is that in which part of the hydrodynamic forces are determined by making use of existing theoretical and empirical formula. Through these studies it is clarified how much we can achieve in the prediction of stopping manoeuvres of a ship and what are needed for further improvement of the prediction accuracy.

INTRODUCTION

To avoid a risk of accidents such as collision or grounding, ship operators should be well acquainted with stopping abilities of their ships. Since it is very tedious and time consuming to carry out various stopping trials of a full scale ship in the sea, it is desirable if we could theoretically predict the stopping abilities. There is also a possibility that some requirements related to stopping abilities of ships may be included in the standards now under discussion in the IMO Design and Equipment Sub-committee. Therefore the establishment of prediction methods of stopping abilities of a given ship without full scale tests (preferably even without model tests) is an urgent task for us.

Because stoppings of a ship are mostly required in shallow water area and it is usually realized by propeller reversing, this is the situation we consider in this paper. In the process of stopping manoeuvres of a ship due to propeller reversing, the effectiveness of a rudder to control ship's heading is significantly diminished and thus the ship is apt to deviate from its original course and heading. Moreover, the hydrodynamic forces acting on a ship vary rapidly as the water depth decreases. Since these phenomena are dominated mainly by viscosity, the accurate prediction of the behaviours of a ship in its stopping manoeuvres without any full-scale or model tests is very difficult even with the state-of-the-art theoretical tools.

We therefore carried out extensive captive model tests while varying water depth in order to investigate the characteristics of hydrodynamic forces acting on a ship when it is stopping. Using the obtained hydrodynamic data and certain equations of motions for the description of the behaviours of a ship, numerical simulations of stoppings are carried out while systematically varying the water depth and the initial state of the ship. The results are compared with the corresponding experimental data. Through these comparisons we discuss how accurate we can predict the behaviour of a ship in its stopping manoeuvres by making use of experimentally determined hydrodynamic forces. Things needed for the further improvemnt of the prediction accuracy are also discussed.

An attempt is also made to predict stopping manoeuvres of a ship by making use of as much theoretical and empirical formula as possible so that we can avoid tedious and time/money consuming full-scale or model tests.

MATHEMATICAL MODELS FOR THE DESCRIPTION OF STOPPING MANOEUVRES

We consider stopping manoeuvres of ships in calm water and thus assume the ship behaviours can be described by the equations of motions in a horizontal plane as:

$$\text{surge} : m(\dot{u} - vr) = X_{\dot{u}}\dot{u} + X(u,v,r) + R(u) + f(J_p) \cdot T \tag{1}$$

$$\text{sway} : m(\dot{v} + ur) = Y_{\dot{v}}\dot{v} + Y(u,v,r) + \Delta Y_0(J_p) \tag{2}$$

$$\text{yaw} : I_{zz}\dot{r} = N_{\dot{r}}\dot{r} + N(u,v,r) + \Delta N_0(J_p) \tag{3}$$

Here u, v, r are the velocities in surge, sway and yaw and m, I_{zz} are the mass of a ship and the mass moment of inertia in yaw respectively. As shown in Fig.1 the equations are described in terms of a coordinate system (x,y,z) with its origin fixed to the center of gravity of the ship. Fig.2 shows the definition of head reach, side reach and stopping angle, which we later use. $X_{\dot{u}}, Y_{\dot{v}}$ and $N_{\dot{r}}$ represent the added mass and the added mass moment of inertia. X(u,v,r), Y(u,v,r) and N(u,v,r) are the forces and the moment acting on a bare hull, which is a hull without a propeller and a rudder. The resistance on a ship advancing without lateral motions is accounted for seperately by R(u) and thus it is not included in X(u,v,r). The last terms of the righthandside $f(J_p) \cdot T, \Delta Y_0(J_p), \Delta N_0(J_p)$ represent the propeller induced effective brake force, the propeller induced lateral force and the propeller induced yaw moment respectively. T is the brake thrust and $f(J_p)$ represents the hydrodynamic interaction between a propeller and a ship hull. J_p is defined as the nominal advancing constant u/(nP), where n is the number of the propeller rotation per unit time and P is the propeller pitch. When a ship is advancing with its propeller rotating in ordinally direction, $f(J_p)$ can usually be expressed as $1 - t$, where t is a thrust reduction factor. When a propeller is rotating in reverse direction, however, since the interactions are heavily dependent on J_p, we express it in a more general form as $f(J_p)$.

It should be noted that in the above equations it is assumed that the total hydrodynamic forces can be expressed by a linear superposition of those on a bare hull and those induced by a propeller. The forces on a rudder is not accounted for because it should be very small compared to others when a propeller is reversing[1]. Figs.3,4,5,6 show our experimental data of $f(J_p)$, $K_T(\equiv T/\rho n^2 D^4)$, $\Delta Y_0^*(\equiv \Delta Y_0/\rho n^2 D^4)$, $\Delta N_0^*(\equiv \Delta N_0/\rho n^2 L D^4)$ respectively. The principal particulars of the model ship used for the experiments are shown in Table 1. These data were obtained while the ship was towed in constant speed U with its propeller reversing. Although it is known that propeller induced asymmetric forces and moments ΔY_0, ΔN_0 are affected by lateral motions(v,r)[2], those effects are not taken into account in the Equations (5),(6) because the amount of experiments required for the identificaton of $\Delta Y_0(J_p, v, r)$, $\Delta N_0(J_p, v, r)$ is enormous.

Among various mathematical models proposed for the description of X(u,v,r), Y(u,v,r), N(u,v,r), we employ the following model which is a slight modification of that of Kose et al.[3].

$$X^*(u,v,r) = a_1 v^* r^* + a_2 u^* v^{*2}/U^* + a_3 u^* r^{*2} \tag{4}$$

$$Y^*(u,v,r) = b_1 U^* v^* + b_2 v^* \mid v^* \mid + b_3 r^* + b_4 u^* r^* + b_5 v^{*2} r^* u^*/U^{*2} + b_6 v^* r^{*2}/U^* \tag{5}$$

$$N^*(u,v,r) = c_1 u^* v^* + c_2 r^* + c_3 r^{*3} + c_4 u^* r^* + c_5 v^{*2} r^* \tag{6}$$

Here the superscripts '*' denote that the variables are nondimensionalized as:

$$X^*, Y^* = X, Y/\left(\frac{1}{2}\rho L^3 g\right), \quad N^* = N/\left(\frac{1}{2}\rho L^4 g\right) \tag{7}$$

$$u^*, v^*, U^* = u, v, U/\sqrt{Lg}, \quad r^* = r\sqrt{L/g} \tag{8}$$

where L is the ship length and U is the total velocity $\sqrt{u^2 + v^2}$.

We also examined the adequacy of the conventional polynomial model and the model proposed by Kose et al.[3] in its original form for the description of X(u,v,r), Y(u,v,r), N(u,v,r). From these examinations we reached the conclusion that the present mathematical model (Equations (4),(5),(6)) is among the best for the prediction of stopping manoeuvres of a ship[4].

The coefficients that appear in the Equations (4),(5),(6) were determined by the least square method so that the equations fit the data of captive model tests. The coefficients are summarized in Table 2 for H/d=4.7, 1.5, 1.3, 1.15, where H is the water depth and d is the ship's draft. Note that the coefficients for N^* in Table 2 are those for the moment about the midship whereas the Equations (1),(2),(3) are described with respect to the reference frame fixed to a ship with its origin at the center of gravity of the ship.

Using the coefficients of Table 2, the Equations (5),(6) fit well with experimental data whereas Equation (4) for X(u,v,r) do not agree very well with the corresponding data. However, since at present we do not have any better alternatives for the description of X(u,v,r), we proceeded with the Equation (4). The added mass and the added mass moment of inertia $X_{\dot{u}}$, $Y_{\dot{v}}$, $N_{\dot{r}}$ for deep water are determined by the chart of Motora[5] and the shallow water effect on them are evaluated according to Yoshimura(Fig.6 in Ref.[6])

NUMERICAL SIMULATIONS OF STOPPING MANOEUVRES

Using the experimental data in the righthandside of the Equations (1)(2)(3), we conducted numerical simulations of stopping manoeuvres of a ship. In order to obtain the corresponding experimental data, free running model tests were carried out in which the propeller of a ship advancing straight freely in constant speed U_0 was instantaneously made to a complete stop and was immediately reversed up to a prescribed number 'n' of revolutions linearly with time. The experiments were conducted for three cases in which

(1)The ship was kept advancing straight with its rudder angle(δ) fixed at 0 deg.

(2)The rudder angle was kept at δ=5deg.

(3)The rudder angle was kept at δ=-5deg.

until the propeller was reversed. (After the propeller reversing, the rudder was returned to its neutral position (δ=0deg.)) The experiments (2),(3) were conducted in order to examine the effects of initial lateral and yaw motions on the subsequent behaviours of the ship. The speed U_0 is 0.797m/s, which corresponds to 12kt. in full scale and the water depth to draft ratio is H/d=4.7 and 1.3.

Although, as mentioned above, the righthandside of Equations (1)(2)(3) were determined through the experiments of corresponding water depth, the exception is $f(J_p)$, for which the data obtained in H/d=4.7 was always used. This is because (1)It is known that when a ship is advancing with its propeller rotating in ordinally direction $f(J_p)$ varies little with the water depth[7]. (2)The experimentally determined $f(J_p)$ in H/d=1.3 becomes very large as $|J_p|$ increases (see Fig.3), which, we thought, should be rechecked carefully.

Fig.7 and Fig.8 show the comparisons of results of the free running model tests and the numerical simulations on ship trajectories from the instant of the propeller reversing to a complete stop for H/d=4.7 and H/d=1.3 respectively. Here 'a complete stop' is defined as the instant at which u becomes zero. Although small discrepancies are observed between the numerical simulation results and the corresponding experimental data, especially in shallow water, where the ship tends to stop in less time in the numerical simulations, the agreements are satisfactory for practical purposes. Fig.9 and Fig.10 summarize and compare the experimentally obtained and predicted stopping abilities of the ship in H/d=4.7, H/d=1.3 respectively. The stopping time is the time necessary for a ship to make a stop from the propeller reversing. r_0 is the yaw rate at the instant of the propeller reversing. 't_r' indicated in the figures is the duration of time between the instant of propeller reversing and that at which the number of propeller rotation reached the prescribed number 'n'. As can be expected from the comparisons of ship trajectories shown in Fig.7 and Fig.8, the numerical simulation results compare fairly well with the experimental results (except for the stopping angle in H/d=1.3). The considerable scattering of the experimental data of the stopping angle in H/d=1.3 may be attributed to the unsteadiness of hydrodynamic forces acting on the ship because of the restricted keel clearance under the ship bottom. In order to further examine the shallow water effects, we conducted numerical simulations for two other water depth H/d=1.5, H/d=1.15. Fig.11 compares the results obtained by the numerical simulations in the four kinds of water depth. The shallow water effects are not manifested in the head reach and the stopping time whereas they are clearly observed in the side reach and the stopping angle. For comparison we also carried out the numerical simulations in which $f(J_p)$, determined from the experiments of the corresponding water depth, was used. (As mentioned above, so far $f(J_p)$ at H/d=4.7 has always been used for the simulations even if H/d is much smaller.) Fig.12 shows the results obtained in this way. Other than in the stopping angle and the side reach, the effects of the change of water depth is also distinct in the stopping time and the head reach. When the propeller of a ship is reversing, the water is pushed toward bow direction and interact with the hull so that the flow field around the hull should vary as the water depth decreases. In fact as shown in Fig.3 $f(J_p)$ varies considerably with the decrease of water depth. Therefore, in principle, the results shown in Fig.12 should be more accurate than those obtained by making use of the value of $f(J_p)_{H/d=4.7}$. However, from the viewpoint of the comparison to the experimental data, it is to the contrary as can be seen if we compare Fig.9, Fig.10 and Fig.12. Although there can be a number of causes for this apparent contradiction, we now suspect that the our pseudo-stationary assumption employed in the experimental determination of $f(J_p)$ is the one that explains it. That is, we used $f(J_p)$ determined from experiments in which the model ship was towed in constant speed U_0. On the other hand, in the stopping process of a ship, the flow field in the stern area is not steady and thus the corresponding propeller brake force may be different from our pseudo-stationary values. This transient nature of propeller brake forces, however, is very difficult to incorporate in the numerical simulations of stopping manoeuvres and is subject to further investigation.

SIMPLIFIED PREDICTION OF STOPPING MANOEUVRES

As shown in the preceding section, once all the hydrodynamic forces in the righthandside of the Equations (1)(2)(3) are known, the stopping abilities of a given ship can be predicted with sufficient accuracy. However it is very tedious and time/money consuming to conduct experiments each time for the determination of those hydrodynamic forces. Therefore we made an attempt to determine the hydrodynamic forces from available theoretical or empirical formula. Specifically, we introduced the following approximations that seem to be justified.

(1)Since the speed of a ship in its stopping manoeuvres should be low, the wave making resistance can be neglected and the resistance $R(u)$ of the ship may be approximated as follows.

$$C_R \equiv R / \left(\frac{1}{2}\rho S U^2\right) = (1 + K + \Delta K)C_F + \Delta C_F \qquad (9)$$

Here S is the wetted surface of a ship and C_F is the frictional resistance coefficient determined by the Schoenherr's formula. K is the so-called form factor and ΔK represents the shallow water effect on K while ΔC_F represents the roughness effect of a hull surface. In our calculation K was dertermined from the resistance test data conducted in H/d=4.7 and assumed unchanged for all H/d. As for ΔK we employed the proposal of Takashina[7] which is given as:

$$\Delta K = a\left(\frac{d}{H}\right)^2 \qquad (10)$$

where $a=0.7$ for a container ship and $a=1.2$ for a tanker. (Our ship is a PCC and thus we used 0.7.) ΔC_F is known to be around 0.0004 for a small ship and we used this value.

The predicted resistance in this way is shown in Fig.13 with the comparisons to the corresponding experimental data. The agreement is quite good except for the resistance in very shallow water H/d=1.15, where the wave making resistance may not be negligible.

(2)The lateral/yaw motion oriented resistance $X(u,v,r)$ in Equation (4) can be simply represented as:

$$X^* = a_1 v * r* \qquad (11)$$

where a_1 is determined from published data such as those of Yoshimura[6]. Considering that X(u,v,r) is usually much smaller than the other forces R(u), $f(J_p)\cdot T$

and that the Equation (4) does not fit very well with experimental data, this sim-
plification may be justified.

(3)The effective propeller brake force $f(J_p) \cdot T$ can be replaced by that of $J_p = 0$.
This is solely for the convenience of calculation because the theoretical calculation
of the brake force for $J_p = 0$ may be possible with satisfactory accuracy.

As for the remaining components of the righthandside of Equations (1)(2)(3), it
seems that at present we can not help but resort to experiments.

The stopping time, stopping angle, side reach and head reach obtained by the
numerical simulations in which the above approximations were introduced are
compared with more rigorous calculation results (shown in Fig.11) in Table.3. It
is apparent that the stopping time predicted in this simplified formula is quite
longer and cosequently the stopping angle, the side reach, the head reach are all
larger than more rigorous results. Considering that the resistance $R(u)$ is well
predicted by the present simplified method (except for H/d=1.15) and $X(u, v, r)$
is much smaller than $R(u)$, $f(J_p) \cdot T$, the approximation (3) seem to be inadequate. Although it is not shown here, this was confirmed through more detailed
comparison of the time history of the forces acting on a ship in its stopping manoeuvres.

Therefore there seems to remain a lot of problems for the establishment of prediction methods of stopping manoeuvres of a ship without any experiments. Specifically, for the accurate theoretical prediction of stopping time or head reach, the
theoretical prediction method of propeller brake forces as a function of J_p should
be developed. For stopping angle or side reach, the estimation of propeller induced asymmetric forces and moment ΔY_0, ΔN_0 as well as the lateral force and
the yaw moment on a bare hull Y(u,v,r), N(u,v,r) seem to be equally important
for their accurate prediction.

CONCLUSION

From the present study the following conclusions are obtained.

(1)Once the hydrodynamic forces acting on a ship in its stopping manoeuvres are
known, the behaviours of the ship in its stopping manoeuvres can be predicted
even in shallow water by the present numerical simulation techniques with satisfactory accuracy.

(2)Among the problems to be solved for the further improvement of the prediction accuracy of stopping manoeuvres, incorporation of transient behaviour of
propeller brake forces into the numerical simulations is important.

(3)For the accurate prediction of stopping time and head reach without any experiments, the resistance $R(u)$ and the effective propeller brake force $f(J_p) \cdot T$
should be evaluated accurately. $X(u, v, r)$ is much smaller than $R(u), f(J_p) \cdot T$
and thus can be approximated in a very simple way (or we would say that it

should be neglected rather than be modelled erroneously). $R(u)$ can be predicted with satisfactory accuracy without experiments (except for very shallow water).

REFERENCES

[1]L. Wagner Smitt and M.S. Chislett: Course Stability while Stopping, J.M.E.S., Vol.14, No.7, pp.181, 1972.

[2]Fujino, M. and Kirita, A.: On the Manoeuvrability of Ships while Stopping by Adverse Rotation of Propeller (1st Report, 2nd Report), Jour. Kansai Soc. Nav. Archit. Japan, No.169 pp.57-70, 1978, No.173, pp.45-55, 1979.

[3]Kose, K., Hinata, H., et al.: On a Mathematical Model of Manoeuvering Motions of Ships in Low Speeds, Jour. Soc. Nav. Archit. Japan, Vol.155, pp.132-138, 1984.

[4]Fujino, M., Kagemoto, H., Kanda A. and Koiso K.: Hydrodynamic Aspects Pertaining to Stopping Manoeuvres in Shallow Water, Proc. Korea-Japan Joint Workshop on Hydrodynamics in Ship Design, pp.107-118, SEOUL, June 1991.

[5]Motora, S.: On the Measurement of Added Mass and Added Moment of Inertia for Ship Motions (Part 2, Part 3, Part 5), J. Zosen Kiokai, Vol.106 pp.59-62, Vol.106 pp.63-68, 1959 and Vol.107 pp.91-95, 1960.

[6]Yoshimura, Y. and Sakurai H.:Mathematical Model for the Manoeuvring in Shallow Water (3rd Report) - Manoeuvrability of a Twin-propeller Twin Rudder Ship -, Jour. Kansai Soc. Nav. Archit. Japan, No.211, pp.115-126, 1988

[7]Takashina, J.: A Study on Calculation Method of Ship Maneuvering Motion in Harbors, Doctoral Dissertation, University of Tokyo, 1992.

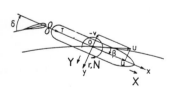

Figure.1 Coordinate system

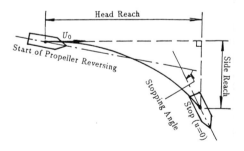

Figure.2 Definitions of head reach, side reach and stopping angle

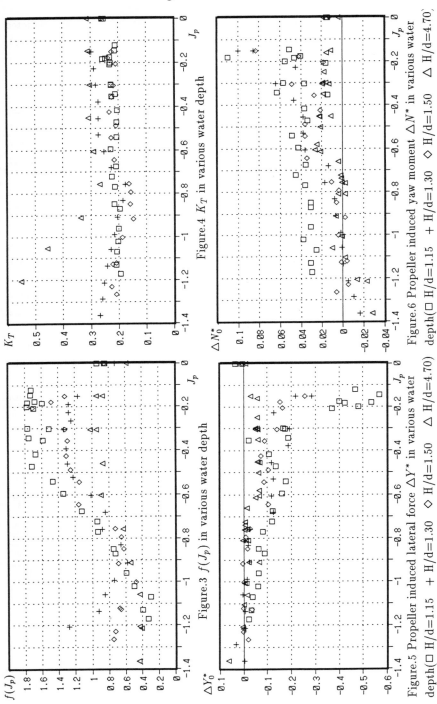

Figure.3 $f(J_p)$ in various water depth

Figure.4 K_T in various water depth

Figure.5 Propeller induced lateral force $\triangle Y^*$ in various water depth($\square$ H/d=1.15 + H/d=1.30 $\diamond$ H/d=1.50 $\triangle$ H/d=4.70)

Figure.6 Propeller induced yaw moment $\triangle N^*$ in various water depth($\square$ H/d=1.15 + H/d=1.30 $\diamond$ H/d=1.50 $\triangle$ H/d=4.70)

Table 1 Principal particulars of the model ship

Length between perpendiculars (L)	3.0000 m
Moulded breadth (B)	0.5367 m
Moulded draft (d)	0.1500 m
Displacement	132.94 kgf
Block coefficient (C_b)	0.550
Propeller diameter (D)	0.1067 m
Propeller pitch (P)	0.0928 m
Number of blades	5
Direction of rotation in forward motion	right
Mass moment of inertia (I_{zz})	7.625 kgf·m·sec²

Table 2 The coefficients for the description of X^*, Y^* and N^*

		H/d			
		1.15	1.30	1.50	4.70
X^*	a_1	-1.1577E-2	-5.1507E-3	-8.5805E-4	7.4351E-3
	a_2	-1.2650E-2	-3.2090E-3	-1.9837E-3	-1.3154E-4
	a_3	-6.7528E-2	-1.0967E-1	-4.4446E-2	-8.0903E-2
Y^*	b_1	-1.1640E-1	-8.8356E-2	-6.8605E-2	-2.6609E-2
	b_2	5.5966E-3	-3.7835E-3	-7.0744E-3	-4.5869E-3
	b_3	-1.5305E-3	-1.9464E-4	-4.3087E-4	-1.4685E-4
	b_4	3.6044E-2	1.2188E-2	7.2303E-3	4.8696E-3
	b_5	3.2517E-2	3.0301E-2	1.7146E-2	1.8126E-3
	b_6	-6.6684E-2	2.8137E-2	-1.8349E-2	-1.1035E-2
N^*	c_1	-2.0832E-2	-1.9070E-2	-1.5590E-2	-6.9866E-3
	c_2	-1.0552E-3	-7.8858E-4	-6.6271E-4	-1.5636E-4
	c_3	3.6640E-2	-2.5320E-3	-1.6483E-2	-1.1490E-2
	c_4	9.9110E-3	7.1489E-3	4.6168E-3	-8.5998E-4
	c_5	1.7473E-1	9.2258E-2	5.0942E-2	-6.2373E-2

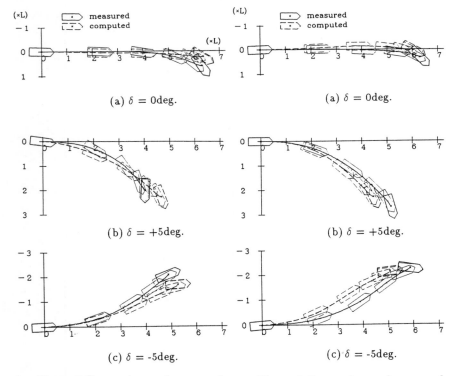

(a) $\delta = 0$deg.

(b) $\delta = +5$deg.

(c) $\delta = -5$deg.

Figure.7 Comparisons of measured and computed ship trajectories (H/d=4.7)

(a) $\delta = 0$deg.

(b) $\delta = +5$deg.

(c) $\delta = -5$deg.

Figure.8 Comparisons of measured and computed ship trajectories (H/d=1.3)

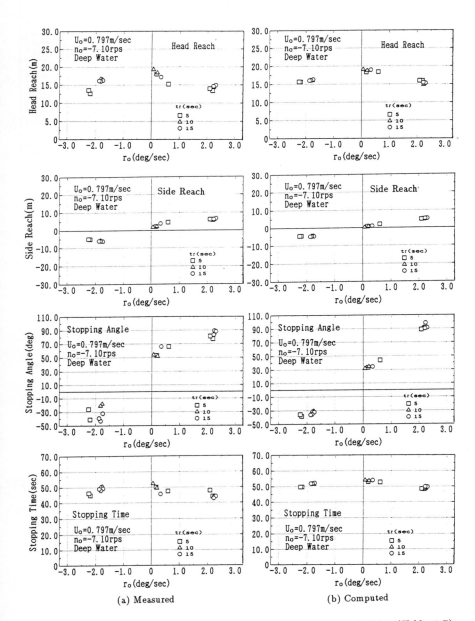

Figure.9 Comparisons of measured and computed stopping abilities (H/d=4.7)

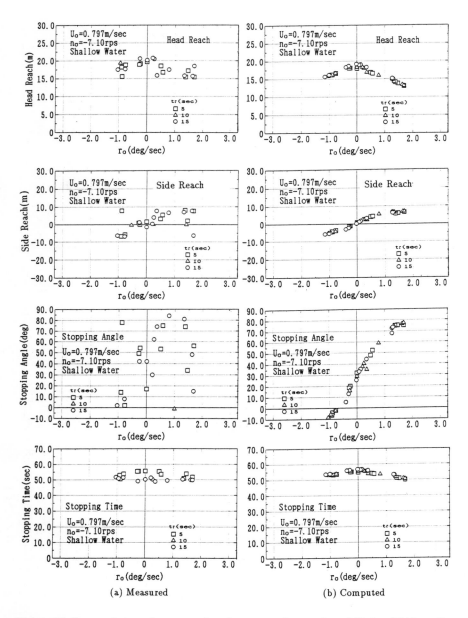

(a) Measured   (b) Computed

Figure.10 Comparisons of measured and computed stopping abilities (H/d=1.3)

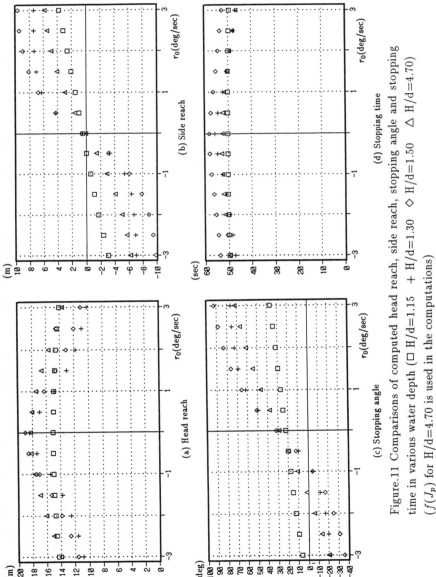

Figure.11 Comparisons of computed head reach, side reach, stopping angle and stopping time in various water depth ($\Box$ H/d=1.15 + H/d=1.30 $\Diamond$ H/d=1.50 $\triangle$ H/d=4.70)

($f(J_p)$ for H/d=4.70 is used in the computations)

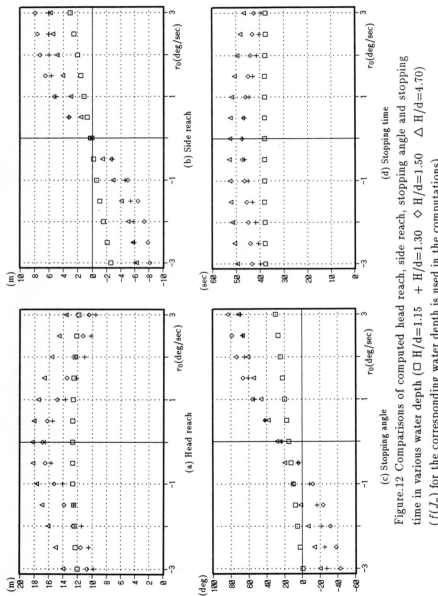

Figure.12 Comparisons of computed head reach, side reach, stopping angle and stopping time in various water depth (□ H/d=1.15 + H/d=1.30 ◇ H/d=1.50 △ H/d=4.70) ($f(J_p)$) for the corresponding water depth is used in the computations)

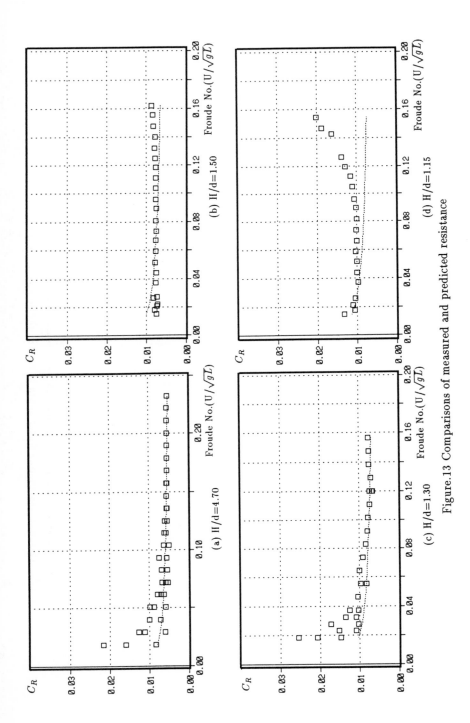

Figure.13 Comparisons of measured and predicted resistance

Table 3 Comparisons of stopping abilities predicted
by the simplified method and the rigorous method

H/d	r_0 (deg/sec)	simplified method				rigorous method			
		stopping time(sec)	stopping angle(deg)	side reach(m)	head reach(m)	stopping time(sec)	stopping angle(deg)	side reach(m)	head reach(m)
1.15	-3.0	68.1	7.30	-6.64	20.35	49.8	6.54	-3.05	14.32
	0	67.2	34.63	2.05	20.72	50.3	22.17	0.48	15.02
	+3.0	68.4	65.71	11.14	18.05	49.7	36.98	3.83	14.08
1.30	-3.0	65.2	-94.04	-14.88	0.38	47.4	-22.32	-7.02	10.84
	0	64.3	38.03	1.19	20.14	55.7	29.57	0.55	18.43
	+3.0	64.8	169.95	13.00	-1.26	47.0	76.43	7.40	10.19
1.50	-3.0	61.9	-45.51	-13.25	10.87	53.8	-35.88	-9.85	11.62
	0	64.8	38.23	1.16	20.87	58.2	31.87	0.65	19.03
	+3.0	60.0	114.63	12.90	9.55	52.7	92.62	9.73	11.10
4.70	-3.0	62.5	-12.02	-8.95	17.22	49.6	-19.80	-6.20	14.03
	0	63.0	38.89	0.51	20.83	52.8	28.74	0.06	18.33
	+3.0	59.6	89.00	9.13	16.09	46.8	71.95	5.85	13.63

Development of SWATHMAN, A Manoeuvring Simulation Tool for Small Waterplane Area Twin Hull Ships

A.F. Miller (*), R.C. McGregor (**)
(*) Vickers Shipbuilding and Engineering Ltd, Barrow-in-Furness, UK
(**) Department of Mechanical Engineering, University of Glasgow, UK

ABSTRACT

This paper describes the adaptation of monohull manoeuvring techniques to SWATH ships. Following a thorough review of SWATH manoeuvring characteristics, conventional monohull manoeuvring theory is adapted and applied to develop a manoeuvring prediction tool for SWATH ships, SWATHMAN. This program will estimate the rudder areas required in order to achieve a specified manoeuvring performance. Conversely, the program will estimate the likely turning performance for a specified rudder area. The program incorporates propeller acceleration effects and will deal with rudders both in and out of the propeller slipstream. Indeed, the program may be used to compare the efficiency of control surfaces mounted in various locations.

The paper concludes with several observations on the nature of SWATH manoeuvring. Results from the simulation program are presented and compared with trial data for a range of existing SWATH vessels. The quality of the correlation observed demonstrates the validity of the approach.

INTRODUCTION

SWATH (Small Waterplane Area Twin Hull) ships are a form of modified catamaran where the underwater form has been distorted to move the supporting buoyancy well below the surface of the sea and away from the wave action. A typical SWATH vessel consists of two totally submerged torpedo-like hulls upon which an above water cross-structure, or box, is supported by means of long streamlined surface piercing struts. The resulting vessels have demonstrated dramatically improved seakeeping performance over conventional monohulls and catamarans at both model and full scale.

Considerable effort has been directed towards improving our understanding of the hydrodynamic forces and moments acting upon these hullforms. Since the primary reason for the very existence of SWATH ships is the excellent seakeeping performance afforded by the concept, most of this effort has been aimed at predicting and quantifying ship motions in a seaway.

Relatively little effort has been devoted to the study and prediction of control of SWATH ship motions in the horizontal plane, i.e. their manoeuvring characteristics. The bulk of available literature originates from the DTNSRDC and largely concerns model tests performed on rotating arm devices. These experiments are performed to calculate hydrodynamic force and moment derivatives for a large number of combinations of initial ship condition and rudder configuration. The resulting database may allow construction of a manoeuvring simulation tool for SWATH vessels but such experiments are time consuming and costly, requiring exclusive use of a large specialised purpose built facility.

In order to make any predictions on the manoeuvring capability of a ship the acceleration and velocity derivatives must be known or approximated. Since direct evaluation of these derivatives is not at present considered a practical proposition, and since model testing is not feasible at the concept design stage, it was decided to examine the possibility of modifying existing semi-empirical techniques for finding monohull manoeuvring characteristics (Clarke et al [1]) in an attempt to provide guidance for the naval architect engaged in the design of rudders and steering gear for SWATH vessels.

LITERATURE REVIEW

General SWATH Manoeuvring Considerations

Very little full scale operational information is available [2,3,4] at present although the situation may change as the number of SWATH vessels in service worldwide increases over the next few years. Study of published information, although limited, nonetheless allows several interesting conclusions to be drawn.

SWATH vessels are by nature of their geometry inherently directionally stable. The centroid of the projected area of the struts is generally aft of the centre of gravity of the vessel, it therefore takes a large side force to initiate a turn at speed. Consequently larger rudders and heavier steering gear must be employed than on equivalent monohulls. However directional stability is an advantage for missions requiring a steady course, particularly in oblique seas. It is especially advantageous if towing a sonar array since the signals from the array will be less confused and thus easier to interpret. Owing to this inherent directional stability and the problem of rudder location on SWATH vessels, close attention must be paid to the design of the steering mechanism in order to ensure that the ship possesses adequate turning performance.

The SWATH form presents a number of unique problems when it comes to siting rudders and steering gear. Naturally this has led to the development of several innovative configurations of control surfaces.

Owing to the transverse separation of propellers, low speed manoeuvrability on SWATH ships using differential thrust is excellent. It is noted that SSP *KAIMALINO* turns within her own length at very low speeds (Fein [5]). Vessels equipped with bow thrusters should be able to turn on the spot. The possibility exists for providing exceptional stationkeeping or docking performance using bow thrusters linked to differential thrust from controllable pitch propellers under active automatic control. Controllable pitch propellers and / or electric transmission is recommended for applications requiring good low speed manoeuvring. With fixed pitch propellers and a conventional drivetrain, unacceptable strains would be placed on gearboxes due to the constant forward / reverse shifts that would be required.

At higher speeds turning performance may be improved by employing canards to bank the vessel into the turn. The asymmetric drag produced, results in sharper turns. SSP *KAIMALINO* has reported reductions in tactical diameter of the order of 20 % using this method. Similarly deployment of a retractable "turning foil" has been found to yield benefits. When the rudder is surface piercing, trim has an important effect on turning performance.

Turning performance is dependent on speed. At 23 knots the tactical diameter of the SSC *SEAGULL* was found to be twice that at 13 knots [4]. This is due to flow patterns along the hull varying considerably with Froude Number. Tank tests [6] reveal that the manoeuvring derivatives are less speed dependent for a long strut design.

With careful design of the control surfaces, turning performance of SWATH ships can be made comparable to that of equivalent monohulls. The often quoted ratio of tactical diameter / ship length is misleading for comparison purposes, since the length of an "equivalent" SWATH is less than its monohull counterpart by about 40% (MacGregor [7])

Rudder Configurations
SWATH hullforms present the naval architect with several options when designing control surfaces since several possibilities exist for both the location and type of control surface used to manoeuvre and stabilize the vessel.

Traditionally in monohulls the rudder(s) is / are placed right aft, usually directly behind the propeller(s). In this location, the turning force exerted by the rudder is increased due to the increase in flow velocity induced by the propeller(s). This increased flow velocity is particularly important at low speed and when trying to manoeuvre from stationary, since without flow there can be no sideforce generated by the hull or rudder. Combined with the presence of suitable otherwise unusable space in the stern directly above for siting steering gear, this location then provides an ideal and hence almost universal solution to the problem for monohulls.

For SWATH ships the answer is not so simple. The same considerations apply, however the lack of suitable protected mounting positions for the rudders, coupled with the problem of locating steering gear, has resulted in a number of innovative solutions.

With "long" strut designs, i.e. designs where the strut length equals or overhangs the lower hull aft, a traditional solution with rudder behind the propeller and steering gear housed in the hull and strut is normal. For "short" strut designs the obvious arrangement is to incorporate the rudder into the trailing edge of the strut. However this solution produces low turning efficiency and necessitates a much larger (by virtue of its location unbalanced) rudder requiring larger and heavier steering gear. Without propeller induced flow over the rudder this arrangement also suffers in its ability to manoeuvre at zero speed.

The most common steering arrangements for SWATH vessels together with the advantages and disadvantages inherent in each concept are shown in fig 1 and set out below.

Strut Rudder   A movable section is incorporated into the trailing edge of the struts controlled by steering gear in the cross deck or in the struts themselves.

This is the simplest and cheapest solution which also adds least drag to the vessel. However the configuration is ineffective at both low and high speeds, since at low speeds there is no benefit gained from the locally increased flow velocity due to propellers, and at high Froude No's the waterline dips towards the stern of the vessel, reducing wetted-effective rudder area. Consequently, greatly increased rudder areas are required to ensure adequate turning performance. It is impossible to balance strut rudders, and so very large powerful, costly and heavy steering gear is required.

Extended Strut Rudder Aft of Propeller   Following traditional (monohull) practice this is the most common arrangement for long strut designs. The flow induced by the propeller increases effectiveness and allows a relatively small rudder to provide adequate turning and directional control. For short strut designs however this is not a practical answer since the provision of a "strut extension" to carry the rudder would increase both drag and cost unacceptably. The problem of rudder protection should also be addressed for ships utilizing this configuration. Although speed loss in the turn per degree of helm is greater for configurations with the rudder behind the screw, the tactical diameter is approximately 30% less for a given helm angle.   Thus the effects on speed loss is counteracted.

(Surface Piercing) Spade Rudder Forward of Propeller This type of rudder is a combination of the two configurations described above.   It offers a compromise for "short strut" vessels where the provision of a rudder behind the propeller is not practical.   The rudder is located above the hull just forward of the propellers to take advantage of the accelerated flow induced by the screws.

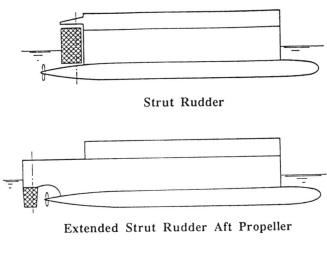

Strut Rudder

Extended Strut Rudder Aft Propeller

Surface Piercing Spade Rudder Fwd of Propeller

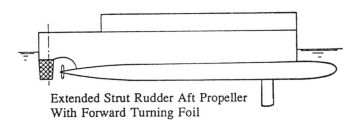

Extended Strut Rudder Aft Propeller
With Forward Turning Foil

Figure 1: SWATH rudder configurations

The steering gear must be located in the lower hulls which produces access problems, however since these rudders can be balanced, unlike strut mounted types, this steering gear may be of minimum dimensions. If the rudder is surface piercing, this allows the possibility of providing additional lateral support above the waterline.

In model tests, the configuration was found to provide adequate turning performance for reasonable rudder areas. In the case of surface piercing variants effectiveness was found to decrease with speed as for strut rudders. Locating the rudder forward of the screw obviously degrades the flow into the propeller, resulting in slightly worse propulsive efficiency. Additionally, in some model tests, rudder ventilation occurred for helm angles greater than 25 degrees.

Canards These closely resemble a cross between conventional ships rudders and fin stabilizers. Generally mounted inboard of the twin hulls in clear protected water at the stern of the ship, they provide combined control of vertical and horizontal motion.

Since only one set of fins are required the designer saves ship drag and weight. Against these savings must be set the additional complexity and cost of the control system required. Further, in the event of a breakdown of this system, independent manual control of vertical and horizontal motion may not be possible. The configuration also suffers from interaction between roll, sway and yaw at low encounter frequencies, this is particularly noticeable in following seas. Otherwise the configuration resembles and shares the same pros and cons as the non surface piercing variant of the spade rudder described above.

Turning Foil This is perhaps the most novel approach to the problem. The device consists of a vertical foil normally housed in a trunk in the forward hull or strut. When a turn is required the foil is lowered or hinged into position beneath the hull which is on the inside of the desired turn. The increased drag produced by the foil acts with the created sideforce to yaw the vessel into the turn.

The device is primarily intended to assist turns initiated by other methods. It cannot be the sole manoeuvring device aboard a ship since it cannot be used in shallow or confined waters. It does however offer several interesting features including the cancellation of side forces created by conventional aft rudders which push the ship sideways out the turn when helm is first applied.

MANOEUVRING THEORY

The SWATH manoevring prediction program, SWATHMAN, is based on manoeuvring theory developed for monohull vessels and fully described in

Clarke et al [1] and Miller [8].   Much of this theory is founded upon multi-variate linear regression and semi-empirical expressions developed from analysis of experimental data.   It is anticipated that the symmetrical nature of SWATH geometry will readily lend itself to study utilizing theory developed in this way.   It is therefore fully expected that calculations based upon this theory will be equally valid for SWATH vessels as for those of monohull form.

Manoeuvring Criteria

Turning Ability It is usual to describe the turning behaviour of a ship in terms of its turning circle.   Values of advance, transfer and diameter are often quoted as a means of quantifying a vessel's inherent directional stability.   However most ships turn with a diameter of two-three times the ship length whether stable or unstable, so that the final turning behaviour is not a very useful means of determining manoeuvrability [1].

As an alternative to considering the turning circle, initial turning ability of the ship will be examined immediately after rudder activation.   Since deviations from a straight course are small, linear theory may be used with confidence.

A more suitable definition of turning ability is the change in heading angle per unit helm angle applied after the ship has travelled one ship length. Norrbin [9] first introduced the idea of a turning index, the "P" number.   This is the heading change per unit helm angle for one ship length travelled, described in terms of the Nomoto indices K' and T'

$$P \approx -\tfrac{1}{2}\frac{K'}{T'} \tag{1}$$

Norrbin suggested a value for P > 0.3, which is equivalent to a 10 degree change in ship heading angle in one ship length, when the helm is placed hard over (30° or more of rudder).   However, Norrbin and Nomoto later suggested that in the case of large tankers this requirement may be relaxed to P > 0.2. From analysis of results to date and considering the fact that SWATH vessels are shorter than "equivalent" monohulls it is recommended that P > 0.2 be taken as standard for SWATH vessels.

Dynamic Stability For a linear dynamic system to be stable it is necessary for the roots of the characteristic equation to be negative.   This reduces to

$$Y_v'(N_r' - m'x_G') - N_v'(Y_r' - m') > 0 \tag{2}$$

Turning Diameter Whilst the terminal turning behaviour of a vessel should not, on its own, be used to define its manoeuvring performance, the information is nonetheless not without value.   A vessel's turning diameter is the most often quoted result from full scale manoeuvring trials, due most likely to the relative ease of measurement and the easily understood physical significance of the value. Similarly current regulations require that this information is permanently displayed in the wheelhouse of most vessels and it is certainly a quantity the prospective operator of a SWATH vessel will wish to know.   For these reasons a routine was incorporated into the SWATHMAN program in order to enable the calculation of turning radii for specified degrees of helm.

For dynamically stable vessels the steady radius of turning, R is given in terms of the non-dimensional derivatives by :-

$$\frac{R}{L} = -\frac{1}{\delta}\frac{Y_v'(N_r' - m'x_G') - N_v'(Y_r' - m')}{Y_v'N_\delta' - N_v'Y_\delta'} \tag{3}$$

where R is the radius of turn, L is the vessel length and δ is the rudder angle

Estimation of Ship Derivatives
Several attempts have been made to derive empirical expressions relating the velocity derivatives to ship geometry.   These formulae were derived after analysis of experimental results obtained on planar motion mechanism and rotating arm devices.

Clarke et al [1] performed a multiple regression analysis of all available data.   Their results are summarised in the following expressions for velocity and acceleration derivatives.   The formulae are given in [1,8].

Estimation of Rudder Derivatives A significant difference arises in the treatment of the side force Y created by the rudder.   This is calculated on the basis that the rudder acts like a low aspect ratio wing, giving the non-dimensional side force / helm angle coefficient as

$$Y_\delta' = \left(\frac{A}{LT}\right)\left(\frac{T}{L}\right)\left(\frac{\partial C_L}{\partial \delta}\right)\left(\frac{c}{u}\right)^2 \tag{4}$$

where c is the flow velocity over rudder, A is the rudder area, T is the draught and C_L is the lift coefficient for the rudder section.

The flow velocity ratio term is dependent on whether the rudder is subject to propeller induced accelerated flow.   For rudders subject to propeller accelerated flow the ratio becomes :-

$$\left(\frac{c}{u}\right)^2 \approx \left\{1 + \%_{Area}\left[\left(\frac{V_A(ACL)}{V_S}\right)^2 - 1\right]\right\} \tag{5}$$

where $\%_{Area}$ is the proportion of rudder area subject to the accelerated flow,

ACL the flow acceleration factor due to the propeller, V_s is the ship speed and V_a is the flow speed into rudder.

The lift curve slope coefficient for the rudder is harder to define. After trying a classical approach, 1.301 rad^{-1} was selected following extensive analysis of full scale data and model test results together with published comparisons and predictions utilizing Clarke's regression routines. This approximation removes the effect of rudder aspect ratio from the calculation procedure. This is unlikely to effect results for low aspect ratio rudders behind propellers, but may introduce small errors when determining side force from high aspect ratio surface piercing strut rudders. This effect is counteracted by the incorporation of a mirror imaging factor into the calculation. This is primarily designed to model the increase in effective aspect ratio which occurs due to the proximity of perpendicular hull surfaces (and rudder fences in the case of surface piercing variants).

For the above cases the standard value of lift curve slope coefficient is modified according to the following formula

$$\left(\frac{\partial C_L}{\partial \delta}\right)_{Modified} = \left(\frac{\partial C_L}{\partial \delta}\right)_{Std} \left[1 + \left(\frac{1-K}{K}\right)\left(1 - \frac{\partial C_L / \partial \delta}{1.8 \, \Pi}\right)\right]^{-1}$$

(6)

where K is the imaging factor for the rudder.

DEVELOPMENT OF SWATHMAN

A manoeuvring prediction tool for SWATH vessels was created incorporating adaptations of currently accepted monohull practice suitably modified to take into account the features peculiar to SWATH forms. The resulting tool allows the user to determine the size of rudder required for a given vessel in order to provide adequate manoeuvring performance. The program can cope with rudders fore and aft of the propellers and will check the directional stability for a given design in addition to estimating the likely turning performance and heel angles for specified degrees of helm.

The first stage is to input the main geometrical details of the vessel or accept default values based upon regression fits of data from existing designs and selected according to the main dimensions of the required vessel. Bounding values defining the acceptable range for Norrbin's "P" No and a first estimate of rudder area and location are also supplied.

At this stage the option of siting the rudders in or out of the propeller slipstream is given and the user is asked what proportion, if any, of the rudder is subject to this slipstream.   Using this information together with values for the Taylor Wake Fraction and a flow acceleration term, from [10,11], the program calculates the ratio of flow velocity over the rudder to the ship speed. This value combined with the lift curve slope for the rudder section, allows estimation of the side force generated by the rudder.   The imaging factor is also input from appraisal of the rudder siting.

At this stage the program calculates "Clarke's Rudder Coefficient". Clarke et al [1] suggested that the product

$$\left(\frac{\partial C_L}{\partial \delta}\right)\left(\frac{c}{u}\right)^2 \qquad (7)$$

may be assumed constant with a value of 3.0 as typical for single screw vessels of normal form.   The program displays this product and allows the user to reassess the data if so required.

The rudder derivatives may be taken from any one of four semi-empirical techniques according to Wagner Smitt, Norrbin, Inoue or Clarke et al [1]. Alternatively the user may input his own values as found from model tests or ship motion packages.   Once the ship derivatives are found the corrections due to the fins/rudders are found and the derivatives modified accordingly if required.

The final stage of the first iteration is completed by calculating Nomoto's turning coefficients [12] and Norrbin's "P" number [9].   If this "P" number falls outside the range initially specified by the user the rudder is resized automatically and further iterations performed until the condition is met.

Once the "P" number falls within the specified range dynamic stability may be checked and if the vessel is found to be unstable one can proceed with the unstable design or attempt to stabilise it by changing overall vessel dimensions or the rudder dimensions only .

Final values of rudder area and corresponding "P" Number are displayed at this stage and the option given to accept or modify the rudder area.   When acceptable values are reached the user may then proceed to calculate the likely steady turning radius for his vessel equipped with the chosen rudders.   Finally the program estimates the probable value of heel angle attained whilst executing a turn of specified radius.

This program, SWATHMAN3, has been run for a number of designs at model and full scale, including the fishing SWATH *ALI*.   Similarly the program has been used to evaluate designs with rudders fore and aft of the screws in an attempt to quantify the effect of rudder type / location upon turning performance.

FULL SCALE TRIALS

Limited full scale manoeuvring performance trials were conducted utilising the 20 tonne SWATH fishing vessel *ALI*. This vessel is a basic SWATH form of single "short strut" design. The rudders are of the strut type, incorporated into the trailing edge of the struts.

The manoeuvring tests formed part of the overall trials program conducted on this vessel during November and December 1990 (McGregor [13,14]).

Although manoeuvring data was not the primary objective of the trials, data was collected by recording simultaneous values of heading, velocity and distance travelled. Since the turns were rather gentle, it was found that the computed distance travelled during a set of 720 degree turns was, on average, only 0.5% different from the measured values (see fig 2). MV *ALI*'s initial turning characteristics and steady turning radius were evaluated for a range of helm angles and speeds.

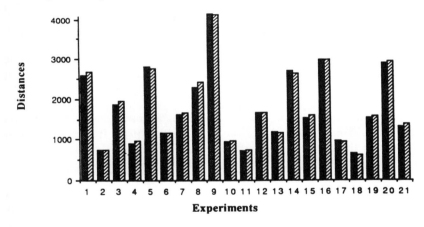

Figure 2: Comparison between measured and predicted length of turning path

DISCUSSION

Predictions
For any given design of SWATH vessel, the program predicts the rudder area and configuration required to provide that vessel with acceptable manoeuvring performance, estimates turning characteristics and will re-design the rudder as required to meet specific requirements.

SWATHMAN was used to evaluate the manoeuvring performance of 7 existing vessels for which full scale manoeuvring trials information was available (table 1). For each of these 7 vessels the program was required to determine suitable rudder areas in order to satisfy a previously specified turning

Table 1: Vessel particulars, predicted and trials turning characteristics

Vessels Name	Patria	Kaimalino	Halcyon	Marine Ace	Seagull	Ohtori	Ali
Year of Build	1989	1973	1985	1977	1979	1980	1990
Builder	FBM Cowes	USCG	RMI Inc	Mitsui	Mitsui	Mitsui	Private
Purpose/Role	Fast Ferry	Workboat	Demostrator	Demostrator	Fast Ferry	Hydrographic	Creel Fishing
Length Over All	37.00	26.41	18.29	12.34	35.90	27.00	12.00
Hull Length	32.00	24.38	16.13	10.47	31.50	24.00	10.48
Strut Length	32.00	14.17	16.78	7.31	32.14	24.00	8.90
Hull Centreline Spacing	10.00	12.19	7.47	5.30	13.50	8.00	4.00
Load Draught	2.70	4.66	2.13	1.55	3.15	3.40	1.60
Maximum Hull Diameter	1.85	1.97	1.52	1.24	2.95	2.30	1.00
Maximum Strut Width	1.00	0.91/1.2	0.75	0.57	1.25	0.60	0.60
Load Displacement (tonnes)	180.00	193.00	50.00	18.40	343.00	239.00	20.00
Type of Rudders	Aft Props on Overhang	Aft Props on Overhang	Aft Props on Overhang	Aft Props on Overhang	Aft Props on Overhang	Aft Props on Overhang	Fwd Props Strut Hung
Rudder Height/Span	-	4.42	1.20	0.75	1.50	1.48	0.68 (1)
Rudder Chord Length	-	0.88	0.70	0.45	0.84	0.8 (mean)	0.60
Total Rudder Area	1.12	3.89	0.84	0.34	1.26	1.38	0.41
Turn Diameter @ 35 Degrees Helm							
Full Scale Trials Results	240-280	229-282	90-100	66	200	165-330	120
SWATHMAN Program Prediction	240	220	98	58	142	132	112
SWATHMAN Prediction Conditions							
% Rudder In Flow	75	40	75	75	75	75	-
Flow Acceleration Due to Propeller	1.8	1.8	1.8	1.8	1.8	1.8	0
Mirror Imaging Factor Applied	1.0	1.0	1.0	1.0	1.0	1.0	1.5
Comment		Rudder NACA Section 15	High span only 40% in propwash	Figures for 30 deg helm Only	Prog selected A=0.3sqm giving TD=66 m	Trial data may not be at 30 deg helm	Prog selected A=1.21sqm Giving TD=148 m	Only vessel fitted with strut hung rudders

(1) Submerged at Load Draught   (2) @ 30 Degrees Helm

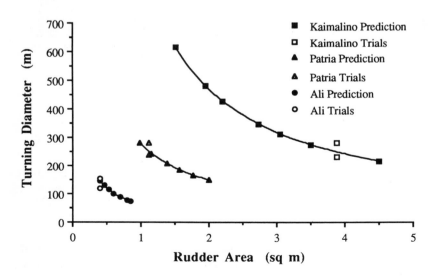

Figure 3:Predicted and Fullscale Turning for *KAIMALINO, PATRIA* and *ALI*

performance and then to simulate the likely manoeuvring performance of the vessels "as built".   In the latter case, real values of rudder area were input together with likely prevailing flow conditions for the region around the rudder.

Miller [8] reports studies which were made into the effects of varying flow conditions around the rudder, free surface imaging and mirroring effects.

Figure 3 presents SWATHMAN predictions together with trials results for minimum turning diameters / rudder area for the vessels *PATRIA*, *ALI*, and *KAIMALINO*.   It may be seen that the predictions agree well with values measured on full scale trials.

Figures 4 and 5 present SWATHMAN predictions of turning performance (Turn Diameter / Helm Angle) for the vessels *ALI* and *HALCYON*. Reasonable agreement with measured values is again observed.   Fig 4 also demonstrates the influence upon manoeuvring performance of rudder imaging effects. This phenomenon occurs where the proximity of large flat areas close to and perpendicular to the rudders produce an increase in rudder efficiency by increasing effective aspect ratio.

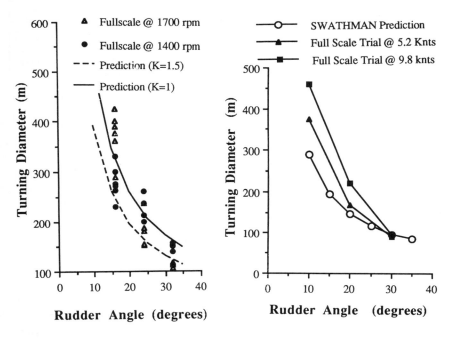

Fig 4: Turning performance for *ALI*   Fig 5:Turning performance for *HALCYON*

Miller [8] showed that the manoeuvring characteristics are quite sensitive to the value assumed for the imaging factor, the acceleration of the flow due to the propeller and the proportion of the rudder that is subjected to that accelerated flow. This can is demonstrated in figs 4, 6 and 7.   These three values are all variables over which the designer has some control.

A comparison of SWATHMAN predictions with full scale trials data for all seven vessels is summarised in Table 1.   The predictions obtained tend to underestimate turning diameter slightly, this was particularly noticeable in the case of the two Japanese vessels, SSC *SEAGULL* and *OHTORI*.   Overall however predictions from the program were found to agree fairly closely with full scale trial results.   This may be expected in the case of the MV *PATRIA* whose geometry was used to calibrate the derivative calculation routines. However the good agreement observed between the predictions and trial results for the other six vessels confirms the validity of the approach.

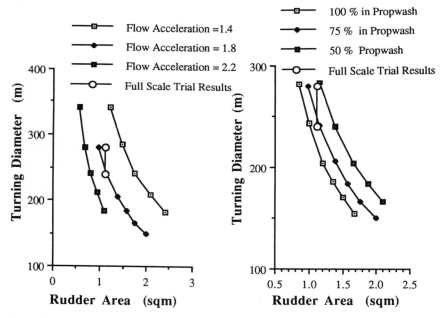

Fig 6: Effect of accelerated flow in propeller wash on *PATRIA*

Fig 7: Effect of proportion of rudder in propeller wash on *PATRIA*

Fullscale Observations
The most obvious manoeuvring characteristic of the MV *ALI* was the directional stability which she possessed.   Despite noticeable yawing in bow quartering seas the overall course remained straight, with little or no correction to the helm necessary.   As anticipated for a vessel with strut rudders medium to high speed manoeuvring ability was fairly poor.

From the linear dependence between yaw rate and rudder angle (fig 8), linear manoeuvring theory is seen to be acceptable for the analysis of MV *ALI*.

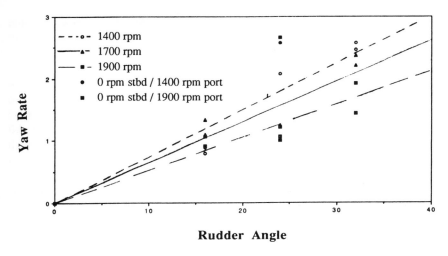

Figure 8: Linear relationship between yaw rate and helm angle in MV *ALI* trials

CONCLUSIONS

A systematic and wide reaching appraisal of the manoeuvring characteristics of SWATH vessels has been carried out by comparing full scale tests and the results from a new manoeuvring prediction program which adapts accepted manoeuvring theory to SWATH forms.

The principal conclusions from the study are :-

1.   SWATH vessels are inherently very directionally stable.

2.   Despite this, SWATH vessels with well designed control surfaces can possess turning diameters equivalent to comparable monohulls [15].

3.   Slow speed manoeuvring is excellent due to the availability of large amounts of differential thrust from widely spaced propellers.

4.   Unlike monohulls turning performance is very speed dependent for most SWATH designs.   Turning diameters increase with speed particularly for designs with surface piercing rudders.

5.   The manoeuvring prediction program may be applied to SWATH vessels, operating in the low to medium speed range, fitted with rudders both in and out of the propeller slipstream and possessing widely different resistance and propulsive characteristics.

6.   The program has been run for a number of existing SWATH designs for which full scale trials information is available.   The results / predictions from the program were found to agree closely with the actual values found on trials.

ACKNOWLEDGEMENTS

The authors would like to acknowledge the financial support of Vickers Shipbuilding and Engineering Ltd and the Science and Engineering Research Council through the Marine Technology Directorate.

REFERENCES

1.   Clarke, D., Gedling, P., and Hine,G., 'The Application of Manoeuvring Criteria in Hull Design Using Linear Theory', TRINA, Vol 125, 1982.
2.   Warren, N., Private Communication regarding manoeuvring performance on trials of the MV "*PATRIA*". Nov 1990.
3.   Nethercote, W.C.E. et al, "Manoeuvring of SWATH ships", Proceedings of 20th American Towing Tank Conference, Hoboken, New Jersey, July 1983.
4.   Narita, H., and Mabuchi, Y., "Design and Full Scale Test Results of Semi-Submerged Catamaran (SSC) Vessels", Proceedings 1st International Marine Systems Design Conference (IMSDC) , London 1982.
5.   Fein, J.A., "Vertical and Horizontal Plane Control of SWATH Ships", Proceedings of 7th Ship Control Symposium.
6.   Hart, C.J. et al, "Rotating Arm Experiment for an Extended Strut SWATH Ship as Represented by SWATH 6E", DTNSRDC SPD Report 0698-03,September 1983.
7.   MacGregor, J.R., "A Computer Aided Method for Preliminary Design of SWATH Ships", PhD Thesis, Glasgow University, May 1989.
8.   Miller, A.F.,"Aspects of SWATH Design and Evaluation", MSc Thesis, Glasgow University. September 1991
9.   Norrbin, N., "Zig-Zag Test Technique and Analysis with Preliminary Statistical Results", SSPA Allmann Report, No 12 1965.
10.   Fein, J.A., "Rotating Arm Experiments for the Stable Semi-Submerged Platform (SSP) Manoeuvring Prediction", DTNSRDC SPD Report 0698-02, September 1977.
11.   Kim, K.-H., and Reed , A.M., 'Propeller Design of U.S. Navy's SWATH T-AGOS19',
12.   Nomoto,K.,Taguchi,T.,Honda,K.,and Hirano,S., "On the Steering Qualities of Ships", International Shipbuilding Progress, Vol 4. No 35, 1957.
13.   McGregor, R.C., 'Full Scale Manoeuvring Trials of SWATH Fishing Vessel', Marine Technology Report in Preparation , Jan 1991.
14.   McGregor, R.C. and Miller, A.F., "On the Full Scale Manoeuvring Characterstics of the SWATH Fishing Vessel *ALI*", proceedings of the 23rd American Towing Tank Confernce, New Orleans, June 1992
15.   Waters and Fein, J.A., "Manoeuvrability of SWATH Ships", Proceedings of 19th American Towing Tank Conference, Ann Harbor, 1980

Development of a Four Degrees of Freedom Linear Ship Manoeuvring Mathematical Model

R.A. Francis, M.J. Dove, M.M.A. Pourzanjani
Maritime Division, Southampton Institute,
Warsash Campus, Warsash, Southampton
SO3 9ZL, UK

ABSTRACT

Many modern vessels have greater freeboard and are experiencing increasing roll angles, with this in mind a series of investigations were undertaken to compare the prediction performance of three and four degree of freedom models.

The study involved the development of three and four degree models to simulate the widest possible range of vessel types. The predictions were for flat calm conditions with no external factors being included.

From the results obtained from this programme it was shown that there is little difference in the predictions and therefore it may be concluded that for linear models no significant improvement in accuracy will be gained by including the fourth degree. It is intended that further study will be carried out which would include external factors, and non-linear hydrodynamic coefficients.

NOMENCLATURE.

B	Beam.
T	Draught.
L	Length.
C_B	Block coefficient.
G	Centre of gravity.
GM	Metacentric height.
I_x	Moment of inertia about x axis.
I_z	Moment of inertia about z axis.
K	Hydrodynamic rolling moment.
K_r, K_p etc	Roll hydrodynamic coefficients.

m	Mass of vessel.
M	Meta centre.
N	Hydrodynamic turning moment.
N_v, N_r etc	Yaw hydrodynamic coefficients.
p	Roll rate.
p	Roll angular acceleration.
r	Yaw rate.
r	Yaw angular acceleration.
u	Forward velocity.
u	Forward acceleration.
v	Lateral velocity.
v	Lateral acceleration.
W.L.	Water line.
WR	Water resistance.
X	Hydrodynamic surge force.
X_u, X_v etc	Surge hydrodynamic coefficients.
Y	Hydrodynamic sway force.
Y_r, Y_v etc	Sway hydrodynamic coefficients.
δ	Rudder angle (radians).
ϕ	Roll angle (radians).
Ψ	Yaw angle (radians).

INTRODUCTION

Many modern ships tend to be larger, have greater freeboard and steam at faster speeds, also passenger and car ferries as well as RO/RO ships have shown a tendency to roll significantly when turning. High superstructures and a relatively low density of the cargo means a small metacentric height, leading to a small righting lever and a greater time for the vessel to recover.

At speed and in close turns the rolling moment induced by the rudder and hydrodynamic forces acting may be considerable and may have a marked effect on the vessels manoeuvrability. A study by Hirano et al [1], revealed that the manoeuvring motion of ships with large roll should be calculated taking the coupling effect due to roll into consideration. For example after the M/S Zenobia accident, demonstrated by Kallstrom and Ottosson [2], when the vessel, in a demonstration of the autopilot, was put into a close turn the ship suddenly heeled over to port and the load began to move, which resulted in a list of 40 degrees. After unsuccessful attempts to right the vessel it eventually sank.

If it can be shown that roll has a significant effect on the manoeuvring motion of a vessel then perhaps details concerning roll should be included in the International Maritime Organisation [3] recommendations on the information to be displayed in the wheel house.

This study aims to see if, by including the effect due to roll into the model there would be any significant improvement in the model's predictions. Both 3 and 4 degrees of freedom models will be used in the study, with the comparison between the 3 degree model (surge, sway and yaw) and 4 degree model (surge, sway, yaw and roll) being made.

VESSELS USED IN SIMULATIONS

A range of vessel types and sizes were used so that the effect of roll could be seen across a range of vessels rather than for only one ship type. The vessels used were:
     i.   25 metre Training Vessel (ITV Somerset),
    ii.   150 metre Container Ship,
  iii.   150 metre Ro/Ro Ferry (M/S Zenobia)
   iv.   63 metre Dredger (Sand Skua)
    v.   161 metre Mariner Class Vessel.

ROLL

Due to the underwater shape of vessel's hull, which is usually of a compromise to achieve a minimum resistance and maximum cargo carrying capability, all ships will roll to same extent. This may be due to external effects and/or the vessel dynamics. Any rolling effect is harmful to the efficiency of ship performance. Among the problems which can occur due to excessive rolling are:
    a)   Loss of speed for a given power output.
    b)   Loss of efficiency of ship staff, either due to the necessity to hang on, or through actual seasickness.
    c)   Loss of commercial effectiveness due to necessity to secure cargo and ship's equipment firmly. An example would be of a ro/ro ferry with hundreds of cars on-board.
    d)   Damage to ship's equipment due to excessive roll.
    e)   Complete loss of vessel due to excessive roll.

Because of the problems associated with roll, considerable attention has been paid to roll reduction. The equivalent problem with pitch is much less severe due to the shape of the ships hull in that its length is five to ten times its beam.

Modelled roll
In this study only the roll caused by the turning of the vessel is considered. That is, it is assumed no wind or wave excitation forces are acting on the vessel, therefore the rolling motion could only be caused by rudder movements and the water's resistance to allowing the vessel to sway as the vessel turns.

How is roll modelled
Roll is modelled the same way as any of the other degrees of motion in that a differential equation containing hydrodynamic coefficients and variables is used. However, account has to be taken of the righting lever as this acts as damping to the roll motion. As the study is only looking at roll in flat calm conditions then roll will only be considered within the limits of initial stability and therefore the righting moment can be represented by the equation:

Weight * Metacentric height * Sine(Roll angle)   **(1)**
or
$$W \ast GM \ast \sin(\phi) \qquad\qquad (2)$$

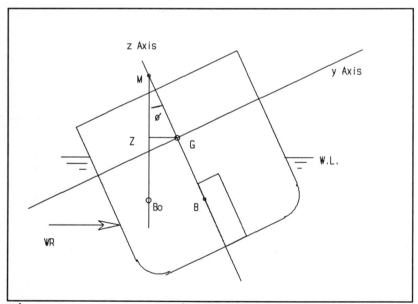

Figure 1   Forces acting on vessel

The resulting moment is given by:

Resultant Moment = Rolling Moment - Righting Moment
(3)

When the resultant moment is zero then the system is at equilibrium and therefore the vessel will not roll to port or starboard and remain at whatever angle it has reached at that time.

MATHEMATICAL MODELS

Mathematical models which are developed for the simulation of ship manoeuvres must be capable of representing a wide range of ship types and design, machinery and propulsion and steering devices.

There are four main types of mathematical models, namely;
  i) Input-Output relationship model,
  ii) Holistic model,
  iii) Force mathematical model,
  iv) Modular manoeuvring model.

These models are described briefly by Chudley [4].

A vessel with six degrees of freedom possess three force equations and three moment equations. The force equation for heave and the moment equation for pitch need not be considered here because they have negligible effect on the prediction, as flat calm conditions and no external factors are assumed.
This gives a set of Eulerian equations in the form, assuming that the body axes are located at the ship's centre of gravity,

equation set (4)

$$X = m\dot{u} - mrv \qquad \text{(the surge equation)}$$
$$Y = m\dot{v} + mur \qquad \text{(the sway equation)}$$
$$N = I_z\dot{r} \qquad \text{(the yaw equation)}$$
$$K = I_x\dot{p} \qquad \text{(the roll equation)}$$

where X and Y are the total force components in the surge and sway directions respectively, N and K are the total moment components about the Z and X axes respectively and I_z and I_x are the moments of inertia about the Z and X axes respectively.

Abkowitz [5] covers techniques used in obtaining expressions for the hydrodynamic forces and moments and by using a Taylor series expansion, equations are obtained for the vessels motion. For the linear models only the first order terms are used. It is assumed in these models that there are no external factors and that all simulations are taking part in a flat calm sea.

In both models it is assumed that propeller revolutions are increased so as to overcome any loss of speed that would otherwise occur, therefore forward velocity is assumed constant.

Three degrees linear model
In the three degrees of freedom linear model only surge, sway and yaw are considered. The equations in set 1 can be written as a function of their relevant components;

$$Y = f_y (\dot{v}, v, \dot{r}, r, \delta)$$
$$\text{and} \quad N = f_z (\dot{v}, v, \dot{r}, r, \delta)$$

equation set (5)

When the Taylor series expansion has been applied to equation set 2, the resultant equations are of the form;

$$m\dot{v} + mur = Y_{\dot{v}}\dot{v} + Y_v v + Y_{\dot{r}}\dot{r} + Y_r r + Y_\delta \delta$$

$$I_z\dot{r} = N_{\dot{v}}\dot{v} + N_v v + N_{\dot{r}}\dot{r} + N_r r + N_\delta \delta$$

equation set (6)

Four degrees linear model
In the four degrees of freedom linear model surge, sway, yaw and roll are all considered together. The equations of set 2 can therefore be written as a function of their relevant components;

$$Y = f_y (\dot{v}, v, \dot{r}, r, \delta, \dot{p}, p, \phi)$$
$$N = f_z (\dot{v}, v, \dot{r}, r, \delta, \dot{p}, p, \phi)$$
$$\text{and} \quad K = f_x (\dot{v}, v, \dot{r}, r, \delta, \dot{p}, p, \phi)$$

equation set (7)

Once the Taylor series has been applied the following equations are present;

$$m\dot{v} + mur = Y_{\dot{v}}\dot{v} + Y_v v + Y_{\dot{r}}\dot{r} + Y_r r + Y_\delta \delta + Y_{\dot{p}}\dot{p} + Y_p p + Y_\phi \phi$$

$$I_z\dot{r} = N_{\dot{v}}\dot{v} + N_v v + N_{\dot{r}}\dot{r} + N_r r + N_\delta \delta + N_{\dot{p}}\dot{p} + N_p p + N_\phi \phi$$

$$I_x\dot{p} = K_{\dot{v}}\dot{v} + K_v v + K_{\dot{r}}\dot{r} + K_r r + K_\delta \delta + K_{\dot{p}}\dot{p} + K_p p + K_\phi \phi - mgGM\phi$$

equation set (8)

MODEL COMPARISON SIMULATIONS

To compare the models certain manoeuvres were required to be performed by both models. These simulations were to be similar to those normally used in assessing ship manoeuvrability. Three different tests were to be used which are detailed below:

i) Turning Circle Test: In this test the rudder is rapidly deflected to and held at a fixed angle. The vessel is allowed to swing until it has reached steady state and, after transients have disappeared. In the models this test was simulated to show the angle of roll that the vessel would obtain during a steady state turn. The simulations were performed for a variety of rudder angles.

ii) Simple Alteration of Heading. A simple alteration of heading by a change of course is simulated to show the roll that is most likely to be experienced in normal use. This test will help to assess the settling time.

iii) Zig Zag Manoeuvre. In this test the vessel's rudder is rapidly deflected to a preset rudder angle, e.g. 20 degrees to starboard, the model was allowed to swing through the angle then the opposite helm of the same magnitude was demanded. This is repeated several more times. The experiment is repeated for different deflections and vessel speeds. This test will show, in the four degrees of freedom model, if there is any build up of roll from sudden changes in heading.

DISCUSSION OF RESULTS

The results will be analysed according to simulation with an overall analysis at the end. For the analysis purposes only the Container Ship manoeuvring simulations will be discussed because they are typical of the overall results.

Turning circle
The turning circle manoeuvring simulations for the 3 degrees of freedom model were found to be unreliable due to problems with the hydrodynamic coefficients and therefore were not considered. The simulation was carried out for rudder angles of 35 degrees to port to 35 degrees to starboard in increments of 5 degrees.

With only results for the 4 degrees of freedom

model, only the level of roll can be seen for a steady
rate of turn. Large angles of roll occurred which must
have some effect on the model.

This large roll, that was seen with all the
vessels simulated for roll, probably explains the fate
of the M/S Zenobia which was put into a close turn as
described in the introduction to this paper.

Alteration of course
With this manoeuvring simulation various angles were
used for the course changes.

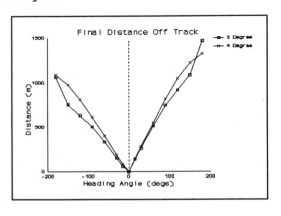

The results
obtained show that
the distances
between the models
predictions were
small for small
alterations in
course and as
expected got worse
for larger angles.
The further
distances off course
by the 4 degree
model was due to the
extra sway that
would be caused by
having roll included in the model and the increased
time that it took to reach the desired course.

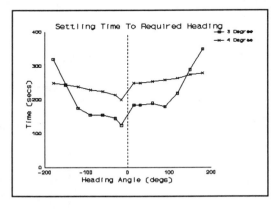

The settling
time to the required
course did show some
differences. The 3
degree model mostly
got to the required
course much quicker
than the 4 degree
model, this was due
to the 3 degree
model holding the
rudder angle larger
for a longer period
of time. The 4
degree model
lessened the rudder
angle to reduce the effect of roll that was
experienced, it also had a small amount of opposite
rudder to counter the roll that it was experiencing.

The amount of roll experienced by the 4 degree

model was up to a maximum of 26 degrees for a 180 degree turn, and had a linear relationship with the angle of heading change, i.e. the greater the change to the new heading the greater the roll. This greater roll was caused by the larger periods of time with the rudder at maximum

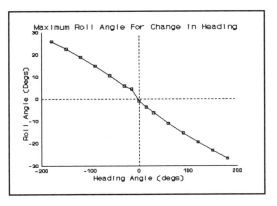

angle or at a large angle. The roll would usually have damped out within 420 seconds of the change to a new course.

Zigzag course

With this manoeuvring simulation various deviations about a due north heading were simulated. This simulation had deviations of between 0 to 35 degrees in increments of 5 degrees.

For small angles of deviation it was seen that the 4 degree model was closer to the required course, but the differences were small and could be neglected. With larger angles the 3 degree model was closer, with a significant difference for deviations greater than 15 degrees.

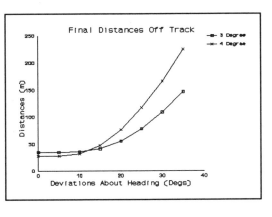

The maximum distances between the models was not at the end of the simulations, but was actually occurring at the penultimate deviation in the simulation. However, the differences between the maximum difference and the final difference was fairly constant for deviations greater than 10 degrees averaging about 9 metres and therefore negligible.

Settling time to the course was not recorded but the time to reach the required heading was plotted and it was seen that the 3 degree model reached the new heading quicker than the 4 degrees model, but again this was due to the 3 degree model holding the rudder angle larger for longer periods of time. The 4 degree model did use a small amount of opposite rudder to counter the roll caused by the change in course as with a simple alteration in course.

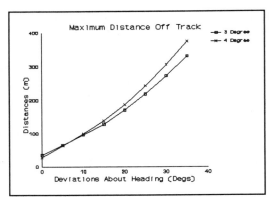

The total distance travelled did show greater differences than with just a simple alteration in course, but again when compared with the total distance travelled by either model was negligible.

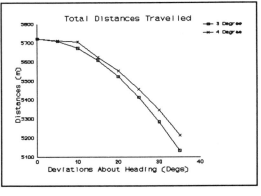

The amount of roll experienced by the 4 degrees model was up to a maximum of 12 degrees for the 35 degree deviation zigzag simulation. It is also seen that again a linear relationship existed between the deviation and the maximum angle of roll. It should be remembered that with this simulation the vessel was allowed to obtain its course before being required to change to a new one, if the change was required before the vessel

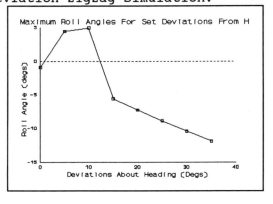

had settled on the new course then a build up for roll may have been seen.

Overall results
Overall the results tend to suggest there was little difference between the two models, the 4 degrees model showed some differences in rudder behaviour and also took longer to reach the required course.

The 4 degrees model was closer to the demanded course for small changes in course and further away for large changes. This was probably due to the roll causing more sway in the model.

CONCLUSIONS

The primary aim of this investigation was to compare the prediction performance of three and four degree of freedom models.

A 4 degrees of freedom linear model should be more accurate than the 3 degrees of freedom model when compared to actual trials data collected from full scale trials. However, as no full scale data was available for comparison then only a subjective view of the results could be made.

It was seen that there was little difference between the models and therefore having roll included in the model would only complicate the model and would entail time consuming full scale trials to evaluate the coefficients. However, with the effect of wind, tide, current and waves being taken into account and the inclusion of the non-linear hydrodynamic coefficients, then perhaps the difference between the models would be greater. For the models as they stand at present there is no real reason for choosing the 4 degrees model in preference to the 3 degrees model as no great improvement in accuracy is gained.

With the advent of ships having greater freeboard and lower density cargoes the amount of roll that the vessel experiences is getting larger and models should start to incorporate this fourth degree of freedom.

An area of further study would be to include these external factors and the nonlinear coefficients, along with the cross-coupling between the degrees of motion, into the model and then compare to actual trials data.

REFERENCES

[1] Hirano, M. and Takashina, J. 'A calculation of ship turning motion taking coupling effect due to heel into consideration,' *Transactions of the West-Japan Society of Naval Architects*, No 59, 1980.

[2] Kallstrom, C.G. and Ottosson, P. 'The generation and control of roll motion of ships in close turns,' *Ship Operation Automation Vol4*, 1983, pp 25-36.

[3] IMO: Recommendations on the information to be included in the manoeuvring booklets, Resolution A. 209 (VII) adopted on 12th October 1971.

[4] Chudley, J. Dove, M.J. and Tapp N.J. 'A Review of Mathematical Models used in Ship Manoeuvres,' *Proceedings of the 3rd Int. Conf. on Computer Aided Design, Manufacture and Operation in the Marine and Offshore Industries*, Key Biscayne, Florida, 1991. Computational Mechanics Publications, Boston, 1991.

[5] Abkowitz, M., Lectures an ship hydrodynamics, steering and manoeuvrability. Hy-A Report, Hy, 5., Denmark, 1964.

[6] Ankudinov, V.K. 'Ship manoeuvrability assessment in ship design - simulation concept,' *Proceedings of the Inter.Conf. on ship manoeuvrability*, RINA, No 19, April-May 1987.

SECTION 3: DIRECTIONAL CONTROL

The Effects of the Environment on the Stability and Turning of Ships

D. Vassalos, C. Delvenakiotis
*Department of Ship and Marine Technology,
University of Strathclyde, Glasgow G4 0LZ, UK*

ABSTRACT

The effect of the environment comprising steady wind, current, second order wave forces and combination thereof on the controls-fixed stability and turning trajectory of a VLCC is investigated systematically and the results are presented and discussed. A dynamical systems theory is adopted in the investigation using a coupled four-degrees of freedom non-linear mathematical model. The need to assess ship manoeuvrability in a realistic environment is demonstrated by considering the influence of wind and current on the recently proposed IMO manoeuvring performance standards.

INTRODUCTION

The ability of a vessel to manoeuvre effectively constitutes an important element of her safety requirements with strong bearing on her efficiency and economic operation. Furthermore, the economic, political and ecological consequences of an accident at sea are far reaching. It would appear, therefore, rather surprising and unfortunate that designers are left to make decisions affecting manoeuvring behaviour unaided, whilst international bodies have so far failed to take responsibility for ensuring safe ship operation with regard to this factor.

Systematic research on the subject of ship manoeuvring started at Strathclyde in November 1987 aimed at improving the existing situation by addressing the manoeuvring problem from fundamental principles. The major development relates to the introduction of dynamical system ideas on studying ship manoeuvring behaviour using a non-linear modular manoeuvring model, [1]. A flexible computer simulation program has been developed and by making use of recent advances in other fields of non-linear dynamics, much insight into ship manoeuvrability has been gained whilst establishing a framework for a systematic study of manoeuvring behaviour, [2] to [7].

In recent years, a lot of work has been done in order to generalise modular mathematical models to cope with the influence of shallow water, [8], and with low speed manoeuvring in the presence of external disturbances which may require the model to be able to work in four quadrants of motion rather than in a narrow band of drift angles as was the case in earlier models, [9]. In relation to this, considerable information is still needed on a range of items, including: hull forces at large drift angles, propeller data in all four quadrants, lateral forces at propellers, deeper understanding of hull-propeller-rudder interaction at large drift angles and yaw rates and of manoeuvring behaviour in the presence of environmental disturbances.

The present paper is an attempt to shed some light in regard to the last item.

BACKGROUND

An assumption that is usually implicitly made is that ship manoeuvrability under ideal environmental conditions would be adequate to ensure safe operation in general. Such an assumption, however, is difficult to defend as indicated in ITTC '90, [10], where the following is stated:

*   Increasing interest is being shown in low speed manoeuvring in shallow and confined waters, (e.g. restricted waterways, approaching harbours and ports, often in the presence of wind, current and other environmental effects).
*   Course-keeping difficulties and directional stability problems in following and quartering seas are phenomena well known.
*   The ability of a vessel to maintain heading in an environment of strong winds is an essential factor for its overall safety, especially when windage is high.
*   For a mathematical model to be used effectively, forces and moments arising from environmental aspects such as water depth, wind, current and waves must be considered in addition to those considered to be of purely hydrodynamic origin.

Many more arguments could be brought forward and cases sited from the literature to support the fact that for many a ship, safe and successful operation in the performance of her mission depends significantly on her ability to manoeuvre adequately in the environment in which she operates (currents, wind, waves, shallow water, etc). Furthermore, to counter the argument that calm water manoeuvring is complicated enough, it has to be emphasised that the reliability of the simulation depends on the incorporation of all relevant aspects in the mathematical model and only secondarily on the accuracy with which the effects have been derived or are described.

Environmental effects on ship manoeuvring have already been considered, e.g. [1], [11], by incorporating wind, current and second order wave forces modules in the manoeuvring simulation. First order wave effects have also been incorporated, e.g. [11], [12] but are normally assumed to be unimportant, a false assumption when considering, for example, directional stability in following/quartering seas.

A systematic investigation of manoeuvring performance in a realistic environment is, however lacking, and considering earlier arguments, long overdue.

The results of the first phase of such an investigation are presented here, within the framework of dynamical systems theory, using a VLCC, a ship type with generally acknowledged poor manoeuvrability, especially at slow speed in the presence of external disturbances.

The terms 'relative manoeuvrability' will be used to denote manoeuvring performance in the vessel's operating environment whereas 'inherent manoeuvrability' denotes the same in calm water, [12]. Both terms refer to open-loop qualities.

PROBLEM FORMULATION

Mathematical Model

For calm water, the non-linear mathematical model used is outlined below:

$$\text{SURGE} : m(\dot{u} - rv - x_G r^2 + z_G pr) = X_H + X_P + X_R + X_O \tag{1}$$

$$\text{SWAY} : m(\dot{v} + ru - z_G \dot{p} + x_G \dot{r}) = Y_H + Y_P + Y_R + Y_O \tag{2}$$

$$\text{ROLL} : I_X \dot{p} - m z_G (\dot{v} + ru) = K_H + K_P + K_R + K_O \tag{3}$$

$$\text{YAW} : I_Z \dot{r} + m x_G (\dot{v} + ru) = N_H + N_P + N_R + N_O \tag{4}$$

The co-ordinate system used is shown in Figure 1 whilst information on the hull, propeller and rudder forces as well as interaction effects can be found in [8].

Following a number of transformations, the motion equations are brought to the dynamical systems form:

$$\dot{z} = F(z, \alpha) \qquad (5)$$

where z is the vector of the state variables of the system, $z = (u, v, r, p, \phi)^T$ and α is a control parameter, such as trim, propeller rate, rudder angle, water depth, etc. Equation (5) is used to investigate either the transient response of the system to changes taking place in its control space, or to analyse long term behaviour by identifying the dependence of its steady states on a varying control parameter. The procedure is described in detail in [6].

An important feature of the algorithm is that it contains a stability analysis routine so that in the vicinity of each steady state identified, local linearisation is performed by substituting $z = z_o + b$ into

equation (5), where b represents the vector of deviations from z_o, yielding

$$\dot{b} = [C] b \qquad (6)$$

where [C] is the Jacobian matrix of F. The criterion then for instability is the existence of positive real parts in the eigenvalues of [C].

Incorporation of wind forces
Wind forces are treated as external forces, expressed normally in the following form, [14].

$$X_W = -U_{rw}^2 \; \rho A_X C_X \; \sin[(9/7)(|\psi_{rw}| - \pi/2)] \qquad (7)$$

$$Y_W = U_{rw}^2 \; \rho A_Y C_Y \; \sin\psi_{rw} \qquad (8)$$

$$N_W = -U_{rw}^2 \; \rho A_Y LC_N \; \sin(2\psi_{rw}) \qquad (9)$$

$$K_W = U_{rw}^2 \; \rho A_Y H_s C_K \; \sin\psi_{rw} \; \cos^2\phi \qquad (10)$$

where, A_X, A_Y are reference areas

C_X, C_Y, C_N, C_K are coefficients depending on ship type

(0.7, 0.8, 0.1, 1.3, respectively, [15])

L = vessel length B.P.

H_s = wind lever

U_{rw}= [$(U_w \cos(\psi_w - \psi) - u)^2 + (U_w \sin(\psi_w - \psi) - v)^2$]$^{1/2}$

ψ_{rw}= arctan[$(U_w \sin(\psi_w - \psi) - v)/(U_w \cos(\psi_w - \psi) - u)$]

Incorporation of current forces

The effect of current can be incorporated in a simple way by using the concept of relative velocity between the vessel and the water, although studies in restricted waters may require caution.

An alternative approach, allowing current forces to be treated as external forces is described in [1]. With this method, adopted in this study, the two acceleration components of the current are formulated in the ship's frame of reference and the derived forces are added on the right hand side of the manoeuvring equations.

Incorporation of wave forces

Wave forces are also treated as external forces. Two types of forces are normally considered to act on a vessel. Second order wave forces or drift forces which are of low frequency and high frequency first order wave forces. The combined effect is generally assumed to be the result of their superposition, [11].

Of the two, second order wave forces are assumed to be the more important and these are considered here in the first instance. In particular, the turning trajectory of a VLCC in regular waves is studied by using the following expressions from [13], with coefficients derived from experimental data.

$$X_D = C_{DX}(\lambda/L, \psi_{WV}) 0.5\rho g L_{PP} \zeta_A^2 \qquad (11)$$

$$Y_D = C_{DY}(\lambda/L, \psi_{WV}) 0.5\rho g L_{PP} \zeta_A^2 \qquad (12)$$

$$N_D = C_{DN}(\lambda/L, \psi_{WV}) 0.5\rho g L_{PP} \zeta_A^2 \qquad (13)$$

$$K_D = 0 \qquad (14)$$

ENVIRONMENTAL EFFECTS

Manoeuvring qualities examined

Controls-fixed stability (zero rudder angle) in the presence of a continuous disturbance, represented by wind, current and waves, would be much more realistic than in the presence

of an instantaneous disturbance which is normally used in
the various definitions of motion stability. In any case, it
would be rather meaningless to examine the straight-line
stability of a VLCC in the presence of an instantaneous
disturbance as she, due to her great inertia, would act as a
"filter" damping away any such disturbance.

Here, the controls-fixed directional stability
properties of a VLCC in full load conditions is examined,
under **continuous** environmental disturbances. The effect of
this environment on the vessel's turning trajectory is also
examined as this manoeuvre is an important practical
manoeuvre that ships frequently perform and one that
reflects both manoeuvring quality and rudder effectiveness
in emergency situations. Moreover, because the final phase
of the turning path is a steady-state manoeuvre, it can be
more easily treated analytically than the rest of the
definitive transient-state manoeuvres, thus enabling further
insight to be gained.

Therefore, the investigation focuses on 'relative
manoeuvrability'.

Range of environmental conditions
Relative manoeuvrability is examined firstly in a wind,
current and wave environment, each considered separately,
followed by selective combined environments comprising
wind+current, wind+waves and wind+current+waves. The range
of conditions investigated in the present study are shown in
Table 1 whilst the vessel particulars are shown in Table 2.

Results and Discussion
For each one of the conditions described above, the
time-history graphs of the unknown state variable are
plotted, together with an appropriate number of phase-plane
portraits to facilitate a global understanding of the
system's sensitivity.

The phase-plane presentation has important practical
significance, primarily of **qualitative** rather than
quantitative nature, due to the difficulty of obtaining
accurate graphical solutions. This information, however,
combined with the quantitative information on individual
trajectories, obtained through simulation, constitute the
next best thing to the actual solution of a non-linear
system of equations. But in a sense, this information is
better than a close-form solution since it describes
geometrically the behaviour of every solution for all time.

Based on the parametric investigation detailed in Table
1, a number of observations are outlined in the following,
pertaining to the two qualities examined.

1.'Controls-fixed' stability

Time-Histories

*   Increasing wind speed results in a oscillatory motion behaviour, Figs 2-3.

*   The effect of waves on the controls-fixed stability is significant only at small values of λ/L ($\lambda/L = 0.3 \div 0.6$). This result was not unexpected, as C_{DY} values become significant in this range, Figs 4 and 5.

*   Variation of the wave direction, from head to beam seas, in a combined wind, current and waves environment, produces a faster response by the ship as a result of increasing energy transfer to the ship system, e.g. Figs 6 and 7.

Phase-Portraits

*   Increasing wind speed, moves the system from a stable region to a region of "structural instability". A non-hyperbolic critical point is developed on the phase plane with two elliptic sectors. In this case, the behaviour near the origin can be very complex. Non-hyperbolic means not robust in relation to small modifications in the system parameters. A consequence of this, is that the trajectories defining the system's behaviour around this point are not, as in other cases, only slightly sensitive to small variations of the parameters, but a tiny change can cause a jump ("catastrophe" although not dangerous in this context) leading to a distantly located state, Figs 8 and 9.

*   In a combined wind, current and waves environment change from beam to head seas at small values of λ/L, reduces the oscillatory behaviour of the vessel and enhances her stability. This can be seen in Figs 10 and 11, where a smaller limit cycle is developed in the latter case. This behaviour seems to be exactly opposite from the behaviour of the ship in a wind-only environment where in a head wind static instability together with a self-sustained oscillation is experienced, [4].

*   Increasing the wave amplitude in a combined head wind and waves environment results in zeroing of the surge motion accompanied by increasing sway oscillatory motion which becomes a limit cycle when the wave amplitude approaches half the vessel draught, Figs 12 and 13. This result corresponds to findings in [12].

2.Turning

Time-Histories

*   With increasing beam wind speed, under a constant rudder angle, the vessel fails to reach a constant rate of turn with the centres of turning trajectories drifting. The drifting effect tends to be accentuated with decreasing rudder area, Figs 14 and 15.

*   Non-zero rudder angle settings again produce similar oscillatory behaviour in surge and sway velocities and in yaw rate in the steady-state phase. Larger rudder areas tend to "smooth out" these oscillations whilst increasing the overshoot values, e.g. Fig 16.

*   The ship fails to follow the same turning trajectory in a beam current, and "jumps" to a distant location executing turns which change into a "pivot" point as the rudder angle increases. Each "pivot" point can be assumed as a stable point that stores and conserves energy, while each "jump" represents the part of the cycle in which energy is emitted, Figs 17 and 18.

*   The effect of waves on the ship's turning trajectory are again significant only at small values of λ/L ($\lambda/L = 0.3 \div 0.6$), with the same tendency of trajectories to drift as was observed with wind-only and current-only environments.

*   For the combined environments considered, the effect of current was dominant.

Phase-Portraits

*   The influence of wave length on the turning quality of the vessel can be seen in Figs 19 and 20 where increasing wave lengths transform the limit cycle to an attractive node.

*   The same influence, as described above can be seen in Figs 21, 22 and 23 in a wind-only environment with decreasing wind speeds.

IMPLICATIONS ON MANOEUVRING PERFORMANCE STANDARDS

Based on the foregoing investigation, it was further decided to examine systematically the influence of a current-only environment on the recently proposed IMO manoeuvring performance standards, [16], particularly those concerned with initial turning and turning qualities. It was thought that owing to the large wetted surface area of a VLCC, the

effect of current will be the more testing with regard to
the effect of external disturbances on manoeuvrability.
Considering current of varying strength and direction, the
advance, tactical diameter, and travel distance were
computed as specified in [16]. The results are shown in
Tables 3 to 5 for the full range of the conditions tested.
Within the range under investigation, the following are
noteworthy:

*   A beam current does not affect the vessel's
advance and travel distance.
*   The tactical diameter is independent of the sense
and speed of current along the fore-and-aft direction.
*   The IMO limits (4.5, 5 and 2.5 ship lengths for
the advance, tactical diameter, and travel distance,
respectively) are threatened in a few occasions and are
actually exceeded in the case of the travel distance in
a 3 Knot following / quartering current.
*   The influence of current in all the cases examined
is significant enough to merit further consideration.

CONCLUDING REMARKS

Mathematical modelling of the environment pertaining to
wind, current, waves, restricted waters, etc. has progressed
to a level where systematic investigation of these effects
on the manoeuvring behaviour of ships is now possible. The
novelty in this paper relates to the introduction of
Dynamical Systems theory to studying relative
manoeuvrability and, in particular, the qualities referred
to as controls-fixed stability and turning in the presence
of continuous environmental disturbances. Based on the
limited investigation presented in the paper, the following
concluding remarks can be made:

*   The richness of behaviour of a manoeuvring ship in
the presence of continuous external disturbances, as
revealed by the present study, is proof in itself of the
usefulness of the approach adopted and of the need to
consider relative manoeuvrability more seriously.
*   Considering that the assumptions made in the
context of conventional analysis and associated
manoeuvring performance standards, regarding the
environment in which ships operate, frequently do not
match the actual conditions encountered in practice, it
would seem that both the analysis and the standards
derived therefrom merit careful scrutiny.
*   The approach presented here is presently being
used to study directional stability in realistic
environments, particularly in the presence of
following/quartering seas which is known to have a
strong bearing on vessel safety, and the results will be

made available in the near future.

REFERENCES

1.MIKELIS, N.: "A Procedure for the Prediction of Ship Manoeuvring Response for Initial Design". Proc. Int. Conf. on Computer Applications in the Automation of Shipyard Operation and Ship Design (ICCAS 85). Pub. North-Holland, 1985.

2.VASSALOS, D. and SPYROU, K.: "A New Approach to Developing Ship Manoeuvring Standards". RINA Spring Meeting, 1990.

3.SPYROU, K. and VASSALOS, D.: "Recent Advances in the Development of Ship Manoeuvring Standards". Proc. MARSIM & ICSM 90, Tokyo, Japan, June 1990.

4.SPYROU, K. and VASSALOS, D.: "A Global Investigation of Directional Stability of Ships in a Wind Environment". Proc. IMAEM '90, Athens 1990.

5.VASSALOS, D. and SPYROU K.: "An Investigation into the Combined Effects of Directional and Transverse Stabilities on Vessel Safety". Proc. STAB '90, Naples, September 1990.

6.SPYROU, K.: "A New Approach for Assessing Ship Manoeuvrability Based on Dynamical Systems Theory". Phd Thesis, University of Strathclyde, 1990.

7.VASSALOS, D. and SPYROU, K.: "The Effect of Trim by Bow: A Dynamical Systems Approach". The 2nd Kimmerman Int. Conf. on Ro-Ro Safety. London, April 1991.

8.HIRANO, H. et al: "A Practical Prediction Method of Ship Manoeuvring Motion and its Application". Proc. RINA Int. Conf. on Ship Manoeuvrability - Prediction and Achievement, London, 1987.

9.KHATTAB, O.: "Ship Handling in Harbours using Real Time Simulation". RINA Int. Conf. on Ship Manoeuvrability - Prediction and Achievement, London, 1987.

10."Report of the Manoeuvrability Committee", Proc. 19th ITTC, Madrid, 1990.

11.CAPURRO, G. and PUCCIO, P.: "Manoeuvring Predictions for Preliminary Ship and Port Design", IMAEM, 5th Int. Congress, Athens 1990.

12. LI, M. and WU, X.: "Simulation Calculation and Comprehensive Assessment on Ship Manoeuvrabilities in Wind, Wave, Current and Shallow Water", MARSIM & ICSM '90, Tokyo, Japan, June 1990.

13. HIRANO, M. et al: "Ship Turning Trajectory in Regular Waves", Trans. of the West Japan Society of Naval Architects, No. 60, 1980.

14. AAGE, C.: "Wind Coefficients for Nine Ship Models", Hydro-Aerodynamics Laboratory, Lyngby, Report n.A-3, May 1971.

15. MC CREIGHT, W.: "Ship Manoeuvring in Waves", 16th Symposium in Naval Hydrodynamics", ONR, Berkeley 1986.

16. IMO, "Manoeuvrability of Ships and Manoeuvring Standards", Sub-Committee on Ship Design and Equipment, DE 34/28, 21 March 1991.

PARAMETERS	WIND	WAVES	CURRENT	WIND+CURRENT	WIND+WAVES	WIND+CURRENT+WAVES
U_w = 10 Kn	*					
30 Kn	*			*		
50 kn	*			*		
ψ_w = -90 deg.	*			*	*	*
180 deg.					*	*
U_c = 3 Kn		*		*		*
ψ_c = 90 deg.		*		*		*
ζ_a = 1 m		*				
2 m		*			*	
3 m		*			*	
4 m					*	
4.5 m		*			*	
4.52 m		*			*	
6 m		*			*	
10 m		*			*	
λ/L = 0.4					*	*
0.5						
0.8		*				
1.0		*				*
1.2		*				*
ψ_{wv} = 0 deg.		*			*	*
-45 deg.		*				*
-90 deg.		*				*
180 deg.		*				*
δ = 0 deg.		*	*	*	*	*
15 deg.			*	*		
35 deg.		*	*	*		*
A_R = 77.56 sq. m		*	*	*	*	*
110.80 sq. m		*	*	*		*
144.04 sq. m				*		*

Table 1 : Parametric Investigation Matrix

VLCC'S TURNING ABILITY (ADVANCE) IN A CURRENT ENVIRONMENT

(VALUES IN SHIP LENGTHS)

CURR. SPEED IN KNOTS	CURRENT DIRECTION IN DEGREES						
	0	30	60	90	120	150	180
0	3.48	3.48	3.48	3.48	3.48	3.48	3.48
1	3.75	3.71	3.62	3.48	3.35	3.25	3.22
2	4.01	3.94	3.75	3.48	3.22	3.02	2.95
3	4.28	4.17	3.88	3.48	3.08	2.80	2.69

Table 3 : Advance

VLCC'S INITIAL TURNING (TRAVEL DISTANCE) IN A CURRENT ENVIRONMENT

(VALUES IN SHIP LENGTHS)

CURR. SPEED IN KNOTS	CURRENT DIRECTION IN DEGREES						
	0	30	60	90	120	150	180
0	2.223	2.223	2.223	2.223	2.223	2.223	2.223
1	2.351	2.334	2.288	2.224	2.160	2.114	2.100
2	2.478	2.444	2.351	2.224	2.100	2.000	1.970
3	2.605 (*)	2.554 (*)	2.414	2.224	2.034	1.895	1.844

(*) : exceedance of IMO'S recommended limits.

Table 5 : Travel Distance

PARTICULARS OF THE V.L.C.C.

Symbol	Particular	Value	Symbol	Particular	Value
L_{PP}	Length B.P. (m)	325	P	Prop. pitch (m)	6.50
B	Breadth (m)	53	a_E	Blade ratio	0.68
T	Draught (m)	21.79	k	Prop. blades	5
C_b	Block coeff.	0.831	x_P	Prop. pos. (m)	-150.8
C_P	Prismatic coeff.	0.835		Prop axis pos. (m)	14.7
t	Trim (m)	0.0	A_R	Rudder area (m²)	110.8
x_G	L.C.G. (m)	5.15	H_R	Rudder height (m)	13.85
z_G	V.C.G. (m)	1	Λ	Rudder asp. ratio	1.73
GM	Metac. height (m)	1.7	x_R	Rudder lift (m)	-165.5
Δ	Displ. (tonnes)	310700	z_R	Rudder lift (m)	12.5
f	Prop. number	1	x_{RLE}	Rudder L.E. (m)	-161
D	Prop. diam. (m)	9.1	z_{RUP}	Rudder Upper E. (m)	7.19
U	Speed (m/s)	9.22			

Table 2 : Vessel Particulars

VLCC'S TURNING ABILITY (TACT. DIAMETER) IN A CURRENT ENVIRONMENT

(VALUES IN SHIP LENGTHS)

CURR. SPEED IN KNOTS	CURRENT DIRECTION IN DEGREES						
	0	30	60	90	120	150	180
0	3.195	3.195	3.195	3.195	3.195	3.195	3.195
1	3.195	3.474	3.677	3.752	3.677	3.474	3.195
2	3.195	3.752	4.159	4.308	4.159	3.752	3.195
3	3.195	4.029	4.640	4.884	4.640	4.029	3.195

Table 4 : Tactical Diameter

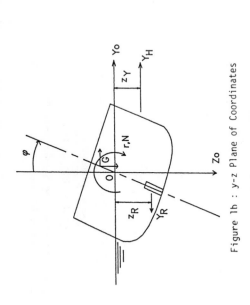

Figure 1b : y-z Plane of Coordinates

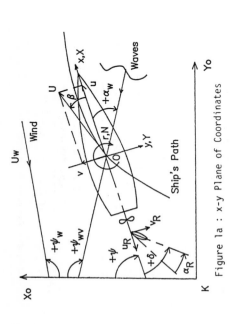

Figure 1a : x-y Plane of Coordinates

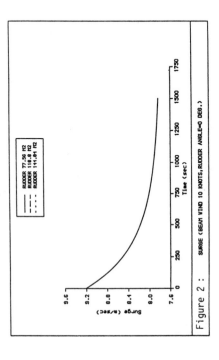

Figure 3 :

Figure 2 :

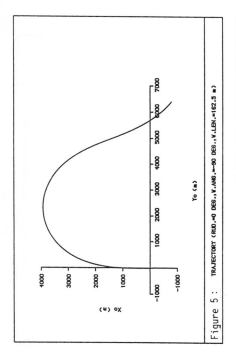

Figure 4 :   TRAJECTORY (RUD.=0 DEG.,V.ANG.=-90 DEG.,V.LEN.=325 m)

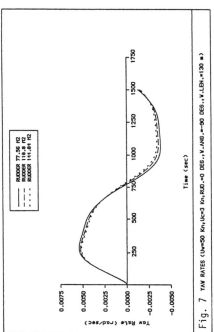

Figure 5 :   TRAJECTORY (RUD.=0 DEG.,V.ANG.=-90 DEG.,V.LEN.=162.5 m)

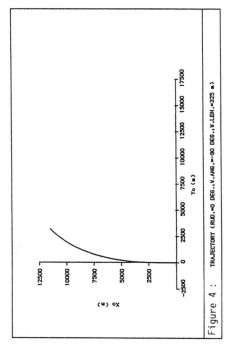

Fig. 6   YAW RATES (Uw=50 Kn,Uc=3 Kn,RUD.=0 DEG.,V.ANG.=0 DEG.,V.LEN.=130 m)

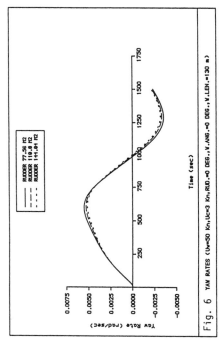

Fig. 7   YAW RATES (Uw=50 Kn,Uc=3 Kn,RUD.=0 DEG.,V.ANG.=-90 DEG.,V.LEN.=130 m)

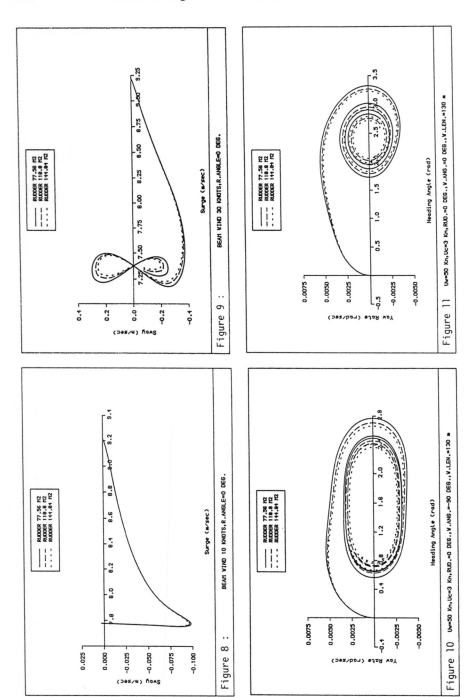

Figure 8 :   BEAM WIND 10 KNOTS,R.ANGLE=0 DEG.

Figure 9 :   BEAM WIND 30 KNOTS,R.ANGLE=0 DEG.

Figure 10   Uw=50 Kn,Uc=3 Kn,RUD.=0 DEG.,V.ANG.=-90 DEG.,V.LEN.=130 m

Figure 11   Uw=50 Kn,Uc=3 Kn,RUD.=0 DEG.,V.ANG.=0 DEG.,V.LEN.=130 m

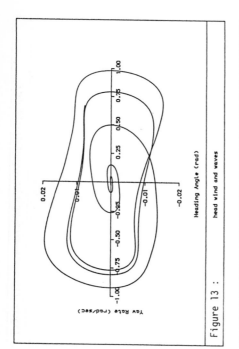

Figure 13 :   head wind and waves

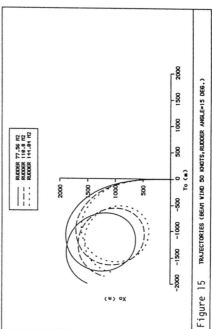

Figure 15   TRAJECTORIES (BEAM WIND 50 KNOTS,RUDDER ANGLE=15 DEG.)

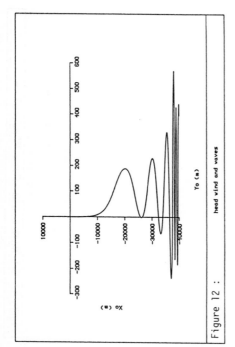

Figure 12 :   head wind and waves

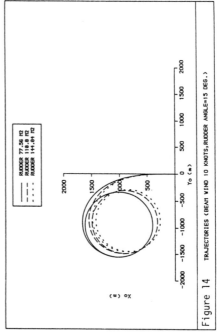

Figure 14   TRAJECTORIES (BEAM WIND 10 KNOTS,RUDDER ANGLE=15 DEG.)

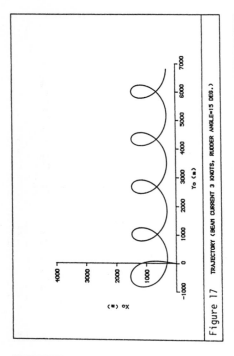

Figure 17   TRAJECTORY (BEAM CURRENT 3 KNOTS, RUDDER ANGLE=15 DEG.)

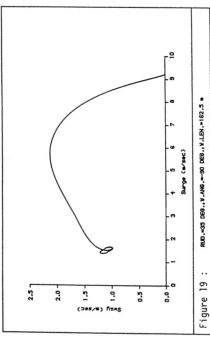

Figure 19 :   RUD.=35 DEG.,V.ANG.=-90 DEG.,V.LEN.=162.5 m

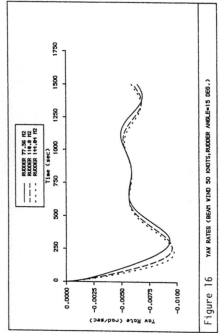

Figure 16   YAW RATES (BEAM WIND 50 KNOTS,RUDDER ANGLE=15 DEG.)

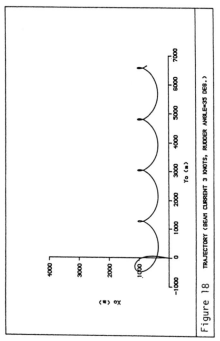

Figure 18   TRAJECTORY (BEAM CURRENT 3 KNOTS, RUDDER ANGLE=35 DEG.)

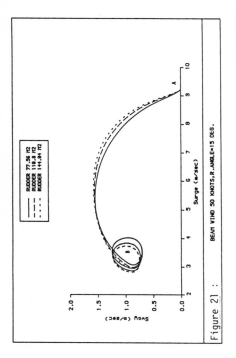

Figure 20 : RUD.=35 DEG.,W.ANG.=-90 DEG.,W.LEN.=325 m

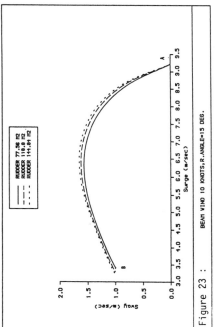

Figure 21 : BEAM WIND 50 KNOTS,R.ANGLE=15 DEG.

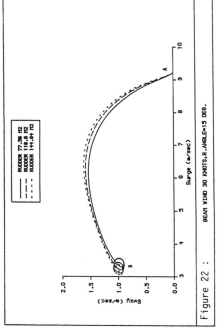

Figure 22 : BEAM WIND 30 KNOTS,R.ANGLE=15 DEG.

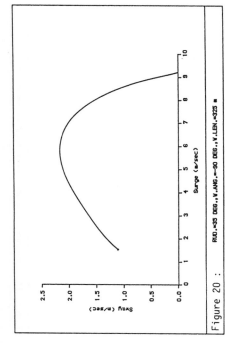

Figure 23 : BEAM WIND 10 KNOTS,R.ANGLE=15 DEG.

The Effects of Skegs and Stern Shape on the Dynamic Stability of Ships

D. Clarke

Hydromechanics Research Group, Department of Marine Technology, University of Newcastle upon Tyne, UK

ABSTRACT

New types of stern shapes, referred to as pram sterns, give rise to a reduction in the directional stability of a ship. Using conformal mapping techniques, the side force generated by the skeg, attached to different shaped after bodies is examined. The results are supported by experimental data and show that a skeg attached to a rectangular body section is far less effective than a skeg attached to a triangular section.

INTRODUCTION

In recent years a type of hull form has been developed with a stern shape known as a "pram stern". This type of stern has a greater degree of buttock flow compared to more conventional stern shapes, and has pronounced almost rectangular body sections. Pram sterns were developed with the aim of improving propulsive performance, but it has subsequently come to light that hulls with pram sterns exhibit a greater degree of directional instability than those with conventional sterns.

The reasons for this significant reduction in stability are not at all clear, and are not explained by the simple slender-body theory or regression formulae that are often used to evaluate the stability derivatives of hull forms, when considering ship manoeuvrability.

It has long been recognised that the skeg or deadwood at the lower part of the stern, immediately ahead of the propeller, plays an important role in adding to the directional stability of a ship. However, the size of the skeg has been much more a consequence of the type of hull form, than having been chosen to satisfy any stability requirement.

It has been found that, not only is the size of the skeg important, but the shape of the body sections above the skeg also greatly influence its effectiveness. This is due to the interference effects between the skeg and the hull, which can be derived by conformal mapping techniques.

In this paper three idealised stern body sections will be considered, triangular, elliptical and rectangular, each having a flat plate skeg below it. The effect on the stability derivatives of a ship with the triangular type stern, when modified to the rectangular type, will be examined.

LINEAR DERIVATIVES

Various attempts have been made to establish a method for predicting the values of the linear stability derivatives, having only a knowledge of the ship geometry. By assuming that the hull may be treated as a flat plate, use was made of the Jones low-aspect ratio wing theory. Here, the assumption was made that the free-surface could be regarded as a mirror, with an image of the ship above the water. However, by this approach the derivatives were only dependent on the square of the length to draught ratio of the ship, and since the hull is represented by a flat plate, all transverse body sections are simply vertical strips having unit added mass.

It is possible to extend this idea into a generalised strip-method, dependent upon the zero-frequency lateral added mass distribution of the hull. Of course the added mass of any transverse two-dimensional body section is entirely dependent upon its geometry, so by this generalisation the added mass strip-method recognises hull form details beyond simply the length and draught. It should also be noted that for elliptical body sections, where the lateral added mass coefficient is unity, the extended method reduces to the result obtained by the Jones low-aspect ratio wing theory, since flat plate section can be regarded as a degenerate ellipse.

The complete expressions for the linear acceleration and velocity derivatives were given by Clarke et al [1], showing their relationship to low-aspect ratio wing theory and to the various attempts at regression analysis. Since we are interested here only in the velocity derivatives, we can write them as [1,2],

$$-Y_v'/\pi(T/L)^2 = [C_H]_S$$

$$-Y_r'/\pi(T/L)^2 = [C_H X']_S$$

$$-N_v'/\pi(T/L)^2 = [C_H X']_S + \int_S^B C_H dX' \qquad (1)$$

$$-N_r'/\pi(T/L)^2 = [C_H X'^2]_S + \int_S^B C_H X' dX' \quad ,$$

where the subscripts are S - stern and B - bow. C_H is the zero-frequency added mass coefficient at the longitudinal station X', which is the non-dimensional distance X/L from amidships.

The ability of this strip-method to predict stability derivatives was examined by Clarke [2] and it was found that the predictions were reasonable over the forward part of the hull, but progressively diverged from the experimental evidence over the after part of the hull. It appeared that the side force generating capability of the skeg at the stern was not being accounted for.

Experimental work reported by Tsakonas [3] and Jacobs [4], indicated that the skeg could be regarded as a separate tail fin, producing side forces additional to those from the hull. This observation would be acceptable if the skeg protruded downwards beneath the keel, but it is difficult to reconcile within the slender-body theory, since the skeg is masked by the fuller body sections forward of it.

One explanation could be that the slender-body theory assumptions have been violated at the stern. The requirement is for almost parallel flow along the hull, since transverse dimensions are supposed to be small compared to the length of the hull. It is well known that there is usually a strong upflow in the region of the skeg, which could be enough to cause the violation of the slender-body theory. This may be just cause to follow the experimental evidence [2,3,4] and treat the skeg as an additional fin added to the hull.

If it is assumed that the skeg can be treated as a low-aspect ratio wing, then its side force generating capability is dependent on its trailing edge span. Nielsen [5] shows that a fin added to a body generates lift from two sources. The first is due to the fin itself and the second is additional lift on the fin due to the interference effect of the body to which it is attached. Accordingly the lift varies with the size and shape of the body.

The expression for the linear derivatives (1) can therefore be extended to include the effects of the skeg as follows:

$$-Y'_v/\pi(T/L)^2 = [C_H]_S + [\triangle C_H]_{SKEG}$$

$$-Y'_r/\pi(T/L)^2 = [C_H X']_S + [\triangle C_H X']_{SKEG}$$

$$-N'_v/\pi(T/L)^2 = [C_H X']_S + [\triangle C_H X']_{SKEG} + \int_S^B C_H dX' \qquad (2)$$

$$-N'_r/\pi(T/L)^2 = [C_H X'^2]_S + [\triangle C_H X'^2]_{SKEG} + \int_S^B C_H X' dX' \quad .$$

Here the term $(\triangle C_H)_{SKEG}$ is the added mass due to the skeg, including the interference effects of the stern shape in its proximity.

If we wished to examine the change in the derivatives, brought about by changes in the skeg itself or changes in the stern shapes, for two different skeg arrangements we get, from equation (2),

$$-\triangle Y'_v/\pi(T/L)^2 = [\triangle C_H]_{SKEG1} - [\triangle C_H]_{SKEG2}$$

$$-\triangle Y'_r/\pi(T/L)^2 = [\triangle C_H X']_{SKEG1} - [\triangle C_H X']_{SKEG2}$$

$$-\triangle N'_v/\pi(T/L)^2 = [\triangle C_H X']_{SKEG1} - [\triangle C_H X']_{SKEG2} \qquad (3)$$

$$-\triangle N'_r/\pi(T/L)^2 = [\triangle C_H X'^2]_{SKEG1} - [\triangle C_H X'^2]_{SKEG2}$$

The added mass coefficient of a skeg, which may be considered to be a flat plate extending from the water line, is simple $\triangle C_H = 1.0$. However its real effective value also depends upon its depth with respect to the draught of the ship. The skeg may not extend from the waterline, but may instead protrude from the stern or transom of the ship, and its effectiveness is then modified by the presence of the afterbody of the hull.

In order to deduce the effective added mass or side force generating capacity of the ship, it is necessary to know the added mass coefficient of the complete body section, with hull and skeg together then to subtract the added mass coefficient due to the hull. This situation is shown in Figure 1 as

$$\triangle C_{H_{SKEG}} = C_{H_T} - C_{H_B}{}^* \quad ,$$

where the subscript T refers to the hull plus skeg section and the subscript B refers to the hull alone. However since $C_{H_B}{}^*$ is only based upon the depth of the body above the skeg, it must be scaled to the full draught T as follows

$$\triangle C_{H_{SKEG}} = C_{H_T} - (1 - h/T)^2 C_{H_B} \quad . \tag{4}$$

In the next section, three idealised stern sections will be considered and their added mass coefficients determined. This will allow the skeg derivatives contribution $\triangle C_{H_{SKEG}}$ to be found.

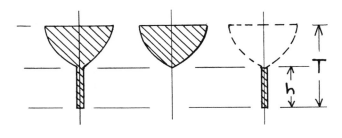

$$C_{H_T} \quad - \quad C_{H_B}{}^* \quad = \quad \triangle C_{H_{SKEG}}$$

Figure 1. Derivation of Skeg Added Mass.

ADDED MASS OF IDEALISED STERN SECTIONS

The added mass coefficient C_H for any general section shape, is the ratio
of the inertia coefficient for that general section to that of an elliptical
section of the same draught. Since a circle is a special case of an ellipse,
the problem of determining the added mass coefficient reduces to finding
the mapping function which maps the section in the z-plane onto a circle
in the ς-plane.

If the mapping function is taken to be an infinite Laurent Series,

$$z = \varsigma + \frac{A_{-1}}{\varsigma} + \frac{A_{-3}}{\varsigma^3} + \frac{A_{-5}}{\varsigma^5} + \cdots \qquad (5)$$

then Summers [6] and Bryson [7] have shown, by means of residue calculus,
that the added mass coefficient is given by

$$C_H = \frac{1}{T^2}[2(r^2 - A_{-1}) - \frac{S}{\pi}] \quad , \qquad (6)$$

where T is the draught of the section and S is the area of the section in
the z-plane. Also r is the radius of the circle in the ς-plane and A_{-1} is the
coefficient of the first term of the Laurent Series.

In the Laurent Series (5), the first two terms represent the well known
Joukowski transformation and the first three terms give rise to the family
of Lewis Sections used to represent ship sections. By including further
terms more general shapes can be mapped onto a circle.

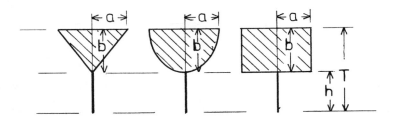

(a) Triangle   (b) Ellipse   (c) Rectangle

Figure 2. Idealised Stern Sections.

Here it is proposed to concentrate on the three shapes shown in Figure 2. These represent a range of possible stern sections, where Figure 2a is a triangle with a thin skeg projecting below, Figure 2b is an ellipse with a thin skeg, and Figure 2c is a rectangle with a skeg projecting below. The case of the ellipse with a fin has been given by Bryson [7], who used a succession of Joukowski transformations to yield the following result for the added mass coefficient

$$C_H = \frac{1}{T^2}(k^2 + b^2)$$

where
$$k = \sigma - (a + b)^2/4\sigma \qquad (7)$$

and
$$\sigma = \frac{1}{2}(T + (T^2 + a^2 - b^2)^{\frac{1}{2}}) \quad .$$

In the above expression a is the horizontal semi-diameter and b is the vertical semi-diameter of the ellipse and T is the total draught. By means of equations (4) and (7) the skeg added mass coefficients may be computed. These are given in Figure 6 for the ellipse with flat plate skeg.

The cases of the triangle and rectangle have to be treated in a different manner. General polygonal shapes can be mapped by means of a Schwarz-Christoffel transformation which usually only determines the derivative of the required mapping function. However Jeffreys and Jeffreys [8] give a modified version of the Schwarz-Christoffel transformation, which directly maps the polygon in the z-plane onto a unit circle in the ς-plane, which is

$$\frac{dz}{d\varsigma} = K \prod_{r=1}^{n}\left(1 - \frac{\varsigma_r}{\varsigma}\right)^{\alpha_r/\pi} , \qquad (8)$$

where subscript r refers to the n vertices of the polygon. It can be shown that the first coefficient of the Laurent Series, determined from equation (8), is

$$A_{-1} = -\frac{1}{2}\left[\left(\sum_{r=1}^{n}\frac{\alpha_r\varsigma_r}{\pi}\right)^2 - \sum_{r=1}^{n}\frac{\alpha_r\varsigma_r}{\pi}^2\right] . \qquad (9)$$

However, to determine the dimensions of the section which maps onto the unit circle, equation (8) must be integrated in the complex plane.

The case of the triangle with a skeg is illustrated in Figure 3, where it can be seen that the slope of the side of the triangle is given by the angle $\gamma\pi$, but the relative size of the skeg and triangle are determined by the angle θ in the ς-plane.

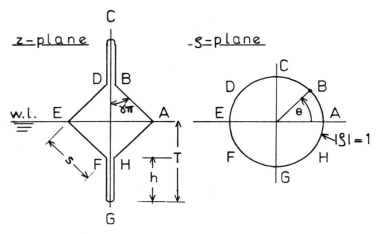

Figure 3. Mapping of Triangle plus Skeg.

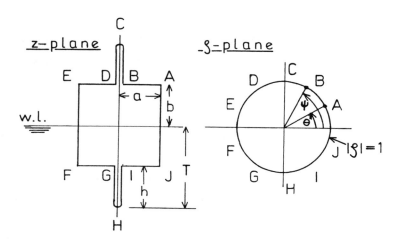

Figure 4. Mapping of Rectangle plus Skeg.

Using equations (8) and (9) for the triangle plus skeg it can be shown that [9],

$$C_H = \frac{1}{T^2}\left[4(1 - 2\gamma sin^2\theta) - \frac{s^2 sin2\gamma\pi}{\pi}\right]$$

where

$$s = \frac{2sin\theta\ \Gamma(\gamma + \frac{1}{2})\Gamma(1 - \gamma)}{\sqrt{\pi}}$$

(10)

and

$$h = \frac{cos\theta^{2(1-\gamma)}}{(1 - \gamma)}F[(1/2 - \gamma), 1; (2 - \gamma); cos^2\theta]$$

with

$$T = h + s\ cos\gamma\pi\quad,$$

where F denotes a hypergeometric series. In the case where there is no skeg, then $\theta = \pi/2$ and the above expression can be shown to reduce to the case of a triangle, as given by Lewis [10] and Lockwood Taylor [11].

Similarly, in the case of the rectangle with a skeg, as shown in Figure 4, the width to height ratio is determined by the angle θ in the ς-plane and the angle ψ determines the relative size of the skeg.

Using equations (8) and (9) for the rectangle plus skeg it can be shown that

$$C_H = \frac{1}{T^2}[4(sin^2\theta + cos^2\psi) - \frac{4ab}{\pi}]$$

where

$$a = 2sin\psi[E(k_1', \pi/2) - k_1^2 F(k_1', \pi/2]$$

$$b = 2sin\psi[E(k_1, \pi/2) - k_1'^2 F(k_1, \pi/2]$$

$$h = 2sin\psi\Big\{k_1'^2[F(k_1, \pi/2) - F(k_1, \psi)]$$

$$-[E(k_1, \pi/2) - E(k_1, \psi)]$$

$$+ cos\theta cot\psi\Big\}$$

(11)

with $k_1 = sin\ \theta\ /\ sin\ \psi$ and $k_1' = (1 - k_1^2)^{\frac{1}{2}}$ and $T = b + h$. Also, F and E denote elliptic integrals of the first and second kind respectively.

In the case of no skeg, then $\psi = \pi/2$ and the above expression reduces to the case of a rectangle as given by Lewis [10], Lockwood Taylor [11] and Riabouchinski [12].

Using the three expressions (10), (7) and (11) the added mass of the triangle, ellipse and rectangle respectively, the added masses have been calculated for a range of the parameters a/b and h/T. These values have been converted into the added mass of the skeg plus the interference effects of the hull by means of equation (4), and are plotted in Figures 5, 6 and 7.

The general shape of the curves in Figures 5, 6 and 7 are similar, but it is immediately noticed in Figure 8, for a/b = 1.0, that the skeg added mass is greatest when attached to the triangular hull shape and least when attached to the rectangular shape.

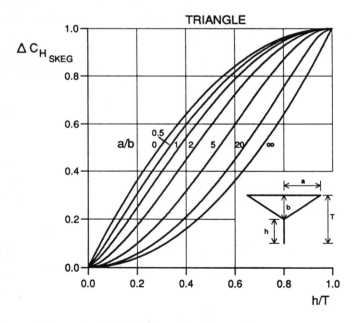

Figure 5. Added Mass Coefficient for a Triangular Stern
Section with a Flat Plate Skeg.

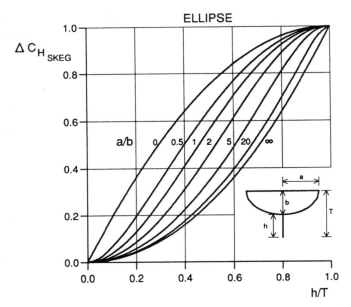

Figure 6. Added Mass Coefficient for an Elliptical Stern
Section with a Flat Plate Skeg.

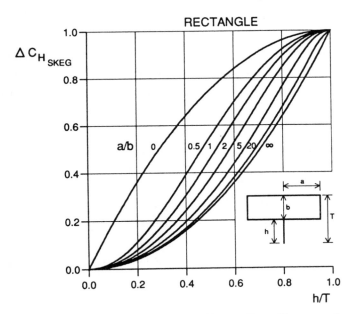

Figure 7. Added Mass Coefficient for a Rectangular Stern
Section with a Flat Plate Skeg.

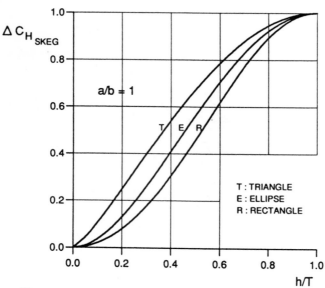

Figure 8. Comparison of the Added Mass for a Triangular, an Elliptical and a Rectangular Stern Section with a Flat Plate Skeg.

MODEL TESTS WITH SKEGS

Measurement of the linear stability derivatives is carried out using either a rotating arm facility or a planar motion mechanism. The experimental techniques are well established and there are a number of sets of derivatives, for a range of ship types, published in the open literature. Unfortunately most of this data is for complete models and very little data exists where any geometrical changes, particularly to the skeg, have been made.

Fortunately, a small amount of data is available, for a modified Taylor Standard Series hull form, where Tsakonas [3] and Jacobs [4] give the linear stability derivatives for hulls with varying skeg sizes. Figure 9 shows the body plan of the modified lines and shows the size and the position of the three skeg configurations tested. Four sets of linear stability derivatives were measured using a rotating arm, for the hull without any skeg, as well as the three skeg variants.

Following equations (2) and (3) the skeg contributions to the measured derivatives have been evaluated from the Jacobs [4] data and these

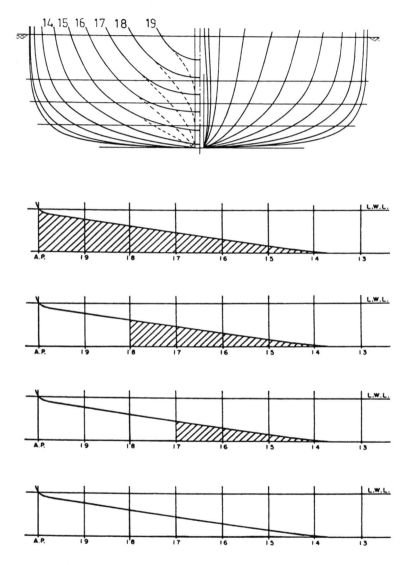

Figure 9. Body Plan for the Modified Taylor Series Model.

are shown in Table 1. The values of the skeg contributions $\triangle C_{H_{SKEG}}$ are shown for three values of h/T and are in columns dependent on the particular derivative measurements used to evaluate them. That is, which of the four expressions in equation (2) was actually used to evaluate the skeg contributions.

Since the body sections above the skeg trailing edges approximate to an ellipse with a/b=1.5, the theoretical line for $\triangle C_{H_{SKEG}}$ has been plotted in Figure 10 by using equation (7). The experimental data points from Table 1 are also shown, where a reasonable agreement can be seen.

Table 1

Skeg Added Mass Values Derived from Experiment, [3] and [4].

h/T	$\triangle C_{H_{SKEG}}$			
	Y_v'	N_v'	Y_r'	N_r'
0.4706	0.462	0.535	0.427	0.525
0.6190	0.629	0.676	0.652	0.789
1.0000	0.993	1.027	1.260	0.946

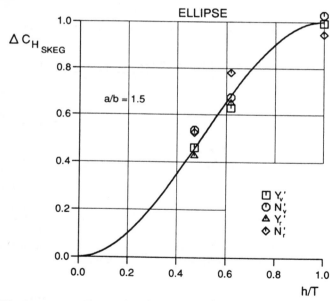

Figure 10. Comparison of the Experimentally Derived Skeg Added Mass Coefficients with Theory.

One data point for h/T=1.0, deduced from the Y_r' data, appears to be 25% higher than the other three points which are close to the theoretical value of unity. This point has not been plotted in Figure 10.

Although this small amount of data has given some confirmation of the theoretical prediction of the skeg contribution to the linear stability derivatives, it is only in the case of the elliptical hull shape. More data is required to confirm the behaviour with the triangular or rectangular hull shapes.

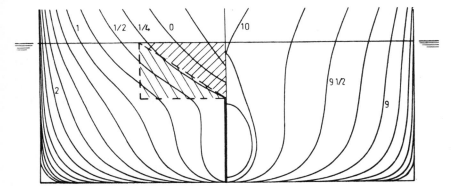

Figure 11. Body Plan for the Tanker *Esso Bernicia*

EFFECT OF CHANGES IN STERN SHAPE

As an example of the effect of stern shape on the values of the linear velocity derivatives, a large tanker with a known triangular stern shape was modified to have a rectangular stern shape.

The derivatives for a 190,000 dwt tanker are given by van Berlekom and Goddard [13]. These were presented in "bis" form, but are converted into the usual "prime" form here. This tanker is known to be the *Esso Bernicia* and the body plan is shown in Figure 11. Also shown in Figure 11 is the approximate triangular section and the hypothetical modification to a square section, similar to a pram stern type. The approximate values for h/T and a/b are shown in Table 2, together with the values of $\triangle C_{H_{SKEG}}$ for the two sterns, taken from Figures 5 and 7.

Table 2

Skeg Derivative Contribution

	Type	a/b	h/T	$\triangle C_{H_{SKEG}}$
Original Stern	Triangular	1.5	0.6	0.76
Modified Stern	Rectangular	1.5	0.6	0.58

If the above values of $\triangle C_{H_{SKEG}}$ are substituted into equation (3) then the changes in the derivatives between the two stern types can be evaluated. It is known [13] that the factor $\pi (T/L)^2 = 1152 \times 10^{-5}$, and $X'_{SKEG} = -0.475$.

Table 3

Changes in Derivative Values ($\times 10^5$)

$\triangle Y'_v$	$\triangle Y'_r$	$\triangle N'_v$	$\triangle N'_r$
207	-99	-99	47

Derivative Values ($\times 10^5$)

	Y'_v	Y'_r	N'_v	N'_r
Original Stern	-1872	385	-701	-322
Modified Stern	-1665	286	-800	-275

Table 4

Stability Levers

	l'_v $= N'_v / Y'_v$	l'_r $= (Y'_r - m') / (N'_r - m' x'_G)$	$l'_r - l'_v$
Original Stern	0.374	0.307	-0.067
Modified Stern	0.480	0.236	-0.234

(From [15], $m' = 1554 \times 10^{-5}$ and $m' x'_G = 37 \times 10^{-5}$)

The stability levers shown in Table 4 indicate the loss of stability incurred by the rectangular stern, compared with the original triangular stern. The stability lever for the original stern is the same as that given by van Berlekom and Goddard [13], and it should be noted that Clarke et al [14] measured the spiral loop width of the *Esso Bernicia* in deep water as $\delta_{LOOP} = 6$ deg. Since the modified stern increases the negative stability lever by a factor of 3.5, it is anticipated that spiral loop width of the hypothetical ship would be in excess of 10 deg.

CONCLUSIONS

The advent of ships with new stern shapes having much more rectangular sections has given rise to a reduction in the directional stability of such ships. By means of conformal mapping techniques, the added mass coefficients for three idealised stern sections have been determined. These added mass coefficients have been used to calculate the skeg effectiveness in the presence of a triangular, an elliptical and a rectangular hull section.

It was found that the rectangular section, which is very similar to those found in pram stern ships causes a significant reduction in the skeg effectiveness, compared to the other two section shapes considered.

A reduction in skeg effectiveness leads directly to a reduction in directional stability for ships with rectangular section sterns, such as the pram stern types.

It was found that in the case of the large tanker *Esso Bernicia*, for which the relevant derivative data was available, an increase in the stability lever of about 3.5 times would result, had that ship been built as a pram stern type.

It is felt that these findings partially explain the stability reduction in pram stern type ships, but that there is also a significant change in the way in which the flow around the stern is shed downstream. This phenomenon may also reduce the stability, but remains for future investigation.

ACKNOWLEDGEMENTS

The author would like to express his thanks to Mr. Kadir Sarıöz and Miss Helen Clough for their valuable assistance in preparing this paper.

REFERENCES

1.Clarke, D., Gedling, P. and Hine, G. 'The Application of Manoeuvring Criteria in Hull Design using Linear Theory'. *Trans. RINA*, Vol. 125, pp. 45-68, 1983.

2. Clarke, D. 'A Two-Dimensional Strip Method for Surface Ship Derivatives. Comparison of Theory with Experiments on a Segmented Tanker Model'. *Journal of Mechanical Engineering Science*, Vol. 14, No. 7 (Supplementary Issue), 1972.

3. Tsakonas, S. 'Effect of Appendage and Hull Form on Hydrodynamic Coefficients of Surface Ships'. *Davidson Laboratory Report*, No. 740, 1959.

4. Jacobs, W.R. 'Estimation of Stability Derivatives and Indices of Various Ships Forms and Comparison with Experimental Results'. *Davidson Laboratory Report*, No. 1035, 1964.

5. Nielsen, J.N. *Missile Aerodynamics*, McGraw Hill, New York, 1960.

6. Summers, R.G. 'On Determining the Additional Apparent Mass of a Wing-Body-Vertical Tail Cross-Section'. *Journal of Aeronautical Sciences*, Vol. 20, No. 12, p. 856, December 1953.

7. Bryson, A.E. 'Evaluation of the Inertia Coefficients of the Cross-Section of a Slender Body'. *Journal of Aeronautical Sciences*, Vol. 21, No. 6, p. 424, June 1954.

8. Jeffreys, H. and Jeffreys, B.S. *Methods of Mathematical Physics*, Cambridge University Press, 3rd Ed. 1962.

9. Clarke, D. *'Some Aspects of the Dynamics of Ship Steering'*. Ph.D. Thesis, University of London, 1976.

10. Lewis, F.M. 'The Inertia of Water Surrounding a Vibrating Ship'. *Trans. SNAME*, Vol. 37, pp. 1-20, 1929.

11. Lockwood Taylor, J. 'Some Hydrodynamical Inertia Coefficients'.

Philosophical Magazine, Series 7, Vol. 9, No. 55, pp. 161-183, January 1930.

12. Riabouchinski, D. 'Sur la Résistance des Fluids'. *International Congress of Mathematicians*, pp. 568-585, Strasbourg, 1920.

13. Van Berlekom, W.B. and Goddard, T.A. 'Manoeuvring of Large Tankers'. *Trans. SNAME*, Vol. 81, pp. 264-298, 1972.

14. Clarke, D., Patterson, D.R. and Wooderson, R.K. 'Manoeuvring Trials with the 193,000 tonne Deadweight Tanker *Esso Bernicia*'. *Trans. RINA*, Vol. 115, pp. 89-109, 1973.

Trials to Investigate the Directional Control of a Fast Lifeboat

I.M.C. Campbell, A.S. Hyde
Wolfson Unit for Marine Technology and Industrial Aerodynamics, University of Southampton, Highfield, Southampton SO9 5NH, UK

ABSTRACT

Extensive instrumented sea trials have been conducted with the RNLI Mersey class of lifeboat both to study its motions and to investigate its directional control in following seas. The paper describes the various trials, procedures, methods of analysis and the application of the results to the study of the directional control of the Mersey and similar boats. The trials described include various calm water manoeuvres as well as runs in following and quartering seas and the results show that the roll motion can have a strong influence on the yaw behaviour of the boat.

INTRODUCTION

As part of an extensive ongoing investigation into the seakeeping of their new lifeboat fleet, the first production Mersey lifeboat constructed from fibre reinforced composite (number 12-12) was trialed in Poole Bay during February, 1991. One aim of the trials was to attempt to measure the differences in the directional control of this particular boat in following seas in its optimum ballast and trim condition and compare this with a condition considered to give poor directional control in large seas.

This paper describes the various trials, procedures and methods of analysis employed in the study. The application of the results to the study of the directional control of the Mersey is then discussed.

BACKGROUND TO DIRECTIONAL CONTROL PROBLEMS

Small craft generally respond quickly to movements of the rudder and because they are small their motions are easily affected by the seastate. It is common for both displacement and planing boats to be manually steered when in a seaway and coxswains are adept at using relatively large and rapid rudder movements to maintain a course. This complicates the study of the directional control of such craft since coxswains can steer craft having different directional control characteristics, which they can assess subjectively, but their actions make these difficult to measure quantitatively.

When control problems are reported they often amount to the failure of the craft to respond to a large rudder application when in some extreme attitude, and again this poses measurement difficulties since it often not possible or desirable to reproduce such events during instrumented trials.

There are isolated reports in the literature of the study into control problems of particular boats, e.g. Dand [1,2], Codega and Lewis [3], Graf [4], and Suhrbier [5]. Improvements are attributed to individual changes to the particular boats.

Various aspects of the problem have also been studied. Early work on the NPL round bilge hulls by Marwood and Bailey [6], was concerned with the study of an apparent loss in transverse stability with speed and it is generally recognised that low statical stability due to a high VCG can contribute to control problems. Wellicome and Campbell [7] conducted a more thorough investigation of the transverse dynamic stability of prismatic hulls, by studying the coupled sway/yaw equations of motion, and showed that for such forms there was generally no loss of transverse stability with speed. Dand [1,2] describes model tests on RNLI lifeboats and the application of turning circle data and the "C" directional stability index to investigate the influence of LCG position and reported marginal differences. There has however been little work to study coupled roll/yaw stability, although it is recognised that it is important to the behaviour of small craft, so it is interesting to note the investigation described in Milburn [8] into heel problems in a turn with a hard chine planing boat. It was found that the addition of a skeg eliminated the high heel angle into the turn but subsequently contributed to broaching problems in waves. Similar effects were found in unpublished work by the author from tests with a free running planing boat model.

The RNLI Mersey class lifeboat provides an interesting case study since in the initial stages of the evaluation trials on an early prototype, it was noticed that the vessel occasionally had directional control problems. Thatcher [9] reported that these were particularly evident when running in large following or quartering seas. The vessel would sit on the face of a wave, with the rudder having no effect on the directional control of the vessel. Thatcher also reported that constant rudder movements were needed to keep the boat running in a straight line.

The directional control of the lifeboat was greatly improved by means of changes to the rudders, bilge keels, displacement, centre of gravity, radius of gyration, and the addition of trim tabs. The improvements were evaluated during operational trials in a variety of sea conditions but without the aid of motion monitoring instrumentation. The particular Mersey used in the measured trials described in this paper incorporated the refinements that had been found to improve control and the trim changes made by altering the tab settings were only expected to make differences when the control became marginal.

THE MERSEY CLASS

The Mersey class is the RNLI 12m Fast Carriage Boat, designed to be a replacement to the Oakley and Rother classes, with a speed of 17 knots, at a displacement of 14.4 tonnes. It has deep V-sections in the bow running into round bilge sections in the mid-body and then to a hard chine bilge near the stern, with tunnels to accommodate the twin propellers and rudders so that they are protected when beaching. The development of the Mersey class is described by Over [10] with updates by Thatcher [9].

Some of the previous instrumented sea trials on the Mersey class have been reported by Campbell [11] and mainly deal with the study of its seakeeping characteristics. As well as rough water trials, some Kempf zig-zag manoeuvres were performed in an attempt to measure its directional stability, an example of which is given in Figure 1. There were practical problems in conducting these manoeuvres due to the rapid rate of turn of the boat but the results showed that the vessel always responded promptly to changes in rudder angle. Experience from these trials indicated that it was difficult to quantify differences in the directional control of the boats in following and quartering seas. This was partly due to the statistical nature of rough water trials data and partly to the rarity of instances involving the loss of control. An example of an instrumented loss of control, on a Mersey, is given in Figure 2. It was therefore decided to use other calm water manoeuvres to investigate the directional control of the boat.

MEASUREMENT SYSTEM

The lifeboat was fitted with a system of transducers and associated instrument-ation to sense the vertical and lateral motions. The data acquisition unit comprised amplifiers, 10 Hz low pass filters and a 12 bit analogue to digital converter with a memory buffer and RS232 interface connected to a host Hewlett-Packard 9816 desktop computer. The transducers consisted of a vertical reference gyro with roll and pitch analogue outputs, a rotary potentiometer mounted on the rudder stock to indicate rudder angle, and a rigidly mounted yaw rate gyro. In addition for rough weather trials, a

Datawell Waverider wavebuoy with Warep receiver was used.   Two piezo resistive accelerometers were also fitted to stiff parts of the lifeboat structure, one near the forward bulkhead and the other at a midships location, for use in head sea trials.

A sign convention was chosen such that a positive starboard rudder would give a positive yaw rate and a positive outward roll in the turn.

TRIALS CONDITIONS

The ballast and trim conditions for the boat were chosen by the RNLI based on their operational experience from earlier trials. Both trim tabs and movable water ballast (in 25 kg cans) were used to alter the running trim of the vessel. Water ballast was also used to heel the boat to a static loll angle for the turning circle trials.

For ideal turning circle manoeuvres there should be absolutely calm conditions with no seas, swell or wind.   Unfortunately due to time constraints on the availability of the lifeboat and trials crew, these weather conditions were not obtained on any day.   On two of the 'calm water' days there was a low swell condition with significant wave height less than 0.3m.

On the other day of calm water manoeuvres, although there was little wind, there was a slight SE swell resulting in a significant wave height of approx. 0.3m.   This swell resulted in conditions, which although adequate to obtain reasonable turning circle data, were far from ideal for other calm water manoeuvres.

TRIALS DETAILS

Turning circle manoeuvres
A freely floating buoy was deployed from the lifeboat to act as a reference point and the boat was positioned such as to approach the buoy into any swell. Data acquisition started when the boat was approximately 30 seconds from the buoy and approaching it on a straight course at the desired speed.   Upon reaching the buoy the coxswain would quickly turn the rudders to the desired indicated rudder angle and hold the rudder at that fixed angle until the boat had completed one and a half turns.   The boat was then pulled out of the turn by the coxswain operating the rudder to hold the boat on a straight course.   Data continued to be acquired throughout this period which was similar to a spiral manoeuvre since the boat was in a turn when the rudder angle was altered.

By approaching the buoy into any swell and leaving with it, the mean rudder angle could be used as a zero, thus reducing the possibility of an offset error. Also by performing one and a half turns there were data on at least one whole turn in the steady turn condition as well as data for the transient response of the vessel to the application of the rudder.

When performing the tests in the heeled condition, the test technique was slightly modified to obtain the steady rate of turn for zero rudder angle. Upon completion on the one and a half turns the coxswain would return the rudder to indicated zero for approximately 15 seconds before holding a steady course for a further 15 seconds. The mean rudder angle from the final period of the run, where a steady course was steered, again gave an offset from zero.

Figure 3 shows a schematic diagram of the turning circle manoeuvres, while Figure 4 shows a typical time history obtained from a turning circle in the upright condition and in a slight swell.

Trials in rough water
Runs were generally started at the deployed Waverider buoy and the boat steered on the required course for the duration of the run. During the run the average, maximum and minimum speeds were estimated from the Autohelm log. Upon completion of the run the boat was manoeuvred back to the Waverider buoy which was located using the VHF/DF. During this period the data for the run was saved and the acquisition system prepared for the next run. A sample time history acquired during a run in following seas is shown in Figure 5.

METHODS OF ANALYSIS

Turning circle manoeuvres
Plots of yaw rate against rudder angle for both the boat upright and heeled are presented in Figure 6. The mean change in heel angle and speed loss for these conditions are plotted in Figures 7 and 8 respectively.

On one of the 'calm water' days there was sufficient swell to cause motion of the vessel whilst in a turning manoeuvre. Analyzing this motion has distinct advantages over analyzing normal seakeeping motions since the rudder angle is fixed. The fixed rudder eliminates the rudder-roll and rudder-pitch coupling. The turns 'in swell' were analyzed to try to quantify the roll-yaw coupling, and to use this as a means of estimating the controllability of the vessel in following seas. A statistical correlation coefficient of the time histories of yaw rate and roll was obtained using their variation from their mean values. Statistical correlation coefficients have a range of ± 1. A high positive value of the coefficient implies that positive variation in roll angle is associated with a positive variation in yaw rate, whilst a high negative value of the coefficient implies that positive variation in roll angle is associated with a negative variation in yaw rate and a low correlation implies that there is no association of roll angle with yaw rate.

In addition the ratio of the rms values of yaw rate to roll was obtained. This ratio was chosen to quantify the effect of roll on yaw rate, for example a vessel which had a high value would have a larger yaw/roll interaction than one with a smaller ratio. Table 1 shows a summary of the analysis of turning circles in swell.

Rough water trials
The results from the analysis of the seakeeping tests are presented in Table 2. This includes a similar analysis to that used for the turns in swell, with the addition of the calculation of the roll-rudder correlation coefficients. Figure 2 shows the time history of the vessel in stern seas. This shows that there is some coupling between roll and yaw rate, but this is 'masked' to some extent by the action of the rudder and its effect on both yaw rate and roll.

DISCUSSION OF TRIALS RESULTS

Turning circles in calm water
The boat remained stable in the turn in all tests and in general the vessel had a tendency to roll outward on the turn. The mean yaw rates from the rate gyro gave very good agreement with those obtained by using a stopwatch to measure the time taken to complete a 360° turn. The stopwatch method is particularly accurate when measuring the time from 180° to 540°, since this eliminates the initial transient phase of the turn where the yaw rate is not constant.

Figure 6 shows that for the upright conditions, there were only small variations in yaw rate for the boat with different trim tab settings and water ballast location. These variations were of the same order as the scatter of the data so making it difficult to identify clear differences in the turn characteristics for the different conditions.

It was also noted that the boat's turning characteristics were slightly asymmetric, with a positive turn to starboard giving a peak yaw rate of $\approx 7.6°$/sec, whilst a turn to port gives a peak yaw rate of $\approx 8.6°$/sec. The asymmetry was much greater with the boat ballasted to a static heel angle of 8.2 deg and it can be seen from Figure 6 that the boat turned at 3 deg/sec with no applied rudder and 5 deg. of rudder was required to maintain a steady course.

The roll variation with rudder angle for the upright case, Figure 7, shows the same characteristic shape as the yaw rate curve in Figure 6. There is, however, more scatter of the data points on the roll curves.

The speed reduction curves for both the upright and heeled conditions are shown in Figure 8. The upright case shows a steady reduction of speed with rudder angle, with the speed dropping to 75% of the straight line speed at 25° of rudder. This makes comparison with data from trials in following seas more difficult because there is less speed loss when large rudder angles are applied in waves, since rudder application is to hold the boat on a straight course. The speed reduction curve for the heeled condition shows the same asymmetric shape as the yaw rate curve. The speed loss is calculated by taking the straight line speed as a reference speed, hence the speed loss curve for the heeled condition reaches unity at -5° of rudder.

Turning circles in swell
The time histories in Figure 4, clearly show two coupling effects. Firstly the roll angle is coupled with yaw rate, the more the vessel rolls out of the turn the quicker it turns. This is a genuine effect and can be observed without the aid of instruments. Secondly pitch angle appears also to be coupled with yaw rate, this can be seen by the higher frequency interaction on the pitch and yaw rate traces but it is believed to be a measurement interaction rather than a genuine effect.

All the turns have a correlation coefficient in the range 0.3-0.7. The correlation coefficients may well be higher and more consistent if the interaction of pitch can be removed from the yaw rate signal, and yaw rate measured on the global axis system rather than the body axis system.

Rough Weather Trials
No control problems were experienced with the boat during the rough weather trials but the sea state was not particularly severe with the significant wave height in the range 2.0m to 2.6m. No clear trends could be seen in the rms values with changes in heading, trim or wave conditions. The rms roll angles were less than 6.5 deg and the maximum roll angle was 15 deg which was less than the roll when control was lost as in Figure 2. It should also be noted that this roll angle does not necessarily represent the attitude of the boat to the local water surface because the boat will tend to follow the wave slope. This point is relevant when comparing the data with calm water manoeuvring data at a fixed heel angle which does represent the attitude of the boat to the water surface.

The rms rudder angles were less than 7 deg. except for runs F11 and F12 in quartering seas which were with the boat in a poor trim condition and in the highest waves. The maximum rudder angles were generally less than 15 deg. and it can be seen from the turning circle data that this was within their most effective range and should produce a yaw rate of 7 deg/sec.

In the rough water trials, the effect that the coxswain has in compensating for roll induced yaw by application of the rudder can be seen in comparing the ratios of rms yaw rate to rms roll for the vessel in rough water to the ratio when the vessel was performing turning circles in swell with constant rudder angle. It can be seen that the coxswain reduces this ratio by approximately 25% by intelligent application of the rudder.

The roll-yaw rate correlation coefficient is significantly lower than that for a turn in swell. The roll-rudder correlation coefficients however are in the range -0.58 to -0.73, indicating that the coxswain reacts to the roll of the boat, so reducing the effect of the roll-yaw rate coupling.

FACTORS AFFECTING DIRECTIONAL CONTROL

The Mersey was directionally controllable during all the calm water manoeuvres since it always responded to rudder applications. The turning circle data show no hysteresis at small rudder angles - indicating that the boat was directionally stable, although, as can be seen from Figure 2, it was necessary for the coxswain to steer the boat to maintain a straight line course because it was sensitive to disturbances from waves. The Mersey was also directionally controllable in the trials seastate although frequent rudder movements were required to maintain a steady heading and, furthermore, no clear differences were found in the trials data for the boat in different trim conditions.

These findings may appear unsatisfactory for two reasons. Firstly one aim of the trials had been to measure differences in directional control due to trim changes, which by subjective assessments had been found to affect the control in waves, and secondly isolated events had occurred on previous trials with other Mersey class boats involving the loss of directional control. In Figure 2 it can be seen that the rudders were held hard over for a 5 second period whilst the boat continued to turn in the opposite direction.

Nevertheless the trials have provided data relevant to the directional control problem and these are summarised below:

i)   It has been shown that the motions of the Mersey exhibit a strong correlation between roll and yaw such that the yaw rate increases when the boat rolls outwards and in a steady turn the boat adopts a slight outward heel which improves its yaw rate.

ii)   In turns where the boat was ballasted to a heel angle the balance between the hydrodynamic and inertia forces acted as described above to reduce the heel angle when heeled into a turn but to increase it when heeled outwards. The maximum yaw rate was also lower when turning heeled inwards.

iii)   In the turns in ii) above the rudder characteristics were asymmetric and displayed more pronounced stall behaviour when turning heeled inwards.

iv)   Study of the Kempf manoeuvres, as shown in Figure 2, showed that large changes in rudder angle produced a small roll transient that initially heeled the boat into the new turn, although as the boat entered the steady part of the turn it would flip over to heel outward again.

v)   It was found from the rough weather trials that there was a strong negative correlation between roll and rudder movements such that as the boat rolled to starboard corrective port helm was applied by the coxswain. This was consistent with the behaviour described in items i) and ii).

vi)   The measured roll angle in these trials was not extreme with the maximum value of 15 degrees, which was only twice the ballasted heel angle used in the turning circle manoeuvres. This was consistent with the analysis of roll data from runs in beam seas to produce the roll response amplitude operator which showed only a small resonant peak - indicating that the boat had high roll damping.

Using the above characteristics it is possible to surmise how directional control was lost in the event shown in Figure 2:

1)   Whilst running before a sea the boat rolled in a wave and corrective rudder was applied to hold the boat on course.

2)   The rudder angle was reduced with the roll but the boat then suddenly began to yaw against the rudder.

3)   Maximum rudder was applied which acted to increase the heel.

4)   The rudders probably stalled and the yaw rate increased, with the boat heeling out of the turn but in the same sense as the rudders.

5)   There was a considerable speed loss due to these events but never the less the coxswain throttled back and as the wave passed, the boat rolled upright and control was regained.

Various features of the boat could affect its behaviour in these circumstances, where the yaw characteristics of the boat at high heel angles are important.

i)   The boat operates in the semi-planing regime so the speed loss in a tight turn is sufficient to reduce the dynamic lift and change the roll/yaw characteristics of the boat. This presents some difficulties in using calm water manoeuvres to simulate the behaviour in a following sea.

ii)   The semi-tunnels in the hull raise the propellers and rudders in the boat, which is desirable for beaching purposes but leads to other effects when underway. The rudders induce less roll in a turn than if they were lower. Their size is restricted by the tunnel geometry and at large angles they partly block the tunnel. The tunnel entry can be close to the surface at high heel angles causing the entry of aerated flow into the propeller on the high side of the boat. If this propeller loses thrust there is an additional destabilising moment in the turn.

iii)   The boat has bilge keels along the outboard edge of the tunnels which help it to sit on its launching carriage and on the beach. These contribute to the high roll damping of the boat, so help restrict the roll angles in waves and thus indirectly aid the directional control. However, the bilge keels also contribute to the slight outward heel of the boat in a turn, although it is unclear whether or not this is beneficial to the control of the boat.

iv)   It is important to restrict the heel of the boat in order to maintain directional control so increasing its statical stability should be beneficial and indeed this was one of the early changes made to the prototype Mersey after the early control problems were discovered.

CONCLUSIONS

1)   Calm water manoeuvres have provided data on both the directional stability of the Mersey and its directional control characteristics when operating in waves.

2)   Turns with the boat ballasted to a heel angle and in a swell yielded data relevant to the directional control of the boat in a seaway.

3)   Loss of directional control of the boat, which only happened with other versions on isolated occasions, is attributed to roll/yaw coupling effects at high heel angles and not to calm water directional instability.

4)   It was not possible to find quantifiable differences in the motions of the boat due to trim changes either in the calm water manoeuvres or the rough weather trials.

REFERENCES

1.   Dand, I.W. 'Directional Stability of High-Speed Lifeboats' *International Conference on Surveillance, Pilot & Rescue Craft for the 21st Century,* Southampton, England, March 1990.

2. Dand, I.W. 'Some Aspects of the Manoeuvrability of a High-Speed Lifeboat' *International Conference on Surveillance, Pilot & Rescue Craft for the 21st Century - 2*, Southampton, England, March 1992.

3. Codega, L. and Lewis, J. 'A Case Study of Dynamic Instability in a Planing Hull' p. 143-163, *SNAME Marine Technology Vol 24, No. 2*.

4. Müller-Graf, B. 'The Effect of an Advanced Spray Rail System on Resistance and Development of Spray of Semi-Displacement Round Bilge Hulls' *Fast '91*, Trondheim, Norway, 1991

5. Suhrbier, K.R. 'An Experimental Investigation of the Roll Stability of a Semi-Displacement Craft at Forward Speed' *R.I.N.A Symposium Small Fast Warships*, March 1978.

6. Marwood, W.J. and Bailey, D. 'Transverse Stability of Round-Bottomed High Speed Craft Underway' *N.P.L. Ship Report 98*, October 1968.

7. Wellicome, J.F. and Campbell, I.M.C. 'The Transverse Dynamic Stability of Planing Craft' *University of Southampton, Department of Ship Science Report 12*, January 1984.

8. Milburn, Lt. D.E. 'Testing the Technical Characteristics of Motor Lifeboats' *International Conference on Surveillance, Pilot & Rescue Craft for the 21st Century - 2*, Southampton, England, March 1992

9. Thatcher, K.C. 'Mersey Class Developments' *RNLI Journal*, Winter 1989/90

10. Over, H.E. 'Development of the Fast Carriage Boat as a New Class of Lifeboat' *International Lifeboat Conference*, 1987

11. Campbell, I.M.C. 'Measurements of the Seakeeping of Two Fast Lifeboats' *International Conference on Surveillance, Pilot & Rescue Craft for the 21st Century*, Southampton, England, March 1990.

ACKNOWLEDGEMENTS

The authors wish to acknowledge the help of all those involved in the trials and are grateful to the RNLI for permission to publish. It is stressed however that any views implied in this paper or given during its presentation are purely those of the authors and not the official attitude of the RNLI.

Run No.	Turn Speed	Mean Rudder	Roll-YR Correl.	RMS ratio YR/Roll
Trim Condition 1				
T11	14.9	-3.18	0.566	0.673
T12	14.8	4.22	0.357	0.690
T13	12.7	-13.24	0.713	0.529
T14	12.1	10.22	0.516	0.624
T15	11.7	-21.35	0.359	0.519
T16	11.5	21.96	0.319	0.595
Trim Condition 2				
T17	14.8	-7.54	0.580	0.619
T18	14.9	2.02	0.612	0.636
T19	13.3	-13.86	0.501	0.660
T20	13.1	11.93	0.681	0.723
T21	11.8	-21.04	0.601	0.434
T22	12.3	23.82	0.735	0.767
T23	12.1	19.11	0.401	0.607

Table 1 : Analysis of turns in swell

Run No.	Speed	Wave Dir.	Roll-YR Correl.	Roll-Rud. Correl.	RMS Ratio Roll/YR
Trim Condition A					
F1	15.5	0	0.279	-0.727	0.462
F2	15.1	45	0.316	-0.717	0.487
F3	15.1	-45	0.261	-0.631	0.511
Trim Condition B					
F7	14.4	0	0.304	-0.659	0.513
F8	14.5	45	0.270	-0.635	0.468
F9	14.9	-45	0.290	-0.587	0.509
Trim Condition C					
F10	14.7	0	0.304	-0.653	0.475
F11	15.6	45	0.311	-0.608	0.446
F12	14.7	-45	0.214	-0.579	0.488

Table 2 : Analysis of runs in following seas

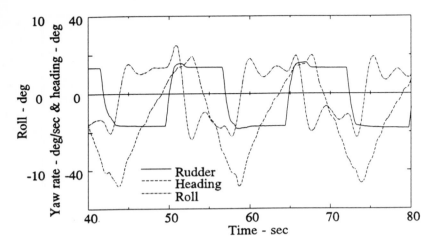

Figure 1 : Time history of a Kempf Manoeuvre

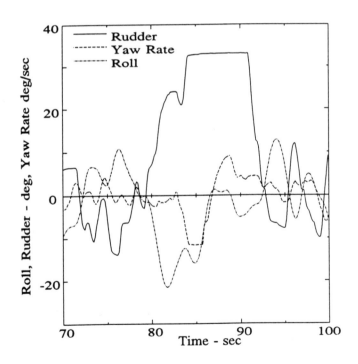

Figure 2 : An example of loss of directional control

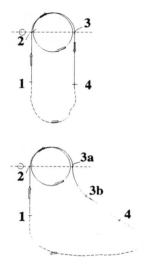

Components of Turning circle manoeuvres

1. Data aquisition started, vessel heading for buoy on straight course.
2. Rudder turned to required indicated angle.
3. Vessel steered on straight course
4. Data aquisition stopped and vessel steered to starting point while data is retrieved and saved.

Differences for 'Heeled' manoeuvres

3a. Rudder returned to 'zero' indicated.
3b. Vessel steered on straight course.

Figure 3 : Turning Circle Manoeuvres

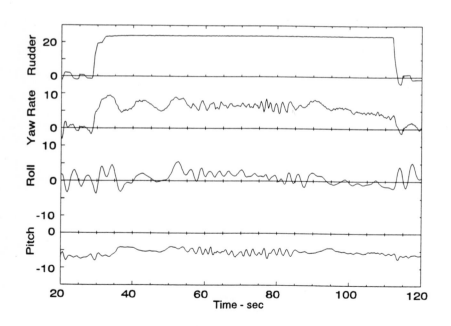

Figure 4 : Time history of a turning circle

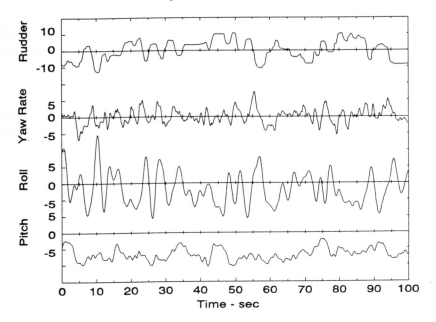

Figure 5 : Time history of the motion in a following sea

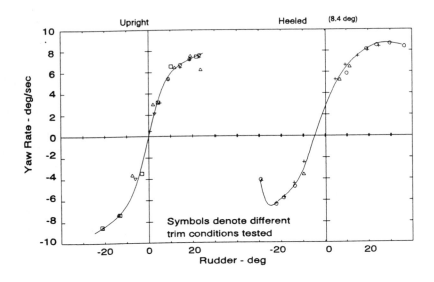

Figure 6 : Rate of Turn both upright and heeled

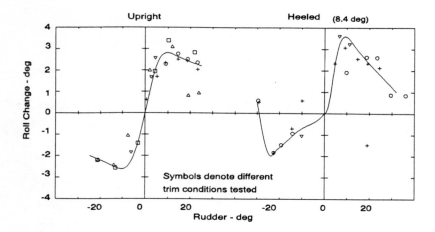

Figure 7 : Roll Change both upright and heeled

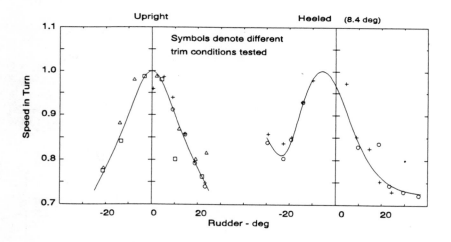

Figure 8 : Speed in Turn both upright and heeled

Investigation of Performance Characteristics of High Speed Planing Craft

J.P. Bate, R. Sutton

Marine Dynamics Research Group, Institute of Marine Studies, Polytechnic South West, Drake Circus, Plymouth PL4 8AA, UK

ABSTRACT

The aerodynamics of planing craft have become an important consideration in recent years, since speeds attained have continually increased. Thus, in this work a method was devised to calculate the aerodynamic lift and drag of a planing hull and is detailed in this paper. The method is based on aerodynamic theory and is used to determine the hydrodynamic lift and drag of the hull. The effect of an aerofoil, the ground effect and trailing vortex drag were also investigated.

INTRODUCTION

The first computer aided design packages for ships were developed in the 1960's and were very crude by modern standards. Today, computing techniques have advanced sufficiently that naval architects have personal computer systems for design work; however, there are relatively few computer programs intended specifically for planing craft design.

The design of planing craft has been primarily an evolutionary process, with hard chine hulls gaining equal status with round chine hulls after the Second World War. Modern applications of planing craft can be summarised briefly as being naval, coastguard and commercial.

This paper considers the aerodynamics and hydrodynamics of high speed monohull planing craft.

Modern high speed planing craft are designed to operate at speeds in excess of 50 knots. As a result, the performance of the craft depends to a greater extent on the aerodynamic forces on the hull, as illustrated by Wikeby [1], where the aerodynamic drag of a high speed raceboat was calculated as 29 percent at 67 knots.

Designers of modern planing craft usually calculate the powering requirements of a specific hull by including the effects of hydrodynamic lift and drag, weight, thrust and buoyancy. It is usually assumed that aerodynamic drag is negligible, as in [2].

The aim of the work detailed herein was therefore to devise a method of calculating the aerodynamic lift and drag of a specific planing craft. Additional calculations for the provision of an aerofoil section were also investigated.

An overall design system was considered; the method devised involved the preliminary design of the craft, hydrostatic calculations and their incorporation into spreadsheet format for dynamic calculations. The commercially available AutoSHIP software was also used, and a design spiral was developed, leading to the completion of the hull form (construction was not investigated). Results are presented which illustrate the effects of variations of transom flap and aerofoil configuration for a final hull shape, operating at high speed.

EQUILIBRIUM OF PLANING CRAFT AT HIGH SPEED

Figure 1 shows a planing craft operating with transom flaps and an aerofoil section, the corresponding moments created by the forces depicted in Figure 1 are given in equation (1) below:

$$[(\Delta.[1-Sin(\tau+\varepsilon).Sin\tau]/Cos\tau) - L_{AH} - L_{AA} - L_{FF}].c$$

$$+ D_F.a + L_{FF}.(LCG+H_f) + L_{AA}.(LCG-LCAA)$$

$$+ D_{FF}.(g+a+\frac{b}{4}.Tan\beta)$$

$$- f.(\Delta.Sin\tau + D_F + D_{FF} + D_{AH} + D_{AH})$$

$$- L_{AH}.(LCAL-LCG) - D_{AH}.(VCAL-(a+\frac{b}{4}.Tan\beta))$$

$$- D_{AA}.(VCAA-(a+\frac{b}{4}.Tan\beta)) + R_{LU}.(VCG+VCLU)$$

$$= 0 \qquad\qquad (1)$$

See appendix A for nomenclature.

FIGURE 1: Forces acting on a high speed planing craft.

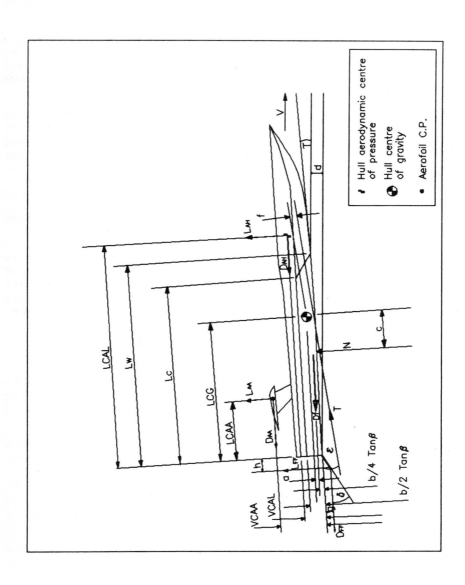

Equation (1) is called the equilibrium equation and describes the balance of moments for a high speed craft.

Note that the moment caused by the resistance of an engine lower unit has also been included in equation (1).

Calculation of Aerodynamic Centre of Pressure

There are only two values in the equation (1) that are not calculated by current methods, i.e. LCAL and VCAL, the longitudinal and vertical aerodynamic centre of pressure of the hull.

Reference [3] shows the individual calculations for evaluating the moments of the aerodynamic forces about the leading edge, the aerodynamic centre and the centre of pressure of an aerofoil. A methodology was devised for calculating the position of the centre of pressure of the aerodynamic forces on a hull, devised by adapting the aerodynamic calculations in [3] to suit a hull, rather than an aerofoil, and connecting them for the required output.

This method treats the hull as a two dimensional object surrounded by one dimensional flow. The fluid is treated as incompressible and inviscid, so that simple aerodynamic theory can be applied to small sections (or elements) of the hull. This essentially involves calculating the pressure on these elements and integrating for the complete hull.

The main problem with this method of calculation is in finding the value of local angle of incidence $'\sigma'$ for the element of the aerodynamic section being considered. Two methods are apparent:

(i)   Using knowledge of the hull coordinates, fit a B-spline to the buttock lines. Differentiate with respect to length and enter the length along the chord to give the gradient, $'\sigma'$, at that point.
(ii) A 'finite element' matrix of the hull can be developed from an AutoSHIP file and then by treating the curvature of the hull as linear over small areas, the incidence can be found.

Alternatively, it was possible to estimate the position of LCAL and VCAL, so as to allow the overall model to continue development. Due to the approximate nature of the points of action of the buoyant and dynamic hydrodynamic forces acting on the hull, it was felt to be acceptable to derive a similar approximate method for calculating VCAL and LCAL, based on aerodynamic theory. i.e. that LCAL=0.25×LOA from the bow and VCAL=0.33×Depth from the transom heel.

AEROFOIL SECTIONS

With the increasing trend towards faster powerboats, the addition of an aerofoil section has become common. On cruising boats this is generally a sales ploy, with horns, aerials, flags and other such items being attached to the aerofoil, reducing what laminar flow there was in the first place. For the more serious powerboat, an aerofoil section can be used to reduce hydrodynamic drag, promote hydrodynamic lift, increase the dynamic transverse stability and provide control of porpoising, hence increasing the top speed of the craft.

Aerofoil Position
The position of the aerofoil is of great importance; if the centre of pressure of the aerofoil is directly above the centre of gravity of the hull, then its effect is mainly that of lift. By moving the centre of pressure of the aerofoil forward or aft of the centre of gravity of the hull, a moment can be introduced whose magnitude is dependant on the speed of the hull. By introducing such an aerofoil to the calculations, this effect of aerofoil position was investigated and some typical results are given in Table 1.

TABLE 1: Effect of variation of aerofoil position with and without trim tabs.

1.   Trim tabs: None
     Aerofoil : None
τ_e = 1.24 Degrees. $R_{\tau e}$ = 109.34 KN.
τ_{max} = 2.61 Degrees. $R_{\tau max}$= 40.16 KN.
τ_{Rmin}= 4.00 Degrees. R_{min} = 35.40 KN.

Possible drag reduction = 69.19 KN = 63.27%

2.   Trim tabs: L(F)=3.3m σ=1 δ=3
     Aerofoil: LCAA=30m (at bow)   VCAA=3.5m
          Span=10m   Chord=3m

τ_e = 1.26 Degrees. $R_{\tau e}$ = 106.56 KN.
τ_{max} = 2.61 Degrees. $R_{\tau max}$= 41.90 KN.
τ_{Rmin}= 4.00 Degrees. R_{min} = 37.60 KN.

Possible drag reduction = 64.66 KN = 60.68%

The above results, and other similar results, showed that the greater the running trim (equilibrium trim), the lower the equilibrium resistance value (the running trim never exceeded the minimum resistance value, which always lay in the 4 to 5 degrees range). Also, since the deadrise was not altered the maximum trim value was not altered significantly. The effect of trim tabs was to reduce trim angle and increase all values of resistance; when trimmed negatively, the flaps served to increase the running trim and reduce resistance. The addition of an aerofoil at the bow increased the running trim and reduced resistance. An aerofoil above the centre of gravity provided mainly dynamic lift, and an aerofoil positioned at the stern reduced the equilibrium trim and increased resistance. Consequently, for high speeds, an aerofoil was shown to be of most use if positioned near the bow, in conjunction with negatively trimmed trim tabs.

Other tests showed that reducing the beam by 10 percent proved to be of greater significance in reducing resistance, which highlights the sort of compromises that the designer faces.

Dihedral
To provide transverse stability, an angle of dihedral should be given to the aerofoil. The angle of dihedral is the amount by which the two halves of the aerofoil are inclined vertically towards each-other. This angle depends on the maximum expected roll angle of the craft. The application is straight-forward; as the craft rolls, the lower aerofoil section provides greater lift than the upper section, hence creating a righting moment.

Sweepback
When an aerofoil section is turned (yawed), it will induce a rolling motion due to the increased lift on the outer wing and reduced lift on the inner wing. To counter this the aerofoil can be given some sweepback. Sweepback also has the effect of increasing the lift coefficient at the outer end of the wing, so some wing washout (reduced incidence at the outer ends) may be required.

The Ground Effect
For a high speed catamaran planing hull the ground effect provides a substantial percentage of the total aerodynamic lift and drag; since this work was concerned with planing monohulls only, calculations for the ground effect were not included, since the ground effect has a less significant result on monohulls.

PERFORMANCE CALCULATIONS

The calculation of the resistance and trim of a bare planing hull is usually performed by naval architects using Savitsky's tabulated method [4], derived from prismatic-like planing surfaces. This method can predict the performance of a planing hull with or without transom flaps and was initially written in spreadsheet form. An aerofoil was included in the calculations and then an approximate method for calculating the aerodynamic lift and drag of the hull was included, as previously mentioned.

Equation (1) is the basis of this theory and was used in spreadsheet form initially, but is now part of a 'C' computer program which performs the same tasks, and also offers the option of varying any of the inputs over a range of values and plotting the outputs (see Figure 2 on the next page). This is useful to the naval architect as a means of preliminary assessment of optimal hull dimensions for a new craft. By careful comparison of the maxima and minima, and by prioritisation of the various parameters (beam, deadrise, velocity, etc.) the designer can select the optimal configuration for the hull.

DISCUSSION, CONCLUSIONS AND FURTHER WORK

A computer program has been developed to assist the naval architect in the preliminary design of planing monohulls, based initially on work by Savitsky [4]. Due to initial time limitations, the calculation of the location of the aerodynamic centre of pressure was simplified to an assumption that was felt to be valid in the context of the empirical nature of other associated calculations. The software produces acceptable results within the limits set out in [4], however it is the intention that present work being undertaken by the Marine Dynamics Research Group will enhance this scope to cover planing catamaran hulls. To this end, research into the ground effect and catamaran hull interaction effects is being undertaken.

Another area that needs clarification is that of the transition to planing of chined craft (i.e. when a planing craft is supported by predominantly buoyant forces), so that the model has a complete range of applicability.

Using hydrodynamic and aerodynamic theory it should be feasible to develop computer software to predict the performance of planing craft. A possible advantage of using a theoretical approach is that novel hullforms could be modelled, i.e. the model would not be restricted to just planing monohulls, or just planing catamarans. The 'finite element' method mentioned earlier would be a suitable starting point for this approach, and could be of a modular form so that different regions of the hull could be modelled individually (bow, gap, wake, sides, etc.).

REFERENCES

1: Wikeby O, 'Aerodynamics of offshore racing powerboats', Ship and Boat International, April 1990, pp 13-16.

2: Blount D and Hankley D W, 'Full scale trials and analysis of high performance planing craft data', Naval Engineers Journal, November 1976, pp 251-273.

3: Houghton E L and Carruthers N B, 'Aerodynamics for engineering students', Edward Arnold pub., Third edition, 1982.

4: Savitsky D, 'Hydrodynamic Design of Planing Hulls', Marine Technology, October 1964, pp 71-95.

FIGURE   2:   Sample   graphs   to   show   some   output characteristics with variation of given inputs.

Resistance
Vs
velocity

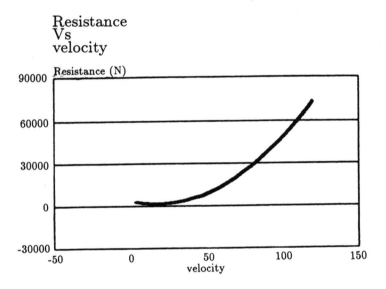

Te
Vs
velocity

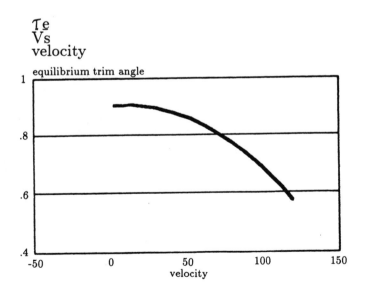

APPENDIX A.

NOMENCLATURE

c   Distance of N from CG, perpendicular to keel. Aerofoil chord length.

λ Mean wetted length:beam ratio.

b   Beam of planing surface.

D_F Frictional drag force component along bottom surface.

g   Acceleration due to gravity.

V   Horizontal velocity of planing surface.

β angle of deadrise of planing surface.

Δ Load on water, mass displacement.

D_{AA} Aerofoil aerodynamic drag.

D_{AH} Hull aerodynamic drag.

d   Vertical depth of trailing edge of hull below water level.

N   Component of resistance force normal to bottom.

a   Distance between D_f and CG, normal to D_f.

f   Distance between T and CG, normal to T.

T   Propeller thrust.

ε Inclination of thrust line relative to keel line.

L_{AH} Hull aerodynamic lift.

L_{AA} Aerofoil aerodynamic lift.

τ Trim angle of planing area.

τ_e Equilibrium trim angle.

τ_{max} Trim angle at which the inception of porpoising occurs.

τ_{Rmin} Trim angle corresponding to minimum resistance at top speed.

LCG   Longitudinal distance of centre of gravity from transom, measured along keel.

LCAA   Longitudinal distance of aerofoil centre of pressure from transom.

LCAL Longitudinal distance of hull aerodynamic centre of pressure from transom.

VCG Vertical centre of gravity of hull from keel.

VCAL Vertical distance of hull aerodynamic centre of pressure from keel.

VCLU Vertical distance of centre of pressure of lower unit from keel, downwards positive.

VCAA Vertical distance of aerofoil centre of pressure from transom heel.

VCG Distance of centre of gravity above keel line, normal to keel.

LCB Distance of centre of buoyancy from CG.

R_{LU} Resistance of lower unit.

D_{FF} Flap drag increment.

H_f Point of action of Δ_F.

SECTION 4: UNCONVENTIONAL VEHICLES

Experimental Verification of Autonomous Underwater Vehicle Behavior Using the NPS AUV II

A.J. Healey

Department of Mechanical Engineering, Naval Postgraduate School, Monterey, California 93943, USA

ABSTRACT

This paper describes recent results in mission execution, and post mission data analysis from the NPS AUV II testbed underwater vehicle. Ongoing research is focused on control technology to meet the needs of future Naval Autonomous Underwater Vehicles. These vehicles are unmanned, untethered, free swimming, robotic submarines to be used for Naval missions including search, mapping, surveillance, and intervention activity. The approach taken at NPS combines integrated computer simulation, real time robust control theory, computer architecture and code development, vehicle and component design and experimentation, sonar data analysis and data visualization.

Started in 1987, the major thrusts of this overall research program are in the areas of **mission planning**, both off-line and on-line, **mission execution** including navigation, collision avoidance, replanning, object recognition, vehicle dynamic response and motion control, real time control software architecture and implementation, and the issues of **post mission data analysis**.

INTRODUCTION

This paper focuses on systems having to do with the Navy's use of Autonomous Underwater Vehicles (AUVs). AUVs are a class of underwater vehicles that are independent from mother ship support with respect to power and control. AUVs are **untethered - free swimmers** - with sufficient on-board intelligence to perceive uncharted and unplanned situations and take action in response. We are interested in these vehicles for a variety of military and/or commercial missions where direct human intervention is difficult or dangerous, and where the use of power cables and fibre optic data links are cumbersome. These vehicles will be used to gather data, provide surveillance, and possibly perform tasks in hostile areas. Research at NPS includes the issues of advanced controls for mission execution, vehicle motion control, sonar data processing for object recognition, and the post mission analysis.

Interest in intelligent **untethered underwater vehicles** has been growing recently. University groups include Texas A&M University, (Mayer et. al. (1987)) who have developed a knowledge based real time controller, hosted on SUN 4 computers with particular attention paid to hardware and software reliability; University of New Hampshire, who under the guidance of D.Blidberg (Chappell, 1987), have built and operated EAVE East vehicles since 1977 with ever increasingly complex computer architectures. EAVE III has a modular, hierarchical architecture using Motorola 68000 series computers running separate PSOS operating systems allowing for multi-processing operation. Lower level tasks are run in "C" while upper level tasks have been run in LISP, with the NIST RCS-3 real time control system (Albus, 1988). At MIT the Sea Grant Program has funded work conducted by Bellingham (1990a), who is exploring the demonstration of intelligent behaviors with a vehicle running on a GESPAC computer having a 68020 CPU with the OS-9 operating system and control code written in "C". The behaviors are hierarchically prioritized using the "Layered Control" concept (Brooks, 1988) although more recently, (Bellingham, 1990b) has seen fit to introduce a state based layered control to coordinate mission specific behavior. The University of Tokyo has recently developed an underwater vehicle for bottom contour following using neural network techniques, (Ura, 1990). At the Naval Postgraduate School, we have developed an underwater testbed vehicle that is specifically designed to test and verify developments in control technology. It is run in the NPS swimming pool as an environment for experimental mission demonstration using a GESPAC computer with a Motorola 68030 CPU a 2MByte RAM card with control code written in "C". The mission planning interface with the vehicle control computer is embodied in a GRiDCASE laptop MS-DOS machine containing mission details in the form of way points and run times that are obtained from an external pre-mission planning analysis. The NPS AUV II, shown as a sketch in Figure 1, is 72" long displacing about 380 lbs. having 2 propellers, 8 control surfaces, 4 thrusters and, at present, 4 single beam sonar channels (Healey and Good, 1992). Many industry groups (UNH Conferences 1987, 1989, the IEEE AUV-90, 91, 92 Conferences) as well as Navy Laboratories, DARPA and the DRAPER Laboratory have work ongoing in this area.

NPS AUV II SYSTEM OVERVIEW

While no formal control system structure has been adopted by all - in fact there are as many as there are investigators - our opinion is that a structure that includes the ability to first perform extensive (if time permits) simulations to verify that the predictable aspects of any mission will be executed in a feasible way, will be necessary. This would be regardless of the mission details. In our structure, this is done with the **Mission Planning Expert System** as shown conceptually in Figure 2. The output is a planned series of geographic way points that avoid charted problem areas and lead the vehicle to its operational site(s) with task descriptors at each target point. This plan encompasses launch, transit to the area, operating in the area, returning to home and recovery.

The **Mission Execution** phase is shown by the structure of activity in Figure 3. **Mission Execution** after launch is conducted between the **Mission Executor** and the **Guidance System** by breaking down the planned mission into a sequence of intermediate way points defined on a finer grid possibly having an adjustable spacing. In more critical areas the spacing would be suitably refined. The **Guidance System** thus interpolates the baseline grid to provide a refined series of way points which are passed to the vehicle **guidance law** and selected according to the degree of precision in path tracking desired by the mission plan. Three guidance laws have been studied viz. line of sight, cross track error, and the cubic spiral laws (Healey et. al., 1990). The **guidance law** generates the commands for vehicle's heading, speed, and depth. These commands are then sent to the vehicle **autopilot systems**. Three autopilots are installed for control over the vehicle's speed,

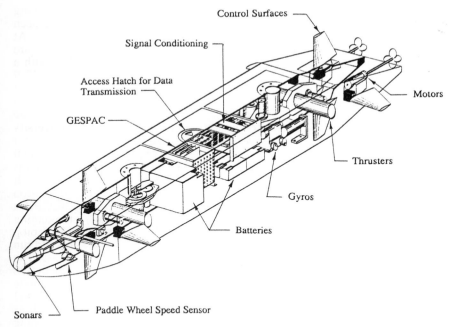

Control Surfaces

Signal Conditioning

Access Hatch for Data
Transmission

GESPAC

Motors

Thrusters

Gyros

Batteries

Sonars   Paddle Wheel Speed Sensor

Figure 1   Sketch of the NPS AUV II

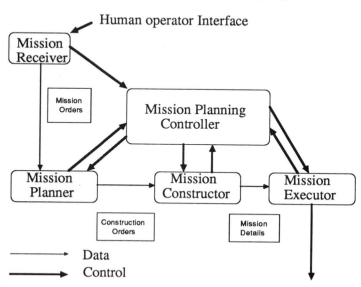

Human operator Interface

Mission
Receiver

Mission
Orders

Mission Planning
Controller

Mission
Planner

Mission
Constructor

Mission
Executor

Construction
Orders

Mission
Details

Data
Control

Figure 2   Mission Planning Expert System

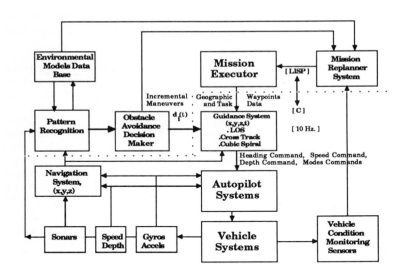

Figure 3   Mission Execution System Diagram

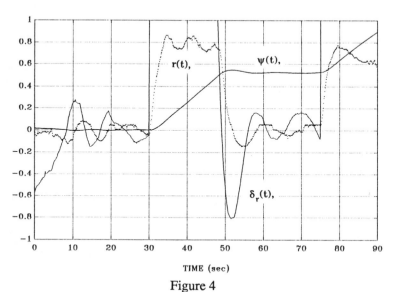

Figure 4

$\delta_r(t)$, $r(t)$, $\psi(t)$, versus Time; Oval Track Run; Combined Diving, Steering, and Speed Control; Standard Control Laws; Scaled as $\delta_r(t)/0.4(\text{rad})$, $r(t)/0.2(\text{rad/sec})$, $\psi(t)/6.0(\text{rad})$

heading, and depth. The servo levels of the vehicle's controller then provide final commands to the vehicle's propulsion plant, control surfaces, and thrusters to drive the vehicle to its planned path.

Obstacle avoidance and reflexive maneuvering logic are to be built into the vehicle's guidance system as a command override structure to respond to signals from the **Obstacle Avoidance Decision Maker (OADM)**. The **OADM** will receive input from **Pattern Recognition** software which correlates information from the sonars and estimates of present location and attitude from the **Navigation System** with an **Environmental Data Base** within the **Mission Executor**. The impending presence of an obstacle is thus flagged. At that time, status as to whether the object is stationary or moving, is to be reflexively avoided, or gradually outmaneuvered (either slow down, speed up, change course, which direction, etc.) is computed. Incremental modifications, $d_i(t)$, to the planned way points and time are then made. Note that for all $d_i(t)$ moves, $d_i(t)$ will be said to tend to zero as t tends to infinity so that the originally planned path will be finally joined. Status signals are sent to the **Mission Replanner** from internal sensors concerning the condition of the internal equipment such as motor and battery status, motor controller system status, servo power and signal conditioning equipment, and power and internal temperature of the main CPU / Data Acquisition / Data Storage hardware.

Post mission data analysis is presently accomplished by down loading data that is stored in onboard RAM storage (19 channels of double precision data at a 10 Hertz rate) to the GRiDCASE laptop computer and then displayed on the data postprocessing computer. The postprocessor at this time lies in an IRIS graphics workstation containing graphics modules that replicate the environment in which the vehicle is operating together with modules for analysis of the vehicle motion data and the sonar sensory data obtained from the mission run (Brutzman et. al., 1992). The results of the planned mission are both simulated prior to mission approval using an IRIS workstation as the environment and vehicle simulator, and then displayed at mission completion. Details of the sonar imagery, or the bottom contour, or other mission specific results can be output in a user-friendly format.

MISSION EXECUTION SYSTEMS AND RESULTS FOR THE NPS AUV II

The execution of a mission begins with downloading the mission plan to the on-board **Mission Executor** followed by the vehicle launch. A time delay must be built into the executor to allow for the launching delay. It has been found important that during this launch phase, and especially with a fully autonomous vehicle, some indicator that the internal systems are functional is desirable - we have used a small movement of one of the control surfaces as this indicator. Upon program initiation, the mission execution plans (defined by the way points and time), are contained in an MS-DOS GRiDCASE laptop computer which is connected via serial link to the vehicle onboard GESPAC MPU30HF single board computer (based on the Motorola 68030 CPU, 25Mhz. with 2Mb of RAM and a 68882 math coprocessor) running with the OS-9 multi-tasking operating system and 2 GESDAC-2B 8 channel 12 bit DA/AD converter cards. Control code is written in "C" language. The GESPAC system is the interface between the mission planning phase and the vehicle hardware, and it houses the **Guidance System**, the **Navigation System**, and the speed, diving, and steering **Autopilot Systems**, each of which can operate under robust Sliding

Mode Control. Figure 3 shows a diagram of the execution functions. Details of the design of the Sliding Mode autopilots have been given elsewhere (Healey, Papoulias, and Lienard, 1990, Papoulias and Healey, 1990) and will not be repeated here. The major interfacing in the execution phase is between the **Mission Executor** and the **Guidance System** and some interplay with the **OADM**. These systems, (in their future embodiment) are to be hosted in PROLOG or C++ language on an interface card running MS-DOS within the GESPAC computer while the **Guidance System** runs in "C" on the main processor board. Missions verified to date by experimental results have included way point following, sonar data analysis and object reconstruction, bottom contour following, and solid object avoidance.

Guidance and Motion Control

Experimental verification of line of sight guidance with PD and Sliding Mode autopilots has been accomplished in several missions run in the NPS swimming pool during the last year. Selected results will be described for missions including a figure eight maneuver using a coarse grid of way points, a depth control and altitude control mission, an obstacle avoidance mission, and missions to record and interpret sonar ranging data for object shape reconstruction.

Initial plans for testbed missions were to perform oval track runs in the NPS swimming pool. The missions were planned where the vehicle, operating under closed loop speed control, closed loop diving and steering control, followed a path with switch points defined at predetermined times at which heading commands were incremented from 0 to 180 to 360 degrees. In this way, the walls of the pool were avoided. This class of test run is helpful to identify the essential characteristics of the autopilot systems and has provided some interesting results shown in the series of Figures 4-7. Other runs including figure of eight, zig-zag, and spiral maneuvers have been completed. In Figure 4 the pertinent steering response variables are shown, Figure 5 gives the corresponding diving variables and Figure 6 shows the vehicle speed response. The path, as identified by dead reckoning ignoring side slip errors, is shown in Figure 7. Many other runs have been made recently and the results here will show a comparison of sliding mode controllers with more standard designs, bottom following performance with a downward looking sonar, and way point following in a figure eight maneuver.

Steering Response

The steering response is shown in Figure 4. The Figure shows the behavior of a PD steering controller given by,

$$\delta_r(t) = K_r r(t) + K_\psi(\psi(t) - \psi_{com}(t)) \qquad (1)$$

where the rudder command signal time history is shown together with the corresponding yaw rate and heading angle. In the first thirty seconds, the vehicle is accelerating to speed, diving to depth, and controlling to the desired heading. At thirty seconds, the command to turn is entered and the response in the turn is clearly seen. The performance of the controller, however, is not elucidated when the turn is entered because the rudders are saturated. It is the control when the vehicle exits from the turn during the period 50 - 70 seconds that is key. The controller represents a balance between responsiveness and stability in controlling the turn and has been designed to have somewhat higher proportional gain than would be necessary if tight turns were not needed. The corresponding heading angle is clearly shown in Figure 4. The oscillatory part of the yaw rate during the period 35 - 45 seconds is possibly generated by inertial cross-coupling that potentially exists between the pitch / yaw modes although nominally assumed to be negligible. Later experiments with tighter control suppressed this phenomenon to a large degree. This is evidence that high gain robust controllers are indeed needed for these separate autopilots in compensating for the induced mode coupling.

Diving Response

The diving response is indicated in Figure 5. There is an initial flurry of dive plane control action as the vehicle accelerates to speed and goes below the water surface. The initial launch is on the surface and the transition to depth is smooth but initially the vehicle speed is slow and the control is less effective than at the nominal running speed about 2 ft/sec. (0.61 meters/sec.). The pitch rate and angle are shown. The pitch angle reaches 0.2 radians then is reduced quickly and the nominal depth of 2 feet (0.61 meters) is achieved. At the end of the test run, the mission calls for a depth change to surface as indicated at the time of 75 seconds. The pitch control law for which the results are shown was a three state proportional law without the nonlinear term, given by,

$$\delta_s(t) = K_q q(t) + K_\theta \theta(t) + K_z [Z(t) - Z_{com}(t)] \qquad (2)$$

Speed Response

The vehicle speed control was initially provided by a PI control law (the Sliding Mode version is now implemented) including an integral term, where with abuse of notation,

$$n_{com}(t) = (u_0/n_0)u_{com}(t) + K_p e(t) + K_i \sum_{i=1}^{10} e_{k-i} \qquad (3)$$

the integral term as a sum over the last ten points was present to help in maintaining speed during the turn where the large centrifugal force and the added plane drag causes significant loss of speed. The response in Figure 6 shows the output from the paddle wheel sensor indicating good acceleration followed by an overshoot at 2.5 ft/sec with a controlled speed reduction during the period 20 - 30 seconds. The speed reduction during 30 - 50 seconds is the effect of the added drag terms which would be much larger without the corresponding increase in propeller speed not shown. (Shown in later runs). The speed gain during the period 50 - 70 is the result of the vehicle coming out of the turn and the speed controller taking over in stabilizing to the set point of 2 ft./sec. (0.61 meters /sec.).

The path obtained by dead reckoning using the paddle wheel speed sensor and the heading gyro output but neglecting side slip errors is given in Figure 7. Recognizing the limitations of the accuracy of this navigation scheme, we have found the results sufficient to guide the vehicle without a collision with the pool walls.

<u>Way point Guidance by Line of Sight</u>

Vehicle autonomous guidance is most simply accomplished by a heading command to the vehicle's steering system to approach the line of sight between the present position of the vehicle and the way point to be reached. In missile guidance this is related to 'proportional navigation'. The difference in guiding AUV's is that the vehicle response is slow compared to the rates of change in command unless the way point is many vehicle lengths away. Separation of guidance and autopilot functions may not always produce stable results underwater. Notwithstanding, we define the line of sight (LOS) to be the horizontal plane angle given by,

$$\psi_{com} = \tan^{-1}\left[\frac{(Y_k - Y(t))}{X_k - X(t)}\right] \qquad (4)$$

in which the $[X_k, Y_k]$ are way points stored in the vehicle's mission planner. Care must be taken to keep the proper quadrant in mind when programming the guidance law. The decision as to whether the way point has been reached is made on the basis of whether the vehicle lies within a 'ball of acceptability', ρ_0 defined around the particular way point. Namely, if, for some distance, ρ_0, an acceptable zone around the way point, $[X_k(t), Y_k(t), Z_k(t)]$, the vehicle location $[X(t), Y(t), Z(t)]$ are such that,

$$\rho^2(t) = [Y_k-Y(t)]^2+[X_k-X(t)]^2+\lambda[Z_k-Z(t)]^2< \rho_0^2 \qquad 0<\lambda<1 \qquad (5)$$

the above condition triggers the selection of the next way point. If, on the other hand, the condition that $d\rho/dt$ goes from negative to positive without the above being met then the way point is not reached. At this juncture, the guidance law must contain logic that will either hold the current way point, directing the vehicle to circle, or the next way point could be entered, depending on a mission planning decision. λ is a parameter relating to the importance of including depth dimension in the acquisition of the way point. In this section, vehicle way point control is examined in experiment using the autopilots described above combined with the LOS guidance. The assumption is made that vehicle speed control is obtained from a separate speed command for each separate leg of a transit mission, although that could be accomplished also by an on line speed command as a function of distance to go and the time to go if a desired time is also associated with each way point. The ability of the LOS method to acquire way points is illustrated by the series of results given in Figures 8 - 11. In Figure 8, the steering response variables are shown with rather oscillatory swings that are characteristic of commands changing as way points are reached and subsequent points entered into the controller. The diving performance is given in Figure 9 where a commanded depth of 2 ft again was used. Figure 10 shows the speed controller response as the vehicle is accelerated and slowed by the turning activity. In Figure 10, the propeller speed command is shown as well as the vehicle speed response from the paddle

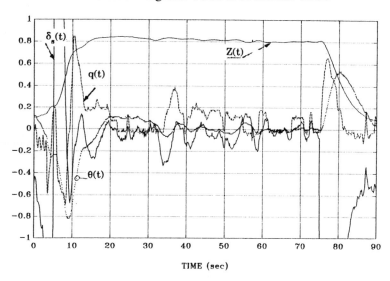

Figure 5
δ_s(t), q(t), θ(t), and Z(t) versus Time; Oval Track Run; Combined Diving, Steering, and Speed Control; Standard Control Laws; Scaled as δ_s(t)/0.4 (rad), q(t)/0.08(rad/sec), θ(t)/0.25 (rad), Z(t)/2.5 (ft.)

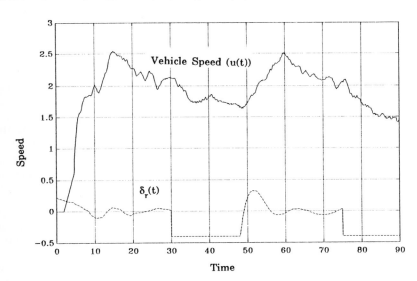

Figure 6
Vehicle Speed (u(t)) versus Time; Oval Track Run; Combined Diving, Steering, and Speed Control; Standard Control Laws

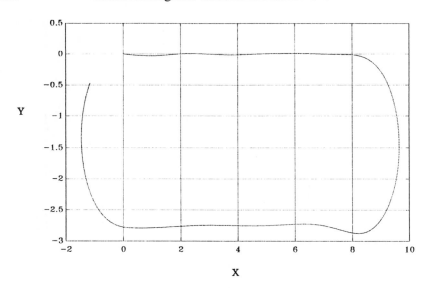

Figure 7
Vehicle Path versus Time; Oval Track Run; Combined Diving, Steering, and
Speed Control; Standard Control Laws; X and Y expressed in Vehicle Lengths

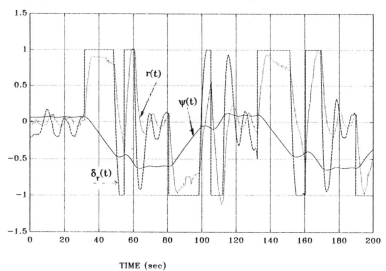

TIME (sec)

Figure 8
Figure Eight Run; Vehicle Steering Response; Combined Diving, Steering, and
Speed Control; Standard Control Laws; $\delta_r(t)$, $r(t)$, $\psi(t)$, versus Time. Shown
During the Run

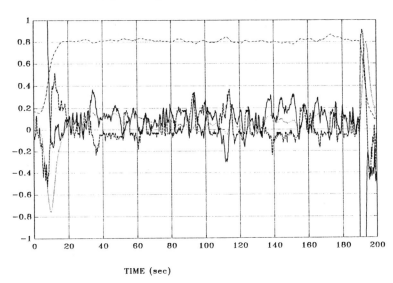

TIME (sec)

Figure 9
Figure Eight Run; Vehicle Diving Response; Combined Diving, Steering, and
Speed Control; Standard Control Laws; Plot As in Figure 5

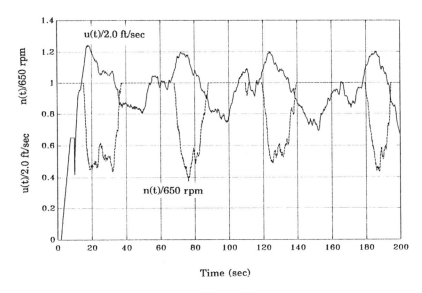

Time (sec)

Figure 10

Figure Eight Run; Vehicle Speed (u(t)) versus Time; Combined Diving,
Steering, and Speed Control; Standard Control Laws. Normalized Plot u(t)/2.0
ft/sec. n(t)/650 rpm

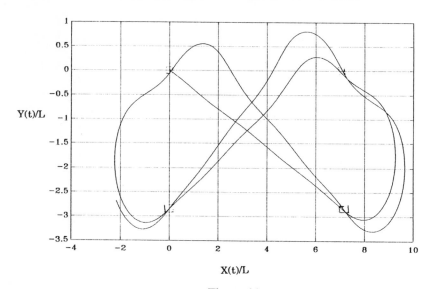

Figure 11
Figure Eight Run; Vehicle Path;   Combined Diving, Steering, and Speed
Control; Standard Control Laws. Way Points Shown. X(t)/L versus Y(t)/L

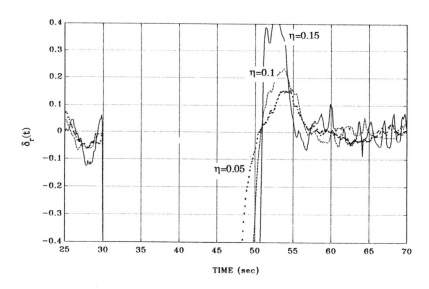

Figure 12 a
Oval Track Run; Vehicle Rudder versus Time; Sliding Mode Steering Control
Laws; Varying Nonlinear Gains η=[0.05, 0.1, 0.15]

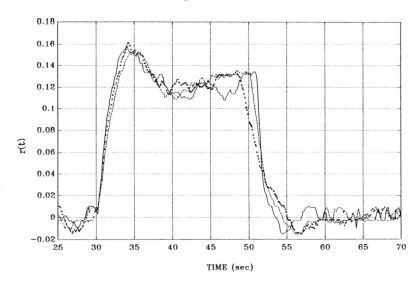

Figure 12 b
Oval Track Run; Vehicle Yaw Rate versus Time;   Sliding Mode Steering
Control Laws; Varying Nonlinear Gains η=[0.05, 0.1, 0.15]

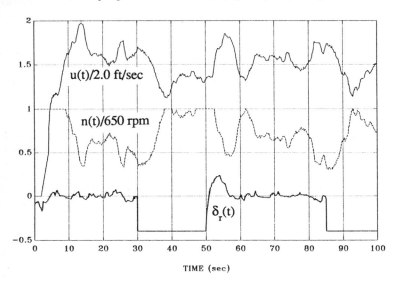

Figure 13
Oval Track Run; Speed Changes [u(t) in ft/sec.], Normalized Propeller Speed
[n(t)/650] and Rudder [δ(t)] versus Time

wheel sensor. Separate experiments, not described here, have determined that the response of the inner loop for the control of motor speed to motor speed commands is fast and has negligible lags in this application. Figure 11 shows that each way point was acquired with excellent precision even though the global locations of those way points may not have been uncertain. In other words, the autopilot functions drove the vehicle to the locations that the vehicle 'thought' it had to meet.

What we see is a vehicle that is capable of tight turns; its steering and diving systems are stable under conditions of combined maneuvering at speeds that are changing; and planned paths, in terms of way points, can be followed with precision consistent with the limits of the vehicle's turning capability.

Sliding Mode Control Compared

The performance of sliding mode control has been compared in a series of runs using the same oval path as in the first series with the steering control law,

$$\delta_r(t)=k_{22}r(t)+k_{23}\dot{r}_{com}(t)+\eta_r\tanh(\sigma_2(t)/\phi_2) \qquad (6)$$

where $\sigma_2(t)$ is the sliding surface.

In Figures 12a and 12b, three controller's results are superimposed with the rudder responses shown in Figure 12a, and the corresponding yaw rate responses shown in Figure 12b. Each shows the effect of increasing nonlinear gains. The effect on the yaw rate response out of the turn is not as strong as thought and increasing gain appears to increase the levels of activity on the control surfaces. However, the overall response is very rapid and much improved over the initial PD controller. It is believed that the sliding mode control is easy to implement and even easier to tune in the field as only one parameter needs to be modified to adjust the speed of the controller from slow to fast and stability is not compromised.

Figure 13 is provided from the same series of runs to illustrate that the propulsion control is disturbed by the continual turning and added drag forces being applied. A careful examination of Figure 13 at the time of 20 seconds shows that the sharp increase in vehicle speed coincides with the control surface changing from a positive to a negative value quickly. Whenever a control surface is brought to a null position there is an attendant change in drag that occurs almost instantaneously. The results reveal that a considerable amount of oscillatory changes occur. It may be evidence of the dynamics and nature of the propeller thrust response having lags. This is the subject of further investigation.

Bottom Following

Incorporation of a downward looking sonar (Datasonics PSA 900) into the depth control system has allowed a test series for altitude control and also using the vehicle depth sensor, a determination of the water column height around the pool. For the basic oval loop, Figure 14 shows the result of the control to a fixed height above bottom, and the attendant estimation of the total water depth.

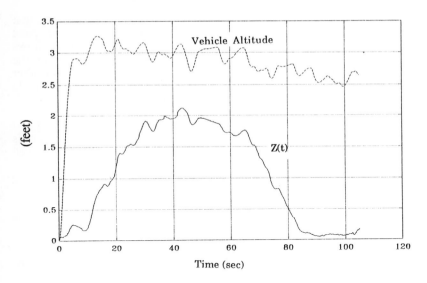

Figure 14
Oval Track Run; Bottom Following; Water Depth versus X.;   Combined
Diving, Steering, and Speed Control;

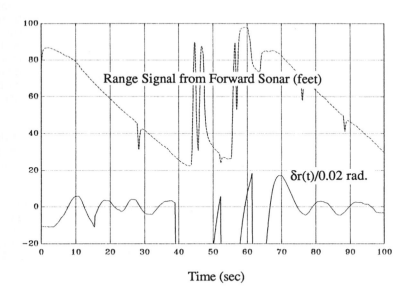

Figure 15
Oval Track Run; Wall Avoidance; Forward Sonar Range and Rudder versus
Time.

Manoeuvring and Control of Marine Craft

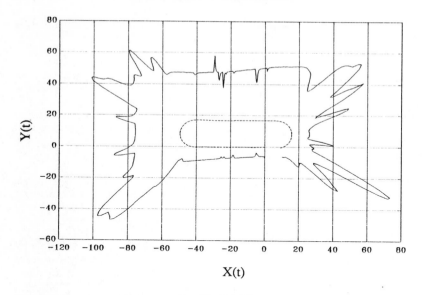

Figure 16
Oval Track Run; Pool Wall Shape from Left Sonar Signature. X and Y units in ft.

Since the water depth in the pool is known at any X location, the result is compared with that known profile.

Obstacle Avoidance

While the **Obstacle Avoidance Decision Maker** is a system that has yet to be defined to its fullest extent at the time of writing, The vehicle has four sonar ranging systems on board that have been providing mapping data to the pool sidewalls. One of the most important obstacle avoidance issues is to prevent the vehicle from running into a solid object in its path. The use of a forward looking sonar to provide range to such an object has been demonstrated in pool tests where a limit of 25 feet has been set after which a hard turn to the starboard is triggered. The quality of the range signals from the Datasonics PSA 900 200 KHz.sonar is shown in Figure 15 where it has been clearly shown that an obstacle avoidance maneuver was triggered at the correct time to turn the vehicle away from the pool end wall.

Using the ranging data from both forward and side looking transducers we show in Figure 16 that the dead reckoning system can be used to reconstruct the shape of the pool side walls with reasonable accuracy. Refinements by taking side slip into account have provided additional accuracy and in fact can be used to calibrate a side slip observer for vehicle navigational enhancement.

CONCLUSION

Much more work needs to done in this community to continue, with appropriate overlap from sufficiently diverse points of view, to illuminate the range and trade-offs of possible structures and technology, hardware and software, needed for precise, reliable control of AUVs in the future. In particular, during the next few years, we plan to

1.   Develop techniques for design of mission planning software using a simulator that has realistic run time and vehicle motion dynamics constraints,

2.   Develop technology for understanding multiprocessor real time computation with transputers for mission control execution,

3.   Understand the precision to which slow speed control can be accomplished in the presence of ocean currents, including the behavior of thrusters,

4.   Understand how to incorporate high resolution imaging sonar into vehicle guidance and control functions to enhance the ability of vehicles to gain acoustic imagery of potential targets,

5.   Understand how to integrate a GPS/INS suite into the vehicle's mission planner and navigation systems,

6.   Further the understanding of the design of system diagnostic reasoners using neural networks to increase vehicle operational reliability.

REFERENCES

Albus, J. S., (1988) "System Description and Design Architecture for Multiple Autonomous Undersea Vehicles" *NIST Technical Note No. 1251*, U.S. Department of Commerce National Institute of Standards and Technology, Sept. 1988

Bellingham, J., Consi, T., Beaton, R., (1990a) "Keeping Layered Control Simple", *Proc. Symposium on Autonomous Underwater Vehicle Technology* June 5-6 1990 Washington DC. Published as IEEE Catalog No. 90CH2856-3, pp 3-9

Bellingham, J., Consi, T., (1990b) "State Configured Layered Control" *Mobile Robots for Subsea Environments*, Proceedings of the 1st NSF IARP Workshop, Monterey Bay Aquarium Research Institute, California, October 23-26, 1990, pp 75 - 80

Brooks, R., (1986) "A Robust Layered Control System for a Mobile Robot" *IEEE Journal of Robotics and Automation*, Vol. 2, 1986

Brutzman, LCDR Donald P., Kanayama, Y., and Zyda, M.J., (1992a) "Integrated Simulation for Rapid Development of Autonomous Underwater Vehicles," presented at IEEE Oceanic Engineering Society *Symposium on Autonomous Underwater Vehicles, AUV-92* Washington D.C., June2-3,1992.

Brutzman, LCDR Donald P., (1992b) "NPSAUV Integrated Simulator", *Master's Thesis, Naval Postgraduate School,* Monterey, California, March-1992.

Chappell, S. G., (1987) "A Blackboard Based System for Context Sensitive Mission Planning in an Autonomous Vehicle" *Proceedings of the 5th International Symposium on Unmanned Untethered Submersible Technology*, University of New Hampshire, June 1987 Vol.2 pp 467-476

Healey, A.J., et. al. (1990) "Mission Planning, Execution, and Data Analysis for the NPS AUV II Autonomous Underwater Vehicle" *Mobile Robots for Subsea Environments*, Proceedings of the 1st NSF IARP Workshop, Monterey Bay Aquarium Research Institute, California, October 23-26, 1990, pp 177-186

Healey, A. J., Papoulias, F. A. Lienard, D., (1990) "Multivariable Sliding Mode Control for Autonomous Diving and Steering of Unmanned Underwater Vehicles " *Modeling and Control of Marine Craft*, Elsevier Publications,1990

Healey, A.J., Good, M., (1992) "The NPS AUV II Autonomous Underwater Vehicle Testbed: Design and Experimental Verification" *Naval Engineers Journal,* ASNE , May 1992 issue.

Mayer, R., et. al. (1987) "Situation based Control Architecture for an AUV" *Proceedings of the 5th International Symposium on Unmanned Untethered Submersible Technology*, University of New Hampshire, June 1987, Vol. 2 pp 430-443

Papoulias, F. A., Healey, A. J. (1990) "Path Tracking of Surface Ships Using Multivariable Sliding Mode Control" *Proceedings of the 9th Ship Control Systems Symposium*, Washington D.C.Sept 10-14 1990

Proc. Symposium on Autonomous Underwater Vehicle Technology June 5-6 1990 Washington DC. Published as IEEE Catalog No. 90CH2856-3

Proceedings of the 5th International Symposium on Unmanned Untethered Submersible Technology, University of New Hampshire, June 1987

Proceedings of the 6th International Symposium on Unmanned Untethered Submersible Technology, University of New Hampshire, June 1989

Proceedings of the 7h International Symposium on Unmanned Untethered Submersible Technology, University of New Hampshire, September 1991

Ura, T., (1990) " Development of AUV 'PTEROA'" *Mobile Robots for Subsea Environments*, Proceedings of the 1st NSF IARP Workshop, Monterey Bay Aquarium Research Institute, California, October 23-26, 1990, pp 195 - 200

Stability and Manoeuvrability Predictions of a Remotely Operated Underwater Vehicle

I. Stewart, S.L Merry, R. Allen

Department of Mechanical Engineering, University of Southampton, Highfield, Southampton, SO9 5NH, UK

ABSTRACT

Control of an underwater vehicle is a complex area of work and the demands on modern vehicle performance continue to tax the applied control engineer. A combination of simulation and underwater trials produces an effective design environment. This paper describes the design of a low cost ROV which will provide a test-bed for underwater vehicle control strategies. A comprehensive simulation of an autonomous underwater vehicle has been adopted to model the ROV and illustrative performance predictions from the package are presented.

INTRODUCTION

In recent years there have been major developments in the technology of Remotely Operated Underwater Vehicles (ROVs). The ROV is extremely versatile and can be used in applications ranging from marine research and inspection to military applications and the leisure market. As the technology has become more advanced and the costs have reduced, a whole new potential market has opened up to the ROV.

Vehicle control is a complex area of work, and is best optimised through both simulation and experimental validation. In addition, it is often difficult to undertake comparative evaluation of control techniques due to the lack of suitably versatile test vehicles. Classical control techniques can be adequate when vehicle hydrodynamics are well defined, as in the case of a torpedo, but may be inadequate when, for example, a modular vehicle configuration changes on different missions and when hydrodynamics are inherently nonlinear, as in the case of many ROVs. Modern methods of control show promise for overcoming such limitations but their effectiveness requires proper assessment.

A project to design and build a small ROV for testing low cost control strategies was initiated through the University of Southampton's Master of Engineering course in October 1991. The project was partially sponsored by Marconi Underwater Systems Ltd., who supplied the main design specifications. At the time of writing, the vehicle hardware has been fabricated and assembled, while the electronics are nearing completion.

A concurrent project, to investigate the stability and manoeuvrability of underwater vehicles by computer simulation has been funded by the National Environmental Research Council. Through a joint research agreement, the Department of Mechanical Engineering has access to a simulation program developed in the Department of Ocean Engineering at Florida Atlantic University, USA , for modelling the performance of their Autonomous Underwater Vehicle (AUV) 'Ocean Voyager'[1]. The program has been modified at Southampton, so that it can be applied to the ROV.

This paper outlines the mechanical design of the ROV and its electronics. The general functions of the simulation program are described and preliminary results for performance prediction of the ROV are presented.

DESIGN OF THE ROV

The design specification for the vehicle included maximum dimensions of 1m length and 0.1m diameter. Although this shape was chosen for the prototype vehicle, different shapes can be added later for testing, for example, the efficiency of a laminar flow hull design. The prototype hull and control surfaces have been produced in 'Perspex' for convenience and to allow the operation of the internal components to be assessed visually. Access to the internal components is a key consideration in the design of a ROV for assembly, maintenance and modification, and is particularly important in a prototype vehicle. The drive and control gear is mounted on a removable tray which is guided by internal rails and sits within the vehicle with a small clearance. A general arrangement of the ROV is presented in figure 1.

Propulsion is achieved through a small d.c. motor; a 200W, 16,000 rpm samarium cobalt motor. The motor speed is reduced by a factor of 5:1 through a gearbox, with power being provided by 8, 1.2V NiCad cells of 1700mAh capacity. The propeller diameter is restricted

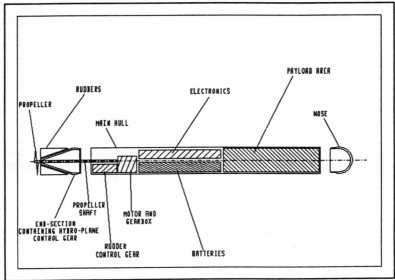

Figure 1 : General Arrangement of the ROV

by the vehicle specification which leads to low section velocities even at high rotational speeds. The propeller was selected to give the most efficient propulsion at the maximum vehicle speed of 4 m/s, this resulting in a pitch of 0.11m and a maximum propeller speed of 3500 rpm.

The optimum blade area ratio of 0.1m was suggested by consideration of cavitation effects. Four control surfaces of low aspect ratio are mounted in front of the propeller; two rudders are controlled by one servomechanism and the two sternplanes are controlled individually to allow for a degree of roll control.

Vehicle control is centred on an IBM AT-compatible computer system, which communicates with the ROV over a bi-directional fibre optic link. Communications are handled by two 8-bit microcontrollers (Motorola 68HC11), one operating within the host computer on a custom-built dedicated communication card, the other on-board the ROV. The communication card has been designed for an 8-bit expansion slot of a PC and could, therefore, be used in a range of computers. Sensor information from the ROV, such as engine RPM, depth, and control surface deflection, is digitised on-board prior to transmitting to the host machine. The host uses this information, together with pilot demands from a joystick, to compute control signals for the vehicle. These are transmitted to the ROV microcontroller which adjusts the pulse width modulated signals to the control surface actuators and the propeller drive system. A transmission bandwidth of 25 frames of information per second has been achieved between the ROV and host and will be increased once the preliminary vehicle trials have been completed.

SIMULATION PROGRAM

The program supplied by Florida Atlantic University (FAU) is a dynamic six degree of freedom model of an AUV. It has been converted in Southampton to run on a PC.

The program itself is written in modular form, and so is relatively simple to adapt to various uses, and different modules can be added to match the output to the individual user's needs, and equipment available. The powerful graphics of the IRIS work-station at FAU produces a three dimensional, fully shaded output depicting the submersible in a real-time simulation. Since this option is currently unavailable at Southampton, a plot procedure has been written to allow the results to be output graphically, rather than in numerical form. This is a self-scaling procedure to allow full use of the screen, and to give maximum definition. Work is currently in hand to develop a real-time program from this, which will allow the progress of the graphs to be seen as the calculations are completed.

All coefficients supplied within the program are for the FAU submersible. Fortunately the geometry of this vehicle is similar to that of the Southampton ROV (torpedo shaped, with a fineness ratio of 10:1), and hence some of the hydrodynamic coefficients have been retained for the preliminary studies of the ROV performance. The propeller characteristics, hull dimensions and control surface specifications have been appropriately modified. This simulation does not take into account any cable dynamics which may have some effect on the manoeuvrability of a ROV. Since the fibre optic link on the Southampton ROV is very narrow and light, with the ROV operating initially at a maximum depth of 3m, it has been assumed that cable drag is negligible.

Data are currently entered into the simulation using a command file, allowing a change in rudder and sternplane position, and/or engine speed to be specified at any time. It also allows the termination of the simulation at a given time. There is a facility to incorporate a command and control procedure into the program, which will be included as a module should the vehicle become fully autonomous. This will permit the addition of other command file inputs such as course or speed, allowing the submersible to calculate its own demands for rudder angle and engine revolutions.

SIMULATION RESULTS

In order to verify satisfactory operation of the modified simulation program, two basic manoeuvres for the ROV have been investigated :

(a) Yaw manoeuvre : steady state straight and level cruise at 4 m/s, followed by application of 5° rudder angle for 20 seconds, returning to straight and level cruise.

(b) Dive manoeuvre : steady state straight and level cruise at 4 m/s, followed by application of 5° sternplane for 20 seconds, returning to straight and level cruise.

Yaw Manoeuvre
Figure 2 shows the rudder deflection input to the simulation as a function of time, with the resultant variation in axial velocity of the vehicle due to the induced drag of the rudder from initial conditions of 4 m/s in straight and level cruise. The path of the ROV in the horizontal plane is illustrated in Figure 3.

The hydrodynamic force from the rudder is misaligned with the vehicle's centre of gravity in the horizontal plane, which induces a rolling moment, as demonstrated in Figure 4. The consequent roll angle of the vehicle generates a vertical component from the rudder force, which in turn produces a negative pitch angle on the vehicle. The pitch angle continues to decrease for the duration of the rudder deflection (20 seconds, see Figure 2) and the resultant total depth gain is approximately 7 metres.

Note that this yaw manoeuvre would not be performed in practice without supplementary roll and pitch control via actuation of the sternplanes.

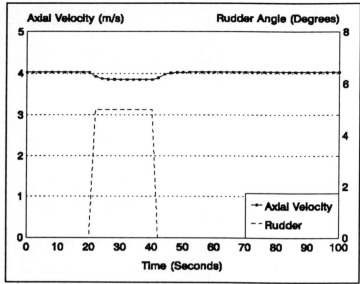

Figure 2 : Reduction in Speed during 5°
Rudder Deflection

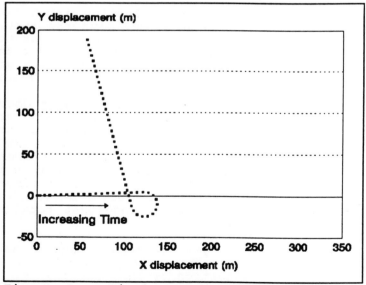

Figure 3 : Displacement of ROV during 5°
Rudder Deflection at 4 m/s Axial Velocity

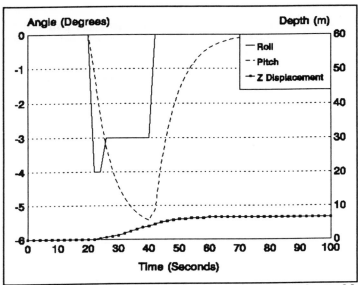

Figure 4 : Variation in Pitch and Roll during 5° Rudder Deflection at 4 m/s Axial Velocity

Dive Manoeuvre
Vehicle response to a sternplane deflection of 5° from
an initial straight and level cruise speed of 4 m/s is
presented in Figure 5.   The corresponding change in
vehicle pitch angle is illustrated and there is a small
reduction in axial speed because of the induced drag
from the control surfaces.

    Figure 6 shows the path of the vehicle in the
vertical plane.   The simulation did not indicate any
coupled motions for a dive manoeuvre ie. there was no
induced yaw, roll or lateral displacement.

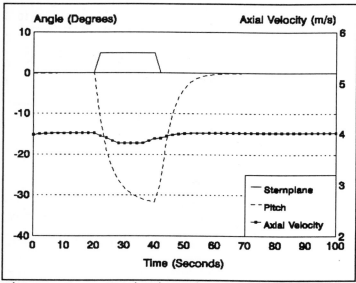

Figure 5 : Variation in Speed and Pitch
During 5° Sternplane Deflection

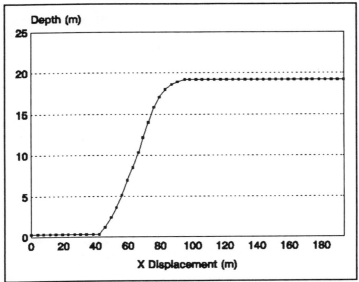

Figure 6 : Depth Profile during 5° Sternplane
Deflection at 4 m/s Axial Velocity

CONCLUSIONS

The hydrodynamic coefficients and hull geometry for a
new design of ROV have been entered into a computer
program for simulating the stability and
manoeuvrability of an underwater vehicle.
Implementation of the program for two basic vehicle
manoeuvres have indicated that the simulation produces
a credible prediction of vehicle performance.

     In the development of strategies for the control
of underwater vehicle dynamics, a combination of a
comprehensive simulation and low cost test vehicle is
considered to be mutually beneficial. Vehicle trials
can be designed more effectively and control strategies
optimised more efficiently. To date, only simple
control of actuators has been used in order to gain
baseline data on vehicle performance. It is our
intention now to integrate modern control techniques
and to assess their performance in overcoming some of
the limitations of classical techniques. Results from
the simulation will be compared with data from vehicle
performance trials in the near future.

References
1. 'Perry Technologies Advances AUV Systems', Waves magazine Jan/Feb 1992, pp18-19.

Acknowledgements
The authors would like to thank the following parties for their contributions to this paper.

Dr. Richard Babb, Institute of Oceanographic Sciences, Deacon Laboratory, and the National Environmental Research Council for financial support of the underwater vehicle simulation project.

Department of Ocean Engineering, Florida Atlantic University, Boca Raton, Florida, for supplying the simulation program.

Mr. Richard Dawson, Mr. Mark Downer, Mr. Geoff Patterson, Mr. Prakash Pattni, and Mr. David Warrender, of the M. Eng. course, Southampton University, for the design and construction of the ROV.

Mr. Peter Gorman, Marconi Underwater Systems Ltd., for his guidance during the design of the ROV.

Experiments To Improve Predictions of Submarine Manoeuvres

B. Ward

Ship and Submarine Dynamics Section, DRA Haslar, Gosport, Hampshire, UK

ABSTRACT

A knowledge of hydrodynamic forces is necessary to determine the manoeuvring characteristics of a submarine design. Computer models have been used for this purpose using derivative data from model experiments. A computer model has been developed at DRA Haslar over the last decade which requires no input derivative data and hence avoids the need to carry out model experiments for each design in the early stages.

This computer model uses a semi-empirical approach which combines classical theory and empirical equations. The empirical equations determine parameters such as forces and moments on the hull, lift forces on control surfaces and positions and strengths of body vortices. Over the last five years various experiments have been conducted to acquire the necessary empirical data and also to gain a greater understanding of how the flow around the submarine affects the manoeuvring characteristics.

Recent validations have shown the predictions of submarine manoeuvring characteristics such as turning circle, speed loss and yaw rate in the turn and vertical pulse manoeuvres to be good. However predictions of depth changes during turns are unsatisfactory.

This paper discusses the experiments to obtain the empirical data.

INTRODUCTION

The prediction of the manoeuvring behaviour of submarines has become more important in recent years whether it is for the early designing of depth and course autopilots or for optimizing appendage sizes. A necessary prerequisite to simulating submarine manoeuvres is a knowledge of hydrodynamic forces and moments which act on the body of the submarine in accordance with momentary velocities, accelerations and appendage positions. Scaled model tests have usually determined hydrodynamic coefficients which are used in a Taylor series or curve approximation to formulate the motion equation in accordance with the Newton Axiom.

Lloyd[1] described a new mathematical model, SUBSIM, which predicts the manoeuvring characteristics of submersible bodies. Subsequent developments were reported in Lloyd[2]. The SUBSIM program is effectively an intermediate step between the traditional derivative approach to the prediction of manoeuvring characteristics and the intensive computational fluid dynamics approach to estimating the force on a body. The purpose of SUBSIM is not to quantify forces exactly but to determine gross manoeuvring characteristics. The use of experiment data to determine empirical functions is a convenient approach to use and overcomes deficiencies in the theoretical methods and the expense of model tests on a particular design. The designer can use SUBSIM at an early stage and arrive at a design before any physical model testing is required. This paper describes some of the experiments used to collect the empirical data.

FORCES AND MOMENTS ON A BODY OF REVOLUTION

Conventional submarines have tended to be near bodies of revolution with pointed tails. It is appropriate for those scientists and engineers involved in submarine design to investigate methods of predicting forces on such shapes. The estimation of forces on a body of revolution has been a problem in the aerodynamics world for much of this century. Early methods such as Munk[3] and Von Karman[4] were unreliable. More recent developments Mendenhall[5] and Tinker[6] tend to be highly computational and therefore time consuming. Lloyd[1,2] opted for a quick empirical approach.

In SUBSIM the forces and moments on the hull are represented by

$$Z'=[Z'_{w}+Z'_{w|w|}\sin\alpha]\sin\alpha \tag{1}$$

$$M'=[M'_{w}+M'_{w|w|}\sin\alpha]\sin\alpha \tag{2}$$

where Z'_{w}, $Z'_{w|w|}$, M'_{w} and $M'_{w|w|}$ are functions of L/D and C_P . The functions were derived by fitting equations to data from 1950's David Taylor

Research Centre (DTRC) data. It was decided that a series of experiments in which fineness ratio was varied from 7.5 to 13 would enhance the database allowing better formulae to be derived as well as verifying the DTRC data. Experiments to measure forces and moments on bodies of revolution were conducted in No 2 Ship Tank (a large towing tank mainly used for submerged body experiments) at DRA Haslar (formerly ARE Haslar).

The model hull consisted of three main sections; nose,tail and middle body. Two identical sections were inserted either side of the middle body to lengthen the model. Diameter was constant at 0.526 metres. Dimensions and other details are given in Table 1.

Table 1

Model	Length(m)	L/D	C_P
DRE1	3.948	7.5	0.64
DRE2	4.210	8	0.66
DRE3	4.736	9	0.7
DRE4	5.264	10	0.73
DRE5	5.790	11	0.756
DRE6	6.316	12	0.776
DRE7	6.842	13	0.793

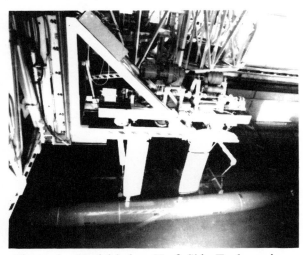

Figure 1 : Model below No 2 Ship Tank carriage

Two swords held the model below the No 2 Ship Tank carriage as shown in Figure 1. The model was pitched over a range of angles from -16 degrees to +16 degrees. Speed was maintained at 2.5 m/s which gives a Reynolds number of 1.15×10^6 (basing R_e on diameter); this is above the critical R_e of 1.0×10^6.

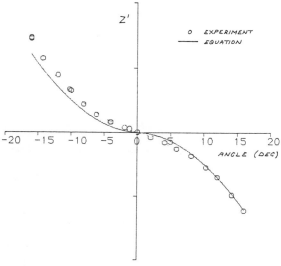

Figure 2 : Model DRE1, L/D=7.5, C_P=0.64

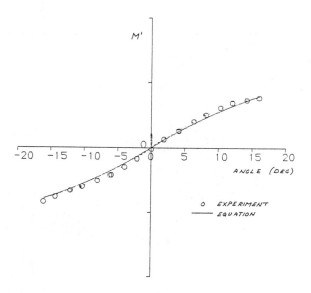

Figure 3 : Model DRE4, L/D=10, C_P=0.73

Regression polynomials of the second degree were fitted to each set of data to yield the four coefficients Z'_w, $Z'_{w|w|}$, M'_w and $M'_{w|w|}$. Figures 2 and 3 show examples of the resulting curve fits to the No 2 Ship Tank data. It was concluded that the data from No 2 Ship Tank and the DTRC data are in good agreement generally.

Further experiments on the rotating arm facility will provide data from which rotary derivatives can be derived.

LIFT ON LOW ASPECT RATIO HYDROPLANES UNDER STATIC AND DYNAMIC CONDITIONS

Figure 4 : Hydroplane experiment in Circulating Water Channel

It was decided that there was a need for data on dynamic effects on lift forces for low aspect ratio hydroplanes. A thorough literature search was carried out; previous papers usually described two dimensional experiments at much higher frequencies than those of relevant interest. It was therefore decided to perform some dedicated experiments to obtain the required data.

Three NACA 0020 hydroplanes were used of aspect ratios 1, 1.5 and 2. Each hydroplane had a chord length of 0.26m and span of 0.13m, 0.195m and 0.26m respectively. A strain gauged stock at the quarter chord position of the hydroplane was attached to a servo to oscillate the hydroplane. Strain gauge bridges on the stock were calibrated to give normal and tangential forces.

The experiment was conducted in the Circulation Water Channel (Figure 4) at DRA Haslar. The horizontal flow velocity was maintained at 2.5 m/s.

Figure 5 shows a plot of non dimensional lift C_L against angle of incidence for aspect ratio 2.

Oscillating runs were carried out at frequencies from 0.055 Hz to 0.386 Hz corresponding to ωc/U values from 0.036 to 0.252. Frequencies were chosen to correspond to full scale angular rates in the region of 5 degs/sec. An example plot is shown in Figure 6.

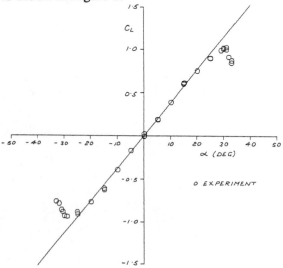

Figure 5 : Lift coefficient - aspect ratio 2, static condition

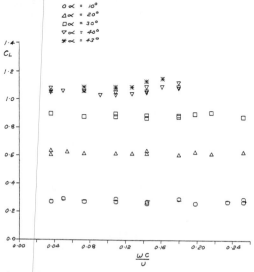

Figure 6 : Lift coefficient - aspect ratio 1, dynamic condition

The experiment showed the dynamic effects to be small but worth noting. No significant variation in C_L was noted over the range of frequencies examined. Phase angles were small; a phase lead of approximately 10 degrees occurs at the highest frequency of 0.386Hz ($\omega c/U = 0.252$).

It was concluded that it was not necessary to model the dynamic effects as they are insignificant at the angular rates likely to be encountered.

VORTICITY AROUND A BODY OF REVOLUTION IN CURVED FLOW

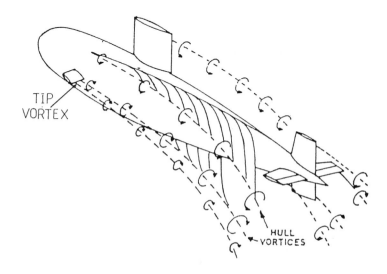

Figure 7 : A typical pattern of vortices around a manoeuvring submarine

The flow around a manoeuvring submarine is dominated by vortices which are shed from the appendages and the hull (Figure 7). The strength and position of appendage vortices may be predicted by lifting line theory (Glauert[7]). The body vortices are affected by incidence and rate of turn of the submarine. The SUBSIM computer program makes use of empirical formulae to represent the positions and strengths of body vortices.

The experiments (discussed in Lloyd[8,9]) were conducted on the rotating arm facility (Figure 8) in the manoeuvring tank at DRA Haslar. They were performed by the Wolfson Unit for Marine Technology and Industrial Aerodynamics (University of Southampton) working under contract.

Figure 8 : The rotating arm experiment

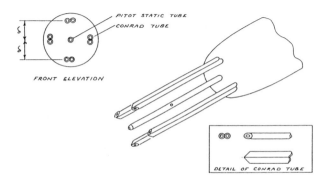

Figure 9 : The Freestone vorticity probe

A 5 metre body of revolution was used with fineness ratio L/D of 8.5. To measure vorticity a Freestone[10] probe (Figure 9) was used which was mounted on a stayed circular strut which could be positioned at one of three locations along the length of the model ($x' = 0.7, 0.85, 0.925$). The probes' radial and angular location could be adjusted. Runs were conducted over a range of angles of incidence and turn rates at the three stations. Measurements were taken at 10 degree angular intervals at 25 mm radial steps from the body surface.

During the analysis of vorticity traverses (Figure 10). A number of salient features were apparent;
a. The peak value was probably missed due to the limited number of data values.
b. The physical dimensions of the probe precluded any measurements close to the local body surface.

c. The traverses appeared to come down to a 'plateau' as the radius increases, whereas it would have been expected that they would decrease smoothly to zero at the 'edge' of the vortical flow. This is probably associated with zero errors in the Freestone probe. It was found during the experiment that the probe gave small levels of 'vorticity' in uniform flow when no vorticity was expected and that these zero errors were functions of the flow direction at the probe. A simple correction was devised based on the results obtained at the outer limits of the strut, and this was applied to each traverse, forcing the vorticity at $r = 1.5 \times D$ to be zero. However, the flow direction changes as the probe is moved towards the body and this will affect the zero error correction. No simple method of quantifying this effect has been devised.

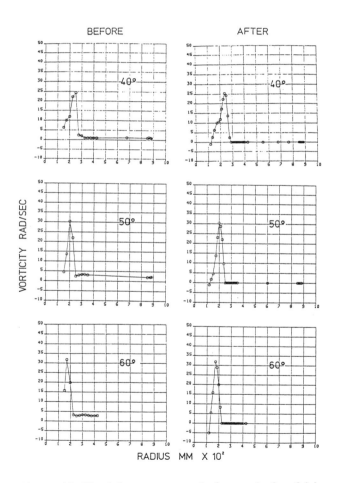

Figure 10: Vorticity traverses - before and after fairing
$(x' = 0.925, r' = 0.3, \alpha = 7.5)$

To overcome these shortcomings the data were faired to a more expected form; ensuring smooth variations as each of the parameters was varied. This involved;

a. Inserting estimated additional points close to the local radius of the body.
b. Interpolating extra points throughout the curve including, at times, a point for peak vorticity.
c. Bringing traverses down to zero at the apparent edge of the vortical flow.
d. Ensuring that the estimated peak vorticity increased smoothly with strut angle. Examples of fairing are shown in Figure 10.

The faired data was reanalysed by the author and new empirical equations were derived for circulation density, centre of circulation and vortex core radius. These equations are functions of angle of incidence, turn parameter etc.

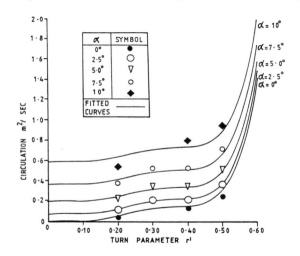

Figure 11 : Total circulation against turn parameter
for varying values of incidence angle

The total circulation was estimated from

$$\Gamma = \int_0^{\pi/2} \Gamma_\theta \theta d\theta \qquad (3)$$

Results for all test conditions at x'=0.925 are shown in Figure 11.

Equations were incorporated into SUBSIM and an extensive validation was carried out. Computed predictions were compared with full-scale trials results. Predictions of turning circle, yaw rate and speed loss in the turn were

consistently good.   Figure 12 shows plots of tactical diameter for three
submarines and as shown for a variety of speeds and rudder angles the
SUBSIM predictions of tactical diameter are very good. However, prediction
of depth change in the turn is poor. This problem has led to further
experimental work to examine the flow over an appended body.

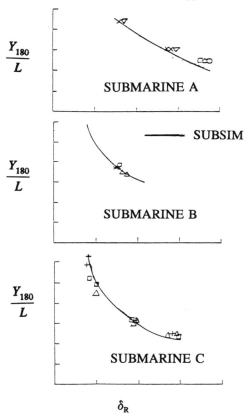

Figure 12 : Computer prediction of tactical diameter

VORTICITY AND PRESSURE ON AN APPENDED BODY OF REVOLUTION

A one metre appended body of revolution was used in the Circulating Water
Channel. This is the subject of Ward, Wilson[11]. Vorticity and pressure were
measured under various static conditions. It was concluded that the appendage,
which is representative of a submarine bridge fin, creates an asymmetry in the
flow which leads to an asymmetry in pressure distribution as shown in Figure
13.

UNAPPENDED   APPENDED

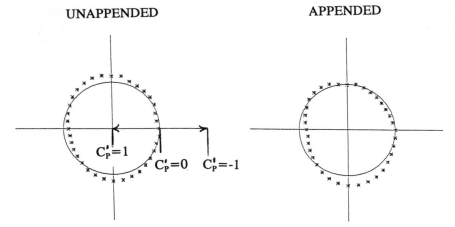

Figure 13 : Pressure coefficients, x'=0.4, α=17.5 degrees

CONCLUSIONS

A description has been given in this paper of various experiments conducted at DRA Haslar to support a programme of research into the prediction of submarine manoeuvres. The experiments conducted were to examine hydrodynamic effects such as dynamic effects on oscillating hydroplanes and the shedding of vortices from the hull of a submerged body. Empirical data was collected in order to obtain estimates of forces and moments on a hull, lift on hydroplanes and positions and strengths of vortices.

ACKNOWLEDGEMENTS

This work has been carried out with the support of the Procurement Executive of the Ministry of Defence.

REFERENCES

1. Lloyd A R J M. Progress Towards a Rational Method of Predicting Submarine Manoeuvres. RINA Symposium on Naval Submarines. 1983.
2. Lloyd A R J M. Developments in the Prediction of Submarine Manoeuvres. Undersea Defence Technology. 1988.
3. Munk M M. The Aerodynamic Forces on Airship Hulls. NACA Report 184. 1924.
4. Von Karman T. Calculation of Pressure Distribution on Airship Hulls. NACA TM No 574. 1930.
5. Mendenhall M R, Spangler S B, Perkins S C. Vortex Shedding From Circular and Non-circular Bodies at High Angles of Attack. AIAA Paper 79-0026. 1979.

6. Tinker S J. A Discrete Vortex Model of Separated Flow Over Manoeuvring Submersibles. Advances in Underwater Technology, Ocean Science and Offshore Engineering. Volume 15: Technology Common to Aero and Marine Engineering. 1988.

7. Glauert H. The Elements of Airfoil and Airscrew Theory. Cambridge University Press. 1947.

8. Lloyd A R J M, Campbell I F. Experiments to Investigate Vortices Shed from a Submarine-like Body of Revolution. 59th Meeting of the AGARD Fluid Dynamics Panel Symposium, Monterey, California, USA. Aerodynamic and Related Hydrodynamic Studies Using Water Facilities. AGARD-CCP 413. October 1986.

9. Lloyd A R J M. Experiments to Investigate the Vorticity Shed by a Body of Revolution in Curved Flow. Advances in Underwater Technology, Ocean Science and Offshore Engineering. Volume 15: Technology Common to Aero and Marine Engineering. 1988.

10. Freestone M M. Vorticity Measurement by a Pressure Probe. The Aeronautical Journal of the Royal Aeronautical Society. January 1988.

11. Ward B, Wilson P A. Experiments to Investigate Vortex Separation from an Appended Body of Revolution. MCMC Conference. University of Southampton. July 1992.

Notation

A	Maximum cross-sectional area of hull	m^2
c	Chord length	m
C_L	Lift coefficient	
C_P	Prismatic coefficient of hull :	

$$\frac{V}{AL}$$

C'_P	Pressure coefficient :	

$$\frac{P}{\frac{1}{2}\rho U^2}$$

D	Diameter of body of revolution	m
L	Length of hull	m
M	Total pitch moment : positive bow up	kNm
M'		

$$M'=\frac{M}{\frac{1}{2}\rho U^2 L^3}$$

M'_w	Non-dimensional linear pitch moment/ heave velocity co-efficient for hull	
$M'_{w\lvert w\rvert}$	Non-dimensional second order pitch moment/ heave velocity coefficient for hull	
P	Pressure	Nm^{-2}
r	Radius from body axis to position of probe	m
r'	Non-dimensional rate of turn or turn parameter ; L/S	
$r_{\bullet}$	Core radius of vortex	m
R_e	Reynolds number :	

$$\frac{UD}{\upsilon}$$

S	Arm radius ; radius of turn	m
U	Flow velocity	m/sec
V	Volume of hull	m^3
w	Velocity in z direction	m/sec
x	Longitudinal distance from nose of body ; positive aft	m
x'	Non-dimensional distance from nose to body ; x/L	
Y_{180}	Tactical diameter of submarine turning circle	m
z	Vertical scale	m
Z	Total force in z direction : positive down	kN
Z'		

$$Z'=\frac{Z}{\frac{1}{2}\rho U^2 L^2}$$

Z'_w	Non-dimensional linear heave force/ heave velocity coefficient for hull	
$Z'_{w\lvert w\rvert}$	Non-dimensional second order heave force/ heave velocity coefficient for hull	
Γ	Circulation	m^2/sec
Γ_θ	Circulation density at a given angle	m^2/sec/rad
α	Angle of Incidence	deg
δ	Freestone probe 'radius'	m
δ_R	Angle of deflection of rudder	deg
ζ	Vorticity	rad/sec
ρ	Density of fresh water	1.0 tonnes/m^3
θ	Angle of strut	deg or rad
υ	Kinematic viscocity of fresh water	1.14×10^{-5} m^2/sec
ω	Frequency	rad/sec

The Effects of Tip Flexibility on the Performance of a Blade-Type Windsurfer Fin

T.W. Chiu (*), T. van den Bersselaar (**),
C.A.M. Broers (*), D.J. Buckingham (*),
M.M.A. Pourzanjani (***)
(*) School of Engineering, University of Exeter, UK
(**) Technische Universiteit Eindhoven, Holland
(***) Southampton Institute, Southampton, UK

1   Abstract

A new Blade-Type sailboard fin has shown promising performance at sea. This paper reports an investigation into the effects of tip flexibility on its hydrodynamic properties. Five fins of different lengths of carbon fibre reinforcement were tested in a closed-circuit wind tunnel. The complexity of the relationship between tip flexibility, bending and twisting of the fin and the Lift-Drag performance was revealed.

2   Notations

α	angle of attack
AR	aspect ratio$=b^2/S$
b	span (fin)
c	chord length (fin)
C_d	drag coefficient$=D/(\frac{1}{2}\rho U^2 S)$
C_l	lift coefficient$=L/(\frac{1}{2}\rho U^2 S)$
D	drag force
L	lift force
Re_c	Reynolds number$=Uc/\nu$
S	planform area (fin)
t	thickness (fin)
U	freestream velocity

3   Introduction

The influence of the fin on the performance and manoeuvring of a surfing or sailboard is well recognised. Recent development of high performance surfer fins is highly diversified. In an earlier research project [1], the hydrodynamic performance of four different wind-surfer fin designs have been investigated. Each design gives high performance under conditions of operation. The ambition of world-class windsurfers to continue to create speed records accelerates the research on fins. Recently a completely new design of fin has been created. This so-called blade-type fin, which resembles the fin of a humpback whale, has been adopted by some well-known wind-surfers and is now considered as one of the best fins ever designed, especially good for high speed windsurfing. It is also widely suggested by windsurfers that a slightly flexible tip gives an even higher performance.

In the manufacturing process, carbon fibre strips could be added to form a layer in the fin-material. This reinforces the fin to form a very strong body which bends or twists much less in normal conditions.

In the present experiment conducted in a closed-circuit wind tunnel, carbon fibre reinforcement was made to extend to full span, $\frac{2}{3}$ span, $\frac{1}{2}$ span and $\frac{1}{3}$ span respectively in four geometrically identical blade-type fins. A fifth fin without reinforcement was also investigated. These fins would thus bend and twist differently under the same flow condition.

4   The Fins

The blade-type fin has a planform that ressembles the fin of a humpback whale. It is characterized by its large aspect ratio ($=4.93$) and its practically straight, but backward swept, lift line. The geometry and dimensions of the standard SAVAGE blade-type fin is shown in fig. 1.

Some advantages of this design are rather obvious. A planing surfing board often bounces on the sea surface, which means that the upper part of the fin rises above the sea surface frequently. Under such a condition, only the lower part of the fin is providing the hydrodynamic force required to counteract the side force caused by the wind on the sail. And very often, the entire fin is out of water, providing no hydrodynamic force at all. With the comparatively longer span of the blade type fin, it would be less probable for the entire fin to be lifted above the sea surface. Therefore the surfing board would more often be in control.

Less obvious is the criterion for the amount of rake (sweep angle relative to the vertical) used. Angle of 10° rake was used, this reduces to 5° during operation as the sailboard travels at a pitch angle of approximately 5° to the horizontal. The rake angle was chosen as a result of water tunnel experiments performed in a previous project [1] to reduce sudden aeration problems. The backward swept planform can also reduce the induced drag quite considerably ([2] and[3]). A smaller chord length also mean that stall due to aeration is less likely to occur.

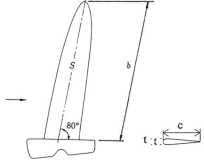

b	span of the fin	0.31	[m]
S	average planform area	0.0195	[m²]
c	chord length at the root	0.080	[m]
AR =b² /S	aspect ratio	4.93	[-]

Fig. 1 Geometry and dimensions of the standard SAV-AGE blade-type fin.

This type of fin is made of fibreglass. In the early design stage, it was thought that the fin would be too flexible because of the large aspect ratio and the smaller thickness ($0.09c$, c.f. $0.11 - 0.12c$ for most other fins). In addition, the bending stress along the fin would be too large and could fracture the fin in extreme conditions. So carbon fibre was added such that the material became a sandwich of 5 layers of materials (fig. 2). The mechanical properties of this composite material is tested by means of a standard four point bending test. Fig. 3 shows a comparison of bending properties between the carbon fibre reinforced fibreglass and the plane fibreglass material. Both materials remain almost linearly elastic up to the fracture point. Fracture was caused by the delamination of the material. The carbon fibre reinforcement improved the fracture strength of fibreglass by 30%, and reduced the flexibility considerably.

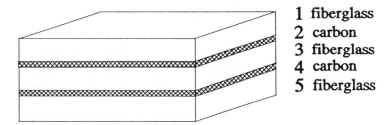

1 fiberglass
2 carbon
3 fiberglass
4 carbon
5 fiberglass

Fig. 2 Layers of the fin materials.

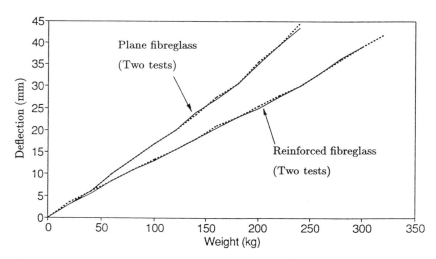

Fig. 3 A comparison of bending properties between the carbon fibre reinforced fibreglass and the plane fibreglass material.

Some questions then arose: How far should the carbon fibre reinforcement extend towards the tip? Test results from experienced windsurfers suggested that an unreinforced tip region seemed to enhance the overall performance. (From the commercial point of view, since the carbon fibre is an expensive material, it would be preferrable if the reinforcement does not *have* to extend to full span.) Flexibility of the fin can have two effects: bending and twisting. Bending tends to reduce the effective angle of attack close to the tip, thus stabilising the local boundary layer at large angle of attack. In the contrary, twisting tends to increase the angle of attack close to the tip, hence destabilising the local boundary layer. At small angle of attack, the situation is reversed: bending tends to reduce the lift force and is thus undesirable, while twisting is favourable because it increases the lift force. The interrelationship between flexibility (or rigidity), bending and twisting under various loading conditions is extremely complex.

In the present work, we would like to determine the optimum amount of reinforcement required. Five geometrically identical blade-type fins were made, with carbon-fibre reinforcement extending from the root to full span, $\frac{2}{3}$ span, $\frac{1}{2}$ span and $\frac{1}{3}$ span, and the fifth one without reinforcement. Fig. 4 shows how the fins were made from the material.

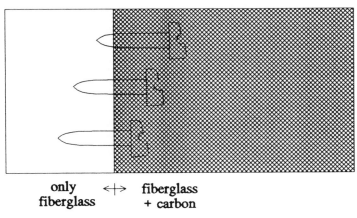

only fiberglass   <+>   fiberglass + carbon

Fig. 4 Manufacture of the fins from the material.

5   The Experiments

A series of wind-tunnel Lift-Drag measurements has been performed on the fins. The fin is mounted in the closed-circuit wind tunnel as shown in fig. 5. The entire fin and mounting block assembly was held by a strain gauge balance (fig. 6). The force experienced by the fin would hence be transformed into electronic signals which are then automatically recorded and analysed by an IBMPC.

A speed of 50 ms^{-1} was used, which corresponds to a Reynolds Number (based on the root chord length) of $Re_c = 2.7 \times 10^5$, or an equivalent speed of 3.47 ms^{-1} (or 6.8 knots approx., c.f. 20-40 knots in actual sailing condition). A test of the effect of Reynolds Number was carried out for the Full-Span reinforced fin at an angle of attack of 5°, which is most typical in actual sailing conditions. If the Reynolds Number is too low, a laminar boundary layer is expected, which separates from the suction side even at very small angle of attack. This is termed the subcritical regime. When the Reynolds Number is high enough, the boundary layer on the fin surface becomes turbulent, which is much more *reluctant* to separate. This is termed the supercritical regime.

above

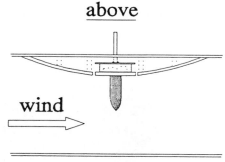

front

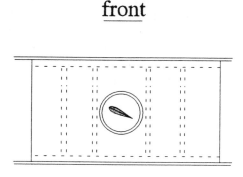

Fig. 5 The wind tunnel set up.

above

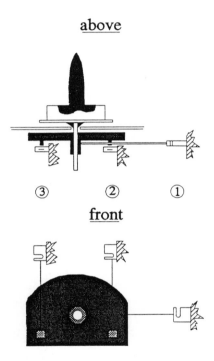

③   ②   ①

front

Fig. 6 Mounting of the fin on the strain gauge balance.

The results of the test (fig. 7) showed that boundary layer transition occurs within the velocity range between 30 ms^{-1} and 40 ms^{-1}. Within this range the drag coefficient fell as the velocity was increased. In the supercritical flow regime above 40 ms^{-1}, the drag coefficient was more or less constant.

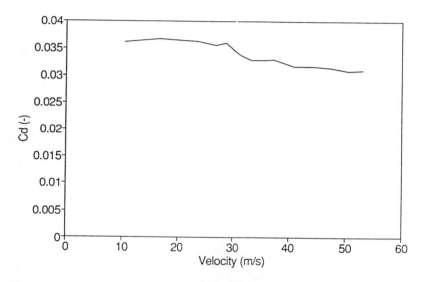

Fig. 7 The effect of Flow Velocity on the Drag Coefficient,
   C_d, **at** $\alpha = 5°$.

Since the supercritical regime is achieved in the chosen Reynolds Number (corresponding to 50 ms^{-1}), it is therefore expected that the force coefficients would be rather insensitive to the Reynolds Number, at least up to an angle of attack of 5°.

6   Results

The results are presented here graphically and the relationship between different quantities are shown:

Fig. 8: C_l against α (angle of attack)

Fig. 9: C_d against α

Fig. 10: Lift/Drag ratio against α

Fig. 11: C_d against C_l (unreinforced)

Fig. 12: C_d against C_l ($\frac{1}{3}$ span reinforced)

Fig. 13: C_d against C_l ($\frac{1}{2}$ span reinforced)

Fig. 14: C_d against C_l ($\frac{2}{3}$ span reinforced)

Fig. 15: C_d against C_l (full span reinforced)

Fig.8 shows that the C_l of all the fins increases with α. All the fins give almost identical Lift characteristics, even at large α above 9°, when the fin has probably stalled. The Drag characteristics (fig.9) of the five fins, however, are quite different. The full span reinforced fin gives the lowest drag when $\alpha > 3°$. At $\alpha < 3°$, the $\frac{1}{3}$ span reinforced one seems to prevail slightly. The drag coefficient of all the fins increases rapidly as α is increased above 7° due to the growth of the leading edge separation bubble which eventually becomes a stall at $\alpha > 9°$.

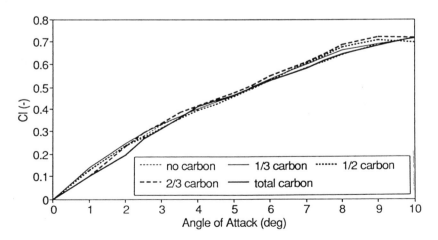

Fig. 8 C_l against α for the five fins, $Re_c = 2.7 \times 10^5$.

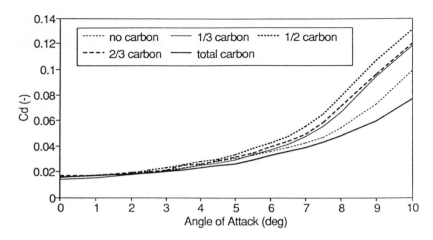

Fig. 9 C_d **against** α **for the five fins,** $Re_c = 2.7 \times 10^5$.

A more important property, the Lift/Drag ratio is shown in fig.10. All the fins possess a peak at $4° < \alpha < 5°$. On the whole, at $\alpha > 4°$, the full span reinforced fin gives the most favourable performances. Below this angle, the $\frac{1}{3}$ span reinforced fin performs substantially better.

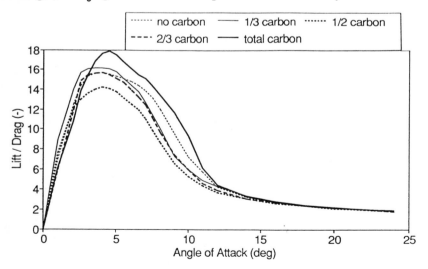

Fig. 10 **Lift/Drag ratio against** α **for the five fins,** $Re_c = 2.7 \times 10^5$.

Stall occurs approximately when the Lift coefficient decreases while the Drag coefficient increases. This is revealed in fig.11-15 . All the fins stall at a C_l of 0.72 (approx.) which corresponds to $9° < \alpha < 10°$.

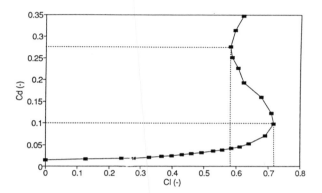

Fig. 11 C_d **against** C_l **for the unreinforced fin,** $Re_c = 2.7 \times 10^5$.

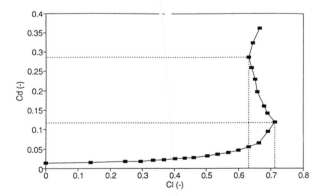

Fig. 12 C_d **against** C_l **for the** $\frac{1}{3}$ **span reinforced fin,** $Re_c = 2.7 \times 10^5$.

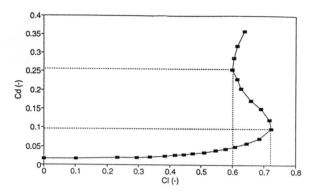

Fig. 13 C_d against C_l for the $\frac{1}{2}$ span reinforced fin, $Re_c = 2.7 \times 10^5$.

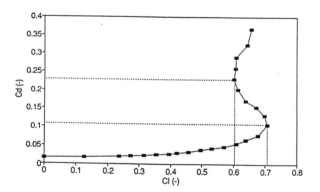

Fig. 14 C_d against C_l for the $\frac{2}{3}$ span reinforced fin, $Re_c = 2.7 \times 10^5$.

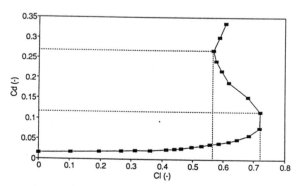

Fig. 15 C_d against C_l for the full span reinforced fin, $Re_c = 2.7 \times 10^5$.

7   Conclusion

It can be perceived from these results that the complex relationship between tip flexibility, bending, twisting and the Lift/Drag performance has resulted in an unobvious conclusion that the full span reinforced fin performs the best when the angle of attack is above 4°, while the $\frac{1}{3}$ span reinforced fin is the most desirable one below 4°, which is typical in high speed windsurfing.

The experiments were carried in air and, of course, did not consider the effects of free surface. So phenomena such as aeration and cavitation are not taken into the scene. More work is being undertaken in the investigation of the blade-type fins, including the measurement of the bending and twisting due to aerodynamic forces by means of photogrammetry, flow visualisation and wake traverse. Attempts are now being made to perform the experiments in water and take due account of the effects of the free surface.

8   References

1. Broers, C.A.M, Chiu, T.W., Buckingham, D.J. and Pourzanjani, M. M.A., "Effects of fin geometry and surface finish on sailboard performance and manoeuvrability", *Presented in the MCMC, the Second International Conference on Manoeuvring and Control of Marine Craft, 14-17 July, 1992.*

2. van Dam, C.P., "Induced-drag characteristics of crescent-moon-shaped wings", *Journal of Aircraft, vol 24, Feb 1987, pp.115-119.*

3. Burkett, C.W., "Reduction in induced drag by the use of aft swept wing tips", *Aeronautical Journal, vol 93, Dec 1989, pp.400-405.*

Acknowledgement

This work is part of a project sponsored by the Marine Technology Directorate Ltd (SERC), to whom the authors would like to express their gratitude.

Effects of Fin Geometry and Surface Finish on Sailboard Performance and Manoeuvrability

C.A.M. Broers (*), T.W. Chiu (*),
M.M.A. Pourzanjani (**), D.J. Buckingham (*)
(*) School of Engineering, University of Exeter, Exeter EX4 4QF, UK
(**) Southampton Institute of Higher Education, Warsash Campus, Warsash, Southampton SO3 9ZL, UK

ABSTRACT

The effect of planforms and surface finishes of fins on the performance and manoeuverability of a sailboard has been investigated. Four different fins and three surface finishes were included in the experiments. Most existing fin design is from practical experience and development "on the water"; tests of these types can be very subjective. The present work uncovers some of the Fluid Dynamics involved in the design of fins.

INTRODUCTION

In general the importance of the performance of fins has been realised by board manufacturers. However, there still is a large amount of mystique as to how they function. In the past a fin was only thought of by most as an appendage to provide directional and rotational stability, now almost any fin can meet this criterion. The lift from a sailboard fin results in a horizontal force perpendicular to the foward direction of the board. Lift from the fin is especially important when dealing with Short Boards (or Boards without centreboards) because it is the main component in coverting side force from the sail into forward motion.

All fins tested are supplied by Savage Surf Systems. Two Slalom racing fins were especially made for the experiments: the World Cup (A) and Competition (B) Slaloms. The length, chord, camber, and surface area are exactly the same but the planforms are reversed. To give a broader spectrum to the experiments two other quite different planforms were tested; the Predator (C), which is for waves and difficult conditions, and the Banana Slalom (D), which is a wave/slalom fin.

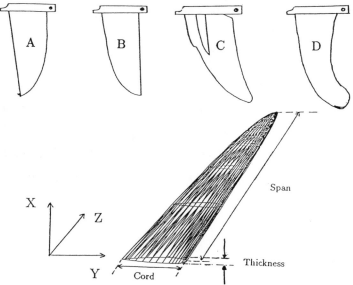

Figure 1. Fin Dimensions & Profiles

All the fins are constructed from glass fibre and no attempt has been made to investigate the use of different materials.

TABLE 1: Fin Dimensions

	Fin			
	W.C. Sl.	Comp. Sl.	Ban. Sl.	Predator
Plan	Straight L.E.	Curved L.E.	Banana	Slotted Crescent
Max. Cord/mm	118	118	138	158
Area/M^2	0.0263	0.0263	0.0245	0.264
Span/mm	290	290	290	245
Thickness/mm	12.0	12.0	15.0	10.0
Aspect Ratio	0.032	0.032	0.0343	0.0227

A wind tunnel was used to take all lift and drag measurements and a Water Tunnel for flow visualisation. The results from the water tunnel are purely photographic and used to investigate phenomena such as aeration (air induced separation as a result of air being drawn in from the surface or air already present in the free stream,) and stall. Lift/Drag calculations and flow visualisation were done for all the fins with three different surface finishes, gloss, sanded and a revolutionary new surface finish Ribcoat (TM British Maritime Technology, Orlando House, Middlesex, England). It is claimed that Ribcoat undermines three–dimensional vortex stretching close to the surface and hence reduces the turbulent skin friction [8]. It is important to note that these are not rough surfaces, as tried in the past, hence the benefits are not limited to a given Renolds Number range. The rough surfaces that have been tried seem to induce a fully turbulent boundary layer sooner, but ultimately the increased surface area increases drag.

EXPERIMENTS

Water Tunnel Experiments

A closed circuit water tunnel with a free surface in the working section was used. Flow speeds up to 6 m/s (22 kph, 13 mph) are attainable in the tunnel, but in the actual experiments, flow speeds of around 3 m/s were used. This may seem an unrealistic speed for sailboards, but the Reynolds number is sufficiently high (i.e. $R_e \approx 400,000 \rightarrow 700,000$) to simulate normal operating conditions. However, the flow speed is not high enough for any unusual phenomena such as cavitation to be observed (the speed at which cavitation occurs, according to windsurfers, seems to rise with each consecutive speed record). Flow speeds were limited by:

1) the maximum flow rate of the tunnel;

2) as the flow speed of the tunnel increased so did the amount of air drawn from the surface into the water, resulting in a flow over saturated with air bubbles;

3) forces from the fin exceeding the support strength of the experimental rig;

4) tank over–flow.

It was found that running the tunnel at higher speeds made no real difference except to block out flow visualisation in the photographs.

The experimental apparatus is designed to imitate the underside of a board and can be set up so that it moves up and down in the flow, imitating the movement of a board through waves. This set up proved to be very satisfactory and allowed phenomena such as aeration to be observed. When the rig was allowed to move freely aeration was more likely to occur, with air being drawn in from the rear surface.

Aeration, or "Spin–out", is a real problem when windsurfing. This is when air is drawn into the flow around the fin destroying the pressure gradient and hence the lift. A momentary loss in lift or total flow separation at the leading edge will result. In practice the sailor either instantly corrects or loses control (the board and sailor will travel at high speed at very large yaw angles). Experienced sailors can recover from this situation, but in a race it can mean the difference between coming first or last.

Aeration seems to be more likely to occur when something triggers it. Because the water tunnel has a free surface the flow has a pressure wave at this section. At slow flow speeds the trough of the wave coincides with the placement of the fin in the water tunnel. Thus, the water flow does not fully immerse the fin until the flow speed is sufficient to have a wave length longer than the free surface. At slow speeds there is a hydraulic jump along the fin (at high a angles attack, e.g. above 9°, the jump is up to 2cm). As the flow speed is increased the free surface rises but the gap from the jump provides a passage for air to be drawn in from behind the hull configuration. This is similar to travelling over a rough sea when at times only part of the fin is immersed in the water. If the board and fin return to the surface at a high angle of attack air is given an entry path ("Spin–out"). Similarly, if air is present in the free stream flow aeration can be triggered at the leading edge. Therefore, a fin will perform better if the board design minimises the injection of air into the flow.

Planform and surface finish play a very strong role in how aeration manifests itself.

Planforms– The Predator was by far the best fin in terms of the suppresion of aeration. Any air–induced separation occured at the leading edge of the hydrofoil in front of the slot and was discharged down the tip by the flow through the slot. The step (refer to photo 1) on the leading edge of the first aerofiol was intended to act as a vortex fence; it is not believed to provide the desired effect. A fairly uniform velocity gradient along the leading edge of the competition slalom led to the stall cell or aeration spreading from the base to the tip of the fin instantly. Catastrophic loss of lift results, leaving the user little chance to recover. On the other hand, the Competition Slalom does not stall at the tip. This is believed to be a result of the tip vortex acting as a vortex fence, the strong downwash induced close to te tip vortex prevents separation even at high angle of attack. The Banana Slalom stalls earliest and has some undesirable trates such as the tip stall appearing at about 12°.

Surface Finish– By far the most significant difference in fin performance in the tunnel was the effect of surface finishes. On fins with the gloss finish, any aeration or stall led to total separation at the leading edge with air pocket forming between the fin surface and the water. Total loss of lift results. Recent experiments show that riblets can reduce the skin friction drag as well as the turbulence intensity in the wake [4]. The fins with sanded and Ribcoat finish rarely had separation, air pockets are broken down into small "bubbles" and discharged into the wake (refer to photo 2) and durring stall the flow over the fin remains attached but turbulent; therefore, the finishes also reduce the the likelyhood of separation. In Windsurfer's terms this equals either total loss of control (gloss finish) or a momentary reduction in lift. This was especially prominent with the more critical Competition and World Cup Slalom fins.

Wake– A photographic and video record of the wake profiles have been made. They will help in understanding fin hydrodynamics and provide a base for determining the boundary conditions for the Panel Method programs. Air in the free stream flow accentuates the tip vortex and streamlines (refer to photo 2). The size and strength of the tip vortex is directly related to the magnitude of the form drag. The World Cup Slalom fin had the smallest and most concentrated tip vortex, while the predator has a turbulent wake. Details of the wake profiles are investigated in the wind tunnel tests.

Surface finish has a noticeable effect on the wake profiles. The Sanded and and Ribcoat finish have the effect of breaking up pockets of air. This is particularly apparent when the fin stalls; the gloss finish discharges large pockets of air into the flow, the two other finishes give off strong swirling three–dimensional vortices exemplified by the tiny air bubbles moving in the flow. The swirling of the tip vortex is much more prominant with the sanded and ribcoat finishes.

Stall

TABLE 2: Fin Stall Angle in Water Tunnel

	Stall Angle		
Fin	Gloss	Sanded	Riblets
Comp. Sl.	17°	16°	17°
W.C. Sl.	15°	16°	17°
Ban. Sl.	12.5°	14°	–
Predator	15 ∼ 20°	15 ∼ 20°	–

The stall angles are approximate for the water tunnel experiments because air in the flow made accurate measurement difficult. The Banana Slalom stalls the earliest and the Predator the last. Two results have been placed in the Predator boxes, the first angle represents when the front foil stalls and the second when the whole fin stalls. Surface finish does not seem to have a large effect on the stall angles of the fins but the results from this table can be misleading. Stall occured catastrophically with the gloss finish, total separation at the leading edge draws air from the free surface. With the sanded and ribcoated finishes any air introduced at the leading edge is dispersed and the flow remains attached but turbulent.

Wind Tunnel Results

A low turbulence (0.01%) closed circuit wind tunnel was used to obtain lift, drag and wake analysis of the fins. The tunnel was run at a flow speed of 40 m/s giving a Reynolds number of $R_e \approx 400,000$ for the fins tested, a boundary layer transition test was performed and proved satisfactory. To obtain the pressure distribution in the wake, a comb of pitot tubes (24 tubes) was traversed horizontally behind the fin and measurements made via manometers. Lift and Drag measurements were done with a spring force balance.

Lift and drag results were found for the Competition and World Cup Slalom fins for three surface finishes and two finishes for the Predator and Banana Slalom. Readings fluctuated intensively on the spring dials, maximum care was taken to obtain the average values.

Results obtained for the gloss and sanded finishes for the lift and drag distinctly show that the sanded finish performs better in the wind tunnel. In some cases the lift was higher and the drag lower and for all cases the Lift/Drag ratio was higher.

TABLE 3: Reduction in Lift/Drag

	Lift/Drag*	
Fin	Sanded	Ribcoat
Comp. Sl.	1.12%	3.27%
W.C. Sl.	1.56%	3.37%
Ban. Sl.	0.48%	–
Predator	2.72%	–

* Average percent improvement over gloss finish

The results from the Competition and World Cup Slalom fins are the most reliable, the first set of data from the Banana Slalom fin was found to be faulty and in reforming the gloss finish the camber and thickness were affected. Average improvements in the lift/drag ratios are very significant for the sanded and Ribcoated finishes respectively, but it should also be noted that the biggest improvement in this ratio comes at normal opperating angles of 3° to 7° (refer to graphs 1, 2 & 3). The Predator gives a relatively low lift/drag ratio when compared to the other fins because; separation occurs on the first hydrofoil in front of the slot, a high surface area/span ratio, and increased form drag due to the contours of the planform. The only two planforms that can be compared directly are the Competition and World Cup Slalom fins.

<u>Stall</u> The stall angle of the fins was recorded and oil flow experiments were performed to further examine flow phenomena. Stall cells, flow separation, wall effects, vortices and others can be seen with oil flow experiments, the following observations were made (refer to photos 3, 4, 5 & 6):

1– flow separation occured at the front foil of the Predator fin;

2– a concentrated stall cell appears just above the tip of the World Cup Slalom;

3– no obvious stall cells were found at the tips of the Banana and Competition Slalom but the flow was slightly turbulent in these regions;

4– a large amount of tip downwash was observed on the Predator fin.

The concentrated stall cell that appears just above the tip of the World Cup Slalom is believed to be due to a very concentrated tip vortex, the Competition and Banana Slalom both had less concentrated tip vortices.

TABLE 4: Fin Stall Angle in Wind Tunnel

Fin	Stall Angle		
	Gloss	Sanded	Ribcoat
Comp. Sl.	13°	14°	13°
W.C. Sl.	13°	13°	13°
Ban. Sl.	13°	13°	–
Predator	n/a*	n/a*	–

* Not Applicable as fin never fully stalled.

Surface finish apparently has little effect on the stall angle of the fins;

this is expected as only the rear surfaces of the aerofoils are sanded or ribcoated.

Wake– A great deal of information about the form drag of a fin can be found by traversing the wake with pitot tubes. However, this particular type of experiment can prove to be very time consuming so the wake profiles were only done for one surface finish. Mesh plots of the total pressure distribution in the wake for the fins with a gloss finish have been made (refer to plots 5, 6, 7 & 8). The plots represent the total pressure contours measured by a comb of 24 horizontal pitot tubes traversed in the wake of a fin (refer to plot 4). To record the free stream pressure the comb is placed in the centre of the wind tunnel, without a fin present, and run at 40 m/s. The plots represent the difference in total pressures when the free stream values are subtracted from measured pressures with the fin in place at 7° (the peaks represent low pressures). Theoretically, the foil with the most uniform wake profile will generate the least vortices in the wake and hence provide the least drag, the results from the wake traverses and drag experiments correlate with this theory.

Conclusions
When looked at qualitatively it appears that the fins with Ribcoat perform significantly better in the Wind tunnel tests than the sanded and gloss finishes. Similarly, the sanded fin perform better than the gloss. All the fins tested have a much better lift to drag ratio with Ribcoat and appear to have much better resistance to aeration. In recent times planforms have moved towards eliptical shapes but the characteristics of the fins tested, such as those highlighted in the wake traverses, help provide insight into the Fluid Dynamics involved. The World Cup Slalom fin is more efficient at low yaw angles but at higher angles the Competion Slalom performs equally well and does not have the poor aeration problems of the former. The predator has a very high stall angle and good aeration characteristics. The Banana Slalom appears to perform well at low angles, under 4°, but has a poor performance in the water tunnel. This is backed up by the feedback from "on the water" testing by windsurfers.

ACKNOWLEDGEMENTS

We would like to thank:
  – SERC for having the foresight to fund the project;
  – Prof. M. Gaster and Dr. L.C. Squire for their valuable advice relating to the experiments performed;
  – British Maritime Technology for "Ribcoating" the fins and Jimmy Mozaffar and Dr Gadd for their help;
  – and Alan Davey owner of Savage Surf Systems for making the fins and sharing his knowledge of the fluid dynamics of sailboards.

References

[1] ABBOT, I.H., VON DOENHOFF, A.E., *The Theory of Wing Sections including a Summary of Aerofoil Data*, Dover, New York, 1959.

[2] ACOSTA, A.J., SABERSKY, R.H. & HAUPTMANN, E,G., *Fluid Flow, a First Course in Fluid Mechanics*, Second Edition, London, 1971.

[3] ANDERSON, J.D.,*Fundamental Aerodynamics*, McGraw Hill, Singapore, 1985.

[4] GRAM, J.M. & AHMED, A, *"Effect of Riblets on Turbulence in the Wake of an Aerofoil "*, AIAA Journal, Vol. 29, No. 11, Nov 1991.

[5] JIMENEZ, C.R., "On the Hydrodynamic Performance of Sailboards", The Society of Naval Architects & Maritime Engineers, Nothern California Section

[6] MARCHAJ, C.A., *Sailing Theory and Practice*, Dodd, Mead & Company, New York, 1982.

[7] SAVITSKY, D., *"Hydrodynamic Design of Planing Hulls"*, The Society of NavalArchitects and Maritime Engineers.

[8] SQUIRE, L.C. & SAVILL, A.M., *"Drag measurement on planar riblet surfaces at high subsonic speeds"*, Applied Scientific Research **46**: 229–243, 1989.

GRAPH 1:

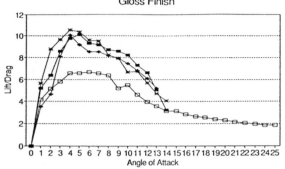

GRAPH 2:

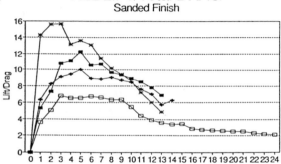

GRAPH 3:

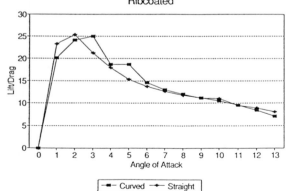

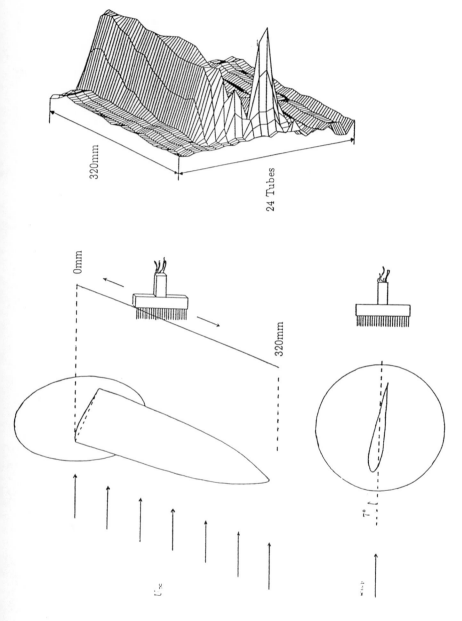

PLOT 4:   WAKE TRAVERSE METHOD

PLOT 5: COMPETITION SLALOM

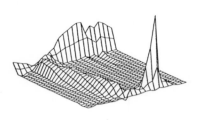

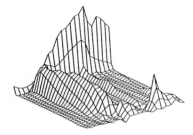

PLOT 6: WORLD CUP SLALOM

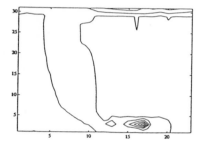

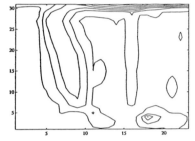

PLOT 7: BANANA SLALOM

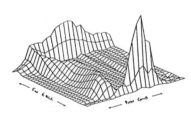

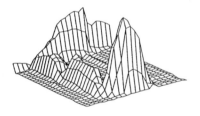

PLOT 8: PREDATOR

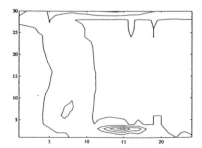

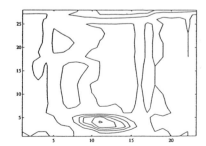

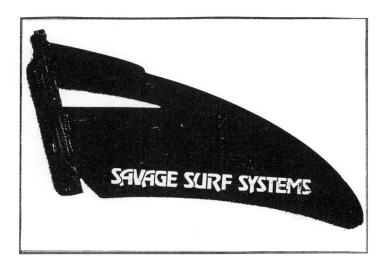

PHOTO 1: PREDATOR FIN.

PHOTO 2: WORLD CUP SLALOM IN WATER TUNNEL.

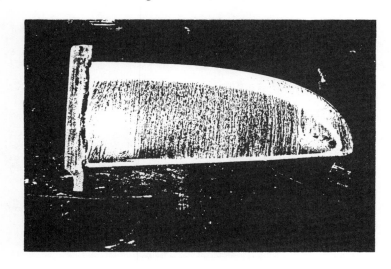

PHOTO 3: OIL FLOW; WORLD CUP.

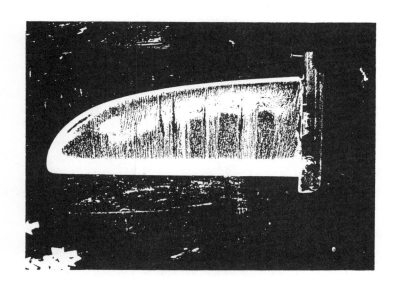

PHOTO 4: OIL FLOW; COMPETITION SLALOM.

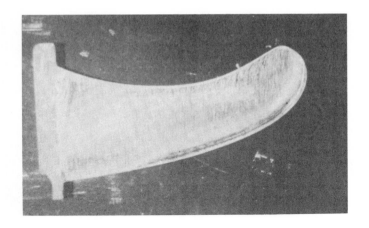

PHOTO 5: OIL FLOW; BANANA SLALOM.

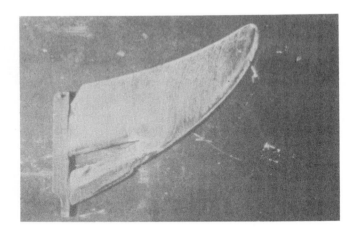

PHOTO 6: OIL FLOW; PREDATOR.

SECTION 5: ADVANCED TECHNIQUES

Failure Diagnostics for Underwater Vehicles: A Neural Network Approach

A.J. Healey, F. Bahrke, J. Navarrete

Department of Mechanical Engineering, Naval Postgraduate School, Monterey, California 93943, USA

ABSTRACT

This paper addresses the proposed use of Kalman filters and Artificial Neural Networks to provide the detection, and isolation of impending system failures. Such system health diagnosis is necessary to the overall success of mission controllers for AUVs. Two examples of network designs are given. The first addresses the identification of anomalous changes to the vehicle's acceleration behavior resulting from possible propulsion system changes, as in a loss of propulsion efficiency from fouling. The second example relates to the identification of excessive frictional loads in the propulsion drive train that may cause motor failure. In each case, the training method and the resulting decision surface characterization of the networks are given.

INTRODUCTION

In the last few years, interest has grown in the use of neural networks for pattern recognition, and more recently, for signal processing, system parameter identification, and automated diagnostics. Two classes of network have received attention; the multilayer static neural network which is a memoryless mapping of inputs to outputs, and the recurrent network which has associative memory of its present state. The static network has been successful in identification of patterns while the recurrent networks have been applied to optimization problems in which emergent dynamic behavior can be mapped. Recurrent networks can be single or multiple layered. The general idea is to provide a mapping of inputs to outputs with sufficient overparameterization of the connection weights. Once identified through training on a set of known conditions, the inherent characteristics of the mapping can be learned, and results for new sets of inputs can be obtained with consistency. While training may take a relatively long time, neural networks are expected to execute rapidly in real time. The learning of nonlinear mappings from known input output data can be very useful especially when recourse to laws of physics is unavailable.

It is believed that neural networks can provide real time solutions to fault diagnostics and error recovery with less effort than other methods. Automatic fault detection is needed for the identification of shifts or changes in the status of the vehicle's operating systems so that corrective action can be considered by the vehicle's mission control computer. In this way, catastrophic failures in the vehicle's ability to conduct its mission may be postponed, or even avoided altogether. As an example of the concept, if a propeller drive shaft developed too much shaft friction, then the added current load may overburden the drive motor. Identification of such a condition before the shaft bearing siezes would allow the mission control computer to assign a slower speed or assign a greater loading to a second shaft (if available), so that a catastrophic condition is averted.

Prior work in dynamic failure detection

Many existing failure diagnostic schemes reported in the literature are concerned about the use of signal processing to indicate a failure condition. Monitoring of sensor signals for change or drift into alarm bands has been routine. Surveys by Willsky, (1976), Walker, (1983), Himmelblau's book (1978), Pau's book, (1981), Isemann, (1984), Basseville, (1988), Gertler, (1986), cover applications to aircraft and nuclear plants and give many examples of the use of algorithms to detect changes in signals which can then trigger alarms. Many algorithms are based on the detection of sensor failures and use system state estimation from banks of Kalman filters which are individually tuned to specified sensor / output failures.

However, more than detection of a failure is required in AUVs because we are also interested in the failure's isolation, the assessment of its level of severity, and ultimately, the institution of an appropriate correction or workaround solution by the mission controller. DeBenito (1990) discusses the use of Kalman filter banks for state estimation, each tuned to a particular sensor failure scenario, followed by a probabilistic post-processor to determine the likelihood of the existence of any particular one of those sensors exhibiting a fault.

The type of failure addressed for AUVs in this paper, however, are not necessarily found using state estimation. Rather it is the variation of the system parameters that would indicate anomalous changes in the vehicle behavior that we wish to consider. We thus adopt an approach that looks at system parameters with a decision processor to isolate the particular mode of operation. Since much computation is needed to perform the post-processing in real time, we prefer to explore the use of Neural Networks that are tuned to recognize and ultimately make decisions based on changes in particular values of the vehicles system dynamic parameters. Neural Networks will execute rapidly in real time and can be supervisorily trained off-line to produce the required decision surface using system parameters as input to determine the system's operating mode. A neural decision maker is expected to enhance the reliability of the detection and isolation process.

One possible structure for an automated failure detection and isolation system is shown in Figure 1. It is proposed that vehicle dynamic maneuvering response health status is to be determined by the current values of the system's dynamic response parameters. Deviations from 'norms' are to be detected using a neural network decision maker the output of which is trained to isolate the failure. The selection of the form of the system parameters to drive the network inputs is key. Whether to have current and prior values of each sensor

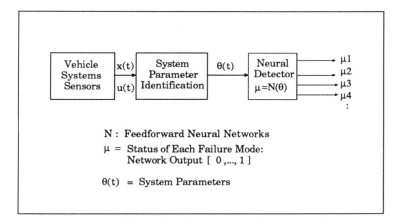

Figure 1. Structure for an Automated Failure Detection and Isolation System

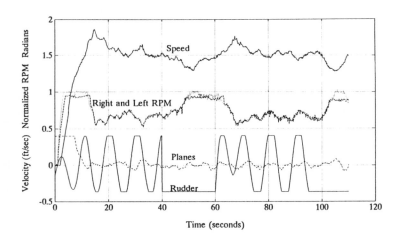

Figure 2. Experimental Results for the Acceleration to Speed and Speed Change during Turning for the NPS AUV II

output sent to the neural network, or whether to perform the parameter identification first and then to send parameter values to the network, is the issue. Problems with the first approach are dictated by the wide range of possible motion time histories that must be taken into account in the training of a neural diagnostic network. Since techniques for the identification of system parameters are well established in the literature, their computation using standard means would lead to a simpler system design. A more compact training set would follow with correspondingly increased chance of convergence and isolation capability.

Signals internal to the vehicle such as motor control voltage and motor current will vary with operating condition but may not change much during maneuvering operations. We choose to provide inputs to the network that vary slowly so that transient changes do not interfere with the failure detection process. At that point, the training of a standard backpropagation network on a set of parameter values and voltage / current combinations can provide the requisite mapping between input data combinations and selected failure conditions.

The two aspects of the problem are therefore the system identification of key parameters that would indicate vehicle operational health, and the supervised training of a neural network to identify if any degraded operational mode has occurred.

System Identification using Kalman filters:

Of the many methods in use for System Identification, the Kalman filter appears to be most suited for the purpose of fault detection. Essentially, the vehicle motion is related by an equation model to outputs from sensors of motion components through system dependent parameters. So long as the model is linear in parameters, the solution for those parameters may be obtained as a least squares fit by a rearrangement of the filter equations so that the evolution of their values over time may be tracked by the filter. An example of its use for identification of the first order propulsion dynamics parameters of an AUV, and in particular, the NPS AUV II vehicle, is the subject of a continuing investigation in this part of the work. The longitudinal response of the vehicle is governed by the balance of inertial forces, hydrodynamic drag forces, propulsion net drive forces, and other loadings arising from control surface activity and centrifugal acceleration forces induced under conditions of turning maneuvers. An equation of motion for straight line accelerations can be expressed by the following.

$$\dot{u}(t) = -\alpha u(t)|u(t)| + \beta n(t)|n(t)| \qquad (1)$$

where the α and β refer to the vehicle's acceleration bandwidth and the propulsion gain respectively. Increases in drag due to added loading are expected to increase α. A loss of a propeller blade would have the effect of a reduction in β.

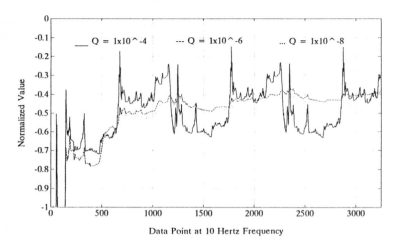

Figure 3. Identification of Normalized α(t); Three Filter Bandwidths Increasing **Q** Increases Filter Speed

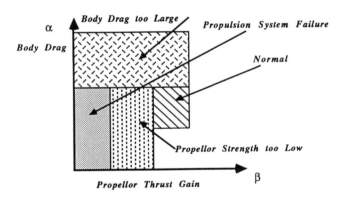

Figure 4. Failure Mode Regions Defined as Map[α, β].

Equation (1) is then reformulated as a single output equation for a system model that has essentially constant parameters, thus the discrete time recursive filter relations become,

$$\underline{\theta}\ (k)=[\alpha(k),\ \beta(k)]' \qquad \text{Parameter Vector}$$

$$\underline{\theta}\ (k+1) = \underline{\theta}\ (k) + Q\ (k) \qquad \text{Parameter Model}$$

$$y(k)=H(k)\underline{\theta}(k) + v\ (k) \qquad \text{Measurement Equation}$$

with

$$\underline{\theta}^-(k+1) = \underline{\theta}^+(k) \qquad \text{Parameter Update}$$

$$\underline{\theta}^+k+1 = \underline{\theta}^-(k+1) + L^+(k)*[y(k+1) - H(k+1) * \underline{\theta}^-(k+1)]$$
$$\text{Parameter Correction}$$

$Q(k)$ and $v(k)$ are white noise processes and the Kalman gain L is computed according to the Kalman algorithms [not given here but available in standard texts as in Gelb (1988)]. Experimental results for the acceleration response from maneuvering runs with the NPS AUV II vehicle are shown in Figures 2 and 3 for the conditions of the vehicle executing a general zig-zag maneuver with a hard port turn superimposed. Three filters are compared with successively faster response designs arising from the assumption of the levels of noise and variability of the parameters. Examining the figure, it is seen that the parameter variability depends on the filter design so that the choice of filter and the training of the neural detection system cannot be separated. It is recommended that the medium speed filter be used as it weights the natural variability exhibited by the chosen parameters with the need to give moderately stable quantities for use in the system failure diagnoser.

NEURAL NETWORK FAULT DETECTION

The neural network fault detector is based on accepting the results of the Kalman filter parameter estimates and detecting when anomalous conditions occur. This aspect of the system requires knowledge of the operational ranges of the actual parameters of the system and the development of a set of input - output data upon which the network can be trained. After training, it is of interest to examine how the network decisions are made in its fault isolation behavior. This is done by executing the network with a set of input data that covers the entire range of its operating map, defined on a fine grid of points. In this way, the change in the network outputs become clear as faults occur.

Operating ranges of the system parameters:

The key to developing an input training set for the failure detection network is to define the ranges of normal operating variability in these parameters. Based on a partial and incomplete study, the authors propose that a 10% variation in β would be 'normal' while a 50% reduction would correspond to the failure of one propellor in a twin propeller vehicle. However, a partial reduction in β would possibly indicate some degree of propeller fouling. Rather than building a set of rules to make the distinction between failures, the network approach

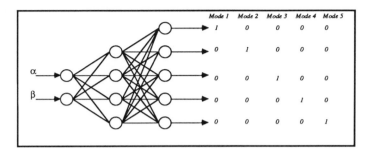

Figure 5. Two Input Five Output [2,4,5] Neural Network for Failure Isolation

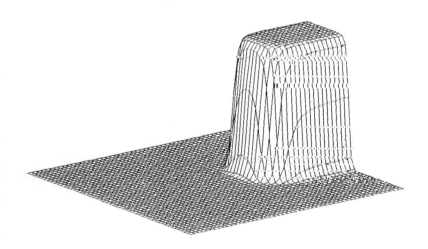

Figure 6. Normal Mode Decision Surface after Network Training is Complete

will allow the additional correlations with other variables such as motor torque and speed to be also taken into account with ease.

Design of the training set

To train the neural detection / isolation system we first define the following ranges of the operating parameters

$$\alpha_{min} < \alpha(t) < \alpha_{max}$$

$$\beta_{min} < \beta(t) < \beta_{max}$$

The decision region for normal / abnormal mapping is then illustrated in Figure 4. Training is then done by generating an input set of values of $\alpha(t)$ and $\beta(t)$ from uniformly distributed random numbers where each combination is assigned a failure mode status for the outputs , μ. Specification of the input training data is the most important part of the neural network design. The training of the network is done by backpropagation until weights are converged. Sometimes up to 200,000 repetitions of input data are required. We use a network that has an equal number of inputs as parameters, a hidden layer of at least twice the number of inputs, and an output layer with as many nodes as failure modes.

The two input networks shown in Figure 5, has been trained to provide the failure detection and isolation mapping given by the combination of α and β values noted in Figure 4. The network, once trained, may then be used in recall mode to exhibit a detection decision surface shown in Figure 6. In Figure 6, the value of the first output node of the network is mapped as a function of α and β using a fine grid of points over the region of interest, and, in this case, shows a solid identification of the normal operating condition as defined by the training set.

More extensive mappings involving larger sets of input parameters can be easily designed.

BUILDING A PROPULSION SYSTEM FAILURE DETECTOR

The approach taken here has resulted in the definition of a feedforward network to act as a diagnostic element for the condition of the propulsion motor based on the mapping of the motor current and speed, given 'normal' loading on the propulsion shaft. The idea is that excess friction will be diagnosed as an extraordinary high level of current for any particular speed; too small a current level for any particular speed will be diagnosed as a loss condition in the propeller; and the attendant reduction in the value of the propulsion gain factor, β, will signify a failure of the propulsion system that may be isolated to a particular motor shaft.

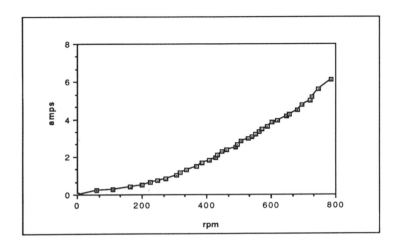

Figure 7. Current (amps) versus Propeller Speed (rpm); Normal In Water Loading.

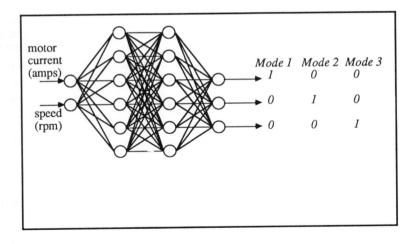

Figure 8. Propulsion Motor Shaft Seal Friction Failure Detection Network

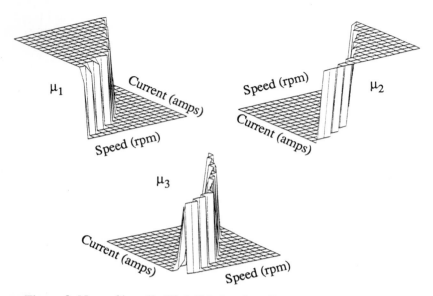

Figure 9. Normal(μ_3=1), High Friction (μ_1=1), and Low Load (μ_2=1)
Isolation Decision Surfaces

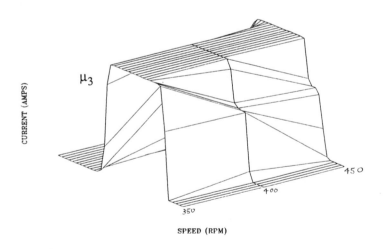

Figure 10. Normal Operation Mode Decision Surface. Trained on Fine Grid

The steady state relationship between current and speed and voltage and speed has been measured by Saunders (1989) and is shown here in Figure 7 The Neural Network shown in Figure 8 was trained on the points illustrated with the three possible failure modes as outputs:

$$\mu=[\ \mu_1\ \ \mu_2\ \ \mu_3\ ]$$

μ_1:   Too much shaft seal friction: [0 - 1];

μ_2:   Normal mode of operation: [0 - 1];

μ_3:   Propeller load too light (Propeller Loss): [0 - 1];

so that the three zones of operation have the following outputs

Failure mode 1	μ=[0 0 1];
Failure mode 2	μ=[0 1 0];
Failure mode 3	μ=[1 0 0]

The decision surface for the detection of which operating mode is prevalent at any time as a function of speed and motor current is shown in Figure 9. The zone around the nominal experimental curve relating the operating variables is of course adjustable. Figure 10 shows details of the normal operating mode decision surface as a slice taken at a fine level of discretization of current values at a particular speed range covering 350 to 450 rpm. The network was trained on a grid of points shown in Figure 11, for almost 2 million trainings using backpropagation on a SUN 4 SPARC station.

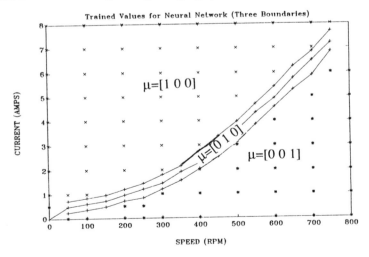

Figure 11. Training Points Used

CONCLUSION

In conclusion it is the authors opinion that a combined system structure having a Kalman filter system parameter identification scheme to provide input to an artificial neural network for the isolation of potential failures in AUV equipment will be useful for enhancing mission control operations. Further work needs to be done to define the ranges of variability expected in system parameters for normal as well as abnormal operational conditions.

ACKNOWLEDGEMENT

The author wishes to thank the Naval Surface Warfare Center, Coastal Systems Detachment for the financial support provided for the study.

REFERENCES

Abkowitz, M., "Measurement of Hydrodynamic Characteristics from Ship Maneuvering Trials by System Identification" *Transactions SNAME*, Vol. 88 1980, pp 283-318

Basseville, M., 1988, "Detecting Changes in Signals and Systems - A Survey", *Automatica*, Vol. 24, No. 3, pp 309-326

DeBenito, C.D., "On-Board Real Time Failure Detection and Diagnosis of Automotive Systems", *Trans. ASME Journal of Dynamic Systems, Measurement and Control*, Vol. 112, No. 4, Dec. 1990, pp 769-773

Gertler, J., 1986, "Failure Detection and Isolation in Complex Process Plants - A Survey" *IFAC Symposium on Microcomputer Applications in Process Control*, Istanbul, Turkey,

Gelb, A., Ed. (1988) "Applied Optimal Estimation" MIT Press, ISBN 0-262-57048-3, 10th Printing, 1988

Healey, A.J., Marco, D.B., (1992) "Experimental Verification of Mission Planning by Autonomous Mission Execution Using the NPS AUV II" Presented at the IEEE Symposium on Autonomous Underwater Vehicle Technology, AUV-92, June 2-3 1992, Washington, DC.

Himmelblau, D. M., 1978, *Fault Detection and Diagnostics in Chemical and Petrochemical Processes* Elsevier Scientific Publishing Company, New York

Hopfield, J.J., 1982 "Neural Networks and Physical Systems with Emergent Collective Computational Abilities" Proc. National Academy of Science, Vol. 79, pp 2554-2558

Hopfield, J. J., 1984 "Neurons with Graded Response Have Collective Computational Properties Like Those of Two State Neurons", Proc. National Academy of Science, Vol. 81, pp 3088-3092

Isermann, R., 1984, "Process Fault Detection based on Modeling and Estimation Methods", *Automatica*, Vol. 20, No. 4, pp 387-404

Ljung, L., Soderstrom, T., 1985*Theory and Practice of Recursive Identification* Cambridge, Mass. MIT Press

Pau, L.F., 1981, *Failure Diagnostics and Performance Monitoring*, Marcel Dekker Inc., New York

Shoureshi, R., Chu, R., 1989 "Neural Space Representation of Dynamical Systems" *Intelligent Control*, Publication of the ASME Winter Annual Meeting

Walker, B. K., 1983, "Recent Developments in Fault Diagnostics and Accommodation", *Proceedings of AIAA Conference on Guidance and Control*, Texas,

Willsky, A. S., 1976, "A Survey of Design Methods for Failure Detection in Dynamic Systems" *Automatica*, Vol. 12, pp 601-611

Applying Object-Oriented Programming Techniques to Ship Modelling

M.A. Baker

Southampton University Computing Services, Southampton University, Highfield, Southampton SO9 5NH, UK

Abstract

This paper describes the development of a large complex computer program using object-oriented programming (OOP) techniques. Specifically, it focuses on the design and implementation of a ship's mathematical model using $C++$.

In the first part of the paper object-orientation is examined. Here the basic principles of object-orientation; data abstraction, encapsulation and inheritance, are discussed. This is followed by a tour through the implementation of object-orientation with $C++$; an explanation of how these features are used is also given.

In the second part of the paper the design of an object-oriented ship model in $C++$ is described. The aim of this part of the paper is to guide the reader through the "top-down" design process and detail the implementation issues that arise.

The penultimate part of the paper is used to discuss the importance of object-orientation. This is followed by a commentary on how this particular methodology fits into the present view of future computing needs.

1. Introduction

The term "object-oriented" relates to a general philosophy and approach to software engineering which can be applied to many different fields. Object-orientation has recently received considerable attention in computing literature. The technique of object-oriented programming (OOP), which at present has no formal definition, is being used in an ever wider range of applications, ranging from programming languages and databases to system analysis and hardware architectures.

The underlying principle of the object-oriented approach is that a real world system may be described by and constructed from interacting objects. These objects relate to real entities as opposed to computer tasks, such as a scheduler or a matrix-multiplier. Object-orientation is not new; the first programming language that exploited object-orientation, SIMULA, made its debut in 1967.

The basic principles of object-orientation are data abstraction, encapsulation and inheritance. It is claimed by the proponents of OOP that these features will help alleviate the growing costs associated with software production and maintenance. Techniques for realising these features have resulted in a plethora of programming languages - Smalltalk, $C++$, Common Lisp Object System and Trellis being the most prevalent.

2. Object-orientation: An Overview

2.1 An Object - the Basic Ingredient
The structure of an object was originally defined in SIMULA and according to Kerr [1] has three elements:

> o An information structure which gives it substance and state.
> o Services or capabilities which enable it to perform tasks but only on requests.
> o Autonomous activity which permits a degree of self-determination.

The first two elements can be interpreted as an object having a set of "operations" and a "state" that remembers the effects of prior operations, Wegner [2]. The third element concerns an object becoming an autonomous process which can interact with other such processes. This quasi-parallel element is rarely implemented but has repercussions when the future of object-oriented languages is considered; this is discussed briefly in the conclusions.

2.2 The Major Features of Object-orientation
There are estimated to be over one hundred object-oriented languages. The number and scope of these languages makes the major features of object-orientation difficult to summarise succinctly. However, the following minimum features must be present for a language to be termed object-oriented.

2.2.1 Abstract Data Types   In order to be called object-oriented, a programming language must have linguistic constructs for implementing abstract data types. An abstract data type (ADT) is an entity whose characteristics and behaviour are being modelled in the system, for example, a message queue in a network application or an account in a banking application. An object can refer to either an ADT or a specific instance (occurrence) of an ADT.

2.2.2 Encapsulation and Data Hiding Encapsulation, or modularisation, binds the state data and functions into a named module, called a class or type, which may be treated as an object in its own right. The declared external interface of the modules describes the visible behaviour of the object. Modularity can be described as the encapsulation of some specific behaviour in a "black box". A user of the black box needs only know the behaviour rather than the internal working of the box. This black box approach is characterised by a precisely defined interface between independent components. Because the data structures and the implementation of the objects are encapsulated, they may be augmented or superseded without affecting the callers or users of the object, as long as the interface remains the same. This property enables systems to be defined as sets of interacting objects which can be extended and modified easily. Modularity also ensures reusability; the ability to reuse standardised modules gives a low development cost over the lifetime of the component.

Data, or information, hiding means that all of the state data private to an object is neither accessible nor visible outside its scope.

2.2.3 Inheritance   Most programming languages support a mechanism to provide inheritance, generally through the class or type construct. Inheritance allows a derived object to inherit the attributes of a base object.

2.3 Other Features of Object-orientated Languages
2.3.1 Polymorphism A method can be defined as some means of manipulating data, for example a function which returns the sum of two int's. It is possible within a typical library of objects for many different methods to have the same name, though they must be unique within a single class. The method may be designated by an operator, symbol or by a function name. In the case of an operator or symbol, the feature is called operator overloading; in the case of a named function, it is polymorphism.

Polymorphism enables abstraction away from explicit data types which can substantially reduce the number of function names that a programmer needs to learn and handle. It can also eliminate the need for conditional statements to manage similar operations on different data types.

Object-oriented languages have an associated embedded run-time system which maintains dynamic lists of objects and their properties. Examples of object properties are a system-generated unique identifier, a symbolic name and the class of an object. The class of an object is used to search for and branch to the appropriate routine called by a message. The search may be implemented statically by the compiler (early binding), dynamically by the run-time system (dynamic or late binding), or by a combination of both depending on the language.

2.3.2 Typing   Object-oriented languages can be either untyped or strongly typed. With strongly typed languages common programming errors such as the incorrect number of arguments, misspelled names and the misuse of pointers can be detected at compile time. A major sacrifice with strongly typed languages is the ability to prototype rapidly, since it is necessary to declare every program element before it is used. The major disadvantages of untyped languages is the more likely occurrence of run-time errors, for example calling a non-existent procedure. There are also greater overheads in procedure calls owing to dynamic address branching.

2.3.3 Run-Time Support   Most object-oriented run-time systems support object memory management in addition to dynamic binding. Memory management functions include allocation of storage for new objects, deallocation and compaction of space for deleted objects. The implementation of these features depends on the language.

2.4 Selection of a Programming Language

The syntax, semantics and functionality of an object-oriented language is very dependent on its ancestry. Some object-oriented languages began with a base language and are still backwards compatible with the parent, for example LISP, C, Pascal and Forth. Other object-oriented languages such as Eiffel, Trellis, Smalltalk and Actor have been specifically designed for object-oriented programming.

For this project the author has chosen *C++*. The main reasons for this choice are:

    o Familiarity with *C*.

    o The availability of public domain *C++* compilers and class libraries.

    o The growing acceptance of *C++* (an ANSI (X3J16) and ISO (WG21) standard are currently being discussed)

    o The greater likelihood of producing portable code in view of the emerging standards.

Table I An example of a $C++$ class

```
//
//   rudder
//
class rudder
{
private:
    int number;                              // int data
    float height;                            // float data
public:
    rudder();                                // def. constr
    rudder(int, float);                      // exp. constr
    ~rudder();                               // destructor
    int get_number() {return number;}        // access funct
    float get_height() {return height;}      // access funct
};
//
// Default constructor for rudder
//
rudder::rudder()
:   number(1), height(3.0)                   // defaults
{
}
//
// Explicit constructor for rudder
//
rudder::rudder(int iI, float fI)
: number(iI), height(fI)
{
}
//
// Destructor
//
rudder::~rudder()
{
   delete number;
   delete height;
}
```

o The presence of all the most desirable object-oriented features (see section 3).

3. A Tour Around $C++$

3.1 Introduction
$C++$ was developed by B. Stroustrup at the AT&T Bell Laboratories, Stroustrup [3,4]. It was strongly influenced by the development of the ANSI C standard and by the Simula67 language with which Stroustrup was very familiar. $C++$ is mostly compatible with C; it enhances some features of the base language as well as providing classes, operator and function overloading, better controlled scope of variables and functions and object constructors and

destructors. *C++* preserves the philosophy of *C*, which is to provide a very efficient, highly portable, untyped, intermediate-level language. Because of this, there is a very minimal run-time system, a standard low-level function library but no standard class library, no memory management system and no standard set of development tools. *C++* has been very well accepted by software developers who have traditionally used *C*; it has already progressed through several versions and is likely to be standardised.

Table II An example of using references

```
//
// function swap
//
void swap(int& i, int& j)
{
    int tmp = i;
          i = j;
          j = tmp;
}
//
// main
//
void main()
{
    int x, y;
    //...
    swap(x, y)
}
```

3.2 The Key Features of *C++*

3.2.1 A C++ Class In *C++* an object is usually used to mean an "instance" of a class. A class (see Table I) is a data type which consists of two things: a set of values and a set of operations which operate on these values. The values are generally referred to as class variables and the set of operations are performed by a set of member functions.

3.2.2 References and Pointers These are common in *C* and *C++*. An *&* is used in a declaration statement to signify a reference variable. It is not a true variable but an alias for another and is used mainly for passing parameters to functions. For example, instead of copying a complete data structure into a function, a reference to the data structure can be passed thus reducing the number of internal memory copies required (see Table II).

The use of pointers is central to *C* and crucial to *C++*. A pointer is a data item not containing an entity, such as a `float` or `int` value, but a pointer to an entity. A pointer provides another mechanism for accessing the information held in an entity. References and pointers are closely linked but different: the main implementation difference is that the aliasing inherent in using a reference is executed by the compiler whereas the use of pointers is explicitly performed by the programmer.

3.2.3 Scoping and security *C++* requires additional control over the scoping, or visibility, of variables and functions. *C* provides automatic variables (local to a function), static variables (global to all functions within a compilation unit) and external variables (global over the whole of the program). Local variables have precedence over static variables where there are name conflicts.

Static variables declared in a class header are class variables. Access to these variables is through the member functions - these are functions declared in the same class as the class variables. $C++$ supports an override operator in order to provide function references for a class and its subclasses. The scope resolution operator (::) before a variable name forces the compiler to use a variable declared in the main body of the code instead of a local variable with the same name.

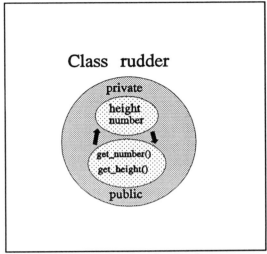

Figure 1 An example of a simple class

$C++$ uses the keywords public, private, protected, and friend to control the scope of functions and variables declared within a class (the member functions). By default, all variables and functions declared in a class are private - scope is restricted to member functions of the class. protected is less restrictive - scope is open to any subclass. public defines the class interface (unrestricted scope) and friend allows an externally derived function or class to have the access rights of a member function. All class variables are private and can only be manipulated via user written access functions. Classes themselves may be declared private or public, which restricts the visibility of the class as a whole.

3.2.4 Storage Classes: Stack Space and Free Storage In order to create classes, $C++$ needed a storage class other than those provided by ANSI C (auto, static and extern). This was implemented for primitive types (char, int, double, etc.) as well as user defined classes with the new and delete unary operators. A variable which is dynamically created using new exists throughout a program until explicitly deleted. The equivalent operations to new and delete are accomplished on a class with constructor and destructor functions.

Constructors are initialisation functions which are used to build valid objects. The usual resource being allocated in a constructor is dynamically allocated memory, but resources could also be internally used fields, files, semaphores or sockets, for example. A destructor is used to release any resources allocated by a constructor. An example of constructors and a destructor is shown in Table I.

3.2.5 Overloading and Polymorphism C++ allows operators and functions to be overloaded. The goal of overloading is to make user defined types "look" like built-in language supplied types. In C++ the keyword `operator` followed by the symbol to be overloaded, when defined as a member function, redefines the symbol within the context of a class. For example, `operator+()` redefines the + operator. Function polymorphism is achieved with the `overload` keyword when used in the declaration of a family of functions with the same name (this is not necessary with C++ version 2.0). It should be noted that each overloaded function should have at least one argument of a different type otherwise the compiler will not know which function to invoke.

3.2.6 Inheritance Inheritance in C++ is implemented using derived classes. The parent (base) class name is given after the new class name and the symbol ':'. For example:

```
class sulzer : diesel_engine{};
```

The derived class `sulzer` is a subclass of `diesel_engine` and inherits its data structures but not its member functions. The subclass can define its interface separately from the base class or inherit most or all of the interface in the base class. For example.

```
class sulzer : public diesel_engine{};
```

Here the subclass `sulzer` inherits the public interface of the base class. The derived class can add additional instance variables and member functions as well as partially redefining the interface of its parent. The parent class can declare a public member to be `virtual` permitting a different definition of the member in the derived classes.

`private` functions and variables of a base class are not exposed to derived classes. C++ has the keyword `protected` to open visibility of member functions to its derivatives. It should be noted that to take full advantage of C++, the visibility of derived classes should be carefully controlled. For example if all derived classes have `public` access to the `private` data of the base class then the advantages of data hiding are lost.

3.2.7 C++ Enhancements The following are enhancements of C++ over C and are not directly related to object-orientation:

    o The I/O operators, >> and <<.

o In-line function expansion.
o Constant declaration for pointers and memory-reference values.
o Unnamed (anonymous) unions.

Table III An Inline Function

```
//
// abs
//
inline int abs(int a)
{
    return (a<0) ? -a : a;
}
```

4. Program Design Using $C++$

4.1 Introduction
In trying to design and develop a large complex computer program there is no substitute for intelligence, experience and taste in programming style, Stroustrup [3,4]. Object-oriented programming does not provide a recipe for replacing the basic attributes required by a good computer programmer, it does, however, coerce a programmer into developing software in a more structured and planned way.

4.2 Design and Implementation Methods
A sound working knowledge of an application and what an end-user expects from it are fundamental prerequisites for writing a successful application. Object-oriented design, according to most authors, for example Brooch [5] and Durham [6], has the following general steps:

o Identify the classes.
o Identify the operations that are performed on each class and those operations that each class must initiate.
o Determine the relationships (visibility) between classes.
o Determine the interface for each class.
o Implement the data structures and methods for each class.

Following these steps is not always trivial. The choice of classes is often subjective and, as in any design process, is an acquired skill. Where possible classes which have been previously tested and used in other programs should be utilised - modularisation should help here. The program that is produced during this work should be built up in an iterative fashion; this should include a testing phase before the start of each new iteration. The normal means of testing a computer program is to build a prototype of the system being modelled. The prototype is run and subjected to a methodical series of conditions to ascertain the likelihood of its failure. At this point "bugs" and features of the code should be rectified before commencing the next iteration. Finally development work is complete when the entire program is fully tested. Stroustrup [4] observes that "a program that has not been tested does not work".

5. Ship Program Design Using C++

5.1 Introduction

The aim of this section of the paper is to discuss the implementation, using a top-down design approach, of a ship model [7], in $C++$. At the time of writing, the project being described is still at a very early stage. The design and structure of the $C++$ ship will evolve as more of the code is developed and tested. Consequently in this section a broad brush will be used to paint a picture of the object-oriented ship design and implementation. This section will cover the following steps:

       o Top-down ship design.
       o Data scoping.
       o Using $C++$ features.

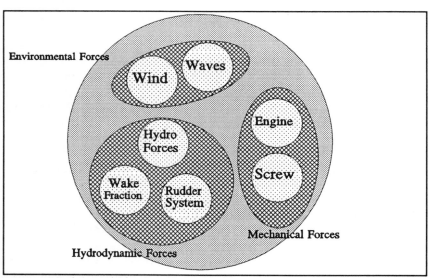

Figure 2 Modules within the ship system

5.2 Top-Down Analysis of the a Ship System

It is normal practice when dealing with a complex program to "divide and conquer". Basically this entails dividing the problem into smaller and smaller "chunks" that are easier and easier to handle individually. The ship system can be split into three interacting sub-systems [7]:

       o Environmental forces   -- external forces (eg wind and waves).
       o Mechanical forces   -- internal forces (eg engine and screw).

o Hydrodynamic forces   -- forces acting on the hull and rudder.

The next step in the design process is to analyse the modules shown in Figure 2 and if necessary divide them into smaller modules. Following the "divide and conquer" rule here, the engine module, for example, can be divided into six overlapping sub-modules, shown in Figure 3. These are:

o Governor.
o Fuel.
o Turbocharger.
o Air.
o Combustion.
o Power.

The decision to pick these sub-modules as objects is subjective, but is primarily based on the fact that:

o They are ADT's of the engine system.

o The data-flow through the engine indicates that they should be treated as separate entities, see Figure 4.

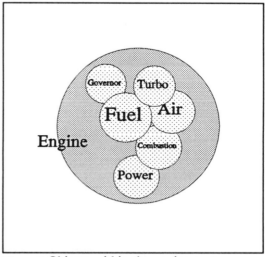

Figure 3 Objects within the engine system

All six objects within the engine module share some common data. Figure 4, which illustrates the dataflow through the engine, also shows that it is necessary to export and import data between modules, for example between the engine and screw modules.

It is normal when two or more objects share data to create a base class from which the other classes share common data. In the case being discussed the base class is engine and the other classes are those shown in Figure 3.

Computer scientists generally frown upon the use of global data and the same is true in object-oriented languages. However, if global data must be used then encapsulation can ensure that the scope and manipulation of the data is carefully controlled.

private members of a class are normally protected against access from functions other than member functions (see Table I). It is only the public members of a class that are usable by non-member functions. This regime can be broken in *C++*. The keyword `friend` allows non-member functions access to private members. Whole classes or just non-member functions can become a `friend` of another class (see Table IV).

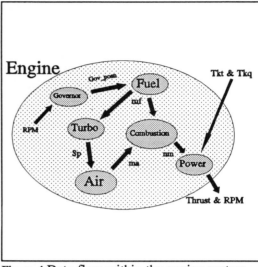

Figure 4 Data flow within the engine system

The base class `engine` has a number of non-member `friend` functions, screw, governor and fuel for example. This design scenario leads to an object hierarchy. Where there is a base class which has a number of non-member `friends` which are members of other classes, such as engine, screw, wind or fuel.

5.2.1 *The User Interface*

A standard interface to the `public` members of a class is an important consideration since some naming/syntax convention will make class functions easier to remember and use. Such a convention will also produce classes which are more likely to be used again and again. A typical example of such a convention would be the use of `read_xxx` or `update_xxx` to read and update class variables.

Table IV A `friend` function

```
//
//   engine base class
//
class engine
{
private:
     double thrust, rps;
public:
     friend double governor::read_rps();
}
//
//   governor
//
{
class governor
{
  private
     double delta_gov_posn;
     double read_rps();
  public
     double update_gov_posn();
}
```

5.3 Other Useful Features

5.3.1 Inheritance During this iteration of the object-orientated ship model no obvious need for inheritance has been found. If the level of detail being modelled was greater then it is likely that many objects would share common attributes. For example a gauge or valve of which there are many types; all have some commonality such as valve diameters or units on a gauge, which could be inherited from a parent class.

5.3.2 Inline Function Expansion A function can be defined as `inline`. The purpose of this call is to increase the efficiency of the code produced. It should only be used when the code contains very small, frequently called functions. The `inline` keyword tells the compiler to do an in-line expansion of the function. This means that wherever the `inline` function is found it is replaced by the actual code of the function (see Table III).

5.3.3 Overloading At this stage in the development of the program it is not clear where the particular advantages of overloading will be useful. As the program evolves this will hopefully become more obvious.

6. Conclusions

6.1 Some Thoughts on *C++*

C++ implements OOP. There are a number of implementation issues:

o There are complex rules for scoping, type checking and syntax.
o Some of its "features" can help produce unreadable and incomprehensible code - this is a feature of C as well.
o The overloading of operators and functions is liable to be problematic.
o There is no wastebasket facility - runtime memory fragmentation is possible.
o It is necessary to delete classes - this could be a problem when multiple inheritance is used. It is possible to destroy a base class before the derived class is finished with.

6.2 The Design and Initial Development of the Object-orientated Ship.

It becomes increasingly obvious when designing object-oriented software that to take advantage of the many features available it is necessary to:

o Have a thorough understanding of the problem being solved.
o Initiate a top-down design scheme.
o Do not code until there is a clear view of object hierarchy and

program dataflow.

o Reuse code that has previously been tried and tested.

o Conform to some standard policy for class data manipulation.

o Conform to some standard data sharing policy. For example have a base class with friends, or some other scheme.

o Identify objects that have a common attributes and use inheritance.

o Use the inline on only small functions.

o Ensure that classes, functions, and variables are self-documented.

o Provide common interfaces to classes.

o Do not try to over-complicate the code, for instance by using overloading; this can be done later.

6.3 Towards the Future

So does object-orientation represent the future for programming or is it just the latest fad? I believe that programming with it will lead towards software that is better designed and has a clean internal structure. It is also clear that object-oriented programming is more likely to survive the trials of time than many other methodologies, such as procedural programming, due to the reasons described in section 2.

Parallel computers are seen by many as the key technology for the future of computers. If object-oriented programming techniques are to become the standard for the future then object-orientation should fit into the model required by computers of the future. According to Kerr [1], objects should be able to have a degree of self-determination. This feature leads an object towards becoming an autonomous process which is a short step away from considering objects as parallel processes.

A number of key issues concerning the implementation of object-oriented languages on parallel computer need to be addressed. For example how to maintain ADT's, achieve load balancing, realise data sharing and message passing. It is obvious that much work is still necessary before the relationship between object-orientation and parallel processing is clear.

Acknowledgements

I would like to thank Ron Kerr at Newcastle University for his help in explaining many aspects of object-orientation. I would also like to thank Dave Gee at Southampton University for proof reading and contributing useful remarks on the text.

References

[1] Kerr, R., *Aspect of Inheritance*, Reprint from the Proceedings of the

Seventeenth SIMULA Users' Conference, Pilsen, Czechoslavakia, 1990.

[2] Wegner, P., *Dimensions of Object-Based Language Design*, 1987 Conf. OOPSLA Proc., ACM, Orlando, FL, October, pp. 168-181, 1987.

[3] Stroustrup, B., *The C++ Programming Language*, 1st Edition, Addison-Wesley Publishing Company, ISBN 0-201-12078-X, 1986.

[4] Stroustrup, B., *The C++ Programming Language*, 2nd Edition, Addison-Wesley Publishing Company, ISBN 0-201-53992-6, 1990.

[5] Brooch, G., *Object-Oriented Development*, IEEE Trans, Software Eng., v. SE-12, pp. 211-221, 1986.

[6] Durham, I., *Abstraction and the Methodical Development of Fault-Tolerant Software*, Report CMU-CS-86-112, Carnegie Mellon Univ, Computer Science Dept, Pittsburg, PA, 1986.

[7] Baker, M.A., *Voyage Simulation: The Whole Ship Model Approach*, International Shipbuilding Progress, Volume 37, No. 411, pp. 289-322, 1990.

Plotting a Route to the Future

H.L. Atkinson, C.T. Stockel
Marine Dynamics Research Group, Polytechnic South West, Drake Circus, Plymouth PL4 8AA, UK

ABSTRACT

This paper commences by drawing attention to the fact that nautical charts and their applications are currently lagging way behind the technological advancements sweeping through the rest of the maritime industry. It continues by suggesting that automation in these areas, in the form of electronic chart systems, could have a profound effect on marine accident statistics.

After presenting the principles of electronic charting and discussing the relevance of the Safety of Life at Sea Agreement of 1974, the paper goes on to outline the functions of the various international committees and working groups involved in the development of electronic chart standards. This is followed by a review of the establishment, operation and findings of the two European, large scale experiments in electronic charting. A brief description of data capture and storage techniques is then presented.

The latter part of the paper is concerned with automatic collision avoidance systems. A short account of stages involved in the development of automatic collision avoidance systems to up to their position level is followed by a more detailed explanation of research currently being pursued in this field at the University of Plymouth. The paper concludes by posing questions about the legal and commercial acceptance of such systems.

BACKGROUND

Over the last few years there has been a significant reduction in the level of bridge manning and the concept of *24 Hour One-man Bridge Operations* has evolved. Det norske Veritas (DnV) have now classified a number ships as W1-OC or, Watch 1-Ocean Areas and Coastal Waters that is, safe for operation by only one person on the bridge day and night. The development of the automatic radar plotting aid (ARPA) has resulted in notable improvements in collision avoidance procedures and, while the hand-written log continues to be an essential feature on the bridge, successful trials have been carried out using *marine black boxes*, similar to those used in aircraft, to record vital voyage information.

As a consequence, the bridges of most ships now contain an ever increasing array of instruments and associated display screens; ARPA sets, echo sounders, logs, compasses, electronic and satellite navigation aids to name but a few. The mariner is thus faced with an enormous volume of information to digest and utilise in his decision making processes. With the introduction of unmanned/minimally manned engine rooms on board many vessels, engine room indicators are now springing up on bridge control consoles. By night ships' bridges are illuminated by digital readouts, cathode ray tube (CRT) displays and coloured indicator lamps.

In the middle of all this electronic equipment and technological advancement the Hydrographic Office publications (navigation charts, tide tables, sailing directions and lists of lights, radio signals and fog signals) have retained their traditional printed format. The mariner is, therefore, obliged to dedicate a large proportion of his on watch time to the arduous task of reading and assimilating this printed information. In addition to this, the officer of the watch (OOW) must be aware of the many sensors on his bridge console and also *maintain a constant look-out*, a task which becomes increasingly onerous at night and in congested waters.

Today, as always, the Master of a ship is responsible for the safe passage of his vessel from port to port. He and his watchkeepers must combine their navigational and seamanship skills together with their knowledge of the Collision Regulations to ensure that this objective is satisfied. Over the last two or three decades escalating traffic densities in waters such as the Dover Straits and the Straits of Singapore, coupled with the increasing size and speed of fast container ships and VLCCs and the resultant decrease in their manoeuvrability, have led to a greater than acceptable number of maritime incidents.

Approximately ninety percent of all marine accidents occur in confined or coastal waters such as channels, fairways and inshore traffic zones; the vast majority taking the form of collisions or groundings [1]. Although the implementation of Traffic Separation Schemes has significantly reduced the number of such incidents this is not a fool-proof solution, nor is it the full story. Human error, in the form of ignorance or negligence, is estimated to be responsible, at least in part, for up to eighty five percent of these accidents [2]. This observation lays, wide open, the argument for the improvement of marine navigation and guidance. Hence the suggestion that electronic charts will have a vital contribution to make to the future safe navigation and operation of vessels in coastal and confined waters, to the efficiency of traffic flow and also, to the protection of the environment from the risk of marine pollution.

INTRODUCTION

Electronic chart is a term which has been applied to a variety of devices ranging from digitally-generated paper chart equivalents to more complex expert systems consisting of interfaced components capable of worldwide navigation without the need for human intervention.

On the whole the charting packages currently available are aimed at specialist markets such as fishermen and yachtsmen. These systems range from those which simply plot a position obtained from an electronic position fixing (EPF) system, such as Decca or Loran, onto a crude representation of the coastline, perhaps including the odd depth contour, to highly sophisticated systems integrating a number of EPF systems and possessing the ability to dead reckon, match the radar image to the coastline and buoys, indicate seabed topography and display traffic routing data.

The International Hydrographic Organisation (IHO) and the International Maritime Organisation (IMO) are currently collaborating to produce the vital standards on which ECDIS (Electronic Chart Display and Information System) will be based. The principles and requirements of the ECDIS concept are defined in section 1.3 of the *Provisional Specifications for Chart Content and Display of ECDIS* [3]. This document specifies that the primary function of an electronic chart should be the provision of safe and reliable navigation offering *paper chart equivalency* or better. Hence, the information shown on the display and that used in updating must comply with the data quality and density specified for paper charts; data availability for the user must be at least equal to that offered by paper charts.

IMPLICATIONS OF THE SOLAS AGREEMENT

When discussing ECDIS, the one of the principal reference documents is the *Safety of Life at Sea Convention (SOLAS), 1974*. This document is supported by more recent Protocols and Amendments including the *Final Report of the IHO Committee on the Exchange of Digital Data, November 1986*. An efficiently designed ECDIS should reduce the navigational workload with the ultimate aim being, to produce a system which can be accepted as a legal equivalent to the nautical publications required by Regulation V/20 of SOLAS 1974:

All ships shall carry adequate and up-to-date charts, sailing directions, lists of lights, notices to mariners, tide tables and all other nautical publications necessary for the intended voyage.

The other SOLAS Convention regulation relevant to ECDIS is Regulation 5 of Chapter I, *Equivalents*; this essentially provides the opportunity for approval of equivalents for some of the nautical publications required by Regulation V/20, subject to adequate testing. Hence, in defining the draft specifications for ECDIS it has been assumed that ECDIS must be equivalent to both the paper chart and its associated publications in every respect. This, in turn, raises the question of reliability of electronic charts versus that of their paper equivalents; the mariner must not be placed in a situation where should his power fail his chart is lost too.

The Radio Technical Commission for Maritime Services (RTCM) of the USA have suggested that there should be different categories of electronic chart for different categories of vessel. IHO experts working on the draft specifications for ECDIS have suggested that the navigator needs two equally sized displays; one for navigating and the other for simultaneous passage planning. The RTCM believe that certain categories of vessel including ferries and tugs, which never migrate far from their defined operating area, have no need for a passage planning display. It could be argued that the answer to the problem is amendment of Regulation V/20 in order to define the requirements for different classes of vessel more explicitly. It has been suggested [4] that whereas *adequate* charts for the *intended voyage* of an ocean-going vessel would most definitely include all of the associated passage planning charts, *adequate* charts for the *intended voyage* of a ferry could be interpreted as only including those charts on which the vessel is actually going to navigate, and thus exclude the need for planning charts.

INTERNATIONAL COMMITTEES AND WORKING GROUPS ON ELECTRONIC CHARTING

In 1986 a study of the repercussions of ECDIS development for hydrographic offices was completed by the North Sea Hydrographic Commission. As a consequence of this the IHO established its own Committee on ECDIS (COE). Under this general administrative title the COE currently has six working groups looking at issues associated with ECDIS standards:

Working Group on ECDIS Overall Standards
This group is responsible for the overall maintenance of the IHO Provisional Standards. Their third draft of the specifications was published in October 1988 and is commonly known as *IHO Special Publication 52*. This document made a significant contribution to the IMO's *Provisional Performance Standards* (PPS) published in May 1989. In view of the presently limited experience with ECDIS the specifications have remained in draft form.

Working Group on Updating of ECDIS

It is recognised that the electronic chart database (ECDB) must be continually updated if ECDIS is to satisfy Regulation V/20 of the SOLAS Agreement. The Working Group maintain that it should be possible to update databases both in port and at sea. The group currently favour the use of the INMARSAT Enhanced Group Call (EGC) Safety Network for this task.

Working Group on Regional Databases
This group considers database development methods, database types and structures, and digitising conventions. The group has, additionally, considered the need for a digital data exchange format for the transfer of data between the integrated database, ECDIS users and the Hydrographic Offices. In October 1989, plans were agreed to develop an entirely new format for data exchange to be known as *IHO DX90*. This format incorporates a unique coding scheme for objects, features and attributes as well as the exchange message itself.

Working Group on ECDIS Glossary
This group is engaged in establishing a glossary of ECDIS terms and dealing with the confusion surrounding the abbreviations and acronyms which always emerge when a technical development project is undertaken.

Working Group on Colours and Symbols
The need for standardisation on the use of colour and symbology became evident during the North Sea Project, where there was little consistency in the colours and symbols displayed by the six electronic chart systems involved in the experiment. It became apparent that the advice of experts in psychology and ergonomics would be needed to design colour and symbol sets.

Working Group on Data Quality
Data quality criteria must be identified for both chart compilation and display. The need to supply the navigator with information about data quality has resulted in the inclusion of source or reliability diagrams in the IHO Chart Specifications.

Together, the IMO and IHO have formed the Harmonising Group on ECDIS (IMO/IHO-HGE) whose findings are subsequently submitted to the IMO Sub-committee on Navigation (SON), and other sub-committees where appropriate. The IMO/IHO-HGE has set 1993 as its target date for finalising the Provisional Performance Standards for ECDIS. Once this target has been met it will be possible for an ECDIS designed in accordance with these specifications to be employed in place of a paper chart. Critical to the meeting of the 1993 deadline is the availability of a database containing data on a sufficiently large sea area to be of use to international shipping.

Two major experiments in the development of regional databases have been carried out; the North Sea Project and the Seatrans Project.

THE NORTH SEA PROJECT

The North Sea Project began in response to concern from the IHO in Monaco that independent commercial developments in electronic charting could misinterpret their carefully compiled guidelines and consequently jeopardise the safety of seafarers, and led to unanswered questions about liability for the chart in the event of an accident.

In June 1987, the Norwegian Hydrographic Service (NHS) and the Royal Danish Administration of Navigation and Hydrography devised an independent enterprise involving themselves and six other North Sea countries. The other countries associated with the project were Sweden, the Netherlands, Belgium, France, the Federal Republic of Germany and the United Kingdom. This led to the voyage of the Norwegian research vessel M/V LANCE and ultimately, to the North Sea Project. During October and November 1988 the vessel sailed from Stavanger calling at a port in almost every country that borders the North Sea.

The project involved the hydrographic offices of each the participating countries digitising the approach charts for the selected ports in their country. The offshore charts for the passage were digitised by the NHS who were also responsible for consolidating all the information in an overall database. Commercial manufacturers of ECDIS were invited to install their systems aboard LANCE and demonstrate their operation using the integrated database.

The aims of the project were to investigate the cooperation needed between hydrographic offices in the development of electronic chart databases; evaluate the resources and costs involved in producing them, examine methods for updating electronic charts, analyse the ability of an existing ECDIS to accept a database developed according to the IHO-COE's specifications, make recommendations for the production of ECDIS specifications and demonstrate the possibilities for ECDIS to the maritime industry while analysing its potential.

Interested parties were able either, to visit the ship and see demonstrations in the ports visited or, to observe the equipment on passage between ports. Over five hundred people observed the systems in operation and their thoughts were recorded in their responses to a questionnaire. The responses given have been considered in the further development of ECDIS standards.

Following the North Sea Project the NHS felt that three issues remained unresolved. They were: agreement on the specifications for ECDIS, the need for a standardised digitising format and a centrally managed database and, the need to ensure that the ship's position as indicated on the electronic chart is an accurate reflection of the vessel's true position as derived from GPS (Global Positioning System). The need for improved graphics together with international agreement on the use of colours and symbology and the combining of different scales also became apparent as a result of the experiment. The project did however, demonstrate the potential of ECDIS as an important navigational aid.

THE SEATRANS PROJECT

The Seatrans Project was undertaken during 1989 and 1990 by the Norwegian Hydrographic Service in response to the findings of the North Sea Project which indicated the need for a realistic investigation of the IMO Provisional Performance Standards for ECDIS and methods for chart updating.

The project aimed to test the first shipboard ECDIS satisfying the provisional IMO regulations during extensive sea trials performed under varying weather conditions and in confined waters. In addition, the project was intended to analyse the effect of electronic charts on operational safety and workloads and also, to provide practical experience of ECDB management. During the project continuous and automatic updating of the chart was performed using the recommended satellite communications. The effectiveness of differential GPS along the Norwegian coastline was also being examined by transmitting differential GPS corrections via existing radio beacons.

The vessel involved in this project was the Norwegian commercial vessel NORNEWS EXPRESS, a 4500 dwt paper carrier built in 1987 and equipped for 24 hour one-man operations in inshore waters. Capt Per Larsen (DnV) believes ECDIS to be the key to true 24 hour one-man bridge operations in all waters. The main navigational instruments are grouped in one central console and the navigator has an all round view from the bridge. During sea trials completed at the end of 1990, the vessel sailed her normal trading route between ports around the North Sea. A large portion of the journey takes the vessel through exceedingly narrow and winding inner channels where the traffic density is high and the depth clearances are minimal. The vessel was equipped with the Robertson Tritech *Disc Navigation System* which was developed in collaboration with the Norwegian Maritime Research Institute AS (Marintek) in accordance with the IMO's PPS.

The specification of trial requirements and the evaluation of the results was undertaken by the Norwegian Maritime Directorate and the Det norske Veritas classification society. The ECDIS digital data was supplied by the NHS who were also responsible for the transmission of automatic chart corrections via INMARSAT-C. Approximately thirty five charts along the 1000 nautical mile test route were digitised and processed to produce the vast quantities of data in the project database.

In contrast with the North Sea Project the Seatrans Project charts included colour fill and area definition. This caused a number of problems and ultimately resulted in a six month delay in the project timetable. When using computer graphic techniques to colour fill a feature such as a shoal bank, a break in the sounding line will allow the colour to seep into the adjoining areas.

In addition to the traditional chart information, the Disc Navigation System is capable of receiving, storing and displaying meteorological data and ice and oil slick movement details via satcom links. The system can also supply tidal information from tide tables stored in the database.

The project has demonstrated the practical use of ECDIS on a one-man operated bridge and also that a suitable ECDB can be developed although, achieving data consistency proved to be a problem. The skipper of NORNEWS EXPRESS felt that the system's greatest advantage was the quality of the advice that it provided. The director of the Norwegian shipping company, Seatrans Ans has been so impressed with the system that he has suggested that its anti-grounding function could be considered as an alternative to the introduction of double hulls as a legal requirement for ships carrying hazardous cargoes. Seatrans have now equipped six of their vessels with the Robertson ECDIS.

The ability of Disc Navigation to interface with ARPA, GPS, echo sounders and other ship sensors has been already been employed in areas where chart information is inadequate or non-existent. POLAR CIRCLE the icebreaking survey vessel, recently purchased from her Norwegian owners by the British Royal Navy, has used the system extensively in Antarctic waters; it enabled her crew to navigate back over the exact same track which they had taken to enter a poorly charting area, thus minimising the risk involved. HMS POLAR CIRCLE will be joined in Antarctic waters in the near future by the new US icebreaker NATHANIEL B PALMER which is also equipped with Robertson Disc Navigation ECDIS. The system developed for this vessel by Robertson Ans will, in addition be capable of integration with an autopilot and dynamic positioning system in order to provide total navigation and positioning control.

DATA CAPTURE AND STORAGE

International agreement has yet to be reached on a single method of electronic chart generation. To date, research has focused on three basic approaches: raster scanning, interactive video and digitisation. Although all three are valid techniques it is assumed in the majority of discussions and publications, including SP 52, that digitisation techniques will be employed. In essence digital generation involves the digitisation of line and point information either from a paper chart or for preference, from hydrographic base documents; the features are stored in a code representing their form as x-y coordinates and can be subsequently displayed in a vector format. Although this approach is ideal for sorting and selecting which features to display, it does, on the other hand, bring to light issues such as ensuring the display of an approved minimum data set for safe navigation.

In parallel with the development of so-called digitised electronic charts consideration is also being given to an alternative interactive video display approach. Fundamental to this technique, is the ability to produce and store photographic images of conventional hydrographic office charts in such a way, that they may subsequently be recalled by a computer and displayed on a suitable high resolution monitor. The technology now exists to overlay the analogue photographic frames with digitally generated graphics, and hence produce a medium for displaying navigation operations including track plotting, chartwork and passage planning.

One significant obstacle in the path of the adoption of this approach to electronic charting is the vast number of individual frames required to store a single chart if it is to be clearly displayed on an appropriately sized monitor. However, on the plus side, with its familiar style of chart presentation evolved over the centuries, the interactive video approach has two obvious advantages: minimal resistance from the notoriously conservative maritime industry and the need for limited retraining only.

ECDIS AND AUTOMATIC COLLISION AVOIDANCE SYSTEMS

For the reasons outlined at the beginning of this paper most of the world's maritime nations are now addressing the problem of collision avoidance. With the pressures placed on today's navigator by one-man bridge operation and the suggestion that human error is responsible for the majority collisions and groundings, automation of the collision avoidance process has become a compelling issue. Early work in this field employed mathematical techniques to develop simulation models which were subsequently run on computers [5] [6] [7]. This approach was limited by the ability of traditional mathematics to mirror human thought processes. In recent years a number of projects have investigated the use artificial intelligence in the development of expert collision avoidance systems [8] [9].

Research undertaken by the Marine Dynamics Research Group at the University of Plymouth, under its former title of Ship Control Group of Polytechnic South West (Plymouth), has examined the issues surrounding automatic collision avoidance in open ocean. The study has resulted in the development of an expert knowledge-based system capable of simulating automatic collision avoidance for multiple ship encounters in open ocean [10] [11]. However, this is not the full story, as previously discussed the vast majority of maritime accidents occur in confined and coastal waters and not in open ocean conditions. In waters such as these so-called *static hazard* avoidance techniques, including anti-grounding procedures, must additionally be considered.

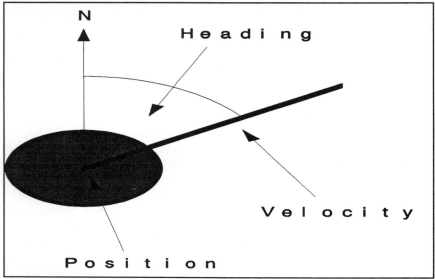

Figure 1   Own Ship Icon Representation

Research work now in progress is concentrating on the development of an automatic collision avoidance system (ACAS) capable of navigating a ship in accordance with the collision regulations, while avoiding both static and dynamic hazards. In order to assess the potential risk posed by static features, including the depth of water under the keel, such a system must have at its heart, a sophisticated electronic navigation chart capable of intelligent interrogation and of interface links with an ARPA.

Preliminary computer-based investigations into own ship representation and routines for coastline avoidance are currently being pursued. The work commenced with the question of icon portrayal of the own ship (Figure 1). In the system devised, the coordinates of the centre of the sphere correspond with the vessel position and the bearing of the vector is concurrent with the ship's heading. The vector length is directly proportional to the vessel's velocity. In future developments the vessel states, namely position, heading and velocity, will be read directly into the computer's serial port from the vessel's EPF system, compass and log; however, in these early stages the vessel states are adjusted in response to user entered keystrokes.

In order to consider hazard avoidance it is necessary to define a safety domain around the own ship and hence the icon. If an object, either static or dynamic, infringes this zone it is deemed to be a potential hazard. When describing a safety domain it is imperative that the extent of the domain is proportional to vessel speed in order to maintain a constant *look-ahead time domain*; a vessel approaching a coastline at 10 knots has less time to implement avoiding action than an identical vessel closing on the same coastline at 5 knots. For this

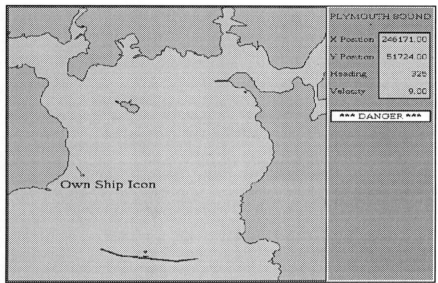

Figure 2   Screen Display for Collision Avoidance Software

reason a domain radius equal to twice the length of the icon velocity vector has been adopted for these preliminary studies. Although the icon is currently positioned at the centre of this domain, decisions regarding its offset to the rear port quadrant will be made in the future. Domain infringement checks are made at each pixel along the domain radius at a bearing coincident with the ship's heading, and then along radii at 45 degree increments of this heading. This scanning procedure can be likened to the technique used by a radar antenna in *searching* the area surrounding a ship.

Using a data set of approximately a thousand digitised points along the coastline of Plymouth Sound, an extremely elementary *chart* of the area has been produced. At the right hand end of the screen display the vessel states are displayed in response to user demand. The chart is limited to two dimensions i.e., it does not incorporate any depth contour data, it is however, a perfectly adequate start point for investigation into coastline avoidance algorithms.The first and most simplistic approach to be considered was *pixel colour determination*. In this case a hazard is defined as a pixel colour differing from that of safe water or the icon itself. As the icon is manoeuvred around the chart the colour of each pixel in which the icon will be drawn is determined by the domain infringement software; if a hazard colour is detected the *distance off* is evaluated. If the distance off drops below a specified tolerance level a danger warning is flashed up on the screen (Figure 2). A second approach to coastline avoidance currently being considered, involves describing the coastline in terms of a complex mathematical curve;

the domain infringement software then being employed to determine on which side of the curve the icon/ship lies.

CONCLUSIONS

While it is now widely accepted that electronic charts will have a vital role to play in the navigation of ships in the next century, their application in allied fields such as automatic control and guidance of ship manoeuvres and automatic collision avoidance is still a matter for debate. Until the legal questions surrounding the implementation of computer-based expert systems for automatic collision avoidance have been addressed, man will remain essential to the collision avoidance loop. However, with the increasing burdens placed on today's mariner and the existing rate of human error in navigation, investigation into the potentials for ACAS must continue.

Future work at the University of Plymouth will build on the existing algorithms with the aim of designing a computer-based system, incorporating a rule base which is able to process single or multi-ship encounters in all circumstances. Although current legislation limits the operation of such systems to an advisory role only, technology does not. In the long term there is no reason why automatic collision avoidance systems should not be capable of accepting full control and responsibility for the collision avoidance action. This type of system would offer the mariner a suggested course of action which he may choose to implement or override however, if after a specified time period has elapsed the mariner has failed to make a selection either way, the system would automatically implement its recommended manoeuvre. At the end of the day though the question still remains, will the maritime industry be ready to accept this change in responsibilty?

REFERENCES

1.   COCKCROFT, A. N. 'Collisions at Sea'. *Safety at Sea*, pp.17-19, June   1984.

2.   Panel on Human Error in Merchant Marine Safety. *Human Error in Merchant Marine Safety*, Washington D. C., 1976.

3.   International Hydrographic Bureau. *Provisional Specifications for Chart Content and Display of ECDIS*, Special Publication 52, Monaco, May 1990.

4.   KERR, A. J. 'The Integration of Navigational Information - The Electronic Chart'. *IALA Bulletin*, pp.35-39, 1989.

5.   CURTIS, R. G. 'An Analysis of the Dangers of Ships Overtaking'. *Proceedings of the Conference on Mathematical Aspects of Marine Traffic*, Academic Press for the Institute of Mathematics and its Applications, 1979.

6.   DAVIS, P. V., DOVE, M. J., & STOCKEL, C. T. 'A Computer Simulation of Multi-ship Encounters'. *Journal of Navigation*, 35, pp.347, 1982.

7.   ZHAO-LIN, W. 'An Alternative System of Collision Avoidance'. *Journal of Navigation*, 37, pp.83, 1984.

8.   IMAZU, H., SUGISAKI, A., TSURUTA, S., INAISHI, M., & MATUMURA, H. 'Basic Research on an Expert System for Navigation at Sea'. *Proceedings of the Academic Symposium Between Chinese and Japanese Institutes of Navigation*, Tokyo, 1989.

9.   COENEN, F. P., SMEATON, G. P., & BOLE, A. G. 'Knowledge-based Collision Avoidance'. *Journal of Navigation*, 42, pp.107, 1989.

10.   RANGACHARI, J. 'A Computer Based Resolution of Multi-ship Encounters'. *M.Phil. Thesis*, Polytechnic South West (Plymouth), 1991.

11.   BLACKWELL, G. K., RANGACHARI, J., & STOCKEL, C. T. 'An Intelligent Interactive Environment for a Maritime Real-time Expert System'. *Proceedings of the Summer Computer Simulation Conference*, Baltimore, July 1991.

SECTION 6: CONTROL

A Self-Organising Fuzzy Control Autopilot for Ship Course Keeping

D. Wang (*), C. McCorkell (**), X.-R. Lu (*)
(*) Department of Marine Electrical Engineering, Dalian Maritime Univeristy, Dalian 116024, P.R. China
(**) School of Electronic Engineering, Dublin City University, Dublin 9, Ireland

ABSTRACT

This paper gives a design scheme for a ship's autopilot which uses a self-organising fuzzy control strategy. For this design the steering behaviour of a human controller is transformed into a fuzzy mathematical model. Because the dynamics of the ship motion is non-linear, high order and contains time-lag, the performance of non-adaptive fuzzy control can not be relied upon under some conditions. Thus a self-organising fuzzy controller is justified. According to a performance criteria the rules of the fuzzy controller are adjusted automatically. Therefore the control performance of the vessel is improved over a wide range of operation and the course precision comes up to the predetermined level. Computer simulation shows that a controller designed in this way can obtain high control performance.

INTRODUCTION

At present all ocean going vessels are equipped with an autopilot system most of which are conventional PID autopilots or adaptive autopilots. Conventional PID autopilots can not adjust the parameters of the dynamic model of ship motion automatically when the speed, load, and sea condition change. Thus at present many ships are equipped with adaptive autopilots which can achieve parameter identification and adaptive control according to the parameter changes of the ship model and disturbance model.

Both conventional PID and adaptive autopilots are designed based on the mathematical model of a ship. When the model is more precise, the response is better. But the model is complicated, non-linear, and of high order. The on-line solution time may be too long for this model to be used to control the ship. Thus the design of an adaptive autopilot is a compromise between precision and realizability. Are there other methods which can be used to solve these problems? It is known that an experienced helmsman who does not know the mathematical model of the ship precisely can steer the ship very well. With fuzzy control theory the experience of a helmsman can be translated into control rules and an autopilot can be designed for course keeping control. In order to improve its control strategy, a self-organising controller may be used. The self-organising fuzzy control autopilot was developed based on a non-adaptive fuzzy control autopilot.

THE SIMPLE FUZZY CONTROL AUTOPILOT

A simple fuzzy control autopilot has been developed and described in [4]. It takes the form of a program running on a digital computer in the block diagram of Figure 1. The fuzzy controller consists of a set of rules which define individual control situations. Each rule connects the COURSE ERROR (E) and CHANGE IN ERROR (C, which is the difference between present and last course error) with the RUDDER ANGLE (δ) that has to be applied. The values e and c are the fuzzy values of E and C. They can be calculated from the sampling values of E and C by multiplying them by a suitable scaling factor and then quantizing the results to the closest elements of the universe of discourse.

Corresponding to e and c, the output g from the controller can be obtained from the decision table which is precalculated from the control rules before the controller is run. Then a suitable rudder angle δ is obtained by multiplying g by a scaling factor K.

The universes of discourse of E, C, δ, e, c and g are:

E: -20 ~ +20	(Degree)	e: -10 ~ +10
C: -0.5 ~ +0.5	(Degree/sec)	c: -9 ~ +9
δ: -20 ~ +20	(Degree)	g: -10 ~ +10

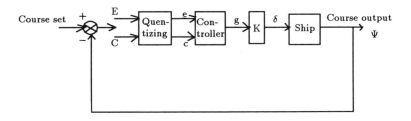

Figure 1: The simple fuzzy control autopilot

THE SELF-ORGANISING FUZZY CONTROL AUTOPILOT

The self organising controller is an extension of the simple fuzzy logic controller that incorporates performance feedback. It is a rule-based type of controller where the control strategy is created by controller itself. The block diagram of self-organising fuzzy control autopilot is shown in Figure 2.

In order to improve its control strategy, the self-organising controller must be able to assess its own performance. Because there is no analytical expression for the fuzzy controller, it is hard to assess its performance using a global criterion. Therefore it can be done only by using local performance measures.

The performance measure unit contains the performance index and the process model. The performance index measures the system output deviation and issues appropriate correcting commands at the controller output, the control inputs chosen are the fuzzy values of course error e and change in error c. The performance index rules are written to generate control rules. The linguistic rules are transformed into a look up table (decision table) of output commands using the standard techniques of fuzzy calculus. An example of the decision table is given in Table 1.

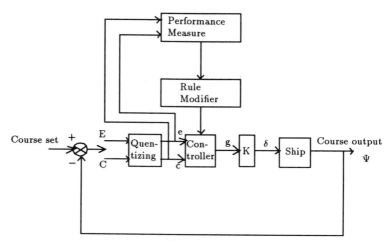

Figure 2: The block diagram of a self-organising fuzzy control autopilot

Table 1: An example of the decision table

g \ c e	-6	-5	-4	-3	-2	-1	0	1	2	3	4	5	6
-6	6	6	6	6	6	5	4	3	2	2	1	0	0
-5	6	6	6	6	5	4	3	2	2	1	0	0	0
-4	6	6	6	5	4	3	2	2	1	0	0	0	0
-3	6	6	5	4	3	2	1	0	0	0	0	0	0
-2	5	5	4	4	3	2	1	0	0	0	0	0	0
-1	4	4	3	3	2	1	0	0	0	0	0	0	0
-0	4	3	2	1	0	0	0	0	0	0	0	0	0
+0	4	3	2	1	0	0	0	0	0	0	0	0	0
+1	0	0	0	0	0	0	0	0	0	-1	-2	-3	-4
+2	0	0	0	0	0	0	-1	-2	-3	-4	-4	-5	-5
+3	0	0	0	0	0	0	-1	-2	-3	-4	-5	-6	-6

+4	0	0	0	0	-1	-2	-2	-3	-4	-5	-6	-6	-6
+5	0	0	0	-1	-2	-2	-3	-4	-5	-6	-6	-6	-6
+6	0	0	-1	-2	-2	-3	-4	-5	-6	-6	-6	-6	-6

It is known that the trajectory of a ship during course keeping has the profile as shown in Figure 3. At time t_1, the autopilot gives a rudder angle δ_1. At time t_2, C is reduced to zero and E is equal to E_{max} and the rudder angle is δ_2. At time t_3 E is equal to zero and C should be very small. For a different track curve δ_1 is the same and the time $T_p = t_2 - t_1$ is varied due to the change in steering characteristics of the ship and sea conditions. Using T_p the steering quality of the ship at any time can be assessed. Furthermore the decision table of the controller can be modified.

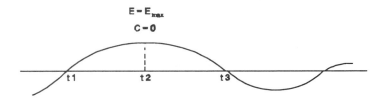

Figure 3: The trajectory of a ship during course keeping

But what is the standard to assess T_p? Here the Nomoto first order model is used.

$$T\frac{dr}{dt} + r = k\delta \qquad (1)$$

where r=dψ/dt and δ denote the yaw rate and the actual rudder angle respectively. From Equation (1) the yaw rate r can be obtained:

$$r = k\delta + (r_0 - k\delta)e^{-\frac{t}{T}} \qquad (2)$$

where r_0 is the initial value of r.

A theoretical value T_c, corresponding to the actual value T_p, can be obtained roughly under normal conditions:

$$T_c = -T \ln(\frac{k\delta}{k\delta - r_0}) \qquad (3)$$

T_c is taken as the standard to assess T_p and the decision table of the controller can be modified as follows:

> If T_p is much larger than T_c (for example $T_p > 1.5T_c$) or T_p is much smaller than T_c (for example $T_p < 0.5T_c$), then the g_1 is increased ,or decreased to the next level. When the time is at t_3 if C is too big (negative big or positive big), the g_2 also will be increased or decreased to the next level.

The rule modifier is the essential part in the process of learning. It changes the rules which form the control strategy and stores them in the rules buffer as a new rule to be used for control and modification purposes. When the process output is not the desired one, it is assumed that some past action taken by the controller has caused that output and should therefore be modified.

Thus according to local performance measures the controller parameters can be modified automatically.

SIMULATIONS

The system was simulated using the single input (rudder angle) and single output (yaw) control system. The yawing response to the rudder motion was derived. The ship's model used was the Nomoto second order model:

$$T_1 T_2 \frac{d^2 r}{dt^2} + (T_1 + T_2)\frac{dr}{dt} + r = k\delta + kT_3\frac{d\delta}{dt} \qquad (4)$$

The parameters T_1, T_2, T_3 and k were determined by actual sea trials. The ships name is *Yuhong* (13 000t). To reduce the effect of the non-linearity, T_1, T_2, T_3 and k were given different values when the rudder angle was different. For comparison, the experimental data and simulation results of the zig-zag trial are given in Figure 4. Figure 5 shows the results of simulation. During this course-keeping process a random disturbance was added to the input.

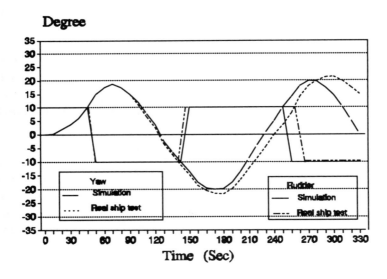

Figure 4: The actual and simulative curves of the zig-zag trial

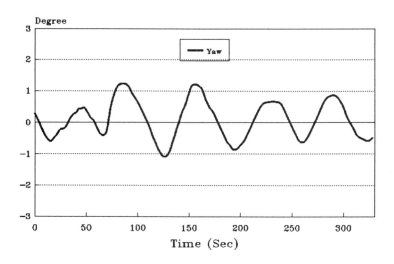

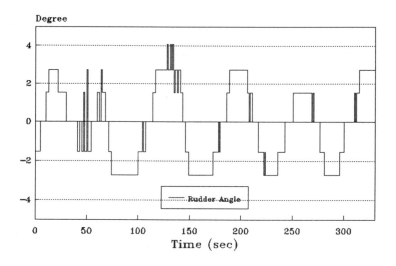

Figure 5: The curves of simulation

CONCLUSIONS

From the simulation result we can see:

1. The accuracy during course-keeping is high (the total area along the zero course error axis between port side and starboard is very closed) and the average error is very small even in case where the disturbance is considerably large.

2. Because the output of the controller, rudder angle, is small, the loss of speed is small also, which means that propulsion energy of the ship can be reduced.

3. The controller is relatively insensitive to noise and thus the number of rudder calls per unit of time is small. It also means that propulsion energy of the ship is reduced.

4. The simulation result is very closed the real ship test as shown in Figure 4.

In the future, further research on the self-organising fuzzy control autopilot based on experiments at sea will be done. These will compare the self-organising fuzzy control autopilot with the non-fuzzy control autopilot.

REFERENCES

1. Procyk, T.J. and Mamdani, E.H. 'A Linguistic Self-Organizing Process Controller' *Automatica,* Vol. 15, pp. 15-17, 1979

2. Amerongen, J. van., Nauta Lemke, H.R. van. and Veen, J.C.T. van der. 'An Autopilot for Ships Designed with Fuzzy Sets'. *Digital Computer Applications to process control,* ed. Van Nauta Lemke, pp. 479 - 488, IFAC and North-Holland Publishing Company, 1977.

3. Naomi, Kato and Michimass, Endo. 'Guidance and Control of Unmanned, Untethered Submersible for Rendezvous and Docking with Underwater Station' in Oceans/89, pp. 804 - 809, *Proceedings of the Conf. Oceans'89,* Publ. by IEEE Service Centre, 1989.

4. Jiang, J.H. and Lu, X.R. 'Development of Adaptive Track-keeping module with the Course Loop of Fuzzy Control' in IMECE/91, pp.187 - 194, *Proceedings of the International Maritime Electrotechnical Conference & Exhibition,* Shanghai, China, 1991.

5. Wakilen, B.A.M. and Gill, K.F. 'Robot Control Using Self-Organising Fuzzy Logic' *Computer in Industry*, pp.175-186,1990.

6. Tanscheit, R. and Scharf, E.M. 'Experiments with the Use of a Rule-Based Self-Organising Controller for Robotics Applications', *Fuzzy Sets and Systems*, Vol. 26, 1988.

A Fuzzy Autopilot for Small Vessels

M.N. Polkinghorne (*), R.S. Burns (*),
G.N. Roberts (**)
*(*) Polytechnic South West, Drake Circus,
Plymouth PL4 8AA, UK*
*(**) Royal Naval Engineering College, Manadon,
Plymouth PL5 3AQ, UK*

ABSTRACT

A fuzzy logic controller is developed for a small maritime vessel. Responses in both course-changing and course-keeping modes are investigated and compared to a classical PID autopilot over a typical range of weather conditions.

1. INTRODUCTION

In the 1920's automation of the ship steering process began. With technological advancements the achievable performance and competence in the range of sea-keeping roles has increased.

The majority of current autopilots are based on the Proportional plus Integral plus Derivative (PID) controller and have fixed parameters that meet specified conditions. In practice maritime vessels are non-linear systems. Any changes in speed, water depth or mass may cause a change in dynamic characteristics. Additionally the severity of the weather will alter the disturbance effects caused by wind, waves and current.

Despite the PID autopilot having settings to adjust course and rudder deadbands [1] to compensate for vessel or environmental changes, the resulting performance is often far from optimal, causing excess fuel consumption and rudder wear. These effects are particularly apparent in small vessels whose sensitivity to disturbances and controller setting is far greater than that with large ships. Modern control techniques of H° [2], Optimality [3], Self-tuning [4], [5], and Model Reference [6] have been applied to such vessels in attempts to improve performance.

Fuzzy logic controllers are thought to be robust enabling them to cope with changes arising in ship dynamics and sea conditions. Based on Fuzzy set theory as proposed by Zadeh [7] they have found maritime applications including submersibles [8], ships [9], [10] and torpedoes [11].

Of the autopilots in use today, a significant proportion can be found on small vessels. Given their increased susceptibility to disturbances, it is important to discover if the fuzzy controller designs applied to large vessels [10] can successfully be utilised on small ships, and whether such a controller can then operate with equal success over the range of typical disturbance conditions.

In this paper the application of fuzzy logic control in the development of an autopilot for small vessels is presented, with comparisons made to a tuned PID autopilot.

2. VESSEL AND DISTURBANCE MODELS

Models for both vessel dynamics in yaw, and for the disturbances and wave, wind and current had to be generated as a pre-requisite for fuzzy logic controller design and evaluation.

2.1 Yaw dynamics

A pc based Runge-Kutta integration routine was utilised for the model simulation. This investigation used a Nomoto model [12] of the form:

$$\frac{\psi(s)}{\delta(s)} = \frac{0.3848(s+0.603)}{s(s+1.656)(s+0.3874)} \tag{1}$$

where: $\psi(s)$ = Yaw (output of vessel model).

$\delta(s)$ = Actual rudder plus disturbance effects (input to vessel model).

The model of the 11 metre vessel for a speed of 8 knots was derived from hydrodynamic coefficients. Rudder dynamics were modelled as a linear function with a time constant of 1 second and saturation limits of ±20°.

2.2 Wave disturbances

In order to simulate ship behaviour with any degree of realism it is essential to include disturbance effects.

In any one place on the sea's surface a combination of waves will be present, all with different frequencies, heights and phase relationships. This combination for a fully developed sea can be described by a wave energy density spectrum. As a simple case all wave components may be regarded as travelling in a single direction giving a one dimensional sea. Pierson and Moskowitz [13] developed such a wave spectrum [Figure 1] based on the wind speed at 19.5 metres above the sea's surface and characterised for differing weather conditions by the significant wave height (swh), ie. the average height of the highest one third of waves.

$$S_{PM}(\omega) = \frac{A}{\omega^5} e^{-B/\omega^4} \qquad (2)$$

where: S_{PM} = spectral density ($m^2rad^{-1}s$)
         A = $0.0081g^2$
         B = $3.11/swh^2$
         g = gravitational acceleration.
         ω = frequency of encounter $rads^{-1}$

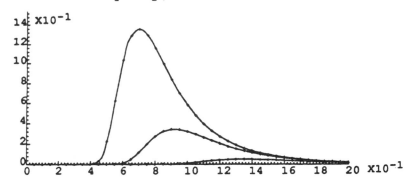

Figure 1: Wave Energy Density Spectrums

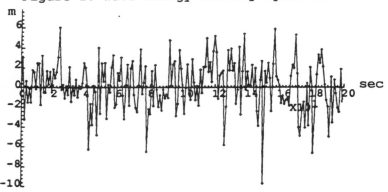

Figure 2: Wave Time History - Sea State 5

Based on the spectrums shown in Figure 1, a wave time history with zero mean for a given sea state code was generated using an Inverse Discrete Fourier Transform [Figure 2]. Table 1 was generated using sea state information and wind data from Sutton et al [15].

Table 1. Data For Sea State Codes

Sea State Code	Significant Wave Height (m)	Mean Wind Speed (ms^{-1})
1	0.05	1.51
2	0.30	3.70
3	0.88	6.34
4	1.88	9.25
5	3.25	14.75
6	5.00	15.11
7	7.50	18.50
8	11.50	22.91
9	>14.00	>23.00

By relating the sea state and wind in this manner it is possible to deduce the mean wind speed for a particular sea state.

2.3 Wind and current disturbance

Both the wind and current disturbances may be considered to act as a constant disturbance with a gusting factor by using a Gauss-Markov function, as developed by Burns [14], of the form:

$$U(k+1) = AU(k) + BW(k) \qquad (3)$$

where:
- $A = e^{T/T_c}$
- $T = 1$ sec (sampling time)
- $T_c = 10$ sec (Break frequency of 0.0159Hz)
- $B = 1-A$
- $U =$ Present value of gust (ms^{-1})
- $W =$ Gaussian random process gusting to ±20% of mean value.

The deterministic and stochastic elements were combined for wind and for current, [Figure 3].

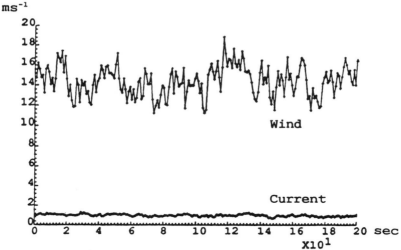

Figure 3: Wind and Current Time Histories
- Sea State 5

Based on the experience of an actual autopilot manufacturer, it was decided that the worst weather conditions that a small vessel would expect to be at sea, under autopilot control, would be sea state 5. The simulation conditions relating to sea state 5, ie. a swh of 3.25m, a wind speed of $14.75ms^{-1}$ and a current of $1.0ms^{-1}$, were therefore used for disturbance purposes in this investigation.

The forces and consequently the moments produced for each disturbance were scaled relative to the rudder moment and summed with the rudder input.

3. AUTOPILOT CONTROL

The autopilot may be considered to act in two modes, namely course-changing and course-keeping. The requirements for these two modes are:

Course-Changing - to reduce the yaw heading error with a minimum overshoot, settling time and rudder action.

Course-Keeping - to maintain the desired course with a minimum yaw heading error, rudder action and number of rudder calls, given the application of disturbances.

The final autopilot design requires both these modes to operate together. However, to aid this investigation the actions have been separated so that each mode may be considered individually.

3.1   PID autopilot

The classical PID autopilot used was of the form:

$$G_{c(s)} = K_p [1 + \frac{1}{T_i s} + T_d s] \qquad (4)$$

where: K_p = Proportional Gain
         T_i = Integral Action
         T_d = Derivative Action

For comparison with a Fuzzy controller, the PID autopilot was tuned for this particular vessel. In practice the autopilot is tuned for an approximate length of boat. The parameter settings then remain constant with the autopilot changing from course-changing to course-keeping modes when the yaw heading error falls within a specified band. The size of the band is set by the user and depends on the weather.

To allow consistent comparison between the PID and fuzzy logic designs, the possible deadbands and weather settings were ignored. The PID controller was tuned to minimise the root mean square (RMS) yaw error with optimum controller parameters being K_p = 1.6, T_d = 2.0 seconds and T_i = 100 seconds for course-changing, [Figures 4 & 5], and K_p = 12, T_d = 10 seconds and T_i = 0.1 seconds for course-keeping, [Figures 6 & 7].

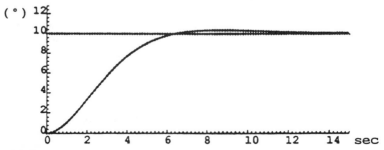

Figure 4: Yaw Response (PID) for 10° Heading Change

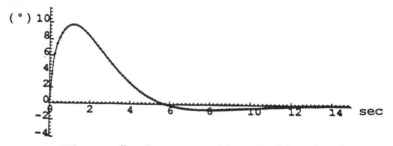

Figure 5: Corresponding Rudder Action

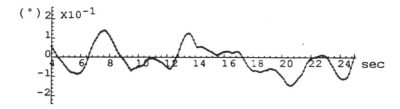

Figure 6: Yaw Response (PID) - Sea State 5

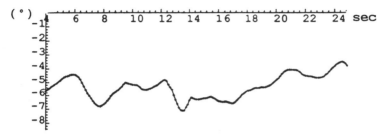

Figure 7: Corresponding Rudder Action

4.   FUZZY LOGIC AUTOPILOT DESIGN

The fuzzy logic controller utilised in this investigation is closely related to the work by Farbrother and Stacey [8] with its descendancy traceable through Sutton [16] back to the early work by Van Amerongen et al [9].

The input variables of yaw error and yaw rate are converted to fuzzy values by their associated input windows, each containing seven triangular fuzzy sets [Figures 8 & 9]. These sets are symmetrical in shape about a set point. Each set is given the linguistic label Positive Big (PB), Positive Medium (PM), Positive Small (PS), About Zero (Z), Negative Small (NS), Negative Medium (NM), or Negative Big (NB).

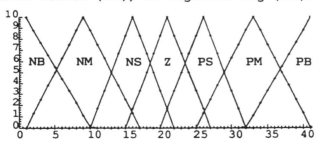

Figure 8: Yaw Error Input Window

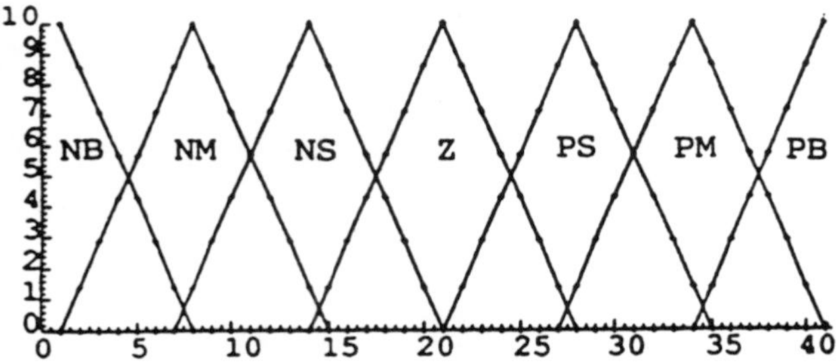

Figure 9: Yaw Error Rate Input Window

The fuzzy logic controller is constructed around a rule base [Figure 10], each rule being of the type:

IF (Condition A) **AND** (Condition B) **THEN** (Action)

ce \ e	NB	NM	NS	Z	PS	PM	PB
NB	NB	NB	NB	NM	Z	PM	PB
NM	NB	NB	NB	NM	PS	PM	PB
NS	NB	NB	NM	NS	PS	PM	PB
Z	NB	NM	NS	Z	PS	PM	PB
PS	NB	NM	NS	PS	PM	PB	PB
PM	NB	NM	NS	PM	PB	PB	PB
PB	NB	NM	Z	PM	PB	PB	PB

Figure 10: Fuzzy Rule Base

The nature of the input windows ensures that several rules may be activated together, the output of each rule being modified by a weighting term. The output window contains seven asymmetrical sets [Figure 11] which due to previous work [8] is known to create a smoother output from the controller. By employing the centre of area method to all the active output sets, a deterministic controller output may be obtained.

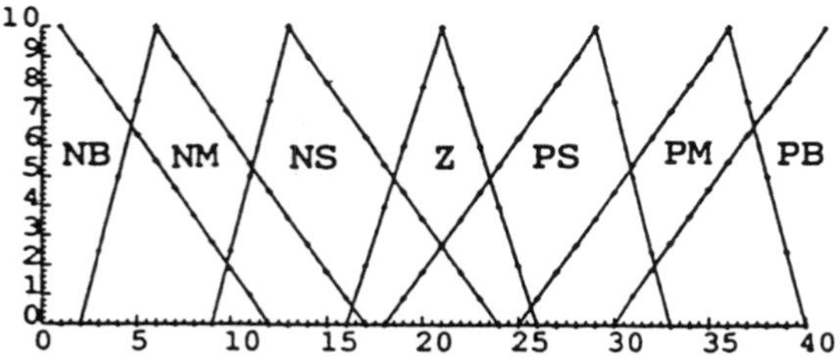

Figure 11: Rudder Output Window

4.1   Course-Changing Fuzzy Logic Autopilot

The window limits for yaw error (e) and rate (ce) were varied to obtain the optimum performance. Output window limits were maintained at ±20° to fully utilise the available rudder movement. The RMS values for both yaw error and rudder action were recorded for analysis.

Based on a step change in yaw of 10°, the fuzzy logic controller was also tuned to minimise the RMS yaw error with final window limits of yaw error ±11.5°, rate ±4.5°s⁻¹ and rudder ±20°, [Figures 12 & 13].

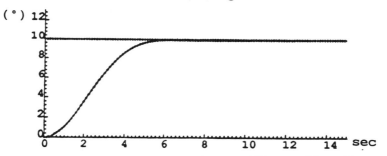

Figure 12: Yaw Response (FUZZY) for 10° Heading Change

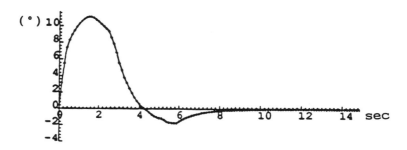

Figure 13: Corresponding Rudder Action

Having established optimum parameters, the controller was subjected to a step change demand in yaw of 30° to indicate the obtainable performance across the typical course-changing envelope. The results are shown in Table 2 where it can be seen that the fuzzy logic controller clearly reduced the RMS yaw error 'across the board' whilst for smaller changes in heading an increase in RMS rudder action was apparent.

Table 2. Course-Changing Results for Fuzzy
Logic and PID Autopilots

	PID Controller	Fuzzy Logic Controller	Fuzzy Logic Improvement
Step Size 10°			
RMS Yaw Error (°)	3.65	3.53	+3.3%
RMS Rudder Action (°)	3.79	4.26	-12.5%
Step Size 30°			
RMS Yaw Error (°)	12.51	10.03	+19.8%
RMS Rudder Action (°)	9.21	8.78	+4.7%

4.2   Course-Keeping Fuzzy Logic Autopilot

As with the course-changing autopilot, the window limits for yaw error and rate were adjusted to obtain an optimum value of RMS yaw error.   The final window limits with the disturbance inputs of sea state 5 were yaw error ±0.3°, rate ±0.2°s⁻¹ and rudder ±20°, [Figures 14 & 15].

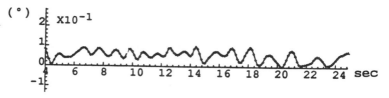

Figure 14: Yaw Response (FUZZY) - Sea State 5

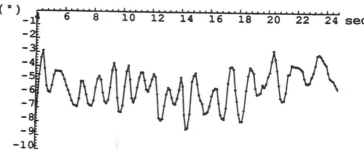

Figure 15: Corresponding Rudder Action

To test the robustness qualities of the fuzzy
logic controller over a range of significant operating
weather conditions, both the controllers were
subjected, without change, to sea state 3 weather
conditions, ie. a swh of 0.875m, a wind speed of
6.34ms^{-1} and a current of 0.1ms^{-1}. The results are
summarised by Table 3.

Table 3. Course-Keeping Results for Fuzzy Logic
and PID Autopilots

	PID Controller	Fuzzy Logic Controller	Fuzzy Logic Improvement
Sea State Code 5			
RMS Yaw Error (°)	0.068	0.059	+12.5%
RMS Rudder Action (°)	5.454	5.579	-2.2%
Sea State Code 3			
RMS Yaw Error (°)	0.022	0.007	+65.0%
RMS Rudder Action (°)	0.671	0.774	+15.0%

For sea state 5 weather conditions the Fuzzy Logic
controller proved more successful at minimising the RMS
yaw error. Following the application of sea state 3
conditions, the fuzzy autopilot demonstrated a further
increase in performance compared to that of the PID
autopilot.

5. CONCLUSIONS

The principles of fuzzy logic have been shown to
successfully control the yaw response of a small
vessel. In both course-changing and course-keeping
modes the fuzzy autopilot reduced the RMS yaw error
with only a slight rise in RMS rudder action. The
output of the fuzzy controller is naturally noisy and
could be improved by the addition of a filter which
would reduce the RMS rudder action.

The general performance of the fuzzy logic
controller has been shown to be superior to the PID
autopilot for the constant speed model. The next stage
in the investigation is to undertake a comprehensive

sensitivity analysis whereby the performance of the fuzzy logic autopilot in course-changing and course-keeping modes will be assessed for suitable variations in vessel dynamic characteristics.

ACKNOWLEDGEMENTS

The authors would like to thank the Marine Technology Directorate (SERC),Marinex Industries Ltd and the PSW for support to undertake the investigation into "Modelling and Control of Small Vessels", (Grant Ref Number GR/G21162).

6. REFERENCES

1. 747 Autopilot Owners Manual. Cetrek Ltd Ref 808-470/03.90. 1990.

2. Fairbairn N.R. and Grimble M.J., 'H° marine autopilot design for course-keeping and course-changing', 9th. Ship Control System Symposium, Vol.3, Bethesda. 1990.

3. Burns R.S., The design, development and implementation, of an optimal guidance system for ships in confined waters. 9th. Ship Control Systems Symposium, Vol.3, Bethesda. 1990

4. Tiano A. and Brink A.W., 'Self-tuning adaptive control of large ships in non-stationary conditions'. Int. Shipbuilding Progress, Vol.28. 1981.

5. Mort N. and Linkens D.A., 'Self-tuning controllers'. Proc. Symp. on Ship Steering and Automatic Control, Genova. 1980.

6. Van Amerongen J., 'Model reference adaptive autopilots for ships'. Automatica. 1975.

7. Zadeh L.A., 'Fuzzy sets'. Inform Control, Vol.8. 1965.

8. Farbrother H.N. and Stacey B.A., 'Fuzzy logic control of a remotely operated submersible'. Proc. Modelling and Control of Marine Craft, Exeter. 1990.

9. Van Amerongen J., Van Nauta Lemke H.R. and Van der Veen J.C.T., 'An autopilot for ships designed with fuzzy sets'. Proc. IFAC Conference on Digital Computer Applications to Process Control, The Hague. 1977.

10. Sutton R. and Towill D.R., 'An introduction to the use of fuzzy sets in the implementation of control algorithms'. Journal of IERE, Vol.55, No.10. 1985.

11. Jones A., Stacey B.A. and Sutton R., 'Fuzzy control of a three fin torpedo'. American Control Conference, San Diego. 1990.

12. Nomoto K., Taguchi T., Honda K. and Hirano S. 'On the steering qualities of ships'. Int. Shipbuilding Progress, Vol.4, No 35. 1957.

13. Pierson W.J. and Moskowitz L., A proposed spectral form for fully developed wind seas based on the similarity theory of S.A. Kitaigorodskii', Journal of Geophysical Research, Vol.69, No.24. 1964.

14. Burns R.S., The control of large ships in confined waters, PhD Thesis, Polytechnic South West. 1984.

15. Sutton R., Roberts G.N. and Fowler P.J.S., 'The scope and limitations of a self-organising fuzzy controller for warship roll stabilisation'. Proc. Int. Conference on Modelling and Control of Marine Craft, Exeter. 1990.

16. Sutton R. 'Fuzzy set models of the Helmsman steering a ship in course-keeping and course-changing modes', PhD Thesis RNEC/University of Wales. 1987.

H∞ Design Applied to Submarine Periscope Depth Keeping: S,KS and 4 Block Controllers Compared

W.B. Marshfield

Defence Research Agency, Haslar, Gosport, Hampshire, UK

ABSTRACT

The paper compares the performance of two submarine depth keeping autopilots in simulations of a submarine at periscope depth in sea state 5.

The two autopilots were both H∞ designs. The first used the S,KS design method while the second used a 4 block design which minimised the effects of heave force and pitch moment disturbances on the submarine.

The 4 block controller is shown to have superior depth keeping qualities as compared with the S,KS design.

1. INTRODUCTION.

This paper concerns the control of depth and pitch of a submarine at periscope depth under waves using H∞ design techniques. Figure 1 shows the axis system used in submarine simulation and controller design.

In this paper the submarine data used is that of the 80m submarine given in [1]. This describes a typical submarine with a length of 80m, a maximum diameter of 10 metres and a displacement of 5176 tonnes.

In general the depth control of a submarine is effected by means of bow and stern hydroplanes as also illustrated in Figure 1. These are fitted in pairs, port and starboard. The bow hydroplanes are usually all moving low aspect ratio hydrofoils with both port and starboard fixed to one shaft and moved by a single actuator. The stern hydroplanes are usually much larger and fixed to the hull. They have rear flaps to provide lift and again both port and starboard flaps are fixed to the same shaft and are moved by a single actuator. The maximum usable plane angle is around 20 degrees. This description applies to the 80m submarine considered here.

To run straight and level when submerged a submarine must be neutrally buoyant with the centre of gravity vertically below the centre of buoyancy, i.e there must be no pitch moment on the boat. Any hydrodynamic forces and moments must also be cancelled out and this is achieved by having small balance angles on the bow and stern hydroplanes.

Most autopilots have depth and pitch errors as inputs. Since depth and pitch rates are desirable these are either estimated in the autopilot or separately estimated using a Kalman filter. Integral terms are also used on occasion.

At high speeds depth control can be achieved using only the stern hydroplanes. In this case the submarine is treated as a SISO (Single Input Single Output) system with depth the output.

At low speeds both sets of hydroplanes are required, with the bow planes most effective in controlling depth and the stern hydroplanes controlling pitch. So in this case we have a 2 input 2 output system so that MIMO (Multi Input Multi Output) techniques are required.

The most difficult depth keeping scenario for a submarine is when it is at periscope depth with a high sea running. Here it is desirable to maintain the submarine at a constant depth relative to the calm surface with a zero mean pitch angle. The waves themselves provide large heave forces and pitch moments at the wave encounter frequency. These are called the first order wave forces. In addition there are smaller second order wave forces and moments which have a frequency content which is related to the envelope of the wave height. They also include a mean upward force and a pitch moment, which in the simulation used in this paper, is proportional to the mean pitch angle. It is the second order wave forces and moments which must be counteracted by the depth autopilot.

The first order wave frequency effects, which are around 0.1 Hz, are outside the control bandwidth of the vessel but they are inside the bandwidth of the hydroplane servos. The depth measurement usually comes from pressure transducers so that the depth signal is contaminated by noise at wave frequencies. Also the pitch moments due to the waves cause small, uncontrollable, pitch motions so that the pitch signal is also contaminated by wave noise. The gain of most autopilots is quite high at the wave frequencies so that the wave noise on the inputs can cause considerable plane motions which serve no useful purpose in controlling the submarine. [2] described tracking notch filters which can be used to reduce hydroplane activity. These filters were used in the simulations described in this paper.

2. SYSTEM DESCRIPTION.
The simulation program in which the controller designs were tested is a version of SUBSEA [3] which uses a subset of the

equations given in [4]. The terms in the equations are mostly
speed dependent hydrodynamic coefficients. By fixing the speed,
and setting any remaining nonlinear coefficients to zero, a
linear set of equations can be defined which adequately describe
the submarine behaviour for small perturbations. For this paper
the speed was set at 6 (UK) knots (3.089 m/s).

For depth autopilot design we are only interested in depth and
pitch equations together with the body axis motions w and q.

The equations are described as follows:
$$E\dot{x} = Fx + Gu$$
where E is the inertia matrix, F is the force matrix and G is the
input matrix.
The state variables are x1 = w (m/s),
$$x2 = q \ (rad/s),$$
$$x3 = depth \ (m) \ and$$
$$x4 = pitch \ (radians).$$
Input 1 is bow planes and input 2 stern planes.
For autopilot design work these are converted to:
$$\dot{x} = Ax + Bu$$
$$y = Cx + Du$$
where D = 0 and the outputs are:
y1= depth (m) and y2 = pitch (degrees)
It is important that the outputs are scaled in units of
comparable size hence the change to degrees in the output. The
ABCD set for 6 knots is given in Appendix A.

3. THE AUTOPILOT.
Previous work applying H∞ techniques to submarine depth control
[5], showed that the S, KS design as proposed in [6] gave
controller designs which provided very good decoupling between
pitch and depth. This method solves the minimization problem

$$\text{Min}_K \left| \begin{matrix} W_1S \\ W_2KS \end{matrix} \right|_\infty$$

However the S,KS design does not explicitly take into account
input disturbances, which in the case of a submarine consist of
out of balance forces and moments, ie errors in obtaining neutral
buoyancy and zero trim or mean suction forces experienced at
periscope depth.

In order to improve performance in the face of trim and
compensation errors a so called 4 block minimization was carried
out. In this case the minimization is

$$\text{Min}_K \left| \begin{matrix} W_1S & W_1SG \\ W_2KS & W_2KSG \end{matrix} \right|_\infty$$

Figure 2 shows the augmented closed loop system for both
arrangements.

Rather than considering the v_2 input as the somewhat artificial disturbance in hydroplane demand the v_2 input was considered as force and moment disturbances. The detail of how this input was applied is shown in Figure 3. The additional B2 input matrix was

$$B2 = E^{-1}.S$$

where S is a scaling matrix which in the design illustrated here was

$$S = \begin{bmatrix} 5e+4 & 0 \\ 0 & 5e+5 \end{bmatrix}$$

The designs were carried out using the Safonov, Limebeer and Chiang algorithm in the Matlab Robust-Control toolbox [7]. In the case of the S,KS design the W_1 and W_2 were

$$W_1 = \begin{bmatrix} 1e+4.(1 + 10.s)/(1 + 2e+5.s) & 0.0 \\ 0.0 & 1e+4(1 + 2.5.s)/(1 + 5e+4.s) \end{bmatrix}$$

$$W_2 = \begin{bmatrix} 1e-6.(1 + 2.5e+6.s/(1 + 2.5e-3.s) & 0.0 \\ 0.0 & 1e-6 (1 + 2.5e+6.s/(1 + 2.5e-3.s) \end{bmatrix}$$

except that in order to get a solution W_2 was divided by 3.

For the 4 block design W_2 was as above and

$$W_1 = \begin{bmatrix} 1e+4.(1 + 20.s)/(1 + 4e+5.s) & 0.0 \\ 0.0 & 1e+4(1 + 10.s)/(1 + 2e+5.s) \end{bmatrix}$$

Simulations were carried out using a single parameter ITTC (International Towing Tank Conference) wave spectrum with a significant wave height of 3.0 m. This is a mid range sea state 5. The wave height spectrum is given by:

$$S(\omega) = \frac{A}{\omega^5} \exp(-B/\omega^4)$$

where $A = 0.0081g^2$ and $B = 3.11/\varsigma^2$.
g is acceleration due to gravity and ς is the significant wave height in metres.

The peak frequency is 0.725 rad/sec which has a wavelength of 117.3 metres. Simulations were carried out for head and following seas which gives the widest range in encountered frequency. At 6 knots in head seas the peak frequency is 0.891 rad/s and in following seas 0.560 rad/s. Figure 3 gives the wave height spectrum and the encountered wave height spectra. Note that in the following sea spectrum there is a discontinuity at 0.794 rad/sec. This is the encountered frequency for the wave whose group velocity is 6 Knots, (group velocity = $\frac{1}{2}g/\omega$). Wave frequencies above this are folded back to frequencies below 0.794.

In the simulation program the waves were represented by 64, regularly spaced, frequency components.

The waves were considered to be long crested, i.e. the crests were long compared with the boat length. This is unlikely to occur in reality but it does represent the limiting worse case as far as heave force and pitch moments are concerned for the headings considered here.

The simulations were carried out for periods of 2200 seconds. In plotting the results and obtaining the statistics of individual runs the first 200 seconds were ignored as these contained start-up transients.

4 RESULTS.
The mean and standard deviations for all the simulation runs are shown in Tables 1 and 2.

TABLE 1

	MEAN	STD DEV.
S,KS CONTROLLER HEAD SEAS		
DEPTH m	16.46	0.310
PITCH deg	0.0	0.392
BOW PLS deg	-6.53	4.79
STERN PLS deg	-5.46	4.10
4 BLOCK CONTROLLER HEAD SEAS		
DEPTH m	16.40	0.265
PITCH deg	0.0	0.423
BOW PLS deg	-6.50	4.67
STERN PLS deg	-5.47	4.32
S,KS CONTROLLER FOLLOWING SEAS		
DEPTH m	16.68	0.430
PITCH deg	0.0	0.771
BOW PLS deg	-2.49	6.09
STERN PLS deg	-2.90	6.00
4 BLOCK CONTROLLER FOLLOWING SEAS		
DEPTH m	16.39	0.343
PITCH deg	0.0	0.880
BOW PLS deg	-2.65	3.98
STERN PLS deg	-2.87	5.22

Figures 5 and 6 show plots of the head sea runs with the submarine properly trimmed. The set depth is 16.4 m to the boat axis. This is maintained by both autopilots (see Table 1), even in the presence of the suction force towards the surface indicated by the non-zero mean hydroplane angles. In the more difficult case of following seas, see Figures 7 and 8 and Table 1, the S,KS controller does show a mean depth error.

In both cases the S,KS controller attempts a stricter control of pitch than the 4 block, hence the larger amount of pitch frequencies appearing in the hydroplane traces, particularly the stern hydroplanes.

The 4 block controller is slightly better at keeping a mean depth at the expense of a small increase in pitch.

If trim error is introduced then a further difference between the two autopilots emerges. Figures 9 and 10 and Table 2 show simulations with a bow up trim error (pitch moment error) of 1.0e5 Nm. This causes the submarine to go off depth in head seas with the S,KS design but not with the 4 block design.

For both autopilots the gains are acceptable in that the full range of the hydroplanes are used without there being long periods in saturation.

5 CONCLUSIONS.
This paper has shown that a submarine depth keeping autopilot that is robust against both neutral buoyancy (compensation) and pitch moment (trim) errors can be designed using the 4 block approach described here. Such an autopilot is particularly useful at periscope depth under waves.

TABLE 2

	MEAN	STD DEV.
S,KS CONTROLLER HEAD SEAS 1E5 Nm TRIM ERROR		
DEPTH m	16.17	0.322
PITCH deg	0.0	0.398
BOW PLS deg	-7.60	4.92
STERN PLS deg	-5.49	4.19
4 BLK CONTROLLER HEAD SEAS 1E5 Nm TRIM ERROR		
DEPTH m	16.40	0.264
PITCH deg	0.0	0.423
BOW PLS deg	-7.26	4.63
STERN PLS deg	-5.25	4.28

REFERENCES

[1]   Marshfield, W. B.
        Submarine data set for use in autopilot research.
        DRA Haslar, Gosport, Hampshire.
        DRA/MAR TM(MTH)92314 1992

[2]   Marshfield, W. B.
        Submarine periscope depth keeping using an H-infinity
        controller together with sea noise reduction filters.
        Trans. Inst. of Measurement and Control vol. 13 No 5, 1991

[3].   Meek, S.F.
        SUBSEA submarine simulation program.
        Defence Research Agency, Maritime Division computer
        program.

[4]   Feldman, J.
        DTNSRDC Revised standard submarine equations of motion.
        DTNSRDC/SPD-0393-09 1979

[5]   Williams, S. J., Marshfield, W. B.
        H-infinity multivariable design of a submarine depth
        control system.
        Proc. AMST 90 Bradford, 1990.

[6].   Postlethwaite, I., O'Young, S., and Gu, D.W.
        H∞ Control System Design: A critical approach based on
        industrial applications.
        10th IFAC Proceedings, Munich 1987.

[7]   Chiang R. Y., Safonov, M G.
        Robust-Control Toolbox for use with MATLAB.
        Mathworks Inc. 1988.

APPENDIX A

80m Submarine at 6 knots.

```
asub =      -3.8063e-2     8.9466e-1     1.9640e-5     1.4649e-3
             1.7116e-3    -9.2033e-2    -1.4455e-8    -5.5997e-3
             1.0           0.0           0.0           0.0
             0.0           1.0           0.0          -3.0886e+0

bsub =                     -7.5580e-3    -2.2909e-2
                            1.7345e-3    -2.2246e-3

csub =       0.0           0.0           1.0           0.0
             0.0           0.0           0.0          57.296

dsub =                      0.0           0.0
                            0.0           0.0
```

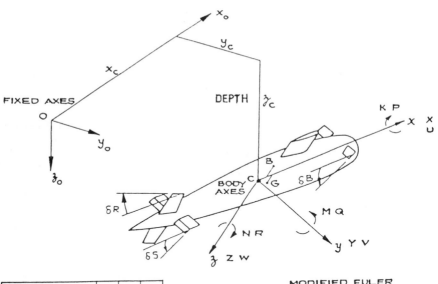

AXIS	x	y	z
VELOCITY	U	V	W
ANGULAR VELOCITY	P	Q	R
FORCE	X	Y	Z
MOMENT	K	M	N

MODIFIED EULER ANGLES.

ROLL ϕ
PITCH θ
HEADING ψ

FIGURE 1: AXIS SYSTEM

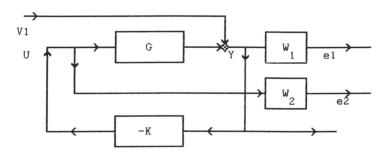

W₁S W₂KS AUGMENTED CLOSED LOOP SYSTEM

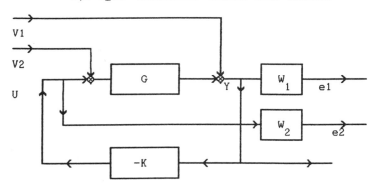

W₁S W₂KS W₁SG W₂KSG AUGMENTED CLOSED LOOP SYSTEM

FIGURE 2

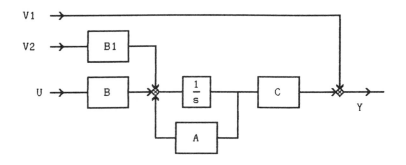

ABCD diagram of G above.

FIGURE 3: DETAILS OF V2 INPUT

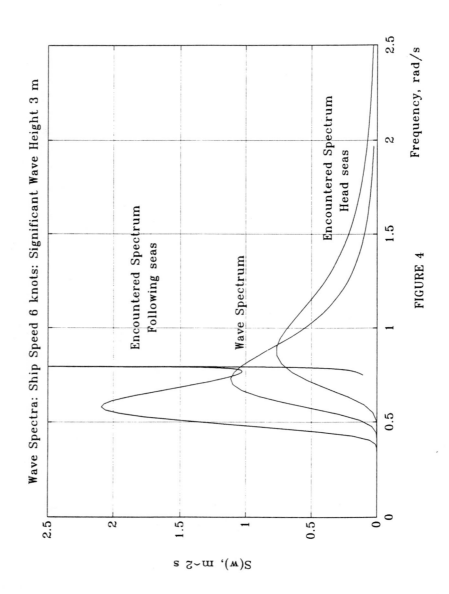

FIGURE 4

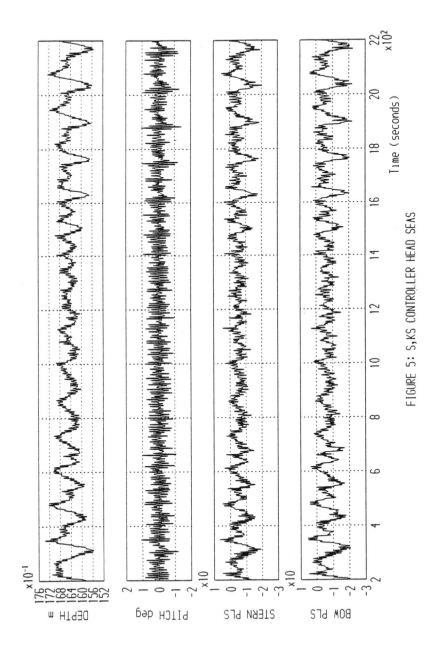

FIGURE 5: S,KS CONTROLLER HEAD SEAS

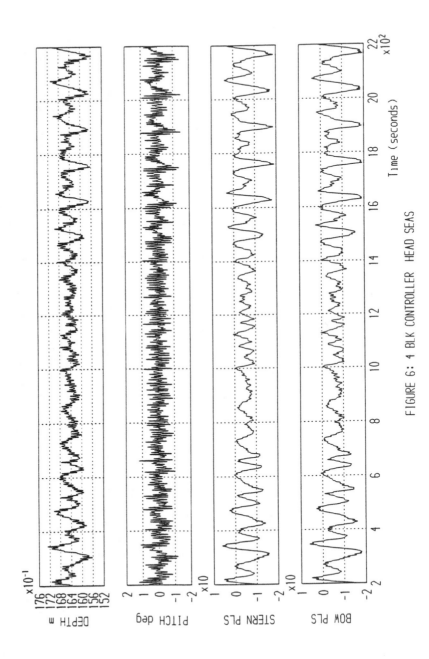

FIGURE 6: 4 BLK CONTROLLER HEAD SEAS

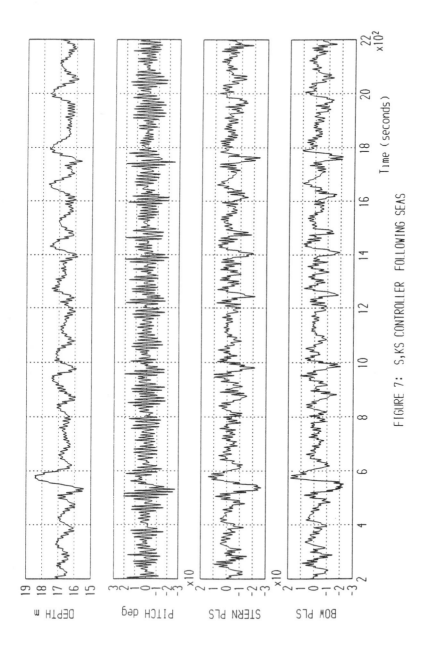

FIGURE 7: S,KS CONTROLLER FOLLOWING SEAS

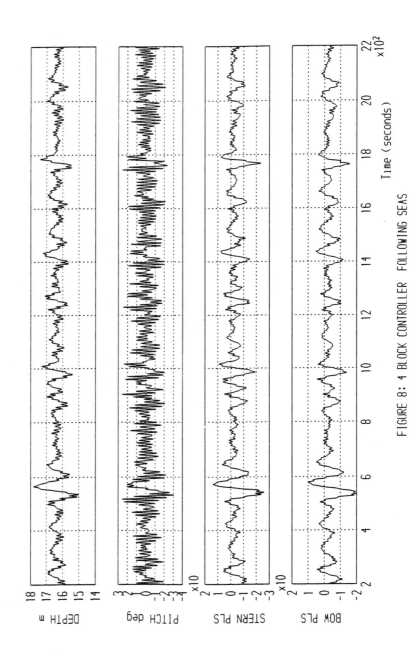

FIGURE 8: 4 BLOCK CONTROLLER FOLLOWING SEAS

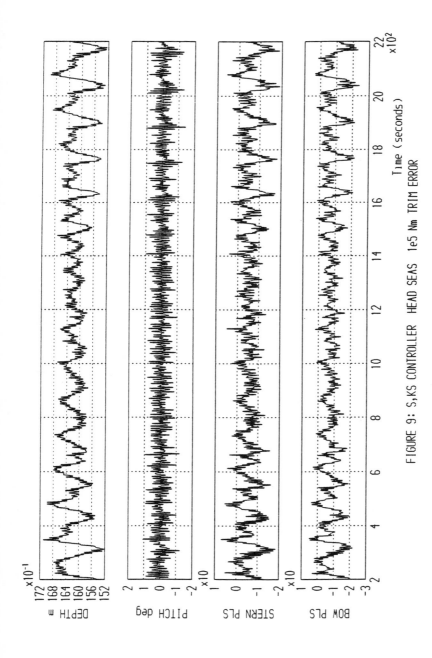

FIGURE 9: S,KS CONTROLLER HEAD SEAS 1e5 Nm TRIM ERROR

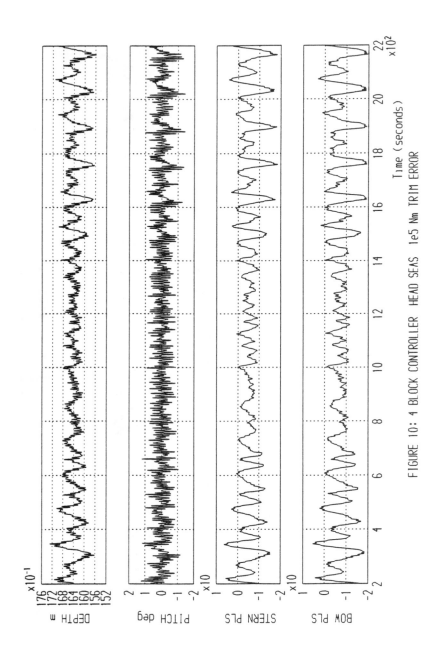

FIGURE 10: 4 BLOCK CONTROLLER HEAD SEAS 1e5 Nm TRIM ERROR

LFE Stabilisation Using the Rudder

A. Tang, P.A. Wilson
Department of Ship Science, University of Southampton, Highfield, Southampton SO9 5NH, UK

ABSTRACT

A numerical study has been carried out to examine the feasibility of LFE stabilisation using the rudder (RLS). Based on the experience gained from rudder roll stabilisation (RRS), comparisons have been made with RRS to assess the present results. It has been shown that LFE stabilisation using the rudder is feasible but an improvement in the frequency content of the feedback signal is needed to upgrade its performance.

INTRODUCTION

For the safe and efficient running of a ship, the motions of a ship in a seaway should be kept within acceptable levels in order that the human operators onboard ship can perform their tasks effectively. However, as the sea conditions worsen, it is inevitable that these limits would be exceeded and consequently, the operational effectiveness of the ship degraded. Based on some earlier studies, it has been shown in Monk [19] that the ability of a human operator to perform manual tasks would be reduced by 20 to 30% when subject to 6° of r.m.s. roll motions and as much as a 50% under 0.07g of r.m.s. lateral accelerations.

Naval architects, seeking to improve the motion characteristics of ships, have been researching into ship motion stabilisers over many years and successful stabilisation schemes have been developed, which have in turn enhanced the operability of ships. Up to now, the active fin stabiliser for reducing roll motions has proved to be very effective and is widely used by naval ships. More recently, the use of the rudder for stabilising roll, generally known as rudder roll stabilisation (RRS), has also shown very encouraging results. In this study, the aim is to apply the concept of RRS, but instead of using the roll angle for the control signal, the lateral force estimator (LFE), which is basically the lateral acceleration has been used.

Lateral Force Estimator

In a recent paper, Baitis et al [2] have introduced a performance index called the MOTION-INDUCED INTERRUPTION INDEX (MII) to assess the likelihood of disruptions to tasks due to ship motions. MII can be defined as an occasion when a crewman would have to stop working in his current task and hold on to some convenient anchorage to prevent loss of balance. Some applications of this index can be found in Baitis et al [2] and Graham [10]. According to Baitis et al [2], MII can be approximated by the perceived lateral accelerations or the so called lateral force estimator (LFE).

LFE is a vector sum of the rigid body accelerations in the plane of the deck, including a term directly proportional to the roll angle. It can be monitored readily on-board ship, providing a measure to quantify task performance. More recently, Monk [19] proposed to use LFE as a criterion for roll motions, suggesting 1.5 m/s^2 LFE at the bridge as a suitable limiting threshold for achieving satisfactory roll motions.

It is thus apparent that LFE has some bearing on the operational effectiveness of a ship and that a threshold LFE level is needed for the assessment of the safe running and maintenance of the ship. As a consequence, it would be natural to seek ways to suppress LFE. Roll stabilization systems that are currently fitted to all ship types are tuned to suppress roll motion only. According to Warhurst et al [30], "lateral accelerations caused by roll-reducing devices may be more harmful to human performance than some greater amount of roll". Thus in the first phase of this work, LFE stabilisation using the existing fin system has been explored (Tang [23]). In this work, encouraging results have been obtained and it was found that LFE levels can be further reduced with LFE stabilisation compared to the normal roll stabilisation, but this was only possible with the proper tuning of the control signal.

Intuitively, as the rudder is located near the flight deck where demanding manual work, it would be possible and beneficial to reduce LFE using the rudder. Furthermore, with the encouraging results from practical RRS installation, it led to the idea of LFE stabilisation using the rudder.

In the past, the LFE type stabilisation was known as stabilisation to the apparent vertical (Bell [4]). In essence, the apparent vertical measures the roll angle plus the equivalent roll angle induced by the sway accelerations relative to an earth fixed frame of reference. It is therefore similar to LFE, *but* they are not quite the same.

Rudder Roll Stabilization

Before embarking on a study of LFE stabilisation using the rudder (RLS), a review has been carried out on the development of RRS in order that information can be drawn to help assess the present work. A brief account of the review is given below to provide some background to the numerical study that follows.

The idea of using the rudder for roll stabilisation can be said to have been described for the first time in Taggart [22], in which excessive ship rolling was reported when the rudder was under automatic steering control. This idea was soon examined by the British researchers, for instance Cowley [7-9], Carley [5] and Lloyd [15], to assess its practical merits. From these studies, RRS seemed to have rather limited scope and be of little general practical interest. Moreover, it was the destabilising behaviour of RRS at high speed operations at quartering seas that has dampened further research temporarily.

The renewed interest in RRS over the last decade and the subsequent successful installation of RRS system on-board ship could be said to have been sparked off by the work published in Baitis [1]. The feasibility of RRS as an anti-rolling device was demonstrated in sea-trials with roll reductions of up to 50% of r.m.s. motions. It was suggested that simple roll rate feedback was the best comprise for simple control when adaptive controllers were not available. Following the recommendation in Whyte [31], Schmitke[21] performed some numerical studies on RRS using a ship motion computer program based on strip theories. Despite the better performance of the fin system for reducing roll motions, it was pointed out that the performance of RRS can be improved by up-grading the rudder actuator dynamics. At this stage of the RRS development, new impetus from the Swedish and Dutch research effort has carried the concept of RRS back to the fore, and eventually brought it to practical realisation in the late 1980s. The Swedish effort can be summarised in the papers by Kallström and co-workers [11-13]. From their work, it was recommended that the minimum ship speed should be at least 10 knots and a rudder rate of 4°/sec if RRS were to be effective. The Dutch work has been fairly well-documented in a series of papers by van Amerogen et al [25-28] and Van der Klugt [29]. In their work, it was found that the major problem was rudder rate saturation, which was due to the fairly sluggish rudder servo dynamics. It was suggested that a rudder rate of 15°/sec would be required for RRS system. During some sea-trials, the destabilising effects due to high speed operations in quartering seas were encountered. More recent work by Baitis et al [3], Katebi [14] and other researchers are now concentrating on refining the controllers of the RRS system.

Numerical Model

The numerical study was performed using a general sea-keeping computer program PAT-86 (Loader [18]) for ship motions predictions and design studies. The lateral motions part of the program is based on the theory in Schmitke [20], and confidence in the numerical predictions has been gained over the years. Although it is common knowledge that roll damping predictions are only accurate in the beam sea conditions (Lloyd et al [17]), it is not unreasonable to expect useful information to be gained on a comparative basis for the LFE system.

From Lloyd [16], it can be shown that

$$LFE = \ddot{y} - z\,\ddot{\varphi} + x\,\ddot{\chi} - g\,\varphi \qquad (1)$$

for small roll amplitudes, where x,y,z are the co-ordinates of the point in question relative to the L.C.G. and φ and χ are the roll and yaw angles respectively. Generally speaking, the yaw acceleration term would be of secondary importance and would only be considered significant near the bow or the stern of a vessel. Close to the centre of gravity (c.g.), the roll acceleration term can be assumed negligible, leaving the sway acceleration coupled with the roll angle term, which is not unsimilar to the apparent vertical in Bell [4].

Equation (1) was used to replace the roll angle term in the transfer function in the numerical model, giving

$$\frac{\alpha}{LFE} = K' \left[\frac{K_1 + K_2 s + K_3 s^2}{b_1 + b_2 s + b_3 s^2} \right]$$

where K_1, K_2 and K_3 which are the LFE, its first derivative and its second derivative gain levels respectively to be specified, while b_1, b_2 and b_3, are the rudder angle, velocity and acceleration gain levels, which are fairly standard for a chosen control system. A tuning procedure discussed in Lloyd [16] has been followed for the selection of the K_i values. More details about tuning for LFE can be found in Theobald [24].

As evident from RRS applications, the rudder rate is an important factor to the success of stabilisation scheme using the rudder. It has been suggested that for most Royal Navy ships, a rudder rate of 6°/sec is a representative value. This corresponds to a r.m.s. value of 2.8°/sec for 10% exceedance. Furthermore, according to Van Amerogen [27], the rudder rate would impose a limit on the maximum rudder angle possible, which is related to the natural roll frequency and rudder rate of the vessel. In the present study, this rudder limit would be about 10°, which corresponds to a r.m.s. value of about 4.5°. However, for the numerical results shown here, this limit has not been exceeded.

Numerical Model Test Case

As the use of the rudder/roll option of this numerical model has been scarce, the first task of the work is to establish some confidence in the numerical predictions when the rudder is applied. This can be accomplished by comparing the rudder forced roll data with some sea-trial measurements. The comparisons are plotted in fig.1, where 'T' denotes sea-trials data. It can be seen that the numerical model compares very well to the measured data. The good comparison is somewhat fortuitous as the wake and the effect of propeller are not modelled. However, from a ship dynamic view-point, it would not be unreasonable to make a comparative study based on this model, especially when the low frequency yaw-roll interaction is so well predicted. The yaw response shown in fig.2 is typical of sea-trial measurements.

The next test was to use the rudder option for RRS to see if the destabilising behaviour of RRS at high speed in quartering seas could be predicted. This was done by means of simple roll rate feedback to the rudder controller. The computer model was set at a ship speed of 15 and 30 knots with an ITTC two parameter sea spectrum of 12.4 seconds modal period and 5.5m significant wave height (long-crested). The resulting r.m.s. LFE and roll response are shown in fig.3 and 4, where 'U' and 'S' denote stabilised and unstabilised respectively. It is evident from these figures that while good reduction both in roll and LFE were obtained at 15 knots, motion amplification did occur in the quartering seas region when the ship was running at 30 knots. This corresponded to the 0.02 Hz predicted in Carley [6] and Lloyd [15]. A glance at the rudder rate response did not reveal any abnormal behaviour and in fact the activities were fairly low.

Thus the rudder/roll dynamics are quite well predicted by the present numerical scheme which is ready to be used for examining RLS.

Tuning for RLS

It was pointed out in Tang [23] that the proper tuning of the LFE control signal is vital if successful LFE stabilisation was to be achieved with active fins. The same would be true when applied to the present case. Therefore, following the procedure in Lloyd [16] for tuning active fins for roll, an optimum tuning frequency was sought for RLS.

It was anticipated that at a certain frequency, a minimum response would be found for a given rudder amplitude as was the case in tuning the active fins for LFE stabilisation. However, it was found that in the RLS, this minimum response did not exist within the practical range of tuning frequencies envisaged. The tuning procedure seemed to suggest that for RLS, the lower the tuning frequency the better would be the response as illustrated in fig.5. This should not be realisable in practice as at low frequency, the yaw induced roll interference would put a lower limit on the tuning frequency.

In order to select the best tuning frequency, it would be easier to make a comparison of different sets of tuning in a sea-way. The gain levels were selected by trial and error till the rudder rate at beam seas would be just below the rate limit of 2.8° /sec. This was a rather time-consuming process but it did allow a better choice to be made. To avoid the likelihood of undesirable yaw interference, the response spectrum value for yaw at the lowest frequency component was examined. An example of these values for tuning frequency is shown in fig.6, where 'B' to 'G' denote different tuning frequencies with 'B' being the lowest frequency. It is apparent that the lowest tuning frequency has given the highest yaw response value as anticipated.

RLS and RRS

Having obtained reasonable performance with the optimum tuning case, a comparison was made between the RRS simple rate feedback, RLS optimum (denoted by 'C') and RLS with simple rate feedback to assess the RLS strategy. A wave spectrum of 5.5 m significant wave height with a modal period of 12.4 seconds was used, and the ship speed was set at 20 knots. The gains of the three cases were adjusted under beam sea condition until the rudder rate of 2.8°/sec was obtained.

The resulting roll and LFE responses are given fig.7 and fig.8. In both cases, it is apparent that RRS performs far better than RLS and that the optimum RLS is better than the RLS with simple rate feedback. Also, looking at the yaw spectrum values for the three cases in fig.9, the RLS options are more likely to interfere with the yaw dynamics.

The main reason behind the better performance of RRS can be explained with the help of the rudder and roll response spectrum, which are shown in fig. 10. The 'l' in the legend denotes RLS while the 'r' denotes RRS. It is obvious that the rudder in the RRS case counteract the roll motion far better especially near the natural roll frequency. Near this frequency, the rudder activities in RRS are about five times the corresponding RLS system value. Furthermore, the RLS rudder shows a relatively high response at high frequency which does little to suppress the dominant rolling near the natural frequency. This high frequency response content is related to the sway term in the LFE signal.

Concluding Remarks

It has been shown that LFE stabilisation using the rudder is feasible. However, improvements should be sought if this strategy is to be of any significance to ship motion control comparing to the RRS approach. One way to improve RLS would be to filter out the high frequency content in the LFE feedback signal. This is currently under investigation.

Symbols

α rudder angle
s   Laplace transform j ω
K_1 displacement gain in controller
K_2 velocity gain in controller

K_3 acceleration gain in controller
b_1 rudder displacement gain
b_2 rudder velocity gain
b_3 rudder acceleration gain

Axis System

x   +ve forward
y   +ve starboard
z   +ve downward
φ roll +ve starboard
χ yaw +ve starboard

Acknowledgement
This project is funded by a MOD (PE) contract and is supervised by Dr. A.R.J.M. Lloyd.

References

1. Baitis   E. et al. 'Rudder roll stabilization for coast guard cutters and frigates' *Naval Engineers Journal*, 1985.

2. Baitis E. et al. 'Human factors considerations applied to operations of the FFG-8 and Lamps MK III' *Naval Engineers Journal*, 1984.

3. Baitis E. & Schmidt L. 'Ship roll stabilization in the U.S. navy' *Naval Engineers Journal*, 1989.

4. Bell J. 'Stabilization to the apparent vertical-measurement of sway' *Transaction of the Royal Institution of Naval Architects*, vol 107, 1965.

5. Carley J.B. & Duberley A. ' Design considerations for optimum ship motion control ' *Proceedings of the 3rd ship control system symposium*, Vol.C, U.K., 1972.

6. Carley J.B. ' Feasibility study of steering and stabilising by rudder ' *Proceedings of the 4th ship control system symposium*, Vol.2, Netherlands, 1972.

7. Cowley W.E. & Lambert T.H. ' The use of the rudder as roll stabiliser ' *Proceedings of the 3rd ship control system symposium*, Vol.C, U.K., 1972.

8. Cowley W.E. ' Development of an autopilot to control yaw and roll' *The Naval Architect*, January, 1972.

9. Cowley W.E. & Lambert T.H. ' Sea trials on a roll stabilizer using the ship's rudder ' *Proceedings of the 4th ship control system symposium*, Vol.2, Netherlands, 1974.

10. Graham R. 'Motion-induced interruptions as ship operability criteria' *Naval Engineers Journal*, 1990.

11. Kallström C.G. ' Control of Yaw and roll by a rudder/fin-stabilisation system ' *Proceedings of the 6th ship control system symposium*, Vol.2, Ottawa, 1981.

12. Kallström C.G. et al ' Roll reduction by rudder control ' *SNAME Spring Meeting STAR Symposium*, Pittsburg, 1988.

13. Kallström C.G. ' An integrated rudder control system for roll damping and course maintenance ' *Proceedings of the 9th ship control system symposium*, Vol.3, Maryland, 1990.

14. Katebi M.R. et al ' LQG autopilot and rudder roll stabilisation control system design' *Proceedings of the 8th ship control system symposium*, Vol.3, The Hague, 1987.

15. Lloyd A.R.J.M. ' Roll stabilisation by rudder ' *Proceedings of the 4th ship control system symposium*, Vol.2, Netherlands, 1975.

16. Lloyd A.R.J.M. *Seakeeping: Ship behaviour in rough weather* Ellis Horwood publisher, 1989.

17. Lloyd A.R.J.M. and Crossland P. 'Motions of a steered model warship in oblique waves' *The Royal Institution of Naval Architects, April Spring Meeting*, 1989.

18. Loader P. and Andrew R.N. 'User guide for the PAT-86 Suite of Ship Motion Computer Programs (U)' *AMTE(UHR) TM86301*, 1986

19. Monk K. 'A warship roll criterion' *Transaction of the Royal Institution of Naval Architects*, vol 130, 1988.

20. Schmitke R.T. 'Prediction of ship roll, sway and yaw motions in oblique waves' *D.R.E.A. report 77/4*, 1978.

21. Schmitke R.T. ' The influence of displacement, hull form, appendages, metacentric height and stabilization on frigate rolling in irregular seas ' *SNAME Spring Meeting STAR Symposium*, California, 1980.

22. Taggart R. ' Anomalous behaviour of merchant ship steering systems ' *Marine Technology*, April, 1970.

23. Tang A. & Wilson P.A. ' Lateral Force Estimator Stabilisation ' *CAMS '92 Control Application in Marine Systems*, Genova, April, 1992.

24. Theobald A.K. 'Initial investigation into lateral force estimator stabilization' *Ship Science report, University of Southampton*, 1986.

25. Van Amerogen J. & Van Cappelle J.C. ' Mathematical modelling for rudder roll stabilisation ' *Proceedings of the 6th ship control system symposium*, Vol.1, Ottawa, 1981.

26. Van Amerogen J. et al ' Rudder roll stabilisation ' *Proceedings of the 4th International Symposium on Ship Operation Automation*, Vol.10, Genoa, 1983.

27. Van Amerogen J. et al ' Roll stabilisation of ship by means of the rudder ' *Proceeding of the 3rd Workshop on Applications Of Adaptive Systems Theory*, U.S.A., 1983.

28. Van Amerogen J. et al ' Model test and full-scale trials with a rudder roll stabilisation system ' *Proceedings of the 7th ship control system symposium*, Vol.1, U.K., 1984.

29. Van Der Klugt P. ' Rudder roll stabilization: The Dutch solution' *Naval Engineers Journal*, May, 1990.

30. Warhurst F. et al. ' Evaluation of the performance of human operators as a function of ship motion' *Naval Ship Research and Development Centre Report 2828*, 1969.

31. Whyte P.H. ' A note on the application of modern control theory to ship roll stabilisation ' *18th A.T.T.C.*, Maryland, 1977.

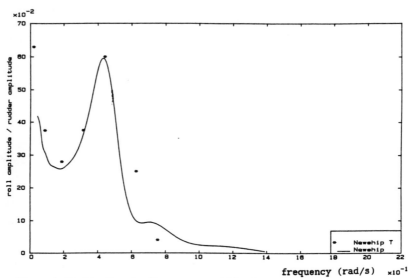

Figure 1: Rudder forced roll response at 18 knots

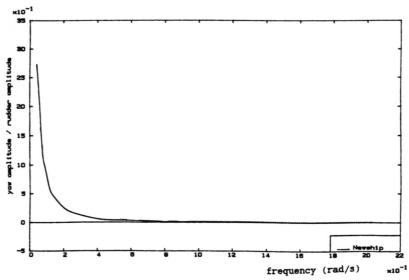

Figure 2: Yaw response due to rudder forced roll at 18 knots

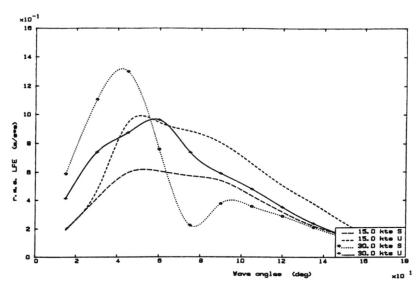

Figure 3: LFE response with rudder roll stabilization

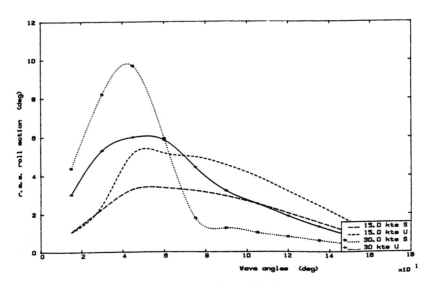

Figure 4: Roll response with rudder roll stabilisation

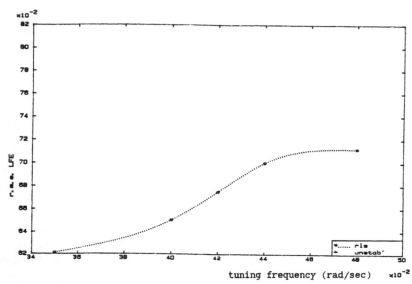

Figure 5: Tuning for RLS stabilisation

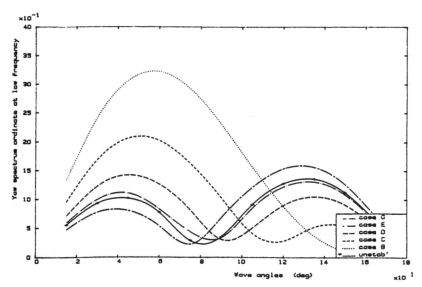

Figure 6: Effect of tuning frequency on yaw response with RLS stabilisation

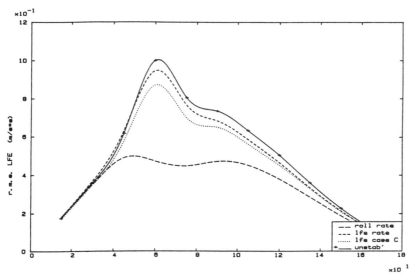

Figure 7: LFE response with different rudder stabilisation control strategies

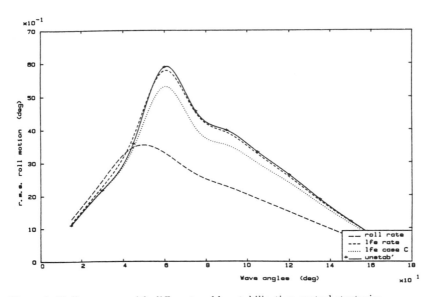

Figure 8: Roll response with different rudder stabilisation control strategies

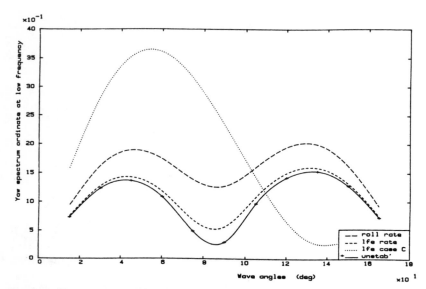

Figure 9: Yaw response with different rudder stabilisation control strategies

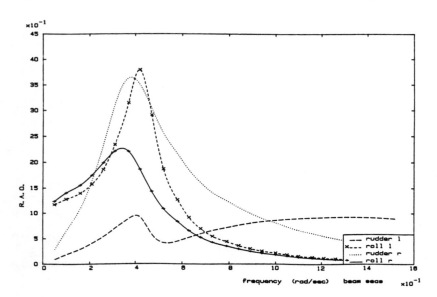

Figure 10: Response spectrum with RRS and RLS

Ship Motion Control

G.N. Roberts

Control Engineering Department, Royal Naval Engineering College, Manadon, Plymouth PL5 3AQ, UK

ABSTRACT

The problem addressed in this paper is the integration of the control surfaces in order to achieve enhanced course-keeping and course-changing characteristics of ships. Integrated control strategies for course-changing and course-keeping are discussed and the results from simulation studies on warship motion control are presented which demonstrate the effectiveness of such control strategies.

1. INTRODUCTION

The need for good ship motion control stems from the requirement for an efficient ship. Often efficiency in this context is defined in terms of; course-keeping, fuel economy, stability, etc. and depends to a large extent on the use of a vessel. Good course-keeping for example, is directly related to fuel economy, whereas the reduction of roll motion is a necessity for passenger and/or crew comfort although improved course-keeping and hence fuel economy also result.

Minorski [1] in 1922 established the six degree of freedom model for the dynamic motions of a ship at sea, and later work by Bhattacharyya [2] and others quantified the cross-coupling which exists between the various degrees freedom. It is however mainly yaw and roll motions which employ active control systems, and it remains normal practice, with very few exceptions, to approach ship motion control as independent designs of individual control loops. This is particularly for warships where autopilots are used to minimise yaw excursions from set course, and an active fin

stabilisation system to regulate roll motion.   This
configuration is depicted by Figure 1.

These single-loop controllers are normally "tuned"
to minimise the effects of the environmental
disturbances ie. wind, current and sea-state.   With
this approach however little or no attempt is made to
take account of output disturbances resulting from the
cross-coupling effects, and as a result a situation can
arise where the two control loops are working in
opposition.   Figure 2 shows the actual multivariable
relationships between roll and yaw and the inputs of
stabiliser fin and rudder positions.   There is
therefore room for improvement upon the current control
strategy depicted by Figure 1, and it would seem likely
that control strategies taking cross-coupling into
account will lead to improvements in ship motion
control.

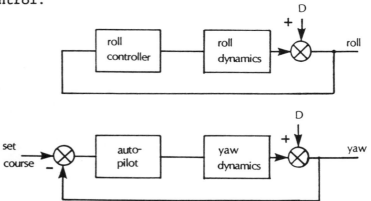

Figure 1: Current Warship Motion Control Configuration

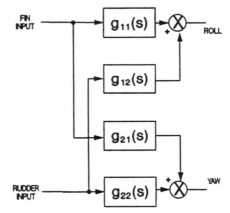

Figure 2: Multivariable Ship Model

It is important to note that it is not the case that all cross-coupling is detrimental to ship motion control and as is the case with flight control systems cross-coupling can be and often is used to advantage. There is a need therefore to consider the multivariable nature of ship dynamics with respect to the two modes of ship operation viz. course-keeping and course-changing.

2. DESIGN STUDY

The warship model used for the design study is that proposed in Whalley and Westcot [3], and later validated by the author [4]. Details of the individual transfer functions of the transfer function Matrix, G(s), are given in Table 1.

Table 1. Elements of Ship Dynamics

$$g_{11}(s) = \frac{0.25k_{11}}{s^2 + 0.235s + 0.25}$$

$$g_{12}(s) = \frac{0.25k_{12}(1 - 4.5s)}{(1 + 8.2s)(s^2 + 0.25s + 0.25)}$$

$$g_{22}(s) = \frac{k_{22}}{s(1 + 0.43s)(1 + 6.62s)(1 + 4.25s)}$$

The ship has two sets of stabiliser fins fitted fore and aft about the ship's turning centre so that the cross-coupling between yaw and stabiliser fin is negligible, ie. $g_{21}(s)$ is zero. The non-linearity of ship dynamics are represented by variation of steady-state gain terms with speed. These variations are shown in Table 2.

Table 2. Speed related Gain Variations

Speed knots	k_{11}	k_{12}	k_{22}
12	0.114	-0.33	0.01
18	0.18	-0.465	0.02

2.1 Course-Changing Mode

In the course-changing or manoeuvring mode large
rudder demands are commonplace and the interaction
between rudder and roll is the significant factor,
particularly during manoeuvres executed at high and
medium speeds. The roll motion induced during such
manoeuvres is undesirable for reasons of safety,
passenger comfort and crew efficiency. Safety is a
factor because successive port and starboard manoeuvres
can under some conditions lead to such excessive roll
motion that capsize is a distinct possibility.
Passenger and crew comfort are also extremely important
for commercial reasons, and in the case of warships
excessive roll motion significantly degrades
operational effectiveness because of reduced crew
efficiency and restrictions imposed on helicopter
operations.

One method for removing interaction of cross-
coupling in multivariable systems is by adopting a non-
interacting-control strategy. This strategy is shown
by Figure 3 where the pre-compensator, D(s), is
introduced to account for the interaction in G(s) ie.
to make the pair G(s).D(s) diagonal.

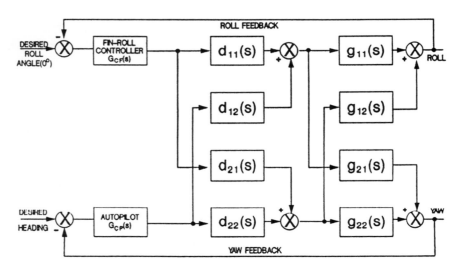

Figure 3: Integrated Course-Changing Configuration

2.1.1 Pre-compensator Design

There are a number of design methods available for

the synthesis of the pre-compensator $D(s)$ ie. Fricker [5] and Whalley [6]. However, in this case as $g_{21}(s)$ is zero then $d_{12}(s)$ will also be zero, and by selecting $d_{11}(s)$ and $d_{22}(s)$ as unity, $d_{12}(s)$ is simply defined as $-g_{12}(s)/g_{11}(s)$. What this means is that the rudder demand signal is fed to the fin servomechanism, via the shaping filter defined by $d_{12}(s)$, so that the resulting fin displacement causes roll motion which anticipates and hence cancels the roll motion which would have been induced by the rudder displacement.

Simulation studies enabled the performance of the pre-compensator over a range of ship speeds to be evaluated.   A typical result is shown by Figure 4, which is taken from the study described in [3] and [7]. This shows the roll motion resulting from a 50% step demand in rudder position, for a ship speed of 18 knots, with and without the pre-compensator included. It is clear from this figure that the rudder induced roll motion is virtually annihilated by the inclusion of the pre-compensator.

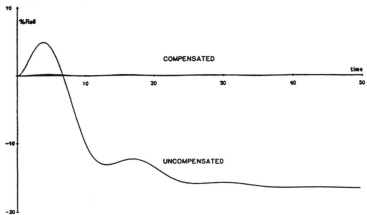

Figure 4: Compensated and uncompensated roll
responses 50% rudder demand - 18 knots

2.2 Course-Keeping Mode

In the course-keeping mode, under autopilot control as in Figure 1, normally rudder excursions not greater than ±5° are experienced. In addition as the rudder position will be constantly varying, average rudder induced roll motion will be negligible. In this mode however the rudder can be utilised to reduce roll motion ie. the so-called rudder roll stabilisation (RRS) technique. With this approach the initial inward heel induced by rudder deflection, as shown by the uncompensated response in Figure 4, can be used to counter roll motion caused by sea state disturbances. The rudder can be used in this way without adversely affecting yaw control because of the relatively fast dynamics of rudder to roll compared with the dynamics of rudder to yaw. When defined in terms of frequency responses the bandwidth of the rudder to roll loop extends in the order of a decade above that of the rudder to yaw loop.

RRS is not a new concept, it was first described by Cowley and Lambert in 1972 [8], and has been an area of active research and development since that time, [9] to [14]. These studies have shown that substantial roll reduction can be provided by RRS although a considerable increase in rudder speed is necessary for the rudder to approach the effectiveness of the stabilising fins. The Royal Netherlands Navy have taken this work further and have decided to adopt RRS for their M Class frigates, the first of which is currently undertaking acceptance trials [15].

The requirement for up to a three-fold increase in rudder speed means that roll stabilisation by the rudder alone can only be achieved after significant redesign and enhancement of the steering gear and therefore can only be considered a viable option for new ships or after a major refit. However, despite the effectiveness of a RRS system being governed by rudder speed, a measure of roll reduction can be achieved using rudder speeds currently available, and it would seem appropriate to use the rudder in concert with the existing stabilisation systems in order to enhance roll stabilisation. Such an integrated control strategy for roll stabilisation in the course-keeping mode is shown by Figure 5.

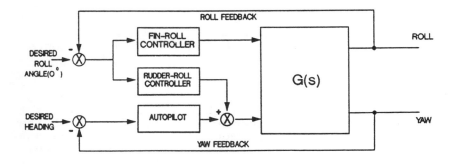

Figure 5: Integrated Configuration for Roll
          Stabilisation

2.2.1 Controller Design

From the configuration shown in Figure 5 it is clear that roll stabilisation results from the combined affects of the rudder and fin control loops, and accordingly controller design should take this into account. However, as the aim of this part of study was to investigate the feasibility of improving roll stabilisation, the existing fin/roll control loop was not disturbed. By adopting this approach the ship's existing roll stabilisation capability is not compromised, and a choice between roll stabilisation using the fins, the rudder or combined fins and rudder is made available to the command. A decision which can be made depending on the requirements at the time. Controller design in this case therefore involves selecting a suitable rudder/roll controller based on the existing "slow" rudder system.

Two distinct control philosophies have dominated the design of active roll stabilisation systems, with classical frequency-domain sensitivity analysis being the basis of the early fin/roll controller designs whilst more recently the Linear Quadratic Gaussian (LQG) technique has been used successfully. These design approaches are equally applicable to controllers designed for rudder/roll stabilisation, although the majority of designs reported in the open literature have employed LQG or derivatives of LQG.

For simplicity, in this study it was decided to use the same controller structure for the rudder/roll controller which is currently used for the fin/roll controller. This was because such a controller would be made available if sea trials were to take place. Hence the rudder/roll controller, $G_{cR}(s)$, was selected as:

$$Gc_R(s) = \frac{K_S(K + K_R s + K_A s^2)}{A_1 + A_2 s + A_3 s^2} \qquad (1)$$

where: K_S = Speed dependent gain

K = Roll angle sensitivity

K_R = Roll rate sensitivity

K_A = Roll acceleration sensitivity

and the denominator coefficients A_1, A_2 and A_3 are selected so that the phase-lag introduced at the ship's natural roll frequency is negligible.

The rudder/roll controller has to compensate for the phase-lag introduced by the rudder to roll dynamics $g_{12}(s)$, and the rudder servomechanism. The aim here is to make the phase-shift of the rudder/roll loop zero at the ship's natural roll frequency. This required phase advance is obtained by the selection of K, K_R and K_A whilst at the same time maximising roll reduction over the widest possible bandwidth and, minimising rudder activity for the whole spectra of sea disturbances.

There are of course many possible permutations of K, K_R and K_A which provide a solution to the zero phase specification at the ship's natural roll frequency. The implied cost function is however to avoid large gain values so that noise does not become a problem, and the position gain, K, should be five to ten times smaller than the velocity and acceleration gains, K_R and K_A, in order to keep yaw disturbances to a minimum. The final settings for the controller gains were arrived at by undertaking a comprehensive simulation study where the performance of the roll stabilisation system was evaluated for a range of ship speeds, encounter angles and sea states.

Having computed the relative settings for K, K_R and K_A, the speed related gain term, K_S, is adjusted to maintain an adequate gain margin. For reasons of brevity only a sample of results are presented here, a more detailed exposition of this aspect of the study can be found in [16] and [17]. A typical set of results is shown in Figure 6 and Figure 7 which give unstabilised and stabilised roll time histories and accompanying yaw disturbances for a beam sea when the ship is travelling at 18 knots in a sea state 5.

The improvement in roll stabilisation achieved the rudder and the fins are operating in concert, and the roll stabilisation which can be achieved by the rudder alone is clearly demonstrated by Figure 6. Results also indicated that because of the contribution to roll stabilisation by the rudder the fin activity was reduced by up to twenty per cent from that when using the fins alone. The relatively insignificant levels of yaw deviation, shown by Figure 7 confirm the bandwidth differences described earlier. The deviations are greater when using the rudder alone than those observed with the combined configuration because when used alone rudder demands are greater. Despite this, however it was found that maximum yaw deviation did not exceed a value of 0.6° for combined rudder and fin stabilis-ation, and 1.0° for rudder stabilisation alone.

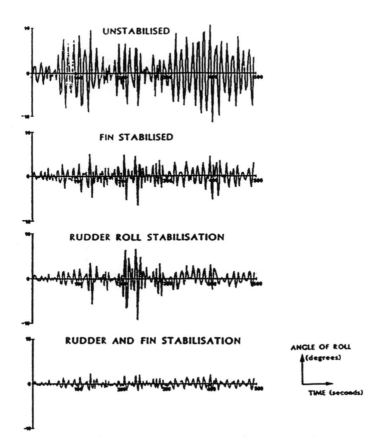

Figure 6: Unstabilised and Stabilised Roll Histories

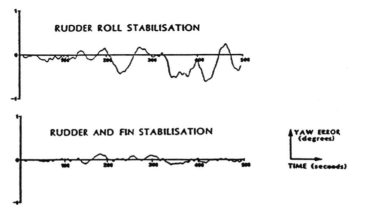

Figure 7: Comparison of Yaw Disturbances

3. CONCLUDING REMARKS

Methods of improving ship motion control for course-keeping and course-changing modes have been described. For course-changing it has been shown that by adopting a decoupled approach it is possible to reduce rudder induced roll motion during manoeuvres. Conversely, for course-keeping an integrated approach is seen to provide enhanced roll stabilisation. It is envisaged that the switch between course-changing and course-keeping modes would be software controlled, based on either the size of yaw error or by simply monitoring the desired course change input to the autopilot.

There is undoubtedly some further research necessary to evaluate maintenance and reliability problems posed by increased rudder and fin duty cycles however, it is clear that the major benefit of adopting the control strategies proposed herein is that the improvements in ship motion control can be achieved using existing sensors and actuators. For either mode the additional controller complexity is minimal and therefore represents an extremely inexpensive solution to the ship motion control problem.

4. REFERENCES

1.   Minorski N., 'Directional stability of automatically steered bodies', Journal of American Society of Engineers, Vol.34, pp280-309. 1922.

2.   Bhattacharyya R., Dynamics of Marine Vehicles, John Wyley and Sons. USA. 1978.

3.   Whalley R. and Westcott J.H., 'Ship motion control', Sixth Ship Control Systems Symposium, vol.3, Ottawa. 1986.

4.   Roberts G.N., 'Ship motion control using a multivariable approach', PhD Thesis, RNEC/ University of Wales College of Cardiff. 1989.

5.   Fricker A.J., 'The application of a direct method for designing decoupling pre-compensators for multivariable systems', Trans. Measurement and Control, Vol.6, No.4. 1984.

6.   Whalley R., 'Computation of decoupling pre-compensators for linear multivariable system models', Proceedings IMechE, Vol.202, No.C3. 1988.

7. Sutton R, Roberts G.N. and Mort N., 'A review of
    ship motion control research undertaken at RNEC
    Manadon', Transactions IMarE. Vol.103. Part 3.
    1991.

8. Cowley J.B. and Lambert T.H., 'The use of the
    rudder as a roll stabiliser', 3rd. Ship Control
    Systems Symposium, Bath. 1972.

9. Lloyd A.R.J.M., 'Roll stabilisation by rudder',
    4th. Ship Control Systems Symposium, The Hague.
    1975

10. Baitis A.E., Woolaver D.A. and Beck T.A., 'Rudder
    roll stabilisation for coastguard cutters and
    frigates', Naval Engineering Journal. 1983.

11. van der Klugt P.G.M., 'Rudder roll stabilisation',
    PhD Thesis, Delft University/van Reitschoten and
    Houwens BV, Rotterdam. 1987.

12. Katebi M.R., Wong D.K.K. and Grimble M.J., 'LQG
    autopilot and rudder roll stabilisation control
    system design', 8th. Ship Control System Symposium,
    The Hague. 1987.

13. van Amerongen J., 'Rudder roll damping experience
    in the Netherlands', IFAC Workshop: Control
    Applications in Marine Systems, Lyngby, Denmark.
    1989.

14. Kallstrom C.G. and Schultz W.L., 'An integrated
    rudder control system for roll damping and course
    maintenance, 9th. Ship Control System Symposium
    Vol.3. Bathesda. 1990.

15. van der Klugt P.G.M., 'Rudder Roll Stabilisation on
    board the HrMS Karel Doorman', Journal of Naval
    Engineering, Dec. 1991.

16. Roberts G.N. and Braham S.W., 'Warship roll
    stabilisation using integrated control of rudder
    and fins', 9th. Ship Control Systems Symposium,
    Bethesda, USA, Sept. 1990.

17. Roberts G.N. and Braham S.W., 'The control of
    warship rolling motion using the rudder and
    stabilising fins, IEE Computing & Control
    Engineering Journal. Vol.2, No.2. March. 1991.

Pitch and Roll Control Systems of the Hydrofoil Catamaran

H. Yamato, T. Koyama, N. Fujita

Department of Naval Architecture and Ocean Engineering, University of Tokyo, 7-3-1 Hongo, Bunkyo-ku, Tokyo 113, Japan

ABSTRACT

The pitch and roll control systems for the Hydrofoil Catamaran are de-signed and actual sea tested in this paper.   The hydrofoil catamaran was a twin hull supported by the fore and aft hydrofoils to achieve the high speed performance.   Hydrofoils have control surfaces to provide forces for the heave, pitch and roll control.   The pitch control system should be essential since the system can avoid the damage in the fore foil due to emergence.   The pitch control system is proposed as a proportional feedback control system using the foil depth.   On the other hand, the roll control system is very appreciable since the roll motion is apt to occur by the beam waves.   The H_∞ control theory was applied to the roll control system.   The system was intended to have the robustness and the less sensitivity to the disturbance.   These two systems were actually sea tested using the prototype ship named "Exceller", and found very prospective for the actual use in hydrofoil catamarans.

1. INTRODUCTION

The hydrofoil supported catamaran named Hydrofoil Catamaran has been developed in the towing tank at the University of Tokyo [1].   The conceptual design based on the towing tank testing has been found feasible upto the size of 4000 displacement ton with the multifoil configuration.   Prior to the development of the ship for commercial use, the small size prototype ship named "Exceller" has been built and tested at sea.   The Exceller was a 12 m in length experimental ship to validate the system which was designed based on the towing tank testing.   In Figure 1, the three-view and principal dimensions of the prototype ship Exceller were shown.   As for the control systems, it is very difficult to determine the characteristics of the control system hardware in the towing tank testing, and it is necessary to configure the system in the actual size.   The Exceller has the digital computer and

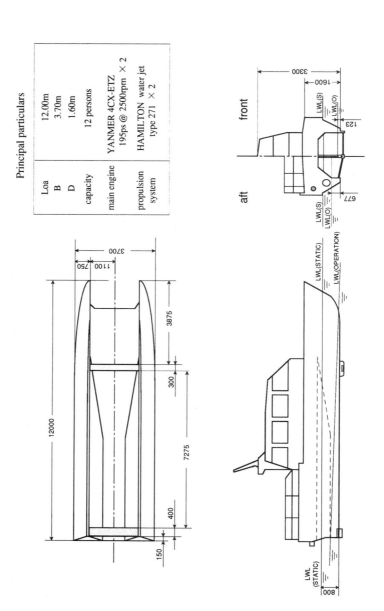

Figure 1: The three view and principal dimensions of the Exceller.

the servoactuator to form the control system using control surfaces on the foil and many kinds of the control can be applied on the ship very easily [2-4].

In this paper, the pitch and roll control systems validated in the Exceller was discussed. The dynamics of the ship was identified by the actual ship for the design of the control systems. The pitch control system will be of practical importance to avoid foil emergence if the ship becomes big and operates in the rough sea. Preliminary discussions for the foil depth control feedback system was developed in this paper. The roll motion which deteriorates the ride quality is very likely to occur due to the catamaran configuration. Taking the system uncertainty and disturbance into consideration, the H_∞ theory is a candidate among the robust control techniques, and it was applied to improve the roll performance [5,6]. Both systems were validated in actual sea and found very promising for the control of the hydrofoil catamarans.

2. THE EXCELLER AND THE ACTUAL SEA TESTING

The Exceller is a catamaran with fore and aft foils installed with the two Hamilton waterjet propulsion systems as shown in Figure 1. The draft of the ship reduces as the ship speed goes high since the foil provides the lift. The details of the foil and control surfaces are shown in Figure 2.

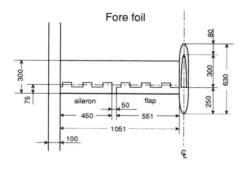

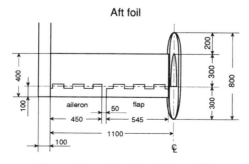

Figure 2:   Details of the foils.

Foils are supported by the demihull and the strut in the center line of the ship.   The aft foil has originally a dihedral angle which was removed later.   The outboard surfaces are used as ailerons to generate roll moment and the inboard ones are used as a flap for the longitudinal control.

In Figure 3, the control and data acquisition system is shown.

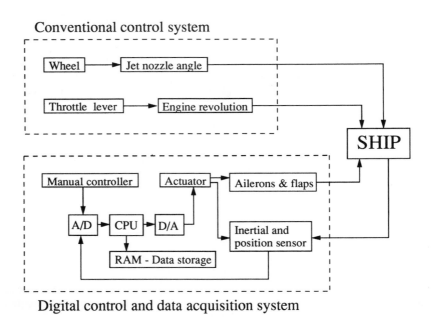

Figure 3:   The control and data acquisition system.

In the upper block, the conventional wheel and throttle lever system was shown.   In the lower block, the digital control and data acquisition system newly developed was shown.   The NEC PC-9801RA, the 32 bit personal computer, was installed as an onboard computer to execute control law algorithm and to accumulate 32 channel data in every 40 msec.   The command to the control surfaces are very easily given from the manual controller and the computer software.

The Exceller was built by Setouchi Craft Company in Onomichi, Japan, with the technical support from the University of Tokyo and Hitachi Zosen Company.   It became seaworthy in July 1990, and engineering sea trials has been made 40 days in an 8 series.

The sea testing was made in the Seto-naikai inland sea where the weather and sea states were basically very mild.   The tested items are listed in Figure 4.

Basic seaworthiness	Speed, Trim capability, Turning Acceleration, Stopping
Maneuver and control system design	(Pitch, heave & roll) Static balance, Control forces, Step & frequency responses (Yaw) Z-test, Frequency response
Control system verification	Pitch damper, Roll SCAS(PD) Roll SCAS(H$_\infty$), Foil depth control

Figure 4:   Tested items at sea.

3. PITCH CONTROL SYSTEM FOR THE HYDROFOIL CATAMARAN

First, the pitch damper was made to moderate the pitching motion of the ship.   However, the hydrofoil catamaran has inherent damping characteristics generated by the foils near bow and stern.
It seems most important to control the foil depth to avoid the damage due to foil emergence.   In this section, very fundamental considera-tion concerning the fore foil depth control system and results from the sea testing are presented.   The system is not fully developed for the practical use, but it provides a basis of the system to be developed.

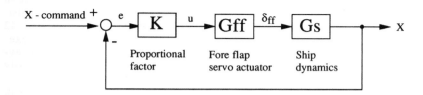

X: Fore foil depth

e : Error in fore frap depth

u : Control inpit

Figure 5:   The foil depth control system.

3.1   Pitch control system configuration

As shown in Figure 5, the foil depth control system was configured as a simple proportional feedback system.   The command was given to move the fore flap only.

The foil depth was estimated by the geometric relations using the ultrasonic height sensor and the pitch attitude from the gyro shown in Figure 6.

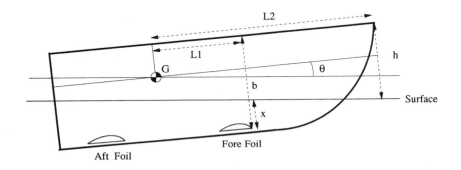

h : Ultrasonic height sensor
θ : Pitch attitude
x : Fore foil depth
G : Center of gravity

$$x = b + (L2 - L1) \tan \theta - h$$

Figure 6:   Geometric relations to obtain the foil depth.

The foil depth was calculated every 40 msec and it could be short enough since the vehicle moved 40 cm forward in that time in case of 20 kt.   The longitudinal position of the height sensor should be determined taking this lead length and the time constant of the pitching motion of the ship into account.

3.2   System verification by the prototype ship "Exceller"

The time history of the pitch control was shown in Figure 7.   In the upper most box, the command to the foil depth and actual foil depth determined by the equation in Figure 6 were shown. At first, the mean depth of the foil was 55 cm, and it increased to 63 cm when the 70 cm command was given in the stepwise at 400 sec.   The difference between the commanded and actual depth would not reduce any more since only proportional feedback was employed. In this chart, it is

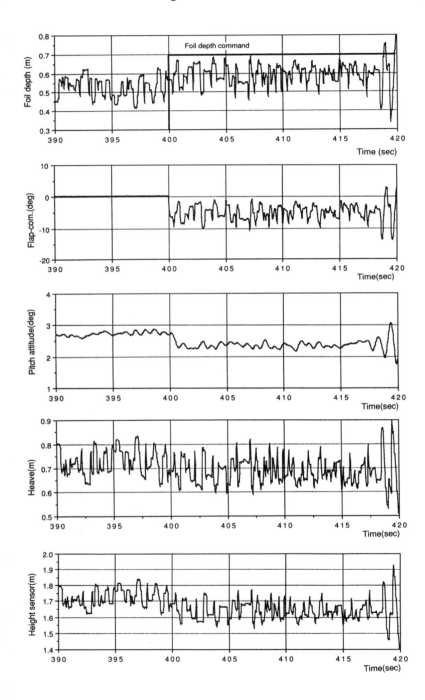

Figure 7: The time history of the foil depth control system.

not clear that the actual foil depth can be kept constant.   However, the system seemed to work well to the dangerous wave which was believed rather long.

The dynamics of the system, that is, measured foil depth to the foil depth command was shown in Figure 8 in terms of the Bode diagram. It can be seen that the system could work well for waves upto 0.5 Hz in the encounter frequency.

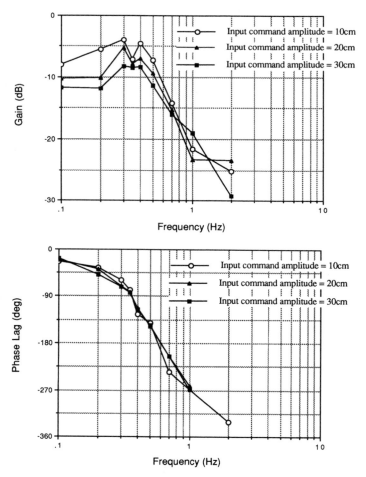

Figure 8:   Bode diagram of the foil depth to the foil depth command.

4. THE ROLL SCAS BASED ON THE H∞ THEORY

In 1990, the Roll Stability and Control Augmentation System (SCAS) was developed based on the conventional control technique and it was revealed to be very effective. In 1991, the H_∞ was applied to the system to add the robustness. The system changes as the speed changes and there are disturbances due to winds, waves and others.   These uncertainties and disturbances could be well managed by the robust control system.

4.1 H_∞ control theory
The idea and the treatment of the H_∞ control technique are summarized in this section.   The system was defined as the mixed sensitivity problem.   In Figure 9, the block diagram representing the problem was shown.

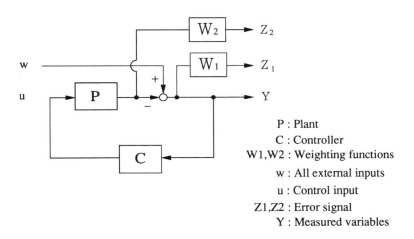

P : Plant
C : Controller
W1,W2 : Weighting functions
w : All external inputs
u : Control input
Z1,Z2 : Error signal
Y : Measured variables

Figure 9:   The mixed sensitivity problem for the H_∞ methodology.

P is the system to be controlled and u is the control input to the system. w_1 and w_2 are the weighting functions for the disturbance suppression and robustness respectively.   The sensitivity of the system to the disturbance y/w is improved by defining the weighting function w_1 in terms of the frequency.   If the sensitivity should be lowered for the specific frequency band, the w_1 should be taken large enough around the frequency band.   The weighting function w_2 should be taken large at some frequency band where the system's uncertainty is likely to occur.
The feedback gain C can be characterized by two weighting functions w_1 and w_2.   Weighting functions w_1 and w_2 have a relation with each other which corresponds to the complementary relationship between sensitivity to disturbance and the robustness to the system uncertainty.
As for the determination of the w_2, the system with uncertainty is assumed to be $P' = P(1 + \Delta)$, that is, $\Delta = (P' - P)/P$. Then the weighting function w_2 should be $|w_2(jw)| > |\Delta(jw)|$.

To obtain the feedback gain, two Riccati equations were derived as shown here.

$$\frac{dx}{dt} = Ax + B_1w + B_2u$$

$$z = C_1x + D_{11}w + D_{12}u$$

$$y = C_2x + D_{21}$$

assume   that

$$C_1^T D_{12} = 0, \qquad D_{12}^T D_{12} = I$$

$$D_{21}B_1^T = 0, \qquad D_{21}D_{21}^T = I$$

Controller is

$$C(s) = \hat{C}\hat{B}(sI - \hat{A}) + \hat{D}$$

$$\hat{A} = A + \gamma^{-2}B_1B_1^T P + B_2F + ZLC_2$$

$$\hat{B} = -ZL, \quad \hat{C} = F, \quad \hat{D} = 0$$

$$F = -B_2^T X_\infty, \quad L = -Y_\infty C_2 T,$$

$$Z = (I - \gamma^{-2}Y_\infty X_\infty)^{-1}$$

where

$$X_\infty = Ric(K_\infty)$$

$$K_\infty = \begin{pmatrix} A & \gamma^{-2}B_1B_1^T - B_2B_2^T \\ -C_1C_1^T & -A^T \end{pmatrix}$$

$$Y_\infty = Ric(J_\infty)$$

$$J_\infty = \begin{pmatrix} A^T & \gamma^{-2}C_1^T C_1 - C_2^T C_2 \\ -B_1B_1^T & -A \end{pmatrix}$$

γ : the positive constant, K_∞, J_∞ : the Hamiltonian matrices and $Ric(\ )$:   the solution of the Riccati equation. If the Hamiltonian matrix is

$$H = \begin{pmatrix} A & R \\ Q & -A^T \end{pmatrix}$$

then Riccati equation is

$$SA + A^T S + SRS - Q = 0$$

S : solution of Riccati equation

4.2   Design procedure of the Roll Stability and Control
       Augmentation System
The system uncertainty can be estimated by the roll dynamics identi-fication by the actual ship in various states.   In Figure 10, the

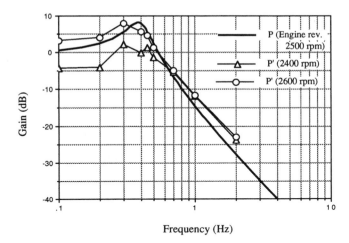

Figure 10:   The roll dynamics of the Exceller.

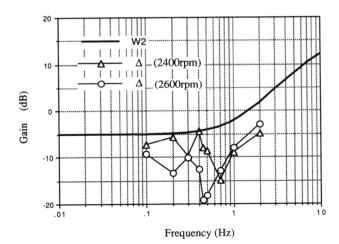

Figure 11:   weighting function w_2 and Δ

transfer function of the roll angle to the aileron deflection was shown in terms of the gain diagram.   The dynamics of the plant P was assumed as shown in Figure 10, however, data dispersed according to the speed change.   The speed change was expressed by the engine rpm.   The absolute value of Δ and the corresponding weighting function w_2 were shown in Figure 11.

According to the weighting function for the robustness w_2, the weighting function for the disturbance w_1 should be defined as shown in Figure 12.

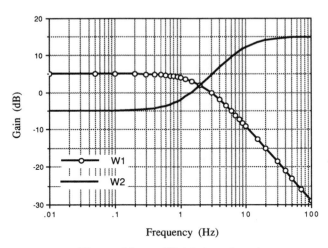

Frequency (Hz)

Figure 12:   Weighting functions.

As is understood here, there is considerable ambiguity to choose the weighting function. And the information concerning the phase lag is not included in the design procedure. It would be necessary to give a design guide to choose the weighting functions. The Riccati equations were solved by the diagonalization method.[7]

4.3   System verification by the prototype ship "Exceller"
The H∞ Roll SCAS was designed and installed on the Exceller and tested at sea.
In Figure 13, the typical time history of the roll motion was shown with the system on and off.   The effectiveness of the system can be seen very clearly.
The effectiveness of the system was tabulated in Figure 14 compared with the results by the roll control system made in 1990 based on the proportional and differential controller.
The system is a simple feedback of the roll angle and roll rate with gains which had been determined in the cabin at the speed of the 2500 rpm.
The roll motion is reduced to 74% by the H∞ Roll SCAS in terms of the root mean squares.   The robustness to the speed change can be seen comparing the roll angle in cases of the 2500 and 2600 rpm.   There is no difference in both values even if the speed changes.   And compared with the conventional system, the suppression was made very effectively with less aileron deflection.

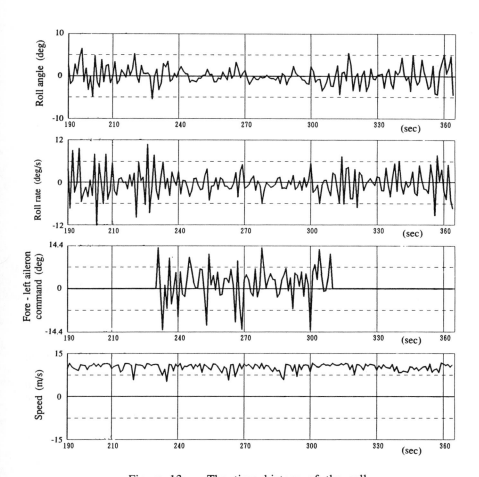

Figure 13:   The time history of the roll.

1	H ∞ Control	Speed : 20kt				
	Ctrl ON/OFF	OFF	ON	Ratios (ON/OFF ; %)	Aileron angle ratio (%)
	Roll angle (deg)	2.26	1.67	74.03	----
	Roll rate (deg/sec)	4.06	2.34	57.66	----
	Aileron angle (deg)	----	6.00	----	73.42
2	H ∞ Control	Speed : 22kt			
	Roll angle	2.13	1.58	74.04	----
	Roll rate	3.99	2.27	56.97	----
	Aileron angle	----	5.68	----	71.78
3	PD Control	Speed : 20kt			
	Roll angle	2.12	1.70	80.20	----
	Roll rate	3.94	2.42	61.37	----
	Aileron angle	----	7.83	----	100.00
4	PD Control	Speed : 22kt			
	Roll angle	2.36	1.86	78.90	----
	Roll rate	3.79	2.43	63.99	----
	Aileron angle	----	8.14	----	102.38
	Sea state : Wave height 40cm				

Figure 14:   The effectiveness of the Roll SCAS.

5. CONCLUDING REMARKS

The conclusion obtained in this paper is presented herein.

(1)   The pitch control system to keep the foil depth can be configured. To avoid foil emergence, the wave height sensor should be installed foreside to have enough time to make pitching motion by fore flaps.

(2)   The Roll SCAS based on the H_∞ methodology was developed and tested at sea and the system was shown to be very effective. The effectiveness of the system depends on the weighting functions. Discussions on the selection of the weighting functions should be necessary.

Through the system's development and the verification by the Exceller at sea, both the pitch and roll control system was reviewed intensively. The fundamental consideration and experience for the design of the control system for the commercial hydrofoil catamaran was provided by this paper.

ACKNOWLEDGEMENT

Authors would like to express their acknowledgements to Prof. Hideaki Miyata, University of Tokyo, Mr. Kiyotaka Matsuno, former president of Setouchi Craft, Co., Mr. Hiroshi Kawaguchi, Setouchi

Craft, Co., Mr. Tadao Takai, Hitachi Zosen, Co. and Mr. Masakazu
Enomoto, University of Tokyo. Prof. Miyata provided the concept and
leaded development of the Exceller. Mr. Matsuno and Mr. Kawaguchi
built the Exceller and gave us a chance and the support to make actual sea
testing. Mr. Takai and Mr. Enomoto were a very nice partnership to build
the control system.

REFERENCES

[1] Miyata, H. et al., Development of a New-Type Hydrofoil
Catamaran (1st Report: Configuration Design and Resistance
Properties.), J. of the Soc. of Naval Architects of Japan, Vol.162, pp.11-
19,1987.(in Japanese)

[2] Miyata, H. et al., Full-Scale Experiments of a Hydrofoil
Catamaran on a Steady Straight Course, J. of the Soc. of Naval
Architects of Japan, Vol.170, pp.15-22, 1991.(in Japanese)

[3] Yamato, H. et al., Full-Scale Experiments of Control System
for a Hydrofoil Catamaran, J.of the Soc. of Naval Architects of Japan,
Vol.170, pp.183-190, 1991.(in Japanese)

[4] Kawaguchi, H. et al., Full-Scale Experiments by the First
Hydrofoil Catamaran WINGSTAR 12 "Exceller", FAST'91,pp.1195-1213,
Proc. from the First International Conference on Fast Sea
Transportation, Vol.2, pp.1195-1213, Trondheim, Norway, TAPIR, June
1991.

[5] Glover, K. and Doyle, J.C., State Space Formulae for All
Stabilizing Controllers That Satisfy an H_∞-norm Bound and Relations
to Risk Sensitivity, Systems and Control Letters, Vol.11, No.3, pp.167-
172, 1988.

[6] Maciejowski, J.M., *Multivariable Feedback Design,* Addison-
Wesley, 1989.

[7] Kato, K., *An Introduction to the Optimal Control Theory*,
University of Tokyo Press, 1987.(in Japanese)

SECTION 7: MATHEMATICAL TECHNIQUES

Numerical Calculation of Steady Turning Performance of a Thin Ship

H. Yasukawa

Nagasaki Experimental Tank, Mitsubishi Heavy Industries, Ltd., 3-48 Bunkyo-Machi, Nagasaki 852, Japan

ABSTRACT

A method was developed to calculate the steady turning performance and the hydrodynamic forces of a thin ship under the assumption of a double-body flow. In the present method the lifting surface theory for expressing the hull and rudder, and the simple sink propeller model[5][6] are adopted. Numerical calculations were made of the turning performance for a simple hull form of full-scale length and of its model size, and the effect due to difference of frictional resistance and wake fraction between them is evaluated. As a result, it was shown that steady yaw rate and drifting angle are almost the same magnitude between two ships, however speed drop ratio of the full-scale ship is larger than that of the model.

1. INTRODUCTION

A ship in steady turning can be regarded hydrodynamically as a lifting body under circular motion. In 1956, Inoue evaluated the lifting force and moment acting on a turning ship hull represented by a flat plate[2] by applying the Bollay's wing theory[1]. This study is the first one of the investigation of ship's turning performance from the viewpoint of hydrodynamics. For evaluation of the turning performance, it is necessary to understand the hydrodynamic forces acting on the ship hull and hydrodynamic properties of the rudder and propeller. Further, interaction effects among them should be taken into consideration. Attempts, however, have not been made so far to deal with theoretically the hydrodynamic performance of the turning ship taking the interaction effects among the hull, rudder and propeller into account.

In this paper, a method is presented to calculate the steady turning performance and the hydrodynamic forces of a ship with single rudder and single propeller under the assumption of a double-body flow. In the present method the lifting surface theory for expressing the hull and rudder, and the simple sink propeller model[5][6] are adopted. In such a way, the problem of the hydrodynamic interactions among the hull, rudder and propeller are dealt with in the framework of the potential theory. For consideration of viscous effect, the empirical coefficients introduced by the present author[7] are also used. The present method features its capability to obtain the turning performance together with the hydrodynamic forces acting on the ship. Therefore, the mutual relation between the turning performance and the hydrodynamic properties of the hull, rudder and propeller can be grasped clearly. Numerical calculations are made of the turning performance for two Wigley parabolic hull forms of full-scale length and its model size. And the effect due to the difference of frictional resistance and wake fraction between them is evaluated. As a result, it was shown that steady yaw rate and drifting angle are almost the same magnitude between two ships, however speed drop ratio of the full-scale ship is larger than that of the model.

2. A METHOD TO CALCULATE THE STEADY TURNING PERFORMANCE
2.1 The Equations of Motion

We consider a steadily turning ship with propeller revolution n_P, rudder angle δ, drifting angle β and steady yaw rate r under constant velocity U. Referring to a right-hand Cartesian coordinate system $o\text{-}xyz$ whose origin is fixed at amidships as shown in Fig.1. We take $z=0$ as the plane of the undisturbed free-surface, the x-axis positive backward, and the z-axis positive upward. Further, we take a coordinate system o_1-$x_1 y_1 z_1$ whose origin is fixed at the leading edge of the rudder. The z_1-axis lies at $x=x_{RO}$, $y=0$. The propeller is located at $x=x_{PO}$, $y=0$, $z=-z_{PO}(z_{PO}>0)$ and we take the propeller axis in the same direction as the x-axis.

The equations of motion for ship maneuvering are expressed as follows:

$$
\begin{aligned}
(m + m_x)\, \dot{u} + (m + m_y)\, v{\cdot}r &= X(U,\beta,r,\delta,n_p) , \\
(m + m_y)\, \dot{v} - (m + m_x)\, u{\cdot}r &= Y(U,\beta,r,\delta,n_p) , \\
(I_{zz} + J_{zz})\, \dot{r} &= N(U,\beta,r,\delta,n_p) .
\end{aligned}
\tag{1}
$$

Here, m : ship's mass,

    m_x, m_y : added mass for surge and sway respectively,

    I_{zz} : moment of inertia around z-axis,

J_{zz} : added moment of inertia around z-axis,

u, v : velocity components of x- and y-axis respectively,

X, Y : surge, sway forces acting on the ship respectively,

N : yawing moment acting on the ship.

In the steady turning motion, eq.(1) can be reduced as:

$$- (m + m_y)\, U{\cdot}r\, \sin\beta = X(U,\beta,r,\delta,n_p),$$ (2)

$$(m + m_x)\, U{\cdot}r\, \cos\beta = Y(U,\beta,r,\delta,n_p),$$ (3)

$$0 = N(U,\beta,r,\delta,n_p).$$ (4)

Here, it is noted that X, Y and N are expressed as the function of U, β, r, δ and n_P. Eqs.(2), (3) and (4) can be regarded as the conditions for steady turning motion. When n_P and δ are given, unknown variables are β, r and U. And the number of the unknown variables coincides with the number of equations.

2.2 Basic Equations for Hydrodynamic Forces Acting on a Ship

Consider the basic equations for X, Y and N. In the present method the assumption of a double-body flow is employed for simplicity of the treatment of free-surface. Further, it is assumed that the ship's breadth is relatively small compared to its length. Then, the hull and rudder are expressed hydrody-namically by distribution of horse shoe vortices and line sources on their center planes. The lifting surface problems with respect to the hull and rudder are solved by using Quasi-Continuous Method(QCM)[3]. According to the QCM, loading and control points are arranged of $N_H{\times}M_H$ and $N_R{\times}M_R$ numbers on the hull and rudder surfaces respectively, where N_H is the number of chordwise (lengthwise) segments of the hull, M_H the number of spanwise (depthwise) segments of the hull, N_R the number of chordwise segments of the rudder and M_R the number of spanwise segments of the rudder. Then, the induced velocity at field point $P_{ij}(x,y,z)$ due to the vortex and source distributions are expressed as follows:

Induced velocity due to vortex distribution of hull:

$$\vec{V}_{HG_{ij}} = (u_{HG_{ij}}, v_{HG_{ij}}, w_{HG_{ij}})$$

$$= \frac{\pi L}{2 N_H} \sum_{k=1}^{M_H} \sum_{m=1}^{N_H} \gamma_{H_{km}} \vec{v}_{ijkm}^{G} \sin\left\{ \frac{(2m-1)\,\pi}{2 N_H} \right\},$$ (5)

Induced velocity due to vortex distribution of rudder:

$$\vec{V}_{RG_{ij}} = (u_{RG_{ij}}, v_{RG_{ij}}, w_{RG_{ij}})$$

$$= \frac{\pi\, l_R}{2\, N_R} \sum_{k=1}^{M_R} \sum_{m=1}^{N_R} \gamma_{R_{km}} \vec{v}^{\,G}_{ijkm} \sin\left\{\frac{(2m-1)\,\pi}{2 N_R}\right\}, \qquad (6)$$

Induced velocity due to source distribution of hull:

$$\vec{V}_{HS_{ij}} = (u_{HS_{ij}}, v_{HS_{ij}}, w_{HS_{ij}})$$

$$= \frac{\pi\, L}{2\, N_H} \sum_{k=1}^{M_H} \sum_{m=1}^{N_H} m_{H_{km}} \vec{v}^{\,S}_{ijkm} \sin\left\{\frac{(2m-1)\,\pi}{2 N_H}\right\}, \qquad (7)$$

Induced velocity due to source distribution of rudder:

$$\vec{V}_{RS_{ij}} = (u_{RS_{ij}}, v_{RS_{ij}}, w_{RS_{ij}})$$

$$= \frac{\pi\, l_R}{2\, N_R} \sum_{k=1}^{M_R} \sum_{m=1}^{N_R} m_{R_{km}} \vec{v}^{\,S}_{ijkm} \sin\left\{\frac{(2m-1)\,\pi}{2 N_R}\right\}, \qquad (8)$$

where L : ship length,

l_R : chord length of rudder,

γ_{Hkm} : vortex strength at the k-th loading point in the m-th strip of hull,

γ_{Rkm} : vortex strength at the k-th loading point in the m-th strip of rudder,

m_{Hkm} : source strength at the k-th loading point in the m-th strip of hull,

m_{Rkm} : source strength at the k-th loading point in the m-th strip of rudder,

$\vec{v}^{\,G}_{ijkm}$: induced velocity at P_{ij} due to the k-th and m-th horse shoe vortex of unit strength,

$\vec{v}^{\,S}_{ijkm}$: induced velocity at P_{ij} due to the k-th and m-th source strip of unit strength.

Here, m_{Hkm} and m_{Rkm} are assumed to be represented by Michell's distributions according to the thin wing theory. $\vec{v}^{\,S}_{ijkm}$ can be calculated easily by combination with the formula of induced velocity due to line source. In the same manner, $\vec{v}^{\,G}_{ijkm}$ can be calculated. The formulae of induced velocities due to line source and line vortex are referred to the paper presented by Nakamura[4]. For the accurate prediction of the hydrodynamic forces, wake vortex models for the hull and rudder should be made clear. In this paper, the following wake models of the turning ship are employed: for rudder, a wake model with a semi-circular vortex is employed which flows out only from the rudder trailing edge, and for ship hull, a combined wake model with straight and a semi-circular vortices[7] is employed as illustrated in Fig.2.

Applying the simple sink propeller model[5][6], the induced velocity due to the propeller is expressed as follows:

Induced velocity at outside of slip stream due to propeller:

$$\vec{V}_{P_{ij}} = (u_{P_{ij}}, v_{P_{ij}}, w_{P_{ij}})$$

$$= -\frac{A\sigma}{4\pi} \nabla G(P_{ij}; x_{P0}, 0, -z_{P0}), \tag{9}$$

where

$$G(x, y, z, ; x', y', z') =$$

$$\frac{1}{\sqrt{(x-x')^2 + (y-y')^2 + (z-z')^2}} + \frac{1}{\sqrt{(x-x')^2 + (y-y')^2 + (z+z')^2}}. \tag{10}$$

<u>Induced velocity at inside of slip stream due to propeller:</u>

$$\vec{V}_{P_{ij}} = (u_{P_{ij}}, v_{P_{ij}}, w_{P_{ij}})$$

$$= \vec{V}_{PS_{ij}} - \frac{A\sigma}{4\pi} \nabla G(P_{ij}; x_{P0}, 0, -z_{P0}), \tag{11}$$

where

$$\vec{V}_{PS_{ij}} = (\sigma, 0, 0).$$

Here, A denotes the propeller disc area and σ the sink strength.
    Next, consider the boundary conditions. Taking a thin ship approximation into consideration, the boundary conditions of the hull, rudder and propeller are expressed as follows:

$$v_{HG_{ij}} + v_{RG_{ij}} + v_{P_{ij}} + v_{HS_{ij}} + v_{RS_{ij}} + v_{I_{ij}} = 0 \quad \text{on ship hull}$$

$$i=1,2,\ldots,M_H, \quad j=1,2,\ldots,N_H, \tag{12}$$

$$-(u_{HG_{ij}} + u_{RG_{ij}} + u_{P_{ij}} + u_{HS_{ij}} + u_{RS_{ij}} + u_{I_{ij}}) \sin\delta$$

$$+ (v_{HG_{ij}} + v_{RG_{ij}} + v_{P_{ij}} + v_{HS_{ij}} + v_{RS_{ij}} + v_{I_{ij}}) \cos\delta = 0 \tag{13}$$

$$\text{on rudder} \quad i=1,2,\ldots,M_R, \quad j=1,2,\ldots,N_R,$$

$$u_I + u_{HG} + u_{RG} + u_{HS} + u_{RS} + \frac{\sigma}{2} = 2\pi n_P a \quad \text{on propeller.} \tag{14}$$

Here, u_I and v_I denote the inflow velocity components. The effective pitch ratio of the propeller a is represented as the function of advanced ratio J[6].
    Hydrodynamic forces acting on the ship is composed of the potential and viscous components. The potential component of the hydrodynamic forces can be calculated by applying the Lagally's and Kutta-Joukowski's theorems when γ_H, γ_R and σ are obtained[7]. The viscous component of the hydrodynamic forces is predicted empirically by combination with Hughes' frictional resistance formula, form factor and rudder viscous drag. In addition to that, the viscous component of the wake fraction is introduced for the inflow velocity to the rudder and propeller[7].

2.3 A Calculation Procedure
    The equations to be solved are eqs.(2), (3), (4), (12), (13) and (14), and the unknown variables are γ_H, γ_R, σ, U, β and r. Fig.3 shows the flow chart of the calculation procedure. First, n_P and δ, and the initial values of β and r are given. The basic

equations are dealt with by the normalized forms using the profile area of the ship hull and U. Then, eq.(2) can be reduced as:

$$- (m' + m'_y) r'\sin\beta \tag{15}$$

$$= X'_H + X'_R - 2\sigma'A' (u'_I + u'_{HV} + u'_{RV} + u'_{HS} + u'_{RS} + \sigma'/2),$$

where X_H' and X_R' denote the hull and rudder resistances respectively, and superscript ′ means the normalized value. Here, the third term of the right hand of eq.(15) represents the propeller thrust. From eqs.(12), (13) and (15), $\gamma_{H'}$, $\gamma_{R'}$ and σ' can be calculated numerically. Next, for obtaining β and r', eqs.(3) and (4) are expressed as:

$$f_Y(\beta, r') = Y' - (m' + m'_x) r'\cos\beta, \tag{16}$$

$$f_N(\beta, r') = N'. \tag{17}$$

The β and r' where f_Y and f_N become zero are solutions which satisfy eqs.(3) and (4). However, eqs.(16) and (17) become in non-linear forms with respect to β and r' since Y' and N' are the function as the β and r'. To solve the non-linear equations numerically, f_Y and f_N are expressed approximately as follows:

$$f_Y(\beta, r') = Y_\beta (\beta+\Delta\beta) + Y_r (r'+\Delta r'), \tag{18}$$

$$f_N(\beta, r') = N_\beta (\beta+\Delta\beta) + N_r (r'+\Delta r'), \tag{19}$$

where Y_β, Y_r, N_β and N_r are given parameters. If the f_Y and f_N can be predicted approximately by using the initial values of β and r', $\Delta\beta$ and $\Delta r'$ can be calculated from eqs.(18) and (19). By adding the $\Delta\beta$ and $\Delta r'$ to the initial values of β and r', new β and r' are obtained. By the iteration of the present procedure, converged solutions of β and r' are obtained. Lastly, U can be predicted from eq.(14).

3. NUMERICAL CALCULATION OF STEADY TURNING PERFORMANCE
3.1 Calculation of Self-Propulsive Performance
        In the calculations, Wigley parabolic hull form is chosen as:

$$y = \frac{B}{2}\left\{1-(\frac{2x}{L})^2\right\}\left\{1-(\frac{z}{d})^2\right\}, \tag{20}$$

where L/B=10.0, L/d=16.0, B the ship's breadth and d the ship's draft. Numerical calculations are carried out for two ships of 150m and 5m in length. In this paper, we shall call hereafter the ship of 150m length as the full-scale ship and of 5m length as the model. Table 1 shows the principal particulars of the ships. The hydrodynamic coefficients for added masses, viscous resistance and wake fraction of the ships are assumed as shown in Table 2.

Numerical calculations are made of self-propulsive performance at Froude number 0.067. Table 3 shows the calculated results of the propeller revolution n_P, propeller advanced ratio at loading point J_P, thrust deduction factor t, propeller efficiency e_P, effective horse power EHP and delivered horse power DHP for the full-scale ship and the model. The calculated results are obtained of the same orders as the experimental results[5][6].

3.2 Calculation of Steady Turning Performance

Next, numerical calculations are made of the turning performance for two Wigley parabolic hull forms of full-scale length and its model size. And the effect due to difference of frictional resistance and wake fraction between them is evaluated.

Figs.4, 5 and 6 show the comparison of $r'(r'=rL/U)$, β and speed drop ratio(U/U_0: U_0 denotes the initial ship speed) versus given rudder angle δ. It seems that the order of magnitude and the characteristics of calculated results agree well with those of the usual turning test results. It can be seen that r' and β are almost the same between full-scale ship and the model, and U/U_0 of the full-scale ship is larger than that of the model.

Figs.7, 8 and 9 show the comparison of the hydrodynamic coefficients of propeller thrust T', ship resistance $X_H'+X_R'$, lateral force on hull Y_H', yawing moment on hull N_H', rudder normal force F_{NR}', and propeller loading point J_P in the turning conditions versus given rudder angle δ. The hydrodynamic force coefficients are represented in the normalized forms using the profile area of the hull and ship speed in turning condition. The resistance of the full- scale ship in the range of small rudder angle is about half of that of the model due to the difference of the frictional resistance. T' of the full-scale ship is also smaller than that of the model, since T' is determined from the force balance among the propeller thrust, ship resistance and the resistance component of the centrifugal force. It is considered that U/U_0 is determined by the ratio of the ship resistance (or propeller thrust) between in the turning and straightly moving conditions. And since its ratio of the full-scale ship is larger than that of the model, U/U_0 of the full-scale ship becomes larger. J_P of the full scale-ship is larger than that of the model due to the difference of the ship resistance and wake fraction. However, F_{NR}', Y_H' and N_H' are almost the same between full-scale ship and the model. Thus, since the effect due to the difference of the propeller load on the lateral force and yawing moment is small, r' and β become almost the same magnitudes between full-scale ship and the model.

4. CONCLUDING REMARKS

A method was developed to calculate the steady turning performance and the hydrodynamic forces of a thin ship. Numerical calculations were made of the turning performance for two Wigley parabolic hull forms of full-scale length and the model size, and the effect due to difference of frictional resistance and wake fraction between them is evaluated. As a result, it was shown that steady yaw rate and drifting angle are almost the same magnitude between the full-scale ship and the model, however the speed drop ratio of the full scale ship becomes larger than that of the model.

ACKNOWLEDGEMENTS

The author would like to express his sincere gratitude to Professor K. Kijima of Kyushu University for his valuable comment and encouragement. Thanks are also extended to all the members of the Nagasaki Experimental Tank, MHI, for their cooperation in carrying out the present study.

REFERENCES

1. Bollay, W.: A Nonlinear Wing Theory and Its Application to Rectangular Wings of Small Aspect Ratio, *ZAMM*, Bd.19, Nr.1, 1939.
2. Inoue, S.: On the Turning of Ships, *Memoirs of the Fac. of Eng. Kyushu Univ.*, Japan, Vol.16, 1956.
3. Lan, C.E.: A Quasi-Vortex-Lattice Method in Thin Wing Theory, *J. Aircraft*, Vol.11, No.9, 1974.
4. Nakamura, N.: Estimation of Propeller Open-Water Characteristics based on Quasi-Continuous Method, *J. Soc. Nav. Arch. Japan*, Vol.157, 1985.
5. Nakatake, K., et al.: Free Surface Effect on the Propulsive Performance of a Ship(1st Report), *Trans. the West-Japan Soc. Nav. Arch.*, No.72, 1986.
6. Yamazaki, R. and Nakatake, K.: Free-Surface Effect on the Hull-Propeller Interaction, *Proc. 15th Symp. on Naval Hydrodynamics*, Washington, D.C., 1985.
7. Yasukawa, H.: Hydrodynamic Interactions Among Hull, Rudder and Propeller of a Turning Thin Ship, *The West-Japan Soc. Nav. Arch.*, 1992(to be read).

Table 1 Principal particulars of Wigley parabolic hull forms

	Full-Scale	Model
Ship Length	150.00m	5.00m
Ship Breadth	15.00m	0.50m
Ship Draft	9.375m	0.3125m
Chord Length of Rudder	4.6875m	0.15625m
Span Length of Rudder	9.375m	0.3125m
Rudder Sectional Shape	NACA0008	
Rudder Area Ratio	1/32.0	
Propeller Diameter	4.6875m	0.15625m

Table 2 Hydrodynamic coefficients for viscous fluid component

	Full-Scale	Model
Added Mass Coeff. m_x/m	0.02	
Added Mass Coeff. m_y/m	0.80	
Form Factor	0.15	
Drag Coeff. of Rudder	0.010	0.023
Wake Fraction Coeff.	0.10	0.19

Table 3 Calculated results of self-propulsive performances

	Full-Scale	Model
U	5.0(knot)	0.470(m/s)
n_P	36.1(rpm)	3.91(rps)
J_P	0.820	0.622
t	0.273	0.281
e_P	0.665	0.571
EHP(ps)	68.8	0.00102
DHP(ps)	128.0	0.00202

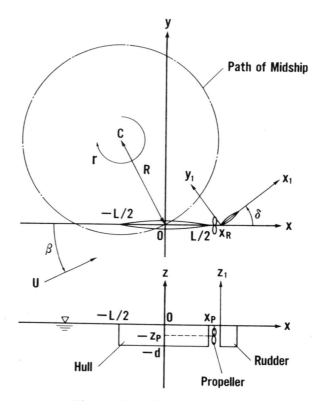

Fig.1   Coordinate systems

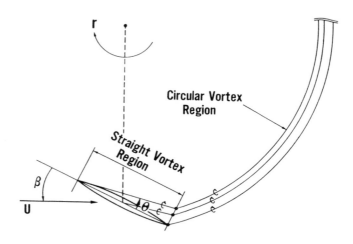

Fig.2   Wake vortex model for ship hull

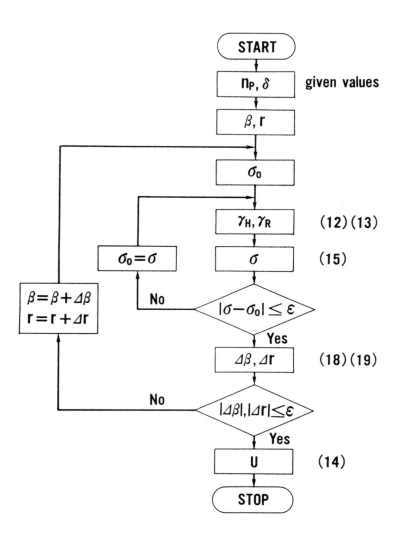

Fig.3   Flow chart of the present calculation

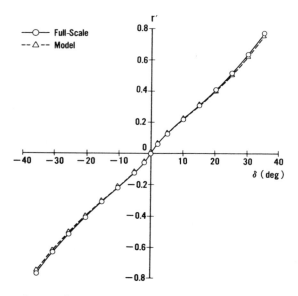

Fig.4   Comparison of steady yaw rate(r') curves versus rudder
        angle(δ)

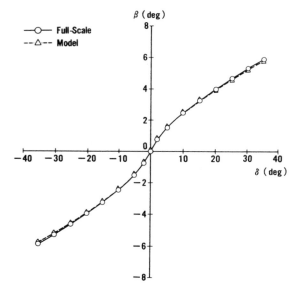

Fig.5   Comparison of drifting angle(β) curves versus rudder
        angle(δ)

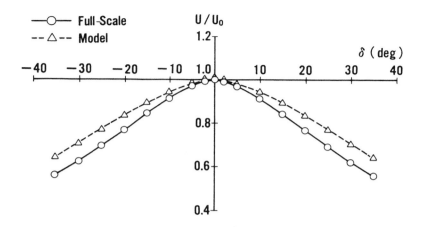

Fig.6 Comparison of speed drop ratio(U/U_0) curves versus
        rudder angle(δ)

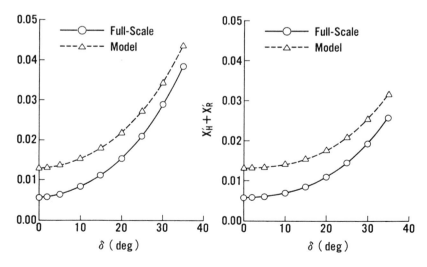

Fig.7 Comparison of propeller thrust(T') and ship
        resistance($X_H'+X_R'$)

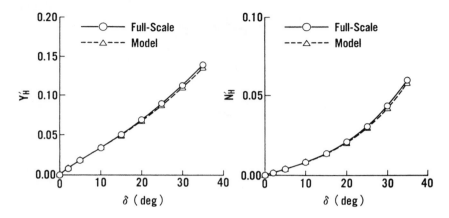

Fig.8 Comparison of lateral force(Y_H') and yawing moment(N_H')
acting on the ship hull

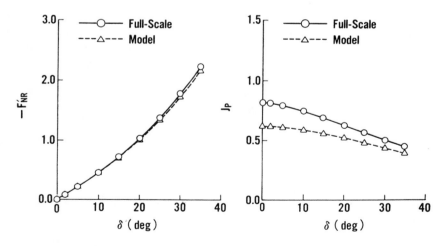

Fig.9 Comparison of rudder normal force(F_{NR}') and propeller
loading point(J_P)

A Viscous Boundary Element Approach to Evaluate Slow Motion Derivatives

W.G. Price, M. Tan

Department of Ship Science, University of Southampton, Highfield, Southampton SO9 5NH, UK

ABSTRACT

A viscous boundary element method is applied to evaluate unsteady fluid flows and fluid actions associated with a body manoeuvring in a viscous fluid. From the proposed mathematical model involving a convolution - integral formulation and fundamental viscous solution, numerical experiments are performed attempting to mirror a steady state towing tank experiment in which the body accelerates from rest to a prescribed constant forward speed and then continues along the tank in this steady state condition. From this preliminary investigation, calculated data are presented showing the variation of the fluid actions (lift and drag forces) with time, Reynolds number and angle of attack between body and flow.

INTRODUCTION

To assess the directional stability, manoeuvrability and control of a ship or other type of marine vehicle requires information on the fluid forces and moments acting on the vehicle. For example, when it departs from steady motion in a straight line the fluid exerts a resultant force and resultant moment about the centre of gravity of the vehicle as a consequence of the disturbance. Such variations of the fluid actions to displacement, velocity, acceleration and their angular motion counterparts provide the hydrodynamic inputs (i.e. the slow motion derivative data) into the assessment exercise [1-4]. In such studies, reliance on experimental data is practically total since little confidence exists in theoretical predictions of the derivative data.

Derivative data are derived from steady state oblique tow tests, steady state rotating arm tests and planar motion mechanism (PMM) oscillatory model experiments [2,4-6]. In the steady state tests, velocity and angular velocity derivative data are measured and the unsteady PMM experiments allow both translatory and rotational velocity and acceleration derivatives to be deduced as well as providing information on the frequency dependence of the hydrodynamic coefficients [7-9]. PMM experiments were initially designed to measure acceleration derivative data - the "added mass or inertia" terms - although now they have a much more prominent role in theoretical studies of the dynamics of ships and other forms of marine vehicles [10].

Theoretical methods have been proposed to calculate the derivative data [4, 11-16] and limited success achieved. But calculations of velocity derivatives are not totally satisfactory because of the dominant influence of the viscous flow components to the fluid actions. To include the viscous description of the fluid in the dynamic interaction between the fluid and body creates many theoretical difficulties. The usual theoretical approach of assuming a potential flow model with its accompanying idealisation of the fluid to describe the fluid-structure interaction mechanism is inadequate. It must be replaced by a more realistic description of the characteristics and flow behaviour of the fluid and therefore by an improved mathematical model to describe the interaction mechanism. In theory this is achieved by resorting to a more fundamental approach involving Navier-Stokes equations to describe the viscous fluid flow.

The method adopted in this paper to evaluate the fluid actions experienced by rigid bodies manoeuvring with prescribed motions is based on such a fundamental approach. It has been shown by Price and Tan [15-17] that from Navier-Stokes equations a viscous boundary element method can be developed to determine directly the fluid actions and velocity field associated with a rigid body moving in a viscous fluid. The mathematical model is based on an integral identity and convolution-integral formulation. The retention of a convolution time integral process allows time history effects to be included as well as accounting for steady and unsteady rotational and translational manoeuvres.

This proposed approach is analogous to methods developed in potential flow calculations of bodies moving in an idealised fluid. Namely, the wetted surface area of the body or vehicle is idealised by a distribution of panels and on the centre of each panel is placed a singularity (source, dipole, etc) of unknown strength which is determined when the imposed boundary conditions are satisfied. The distribution of potential singularities over the panels provides a framework to evaluate the fluid actions.

In the viscous boundary element method adopted herein, the potential singularity is replaced by a fundamental viscous solution and these are distributed over panels which cover the wetted surface area of the body and extend into the surrounding fluid.   This fundamental viscous solution is the solution of the Oseen equation, its variant or a modified form depending on the type of motions (translations and/or rotations) prescribed in the manoeuvres.   Here, we concentrate on translational motions in an attempt to model mathematically a typical towing tank experiment used to measure slow motion derivatives, e.g. the sway velocity derivative.   Namely, the body or vehicle is accelerated from rest and then travels at constant speed along the tank.   This experiment is repeated at different angles of attack or drift angles and the variation of the fluid action with angle deduced.   In this way, the variation in sway force (lift, Y) and surge force (drag, X) with drift angle or sway velocity can be obtained and a velocity derivative extracted.   Naturally, the theoretical method allows more complicated numerical experiments to be devised and more refined non-linear data involving products of disturbances to be produced.   However, in this preliminary study, we shall confine our attention to the simple experiment discussed and to low Reynolds number (Re) flows.   This will provide a measure indicating whether the proposed approach is suitable to derive the necessary data required in an assessment of the directional stability, manoeuvrability and control of a marine vehicle.

MATHEMATICAL MODEL

It has been shown previously [17] that for a body translating with velocity $U(t)$ and angular velocity $\Omega(t) = 0$, the non-dimensionalised convolution integral equation describing the force R and fluid velocity v is given by

$$C(q)v(q,t) = \{ 1 - C(q,t) \} U - \int_{\Omega_b} v_s^* U d\Omega - \int_{\Sigma_b} v_s^* R d\Sigma - \int_{\Omega} v_s^* \left[(v.\nabla)v - f \right] d\Omega$$

$$\tag{1}$$

$$= \{ 1 - C(q) \} U - \int_{\Sigma_b} v_s^* \{ R + (\dot{U}.x)n \} d\Sigma - \int_{\Omega} v_s^* \left[(v.\nabla)v - f \right] d\Omega$$

Here $v_s^*(r,t)$ with components $v_{sj}(r,t)$ is the fundamental viscous solution, $r=x-q$ represents the position of the field point at q relative to the source point at x and the subscripts i,j,s, etc take values 1,2,3 in a three dimensional problem and 1,2 in a two dimensional problem.   In this equation, Ω denotes the fluid domain, Σ represents the boundary surface enclosing Ω and the subscript b to these parameters refers to the body. The unit normal **n** points outwards from the fluid domain Ω and a summation convention i.e.

$$U_j\, n_j = \sum_{j=1}^{3} U_j\, n_j = \mathbf{U} \cdot \mathbf{n}$$

is adopted. The asterisk multiplier (*) denotes a convolution operator, i.e.

$$\mathbf{a} * \mathbf{b} = \mathbf{b} * \mathbf{a} = \int_0^t \mathbf{a}\,(t\text{-}y) \cdot \mathbf{b}(y)\, dy,$$

$$\check{U}(t) = U(\tau\text{-}t),$$

$$
\begin{aligned}
C(\mathbf{q}) &= 0 && \text{if } \mathbf{q}\, \bar{\epsilon}\, (\Omega U \Sigma) \\
&= 0.5 && \text{if } \mathbf{q}\, \epsilon\, \Sigma \\
&= 1 && \text{if } \mathbf{q}\, \epsilon\, \Omega,
\end{aligned}
$$

$v_s(\mathbf{q},t)$ represents the sth component of the fluid velocity $\mathbf{v}(\mathbf{q},t)$ and **f** denotes an external body force.

The fundamental viscous solution $v_{sj}{}^*$ associated with the prescribed translational motion satisfies the equation

$$\dot{v}_{sj}^* - (\hat{\mathbf{U}}.\nabla)v_{sj}^* - \nabla^2 v_{s\,j}^* - p_{s,j}^* = \delta_{sj}\delta(t)\Delta(r) \qquad (2)$$

$$\nabla.v_s^* = 0$$

together with the constraints $v_{sj}{}^*$ (r,0) = 0 and $v_{sj}{}^*$ (∞,t) $\rightarrow$ 0. Here $p_s{}^*$(r,t) denotes an auxilliary function, δ_{sj} = 1 when s = j otherwise it is zero, $\delta(\ )$ and $\Delta(\ )$ both denote Dirac delta functions and $p_{s,j} = \partial p_s/\partial x_j$, $v_{sj,k}^* = \partial v_{sj}^*/\partial x_k$, etc.

This equation is a variant of the Oseen equation [18] and it has

been shown [17] that for a two dimensional problem (s,j = 1,2) its
solution is given by

$$
v^*_{sj}(\mathbf{r},t) = \frac{\delta_{sj}}{4\pi t} e^{-(\bar{r}^2/4t)} + \frac{1}{4\pi} \left\{ \ln\left(\frac{1}{\bar{r}^2}\right) - E_1\left(\frac{\bar{r}^2}{4t}\right) \right\}_{,sj}
\tag{3}
$$

$$
p^*_s(\mathbf{r},t) = \frac{\delta(t)}{4\pi} \left\{ \ln\left(\frac{1}{\bar{r}^2}\right) \right\}_{,s}
\tag{4}
$$

whereas, for the three dimensional case (s,j = 1,2,3) we have

$$
v^*_{sj}(\mathbf{r},t) = \frac{\delta_{sj}}{(4\pi t)^{3/2}} e^{-(\bar{r}^2/4t)} + \frac{1}{4\pi} \left\{ \frac{1 - \operatorname{erf} c(|\bar{r}|/2t^{1/2})}{|\bar{r}|} \right\}_{,sj}
\tag{5}
$$

$$
p^*_s(\mathbf{r},t) = \frac{\delta(t)}{4\pi} \left(\frac{1}{\bar{r}}\right)_{,s}
\tag{6}
$$

Here,

$$
\bar{r} = \mathbf{r} + \zeta, \qquad \zeta(t) = \int_0^t U(\eta)d\eta
$$

and r = |x - q| is the distance between the field point x and source point
q, r_s is the sth component of the vector $\bar{r}$ and the exponential integral

$$
E_1(x) = \int_x^\infty \frac{e^{-\sigma}}{\sigma} d\sigma, \qquad |\arg(x)| < \pi,
$$

and complementary error function

$$
\operatorname{erfc}(x) = \frac{2}{\sqrt{\pi}} \int_x^\infty e^{-\sigma^2} d\sigma
$$

as defined by Abromowitz and Stegun [19].

NUMERICAL COMPUTATIONS AND DISCUSSION

The numerical experiments discussed herein describe a towing tank experiment in which a model starts from rest, accelerates to constant speed and then travels along the tank before stopping. The body, in the form of an ellipse of length to beam ratio 10:1, is towed at an angle of attack β (or sway velocity, v) to the forward direction of the prescribed motion and the variation of force (i.e. lift and drag) to disturbance calculated.

An examination of equation (1) shows that, for no external force excitation $\mathbf{f} = \mathbf{0}$, the proposed theoretical model can be used in two modes, i.e. as a linear model, or, as a non-linear model. In the former, the integral term involving products of flow velocity $\mathbf{v}$ is discarded whereas this term is retained in the non-linear model.

For small Reynolds number flows, the fluid flow is small and the non-linear convective term is negligible, thus justifying the linear model. This simplifying approximation reduces the computation to a linear one involving only a boundary integration over the body surface since the troublesome integration over the fluid domain is discarded.

In reality, for higher Reynolds number flows, the non-linear convective term must be retained and this produces a non-linear computation involving boundary integrations over the body and into the fluid domain. This greatly increases the complexity of the computations and causes restrictions to the range of applicability of the model because of possible numerically created difficulties. In principle, the non-linear approach should provide a better qualitative and quantitative description of the fluid flow field, the fluid actions and the physical mechanisms associated with the fluid-structure interaction. However, for some practical cases, the linear model may be adequate and linear computations sufficient especially when undertaking a comparative study of the expected manoeuvring behaviour of two bodies of similar but slightly different forms rather than calculating the absolute derivative data of the bodies.

Figure 1(a) shows a typical velocity-time history of the prescribed forward motion of the ellipse. During the unsteady phase, the ellipse starts from rest, accelerates to the prescribed constant forward speed and remains travelling in this steady state condition. An examination of the flow field around the ellipse during this experiment shows the creation of a starting vortex which sheds into the wake, passing downstream. The strength of this vortex depends on the intensity of the acceleration.

Figure 1(b) shows the variation of the steady state drag force over a range of Reynolds number. In this experiment, the ellipse is towed at zero angle of attack and the results presented correspond to calculations performed at a large time interval from the start when the ellipse is travelling at constant forward speed and uninfluenced by previous unsteady motions. Alternatively, rather than undertaking time dependent calculations we could have adopted a steady state model (i.e. $U(t) = U$, a constant), derived the appropriate fundamental viscous solution and calculated the steady state drag forces [15-17]. It is pleasing to note that for the low Reynolds number flows examined both approaches produce similar estimates of the values of the fluid actions but the steady state model is more restrictive in its range of application and its ability to describe flow fields.

Figure 1(c) shows the variation of the drag force with time, including both unsteady and steady phases of motion. These calculations are for Reynolds number Re = 1000 and they illustrate the effect of including or excluding the non-linear terms in the mathematical model. The fluid action time histories illustrate an overshoot before attaining their steady state values.

Figure 2(a,b) shows the variation of the fluid actions (lift and drag) with angle of attack between the ellipse and the direction of motion for fixed values of Reynolds number. Here, in essence, we are calculating derivative data which within the range of the numerical experiment show dependence on Reynolds number.

Although these records have not been examined in detail, in principle the unsteady portion of the recording should reveal information on acceleration derivative data and therefore, could eliminate the need to do unsteady oscillatory testing. For example, it has been shown previously [3,7,8] that the change in sway force ΔY to sway velocity $v(t)$ can be expressed in terms of the convolution integral

$$\Delta Y(t) = \int_{0}^{\infty} h(\tau) \, v(t-\tau) \, d\tau$$

where $h(\tau)$ is an impulse response function. In principle we are at liberty to choose the imposed or prescribed sway motion as we like and, for illustrative purposes, this may have the simple form

$$v(t) = at \quad , \qquad \dot{v}(t) = a \qquad\qquad 0 \leq t \leq t_{us} \qquad \text{(unsteady)}$$

$$v(t) = v_0 \quad , \qquad \dot{v}(t) = 0 \qquad\qquad t > t_0 \qquad\quad \text{(steady)}$$

where $a = v(t_{us})/t_{us}$.

Now in the steady phase we find

$$[\Delta Y(t)]_S = v_0 \int_0^\infty h(\tau) \, d\tau \; = \; v_0 \, Y_v$$

or

$$Y_v \; = \; (\Delta Y)_S / v_0$$

whereas in the unsteady phase

$$[\Delta Y(t)]_{us} = at \int_0^\infty h(\tau) \, d\tau - a \int_0^\infty \tau h(\tau) \, d\tau$$

$$= v(t) \, Y_v + a \, Y_{\dot{v}}$$

where Y_v, $Y_{\dot{v}}$ are velocity and acceleration derivative data respectively and previously these were shown to be related to the impulse response functions by the above integral expressions [3,7,8].   Hence the expression

$$\frac{[\Delta Y(t)]_{us} - [\Delta Y(t)]_S \, (at/v_0)}{a} \; = Y_{\dot{v}}$$

allows the acceleration derivative to be determined.

CONCLUSIONS

Although the proposed viscous boundary element approach

developed to solve manoeuvring problems is still in its infancy in the realms of both research and development, the evidence presented here suggests that it is a viable method to use in investigations of the fluid actions experienced by a body manoeuvring in a viscous medium. Naturally many more studies have to be undertaken especially in the development of reliable and efficient numerical algorithms as well as validating the predictions and descriptions of the flow fields against experimental evidence. The inclusion of time dependence in the mathematical model allows realistic manoeuvring operations to be modelled and to extend investigations into areas which hitherto have been difficult to perform experimentally.

ACKNOWLEDGEMENT

We are grateful to Dr. A.J. Musker of the Defence Research Agency (Maritime), Haslar for his encouragement in this project and to DRA for financial support.

REFERENCES

1.   Duncan, W.J. 'The principles of the control and stability of aircraft'. Cambridge University Press, 1952.

2.   Mandel, P. 'Ship manoeuvring and control'. In Principles of Naval Architecture, (ed. J.P. Comstock). Soc. Nav. Archit. Mar. Engrs., New York, 403-606, 1967.

3.   Booth, T.B. and Bishop, R.E.D. 'The planar motion mechanism'. Admiralty Experiment Works, 1973.

4.   Burcher, R.K. 'Developments in ship manoeuvrability'. Trans. RINA 114, 1-32, 1972.

5.   Gill, A.D. and Price, W.G. 'Determination of the manoeuvring derivatives of a ship model using a horizontal planar motion mechanism in a circulating water channel'. Trans. RINA 119, 151-160, 1977.

6.   Gill, A.D. and Price, W.G. 'Experimental evaluation (in a C.W.C.) of the effects of water depth and speed on the manoeuvring derivatives of ship models'. Trans. RINA 120, 149-160, 1978.

7.   Bishop, R.E.D., Burcher, R.K. and Price, W.G. 'The use of functional analysis in ship dynamics'. Proc. Roy. Soc. London A332, 23-35, 1973.

8.   Bishop, R.E.D., Burcher, R.K. and Price, W.G.   'Application of functional analysis to oscillatory ship model testing'.   Proc. Roy. Soc. London A332, 37-49, 1973.

9.   Gerritsma, J. and Beukelman, W.   'The distribution of the hydrodynamic forces on a heaving and pitching ship model in still water'. Fifth Symposium on Naval Hydrodynamics, 219-251, 1964.

10.   Price, W.G. (Ed).   The Dynamics of Ships.   Proceedings of a Royal Society Discussion Meeting. The Royal Society, 1991.

11.   Clarke, D. 'A two dimensional strip method for surface ship hull derivatives: Comparison of theory with experiments on a segmented tanker model'. J. Mech. Eng. Sci. 14, 53-61, 1972.

12.   Mikelis, N.E. and Price, W.G.   'Calculation of hydrodynamic coefficients for a body manoeuvring in restricted waters using a three dimensional method'. Trans. RINA 123, 209-216, 1981.

13.   Mikelis, N.E. and Price, W.G.   'Calculation of acceleration derivatives and correction factors associated with ship manoeuvring in restricted water: Comparison between theory and experiments'. Trans. RINA 123, 217-232, 1981.

14.   Price, W.G. and Tan, Mingyi. 'A preliminary investigation into the forces acting on submerged body appendages'. Int. Conf. on Ship Manoeuvrability, Prediction and Achievement. The Royal Institution of Naval Architects, Paper 13, 1987.

15.   Price, W.G. and Tan, Mingyi. 'The calculation of fluid actions on manoeuvring arbitrary shaped submerged bodies using viscous boundary elements'. Eighteenth Symposium on Naval Hydrodynamics, Office of Naval Research, Ann Arbor, 801-814, 1991.

16.   Price, W.G. and Tan, Mingyi. 'The evaluation of steady fluid forces on single and multiple bodies in low speed flows using viscous boundary elements'. Dynamics of Marine Vehicles and Structures in Waves (ed Price, W.G., Temarel, P. and Keane, A.J.), Elsevier, 125-133, 1991.

17.   Price, W.G. and Tan, Mingyi. 'Fundamental viscous solutions or 'transient oseenlets' associated with a body manoeuvring in a viscous fluid. Phil. Trans. Roy. Soc. London, 1992 (To appear).

18. Oseen C.W.   Ubër die Stokessche Formel und über die verwandte Aufgabi in der Hydrodynamic. Arkiv Math., Astronomic och Fysik 6, 29, 1910.

19.   Abramowitz, M. and Stegun, I.A. (Eds.)   Handbook of Mathematical Functions. New York, Dover Publications, 1972.

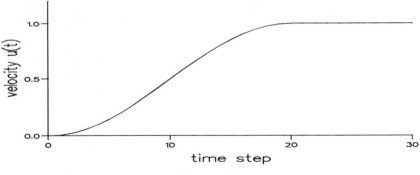

Figure 1(a)

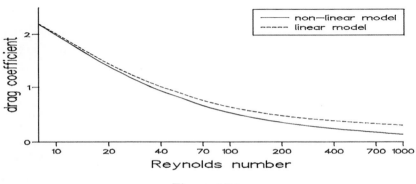

Figure 1(b)

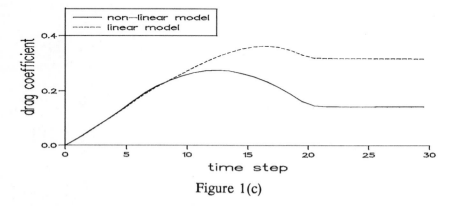

Figure 1(c)

Figure 1 (a): Velocity-time history of the prescribed forward motion of the ellipse. (b): Variation of drag coefficient with Reynolds number. (c): Variation of drag coefficient with time. Re = 1000.

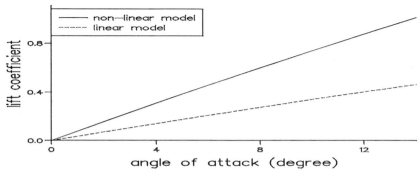

Figure 2(a)

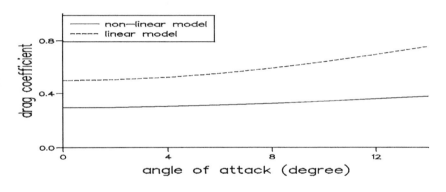

Figure 2(b)

Figure 2 (a): Variation of the steady state lift coefficient with angle of attack. Re = 200. (b): Variation of the steady state drag coefficient with angle of attack. Re = 200.

Some Notes on the Added Masses in Mathematical Manœuvring Models

M.J. Krężelewski

Faculty of Ocean Engineering and Ship Technology, Technical University of Gdańsk, Malczewskiego 78/209, 80-107 Gdańsk, Poland

ABSTRACT

It is well known that for a rigid body moving in any infinite space added masses are constant. The hydrodynamical theories of surface ship motions, however, show, that added masses are dependent on frequency and ship speed of advance. But, in existing mathematical manœuvring models these quantities are assumed to be constant. This assumption may be a good approximation for a ship moving at very low speed. For a fast ship, like container or ferry, however, these models may be a source of significant errors.

In the paper, the problem of surface ship moving in horizontal plane was formulated. Special attention was paid to a boundary condition on the free surface. Applying Kirchhoff's decomposition method to this boundary condition, the differential equations for unit potentials were developed. Finally, on this base it has been concluded that added masses of a manœuvring surface ship are very complex functions of ship velocity components and accelerations. Moreover, it has been shown that added masses are directly depended upon direction of ship movement.

The considerations of the paper may be a good base for improvement of the existing mathematical manœuvring models of surface ship.

INTRODUCTION

As we know, there are many kinds of mathematical models, used to simulate ship manœuvring. A critical survey of these models was made by the author in report [1].

It seems that from all existing manœuvring models of a surface ship, the Oltmann-Sharma model [2] is most based on hydrodynamical principles. However, the hydrodynamical basis, adopted there, is in some cases oversimplified.

The main purpose of this paper is to give a deeper insight into the dependence of hydrodynamical forces in potential flows with the presence of free surface and in particular into the dependence of added masses upon the kinematic parameters of manœuvring ship.

FORMULATION OF THE PROBLEM

In the problem of surface ship manœuvring in the horizontal plane on calm water, the two right-hand Cartesian coordinate systems are adopted: the first $0x_0y_0z_0$, fixed in space, with axes $0x_0$ and $0y_0$ coinciding with undisturbed free surface and $0z_0$ axis pointed vertically down. The second system $Axyz$ with the xy plane also in the calm free surface and the Az axis positive downwards, is fixed to the ship. In the moving system $Axyz$ the Ax axis lie in ship centre plane and is directed to the ship's bow.

Similarly to the problem of general motion of a body in unbounded space, the problem will be formulated in the moving coordinate system. As usual, we assume that the water is unviscid, incompressible and that free surface has no surface tension. Furthermore, the field velocity $\vec{v}$, induced in the water by the ship motion, is irrotational and the generated free surface waves are small. The last assumption allows us to apply linearized free surface condition (which will be discussed further in details).

In the moving system the translatory velocity

$$\vec{v}_e = \vec{v}_A + \vec{\omega} \times \vec{r}$$

where:
$\vec{v}_A$ is velocity of the orgin A of the moving system,
$\vec{\omega}$ is rotational velocity of $Axyz$,
$\vec{r}$ is position vector.

In the moving system

$$\vec{v}_A = \vec{e}_1 u + \vec{e}_2 v; \qquad \vec{\omega} = \vec{e}_3 r$$

Thus, for the considered problem we have:

$$\vec{v}_e = \vec{e}_1(u - ry) + \vec{e}_2(v + rx) \tag{1}$$

If we define the velocity, inducted in water by ship motion, as

$$\vec{v} = \nabla\varphi \tag{2}$$

where potential φ, following Kirchhoff, can be written as:

$$\varphi = \varphi_k v_k = \varphi_1 u + \varphi_2 v + \varphi_3 r = v_k \varphi_k \tag{3}$$

$$\text{with} \qquad v_1 = u, \ v_2 = v, \ v_3 = r$$

then the boundary value problem for unit potentials will be

$$\nabla^2 \varphi_k = 0 \qquad \text{in} \ \ z > 0 \tag{4}$$

$$\frac{\partial \varphi_k}{\partial n} = n_k \qquad \text{on hull wetted surface } S_w \tag{5}$$

where $\vec{n}$ is outward normal vector to S_w;

$$\frac{\partial \varphi_k}{\partial z} = 0 \qquad \text{at the sea bottom} \tag{6}$$

and an appropriate radiation condition at infinity. To this end, the problem is the same as that for general body motions in unbounded space. In the considered problem the difference is that a proper boundary condition on the free surface must additionally be imposed.

According to the above given assumptions, the linear boundary condition on free surface has the form:

$$\frac{\partial'^2 \varphi}{\partial t^2} + \vec{v}_e \cdot \nabla (\vec{v}_e \cdot \nabla\varphi) - 2\vec{v}_e \cdot \nabla \frac{\partial \varphi}{\partial t} - \frac{d'\vec{v}_e}{dt} \cdot \nabla\varphi - g\frac{\partial \varphi}{\partial z} = 0 \tag{7}$$

where

$$\frac{d'\vec{v}_e}{dt} = \vec{e}_1(\dot{u} - \dot{r}y) + \vec{e}_2(\dot{v} + \dot{r}x) \tag{8}$$

The expression (7) will be later discussed in detail. Now, we may point out here that from condition (7) we can obtain equations, valid for each of the unit potential φ_k.

If we, further, assume that the solution of this boundary - value problem exists, then we can obtain the hydrodynamical force and moment relative to the origin A of the moving reference frame, for which the following general expressions hold:

$$\vec{R} = \rho \int_{S_w} \vec{n} U dS + \rho \frac{d}{dt} \int_{S_w} \vec{n}\varphi dS + \rho \int_{S_w} \left[\frac{1}{2} v^2 \vec{n} - (\vec{v}_s \cdot \vec{n})\nabla\varphi \right] dS +$$

$$+ \rho \oint_{\partial S_w} d\vec{r} \times \varphi \vec{v}_s \tag{9}$$

$$\vec{M} = \rho \int_{S_w} U\vec{r} \times \vec{n} dS + \rho \frac{d}{dt} \int_{S_w} (\vec{r} \times \vec{n}) \varphi dS + \vec{v}_A \times \rho \int_{S_w} \varphi \vec{n} dS +$$

$$+ \rho \int_{S_w} \left[\frac{1}{2} v^2 (\vec{r} \times \vec{n}) - \vec{r} \times (\vec{v}_s \cdot \vec{n}) \nabla \varphi \right] dS + \rho \oint_{\partial S_w} \vec{r} \times (d\vec{r} \times \varphi \vec{v}_s) \quad (10)$$

where

$u = -gz$

$\vec{v}_s$ - velocity of surface S_w; for rigid hull $\vec{v}_s = \vec{v}_e$.

For a fully submerged ship, the boundary of S_w, $\partial S_w = 0$ and expression (9), (10) take well known form.

Hence, according to usual practice, we can write the (9) and (10) as

$$\vec{R} = \vec{R}_H + \vec{R}_I + \vec{R}_S$$

$$\vec{M} = \vec{M}_H + \vec{M}_I + \vec{M}_S$$

where

$\vec{R}_H, \vec{M}_H$ have hydrostatic character,
$\vec{R}_I, \vec{M}_I$ are inertia forces, and
$\vec{R}_S, \vec{M}_S$ are the quasi steady terms.

In particular, we thus get

$$\vec{R}_I = \rho \frac{d}{dt} \int_{\dot{s}_w} \vec{n} \varphi dS \quad (11)$$

$$\vec{R}_S = \rho \int_{S_w} \left[\frac{1}{2} v^2 \vec{n} - (\vec{v}_e \cdot \vec{n}) \nabla \varphi \right] dS + \rho \oint_{\partial S_w} d\vec{r} \times \varphi \vec{v}_e \quad (12)$$

Introducing the usual notations

$$\vec{Q} = -\rho \int_{S_w} \vec{n} \varphi dS \quad (13)$$

$$\vec{K} = -\rho \int_{S_w} \vec{r} \times \vec{n} \varphi dS \quad (14)$$

the inertia force and moment can be written as

$$\vec{R}_I = -\frac{d'\vec{Q}}{dt} - \vec{\omega} \times \vec{Q} \quad (15)$$

$$\vec{M}_I = -\frac{d'\vec{K}}{dt} - \vec{\omega} \times \vec{K} - \vec{v}_A \times \vec{Q} \quad (16)$$

Furthermore, by substitution (3) and (5) into (13) and (14) we get the following expressions for the components of vectors $\vec{Q}$ and $\vec{K}$

$$Q_j = v_k m_{kj} \quad (17)$$

$$K_j = v_k m_{k(j+3)} \qquad (18)$$

where

$$m_{kj} = -\rho \int_{S_w} \varphi_k \frac{\partial \varphi_j}{\partial n} dS = -\rho \int_{S_w} \varphi_k n_j dS \qquad (19)$$

are the added masses.

For the considered case it is assumed that only φ_1, φ_2 and φ_6 are not equal to zero. Thus, we get

$$Q_1 = v_1 m_{11} + v_2 m_{21} + v_6 m_{61}$$

$$Q_2 = v_1 m_{12} + v_2 m_{22} + v_6 m_{62}$$

$$Q_3 = 0; \quad K_1 = K_2 = 0 \qquad (20)$$

$$K_3 = v_1 m_{16} + v_2 m_{26} + v_6 m_{66}$$

In order to receive more information about the added masses, we have to expand the condition on the free surface (7).

BOUNDARY CONDITION ON FREE SURFACE

By substitution of (1), (3) and (8) into the free surface boundary condition (7) we obtain

$$v_k \left\{ \frac{\ddot{v}_k}{v_k} \varphi_k + 2 \frac{\dot{v}_k}{v_k} \frac{\partial' \varphi_k}{\partial t} + \frac{\partial'^2 \varphi_k}{\partial t^2} - \frac{2}{v_k} \left[(u - ry) \left(\dot{v}_k \frac{\partial \varphi_k}{\partial x} + v_k \frac{\partial'^2 \varphi_k}{\partial x \partial t} \right) + \right. \right.$$

$$\left. + (v + rx) \left(\dot{v}_k \frac{\partial \varphi_k}{\partial y} + v_k \frac{\partial'^2 \varphi_k}{\partial y \partial t} \right) \right] + (u - ry)^2 \frac{\partial^2 \varphi_k}{\partial x^2} +$$

$$+ 2(u - ry)(v + rx) \frac{\partial^2 \varphi_k}{\partial x \partial y} + (v + rx)^2 \frac{\partial^2 \varphi_k}{\partial y^2} +$$

$$+ (u - ry) r \frac{\partial \varphi_k}{\partial y} - (v + rx) r \frac{\partial \varphi_k}{\partial x} - g \frac{\partial \varphi_k}{\partial z} -$$

$$\left. - (\dot{u} - \dot{r}y) \frac{\partial \varphi_k}{\partial x} - (\dot{v} - \dot{r}x) \frac{\partial \varphi_k}{\partial y} \right\} = 0 \qquad (21)$$

where: $k = 1, 2, 6$

For $u \neq 0$, $v \neq 0$ and $r \neq 0$ the condition (21) can be decomposed in three separated conditions:
• for surge:

$$\ddot{u}\varphi_1 + 2\dot{u} \frac{\partial' \varphi_1}{\partial t} + u \frac{\partial'^2 \varphi_1}{\partial t^2} + \left[-3u\dot{u} + 2\dot{u}ry - uvr - ur^2x + u\dot{r}y \right] \frac{\partial \varphi_1}{\partial x} +$$

$$+\left[-2v\dot{u}-2\dot{u}rx+u^2r-ur^2y-u\dot{v}-u\dot{r}x\right]\frac{\partial\varphi_1}{\partial y}+\left[u^3-2u^2ry+ur^2y^2\right]\frac{\partial^2\varphi_1}{\partial x^2}+$$

$$+\left[uv^2+2uvrx+ur^2x^2\right]\frac{\partial^2\varphi_1}{\partial y^2}+2\left[u^2v+u^2rx-uvrx-ur^2xy\right]\frac{\partial^2\varphi_1}{\partial x\partial y}+$$

$$+\left[-2u^2-2ury\right]\frac{\partial'^2\varphi_1}{\partial x\partial t}+\left[-2uv-2urx\right]\frac{\partial'^2\varphi_1}{\partial y\partial t}-ug\frac{\partial\varphi_1}{\partial z}=0 \qquad (22)$$

- for sway:

$$\ddot{v}\varphi_2+2\dot{v}\frac{\partial'\varphi_2}{\partial t}+v\frac{\partial'^2\varphi_2}{\partial t^2}+\left[-2u\dot{v}+2\dot{v}ry-vr^2x-v\dot{u}+v\dot{r}y-v^2r\right]\frac{\partial\varphi_2}{\partial x}+$$

$$+\left[-3v\dot{v}-2\dot{v}rx+uvr-vr^2y-v\dot{r}x\right]\frac{\partial\varphi_2}{\partial y}+\left[vu^2-2uvry+vr^2y^2\right]\frac{\partial^2\varphi_2}{\partial x^2}+$$

$$+\left[v^3+2v^2rx+vr^2x^2\right]\frac{\partial^2\varphi_2}{\partial y^2}+2\left[uv^2+uvrx-v^2ry-vr^2xy\right]\frac{\partial^2\varphi_2}{\partial x\partial y}+$$

$$+\left[-2uv+2vry\right]\frac{\partial'^2\varphi_2}{\partial x\partial t}+\left[-2v^2-2vrx\right]\frac{\partial'^2\varphi_2}{\partial y\partial t}-vg\frac{\partial\varphi_2}{\partial z}=0 \qquad (23)$$

- and for yaw:

$$\ddot{r}\varphi_6+2\dot{r}\frac{\partial'\varphi_6}{\partial t}+r\frac{\partial'^2\varphi_6}{\partial t^2}+\left[-2u\dot{r}+3\dot{r}ry-r^2v-r^3x-r\dot{u}\right]\frac{\partial\varphi_6}{\partial x}+$$

$$+\left[-2v\dot{r}-2\dot{r}rx+r^2u-r^3y-\dot{u}r-r\dot{r}y\right]\frac{\partial\varphi_6}{\partial y}+\left[ru^2-2ur^2y+r^3y\right]\frac{\partial^2\varphi_6}{\partial x^2}+$$

$$+\left[rv^2+2vr^2x+r^3x^2\right]\frac{\partial^2\varphi_6}{\partial y^2}+2\left[uvr+ur^2x-vr^2y-r^3xy\right]\frac{\partial^2\varphi_6}{\partial x\partial y}+$$

$$+\left[-2ur+2r^2y\right]\frac{\partial'^2\varphi_6}{\partial x\partial t}+\left[-2vr-2r^2x\right]\frac{\partial'^2\varphi_6}{\partial y\partial t}-rg\frac{\partial\varphi_6}{\partial z}=0 \qquad (24)$$

From the above given conditions (22), (23) and (24) it is clear that the boundary value problem for unit potentials φ_k can be formulated in a way similar to that for general motion of a rigid body in unbounded space. But in the problem under consideration, as we see from (22) to (24), the unit potentials φ_k are not so simple. They are very complicated functions:

$$\varphi_1 = f_1(x,y,z,u,u^2,u^3,uv,ur,uvr,uv^2,ur^2,u^2v,u^2r,$$
$$\dot{u},u\dot{u},v\dot{u},r\dot{u},\ddot{u},\dot{v}u,\dot{r}u) \qquad (25)$$

$$\varphi_2 = f_2(x,y,z,v,v^2,v^3,uv,ur,uvr,vu^2,vr^2,v^2u,v^2r,$$
$$\dot{v},u\dot{v},v\dot{v},r\dot{v},\ddot{v},\dot{u}v,\dot{r}v) \qquad (26)$$

$$\varphi_6 \;=\; f_6(x, y, z, r, r^2, r^3, ru, rv, uvr, ru^2, rv^2, r^2u, r^2v,$$
$$\dot{r}, u\dot{r}, v\dot{r}, r\dot{r}, \ddot{r}, \dot{r}u) \tag{27}$$

The second remark is that for special cases of ship motions, the boundary condition on the free surface can be simplified.

For example, considering ship movement on straight course, $v = r = 0$, we have

$$\ddot{u}\varphi_1 + 2\dot{u}\frac{\partial'\varphi_1}{\partial t} + u\frac{\partial'^2\varphi_1}{\partial t^2} - 3u\dot{u}\frac{\partial\varphi_1}{\partial x} + u^3\frac{\partial^2\varphi_1}{\partial x^2} - 2u^2\frac{\partial'^2\varphi_1}{\partial x\partial t} - ug\frac{\partial\varphi_1}{\partial z} = 0 \tag{28}$$

If we, further, assume $\dot{u} = a = const$, then equation (29) takes forms:
• for accelerating motion

$$\frac{\partial'^2\varphi_1}{\partial t^2} + \frac{2a}{u}\frac{\partial'\varphi_1}{\partial t} - 3a\frac{\partial\varphi_1}{\partial t} + u^2\frac{\partial^2\varphi_1}{\partial x^2} - 2u\frac{\partial'^2\varphi_1}{\partial x\partial t} - g\frac{\partial\varphi_1}{\partial z} = 0 \tag{29}$$

• for decelerating movement

$$\frac{\partial'^2\varphi_1}{\partial t^2} - \frac{2a}{u}\frac{\partial'\varphi_1}{\partial t} + 3a\frac{\partial\varphi_1}{\partial t} + u^2\frac{\partial^2\varphi_1}{\partial x^2} - 2u\frac{\partial'^2\varphi_1}{\partial x\partial t} - g\frac{\partial\varphi_1}{\partial z} = 0 \tag{30}$$

where $u = at$.

Furthermore, assuming $u = const$, equations (29) and (30) become the well known linear condition on the free surface for ship movement on straight course with constant speed of advance, i.e.

$$u^2\frac{\partial^2\varphi_1}{\partial x^2} - g\frac{\partial\varphi_1}{\partial z} = 0$$

Now, the above obtained results can be applied to the formula for added masses.

ADDED MASSES

Taking into account the formula for the added mass matrix (19) and relations (25) to (27), it can be stated that, for a given ship, added masses *are not constant*; they are dependent upon the same kinematic parameters as the unit potentials φ_k, i.e.

$$m_{11} \;=\; f_{11}(u, u^2, u^3, uv, ur, uvr, uv^2, ur^2, u^2v, u^2r,$$
$$\dot{u}, u\dot{u}, v\dot{u}, r\dot{u}, \ddot{u}, \dot{v}u, \dot{r}u) \tag{31}$$

$$m_{22} = f_{22}(v, v^2, v^3, uv, ur, uvr, vu^2, vr^2, v^2u, v^2r,$$
$$\dot{v}, u\dot{v}, v\dot{v}, r\dot{v}, \ddot{v}, \dot{u}v, \dot{r}v) \tag{32}$$

$$m_{66} = f_{66}(r, r^2, r^3, ru, rv, uvr, ru^2, rv^2, r^2u, r^2v,$$
$$\dot{r}, u\dot{r}, v\dot{r}, r\dot{r}, \ddot{r}, \dot{r}u) \tag{33}$$

The above considered case of ship accelerated movement on straight course may be of some interest. From conditions (29) and (30) it can be deduced that m_{11} is a function

$$m_{11} = f_{11}(u, u^2, u^3, \dot{u}, \ddot{u}) \tag{34}$$

Hence, it follows directly that added masses for accelerating motion *differ* from that for decelerating ship movement. This conclusion is consistent with results of experiments, made by J. Obokata, pointed out in [3].

To check for symmetry in the added masses matrix, the same way as in the case of ship motion in unbounded space or in the problem of small ship motions on waves with a very low speed of advance can be applied. It is easy to see that the following integral on the free surface

$$\int_{S_F} \left(\varphi_k \frac{\partial \varphi_j}{\partial n} - \varphi_j \frac{\partial \varphi_k}{\partial n} \right) dS \neq 0$$

Hence, it follows that for ship manœuvring motions the added masses matrix m_{kj} is unsymmetrical. Results of experiments, shown in [2] partially confirm the above conclusion: $m_{26} \neq m_{62}$ ($N_{\dot{v}} \neq Y_{\dot{r}}$).

Furthermore, it seems to the author, that in spite of the ship being symmetrical, the following added masses: m_{12}, m_{21}, m_{16} and m_{61} are different from zero.

On the basis of the last statement and the above given conclusions and also taking into account formulae (15) to (18) we have the expressions for the inertia hydrodynamical forces taking the following form:

$$X_I = R_{I1} = -m_{11}\dot{u} - m_{21}\dot{v} - m_{61}\dot{r} + m_{12}ur + m_{22}vr + m_{26}r^2$$

$$-u\frac{dm_{11}}{dt} - v\frac{dm_{21}}{dt} - r\frac{dm_{61}}{dt}$$

$$Y_I = R_{I2} = -m_{12}\dot{u} - m_{22}\dot{v} - m_{62}\dot{r} - m_{11}ur - m_{21}vr - m_{61}r^2$$

$$-u\frac{dm_{12}}{dt} - v\frac{dm_{22}}{dt} - r\frac{dm_{62}}{dt}$$

$$N_I = M_{I3} = -m_{16}\dot{u} - m_{26}\dot{v} - m_{66}\dot{r} + (m_{22} - m_{11})uv - m_{12}u^2 - m_{21}v^2$$

$$+r(m_{61}v - m_{62}r) - u\frac{dm_{61}}{dt} - v\frac{dm_{62}}{dt} - r\frac{dm_{66}}{dt}$$

CONCLUSIONS

From the above considerations some conclusions follow. The first is that the problem of inertia forces for surface ships in plane motion on calm water is a very complicated one. The second is that the added masses matrix is unsymmetrical and the third is that the added masses in accelerating and decelerating movement of ship on straight course *are different*.

The last conclusion is that the results of the paper may be a good base for improvement of mathematical models used in ship manœuvring simulations.

REFERENCE

1. Krężelewski, M.J. 'Present Mathematical Models of Ship Manœuvring,' *FOESTTUG Report*, No 191/CPBR 9.5-204/87, Gdańsk, 1987 (in Polish).
2. Oltmann, P. and Sharma, S.D. 'Simulation of Combined Engine and Rudder Maneuvers Using an Improved Model of Hull-Propeller -Rudder Interactions,' *Proceeding of the Fifteenth Symposium Naval Hydrodynamics*, pp. 83 to 108, Hamburg, Germany 1984. National Academy Press, Washington, D.C. 1985.
3. 18th ITTC, *Report of the Manœuvrability Committee*, Vol. 1, pp. 361 Kobe, October 1987.

A Six Degree of Freedom Model for a Small Vessel

B.D. Wallis, M.M.A. Pourzanjani

Research Unit, Southampton Institute of Higher Education, Warsash Campus, Warsash, Southampton SO3 9ZL, UK

ABSTRACT

There are several methods for modelling the motion of a vessel. Each method has its advantages and disadvantages according to its application. This paper endeavours to assess these methods in relation to their application to small vessels.

Also assessed in this paper are, the motions of the hull in waves, the affect of wind, current and tide and the contribution of the propellers and rudders on manoeuvring. This was in order to give an over all view of the total forces and moments experienced by a small vessel in a variety of conditions.

To conclude this paper it is shown how a modular force mathematical model may be translated into a simulation of a nonlinear system by using a stepwise linear model.

INTRODUCTION

For many years researchers have studied methods for describing ships' dynamic response by utilization of mathematical models. For large vessels this has been successful, Burns [1], Inoue et al [2]. Perhaps this success is due to the fact that several research groups have made extensive full scale and scale model experiments using Mariner type hulls (Morse and Price [3]). As the experimental data was available this made it slightly easier to describe the vessel's dynamics using a mathematical model.

However not such extensive data has been

collected in relation to small vessels. Small vessels
are those which can be defined as having significantly
different shaped hulls to tankers and supertankers,
which are said to be large vessels.

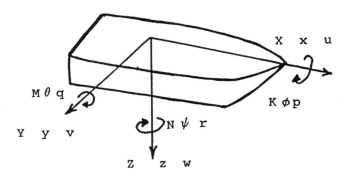

Figure 1: Co-ordinate system.

METHODS USED FOR MATHEMATICALLY MODELLING VESSELS

Although there are many different types of
mathematical models, Chudley et al [4] was able to
generalize and place each model into one of the three
following categories.

    i) Input-Output relationship model
    ii) Holistic model
    iii) Force mathematical model

a) Input-Output relationship model
This method of modelling can best be described as
the fitting of a model response to a real system. The
motion of a vessel is very complex and could be of a
large order which is hard to compute easily. It is
then that the system is represented by a lower order
model. One of the most commonly known of this type of
modelling is Nomoto's model of yaw response given by

$$T\ddot{\psi} + \dot{\psi} = K\delta \qquad \_\_\_(1)$$

This first order model can also be described better
as a second order model :

$$T_1T_2\dddot{\psi} + (T_1 + T_2)\ddot{\psi} + \dot{\psi} = K(\delta + T_3\dot{\delta}) \quad \underline{\quad\quad}(2)$$

Where T_1T_2 , $(T_1 + T_2)$, T_3 and K are coefficients of, and in turn a function of, the yaw rate and rudder angle.

The same approach can be taken in describing the sway speed of the vessel and so on.

The drawback with this model is that non-linearities in the ship's response are not described using this input-output approach. This is because this method neglects the cross coupling terms.

b) Holistic model

This model is sometimes known as a black box technique. As such it models the ship as an entire system. This theory makes the assumption that a manoeuvre is a small perturbation from the steady state forward motion. This method has worked well in many cases with large vessels.

Eda and Crane [5] and Burns [6] have all proved that this style of modelling does contain the capability of describing non-linear functions very competently. However as the vessel is treated as one entity it is hard to change the individual elements which make up the system. Therefore the model may only describe one particular vessel leaving no room for flexibility.

c) Force mathematical model

The force mathematical model essentially treats the ship's hull as a lifting surface inclined at a drift angle to the flow of water, the rudder is assumed to be the same. These lifting surfaces produce lift and drag forces perpendicular and parallel to the flow respectively. This method was originally worked out by Munk and further extended by McCallum [7]. They both assumed the lift force was a linear function and the drag force a quadratic function both with respect to the angle of incidence. These are known today to be inaccurate approximations. There is still a lot more to be learnt about the hydrodynamic forces on a vessel, Pourzanjani [8] using wind-tunnel tests and slender body theory has investigated this.

However taking a force mathematic model as a basis, then the way in which a vessel will respond dynamically whilst manoeuvering or whilst effected by it's environment can be investigated.

For small vessels the variety of hulls and the number of different combinations of propellers, fins and rudder designs are so diverse that none can be classed as a typical small vessel. Because of this problem the model chosen needs to be flexible to cope

with many designs.
    Another requirement for the model is that it can
cope with non-linearities as a nonlinear equation or
as a linear equation as a function of time, which can
simulate non-linearities using a stepwise procedure.
    From the above criteria the input-output
relationship model can be ruled out as it is unable to
easily handle non-linear effects. The holistic model
must be ruled out as it is inflexible by design. In
contrast to the other methods the force mathematical
model is both flexible and able to cope with the
nonlinear effects.

HULL MOTION IN WAVES

Fluid Mechanics
    With hydrodynamic theory the best way of
describing the total force in waves is by using a tree
diagram.

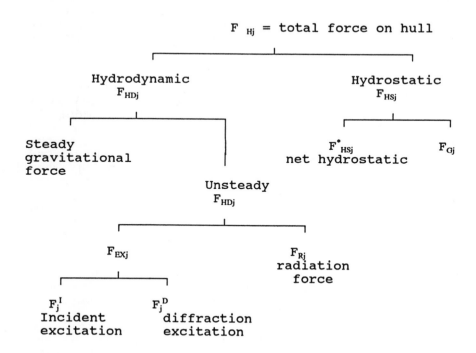

Figure 2: Tree Diagram Showing Total Forces On
         The Hull

From the diagram it can be seen that the total force is the summation of the incident, diffraction, radiation,net hydrostatic and gravitational forces, which means the excitation forces can be expressed in the following manner.

$$F_{Hj} + F_{Gj} - F^{\bullet}_{HSj} - F_{Rj} = (F_j^I + F_j^D) \; e^{i\omega et} \qquad \underline{\hspace{1cm}}(3)$$

which in turn translates to give the equation

$$\sum\nolimits_{k=1to6} [-\omega_e^2 \; (\Delta_{jk}+a_{jk})+i\omega_e \; b_{jk} \; + \; c_{jk}] \; \eta_k \; = \; F_j^I + F_j^D \underline{\hspace{1cm}}(4)$$

Different theories will reveal different co-efficient values for $(\Delta_{jk} + a_{jk}) = A_{jk}$ the added mass, b_{jk} the damping coefficient,Δ_{jk} the inertia matrix, c_{jk} the hydrostatic restoring force coefficients, and the exciting forces F_j^I and F_j^D . The format of these will dictate whether the planes of motion are coupled or uncoupled.

When the values for the coefficients and exciting forces have been estimated then equation (4) can be solved for the only unknown , which is η_k . This is the complex amplitude of the vessel's response in the kth direction.

As η_k is a sinusoidal function relating to ω_e then

$$-\omega_e^2 \; \ddot{\eta}_k \; = \; \ddot{x}_k$$

$$i\omega_e \; \dot{\eta}_k \; = \; \dot{x}_k$$

$$\eta_k \; = \; x_k$$

and excitation forces $F_j^I + F_j^D$ can be called F_{jw} denoting that the excitation force is created by waves.

Equation (4) can now be rewritten with the new notation.

$$\sum\nolimits_{k=1to6} [\; A_{jk} \; \ddot{x}_k \; + \; b_{jk} \; \dot{x}_k \; + \; c_{jk} \; x_k] \; = \; F_{jw} \underline{\hspace{1cm}}(5)$$

This equation (5) may be expanded

For j=1 ie surge direction:-

$$[A_{11} \; \ddot{x}_1 \; + \; b_{11} \; \dot{x}_1 \; + \; c_{11} \; x_1] \; + \; [A_{12} \; \ddot{x}_1 \; + \; b_{12} \; \dot{x}_1 \; + \; c_{12} \; x_1 \;]$$

$$+\dots\dots\dots\dots+[A_{16} \; \ddot{x}_1 \; + \; b_{16} \; \dot{x}_1 \; + \; c_{16} \; x_1] \; = \; F_{1W}$$

This is repeated for j = 2...5 with each of the equations containing eighteen co-efficients. It is at

this point that co-efficients can start to be
eliminated. There are several reasons for eliminating
certain equations, some are eliminated due to symmetry
some due to position and others are neglected as they
are found to be small by experimentation.

The co-efficients that are left form the equation
of motion for small hulls in waves.

SMALL VESSEL WHILST EFFECTED BY EXTERNAL FORCES.

<u>Definition of: Centre Of Lateral Resistance CLR,
Centre Of Pressure CP,Centre Of Effort CE.</u>

The Centre of lateral resistance is the centre of
area of the underwater profile of the vessel. It is
the point around which the vessel will pivot due to
external forces. The importance of these points are
described in The Macmillan and Silk Cut Handbook [9]

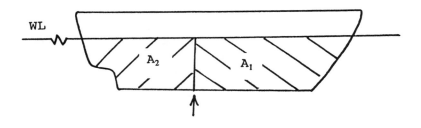

Fig 3: The pivot point CLR

when A_1 = A_2 then this is the pivot point and the
distance x can be found. It is useful to study the
line plan in order to ascertain the position of the
CLR. The forces which will act through this point are
the current and tide. This is because the current and
tide will move the vessel bodily as a translation.

The centre of pressure is the point through which
the resultant force due to directional velocity, will
act upon the vessel. The CP will move as the angle of
attack of the vessel changes. It's position can be
found by using aerodynamic theory. It may be defined
as the point about which the aerodynamic moment is
zero.

The Centre of effort for motorized vessels is the

centre of the profile area of the hull and superstructure. It is the point through which the restoring force acts as well as being the point through which the wind acts. For motorized vessels the wind is very important when it comes to the handling of it. The wind has the effect of not just blowing the vessel away from it's initial position but also turning it. When the wind is not directly on either the bow or the stern then the bow will blow away from the wind direction. This happens most dramatically when the vessel is moving at slow speeds. It also happens when the vessel is moving directly into the wind and the helmsman inadvertently steers slightly off course. The wind will then grab the bow and swing it round.

The lateral centre of gravity LCG, that is the point through which the mass of the vessel acts, is also the point through which the wave force acts causing a yaw moment about the centre of lateral resistance. The LCG remains virtually in the same place but the centre of lateral resistance, the centre of effort and the centre of pressure move as the vessel gets underway. It is difficult to predict the exact position of these points without previous experimental data. The effects of the different positions of the CLR, CP and CE in relation to one another and to the LCG is the hull balance and in turn the hull balance effects the handling of the vessel.

<u>Hull Balance</u>

Of the factors which effect the hull balance the most significant is the trim of the vessel. The trim of a vessel is the way in which the vessel sits in the water. It is set by the designer but can be affected by the shape of the hull below the waterline, the distribution of the weight along it's length and the positioning of heavy weights such as the engine and fuel and water tanks.

(a)

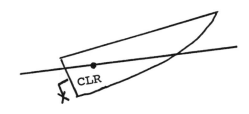

(b)

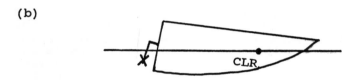

Fig 4: The trim of a vessel

In Fig 4a the stern is too deep in the water. There will be a tendency for the bow to be blown round. As the bow is higher out of the water the CLR will have moved back towards the stern of the vessel.

In Fig 4b the bow is low in the water and this will cause the vessel to turn much more sluggishly and the propeller is nearer the surface so will perform less efficiently. The CLR will be nearer the stern.

Another factor which affects the hull balance is when a vessel is heeling. When a vessel heels the shape of the vessel below the waterline changes so the CLR changes. The centre of effort is often nearer the bow than the LCG and the CLR so when a vessel is heeling and the wind blows then the CE force increases forcing the bow down which alters the CLR. The vessel then pivots about the new CLR.

In waves the hull balance will be affected, in particular in a following sea. Waves hitting the stern will cause the bow to dig in, making it like a brake. The stern is then pushed by the waves causing it to swing round so that the vessel ends up in a beam sea.

If all these factors are taken into consideration then a diagram showing the forces and moments caused by external forces on a vessel can be drawn. Fig (5).

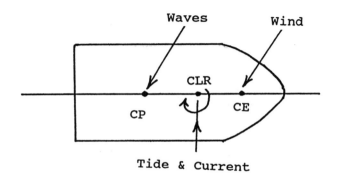

Fig 5: External Forces

PROPELLERS AND RUDDERS

One of the greatest aids in manoeuvering is the use of the propeller in conjunction with the rudder. Propellers will cause a sideways force call the paddle wheel effect when the propeller is rotating. That is the right hand propeller ahead will push the stern to starboard, this will then cause a turning moment about the pivot point. The paddle wheel effect is the strongest when the propeller first starts turning.

This sideways force can be used in order to aid manoeuvering. A short burst of the propeller accompanied by the rudder, which is hard over will cause the stern to be pushed round so the vessel can make a tight turn with very little forwards motion. This can be used when it is necessary to manoeuvre in a restricted water.

MODULAR MODELLING USING THE FORCE MODEL METHOD

Modular modelling is a method by which the forces and moments involved in the motion of a vessel in six degrees of freedom are shown as individual elements broken down into the modelling of the hull, rudder, engine, propellers and so on. Due to the development of this method this means that each element or module can be changed without changing any other module. This gives the system much more flexibility to design a model for any vessel in any manoeuvre at any speed.

A full explanation of this method is given in a paper by Dand[10].

A forces and moments diagram can be drawn showing all the forces involved in the dynamic response of the small vessel at any time.

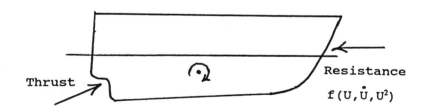

Thrust

Resistance
$f(U,\dot{U},U^2)$

Fig 6:   Total Forces On Small Vessel In The Vertical Plane

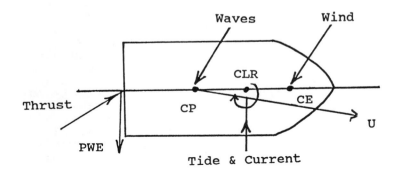

Fig 7:   Total Forces On Small Vessel In the
          Horizontal Plane

     The forces from Fig 6 can be resolved in the
X,Y,Z directions and summed as suggested by the method
of modular modelling   to give the total dynamic
translatory forces in those directions. The same can
be done to the moments from Fig 7 which are taken
about the centres of rotation i.e. in the K,M,N
directions and summed to give three equations of
rotation.
     This then means that the three translatory forces
and the three moments forces describe the small vessel
in six degrees of freedom.

CONCLUSION

     The equations of motion in six degrees of freedom
attain from this method of modelling will be basically
linear. As has been previously stated it is essential
that the model can cope with the nonlinearities
involved in the motion of a small vessel. The total
forces and moments on the vessel will be related to
the time, velocity of the vessel and the angle of
heading. So it may be assumed that for small time
intervals that the heading and velocity of the vessel
will remain constant.
     An example of this can be shown for a vessel
making a standard turning circle, see Fig 8. It can be
seen that effectively a polygon has been fitted to the
actual path simulating the nonlinearities which would
occur in this manoeuvre, using a stepwise linear
model.

_____   Stepwise model

...   Actual path

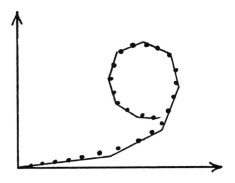

Fig 8: Turning Circle

REFERENCES

[1]   Burns R.S, M J Dove, T H Bouncer and C T Stockel
      'A   Discrete,   Time   Varying,   Non-Linear
      Mathematical Model For The Simulation Of Ship
      Manoeuvres'.
      1st Intercontinental Maritime Simulation Symp,
      Control Data Corp, Schliersee, Germany 1985.

[2]   INOUE S, HIRANO M, KIJIMA K,TAKASHINA J.
      'A   Practical   Calculation   Method   Of   Ship
      Maneuvering Motion'. International Shipbuilding
      Progress vol 28, No 325,1981

[3]   Morse R.V, PRICE D.
      'Manoeuvring Characteristics Of The Mariner Type
      Ships (Uss Compass Island) In Calm Seas'. Sperry
      Polaris Management, Sperry Gyroscope Company, New
      York, Dec 1961.

[4]   CHUDLEY J, DOVE M, STOCKEL C, TAPP N.
      'Mathematical Models In Ship Manoeuvring'. Paper
      Polytechnic South West.

[5]   EDA H, CRANE C.
      'Steering Characteristics Of Ships In Calm Waters
      And Waves'.
      Annual S.N.A.M.E. Meeting, New York, Nov 1965.

[6]   BURNS R.S.
      'The Automatic Control Of Large Ships In Confined
      Waters'. PhD Thesis, Plymouth Polytechnic, 1984.

[7]   McCALLUM I.R.
      'A Ship Steering Mathematical Model For All
      Manoeuvring Regimes'. Symp On Ship Steering And
      Automatic Control, Genova, 1980.

[8]   POURZANJANI M.M., ZIENKIEWICZ H, FLOWER J.
      'A Hybrid Method Of Estimating Hydrodynamically-
      Generated Forces For Use In Ship Manoeuvring'.
      International Shipbuilding Progress, Vol 34, No
      399, Nov 1987

[9]   The Macmillan and Silk Cut Yachtsman's Handbook
      (Macmillan 1988).

[10] DAND I.W.
      'On Modular Manoeuvring Models'.
      Proceedings of the International Conference on
      Ship Manoeuvrability, London, R.I.N.A., Paper #8
      April/May 1987.

SECTION 8: EXPERIMENTAL ANALYSIS

The Prediction of Ship Rudder Performance Characteristics in the Presence of a Propeller

A.F. Molland, S.R. Turnock

Department of Ship Science, University of Southampton, Highfield, Southampton SO9 5NH, UK

SUMMARY

A detailed series of wind tunnel measurements have been carried out to investigate the interaction between a representative ship rudder and propeller.

These tests used a series of six all-movable rudders and a propeller modelled on a Wageningen B4.40. Parameters varied were propeller advance ratio, pitch ratio, rudder aspect ratio, stock position and the longitudinal, vertical and lateral separation of the rudder and propeller. The experimental data are supported by theoretical investigations involving both the use of rudder lifting line/ propeller blade element momentum theory and the application of lifting surface theory to the rudder-propeller combination.

The results of the tests are reviewed and qualitatively discussed with respect to the influence of the governing parameters on rudder lift, drag and centre of pressure for different rudder incidence. The results are also used to derive practical parametric relationships suitable for predicting the lift and drag of various rudder-propeller combinations. Use of the relationships will provide a more physically realistic approach to the generation of rudder forces in manoeuvring models.

1. INTRODUCTION

Research into the determination of ship manoeuvring characteristics has been on-going over many years. It is apparent that there is still a lack of understanding of the fundamental forces and moments acting on the hull and the forces developed due to rudder action.

There is a reasonable amount of information available for rudders working in a free-stream but detailed information on the forces developed by the rudder in the presence of a propeller is sparse.

To fulfil some of these needs for a better understanding of fundamental rudder forces, work has been carried out at Southampton University over a number of years. Firstly, this entailed a detailed investigation into the free-stream characteristics of skeg rudders, Refs. 1 and 2, and more recently experimental and theoretical investigations into propeller-rudder interaction taking the propeller-rudder case in isolation and in the absence of the hull, Refs 3, 4, 5, 6, 7. An underlying objective of the work has been to develop practical relationships, for use in manoeuvring, to predict rudder performance.

Rudder performance characteristics are required at two levels of application, namely the use of sideforce and drag characteristics in manoeuvring models and more detailed information for rudder design purposes. This paper is mainly concerned with applications of the work to the manoeuvring model.

In the present paper the physical parameters governing rudder-propeller interaction are firstly identified. After brief descriptions of the experimental and theoretical techniques used, the derived data is reviewed and used to ascertain the relative importance of the identified parameters. In the final sections practical relationships are proposed for predicting rudder forces in the presence of the propeller.

2.   PHYSICAL PARAMETERS GOVERNING RUDDER-PROPELLER INTERACTION

In addressing the rudder-propeller interaction problem it is necessary to identify the various independent parameters on which the rudder forces depend. In the work to date the influence of the flow over the ship hull has not been considered. This allows the underlying physics of the flow for an isolated rudder and propeller to be investigated. Once this is understood the interaction between a hull and rudder-propeller combination becomes a more tractable problem. Free-surface effects and cavitation are not included as they are not considered fundamental in determining the operating conditions of the rudder and propeller.

In discussing the parameters which govern the interaction it is convenient to group them into four categories. These groups of parameters can then be used to assess their affect on rudder sideforce (lift C_L) which is of primary importance in ship manoeuvring. Additional dependent variables to be considered are the centre of action of the rudder sideforce (CP_c, CP_s), rudder stall angle and, for ship resistance and propulsion, the total thrust of the rudder-propeller combination (propeller thrust - rudder drag).

The four groups of parameters are defined as follows.

i) Flow variables which control the magnitude of the forces developed. These include the time dependent quantities V (free-stream velocity) and n (propeller rate of revolution) and the properties of the fluid, density (ρ) and dynamic viscosity (μ). Also included is the yaw angle γ between the combination and the free-stream.

ii) Rudder geometric variables which determine how the flow passes over the rudder and hence the force developed. This is controlled by the rudder incidence α, span S, mean chord c, stock position X_1, thickness t, section shape, sweep and twist.

iii) Propeller geometric variables which control how the propeller imparts energy into the flow and generates thrust. This is determined by its diameter D, pitch P, boss diameter, sweep, pitch and thickness distributions, number of blades and blade area ratio.

iv) Relative position and size of the rudder and propeller. The two units can be separated longitudinally (X), laterally (Y) and vertically (Z). The relative size is defined as the coverage ξ and is equal to the proportion of the rudder span in way of the propeller race. This can be expressed as $\xi = \lambda\, D/S$ where λ is the fraction of propeller diameter impinging on the rudder.

The sideforce (and other dependent variables) can be expressed as a function of the following non-dimensional variables, where the section shape, twist distribution etc. of the rudder and propeller are assumed fixed:

$$C_L = f\,\{\ [J, Rn, \gamma],\ [\alpha, AR, t/c, X_1/c],\ [P/D],\ [X/D, Y/D, Z/D, \xi]\ \}$$

From the above it can be seen that for a particular rudder-propeller combination the parameters reduce to:

$$C_L = f\,\{\ [J, Rn, \gamma],\ [\alpha],\ [P/D]\ \}$$

It follows that, for a given ship, relationships for manoeuvring should consider the above parameters. From these, the two fundamental controlling parameters (for a fixed pitch propeller) are the propeller advance ratio J and rudder incidence α. Reynolds number and yaw angle γ will be of less importance. Momentum theory indicates that propeller induced velocities are a function of propeller thrust loading (K_T/J^2) which is independent of P/D and this is a parameter commonly used in propeller-rudder interaction studies.

The geometrical groups of parameters (rudder, propeller, and position) will determine the magnitude of the influence of J and α on the performance of the rudder and propeller. To provide this information on a systematic basis was one of the aims of this work. In the experimental tests a representative ship propeller, based on the Wageningen B4.40 series, and all-movable rudders with a constant NACA0020 section were used. At present the only parameters not investigated were the effect of yaw angle and rudder thickness ratio. The theoretical methods developed will allow the influence of the actual propeller and rudder geometry to be investigated in more detail.

3.   EXPERIMENTAL INVESTIGATIONS

3.1 Test Rigs

The tests were carried out in the 3.5m x 2.5m low-speed wind tunnel at the University of Southampton where effective rudder Reynolds numbers of up to 1×10^6 could be achieved. A schematic view of the models in the tunnel are shown in Fig. 1. The rig consists of two independent units which allow free-stream (open water) tests to be carried out independently on rudders and propellers as well as the investigation of their interaction. Descriptions of the rudder and propeller rigs are given in Ref. 7.

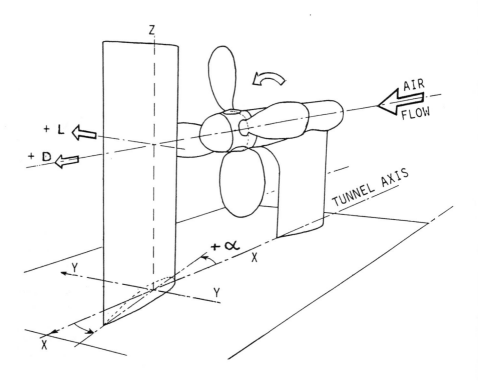

Fig. 1 Schematic of Rudder and Propeller in Wind Tunnel.

Rudder forces and moments were measured using a five-component strain gauge dynamometer. Surface pressure distributions over the rudder were also obtained in order to provide a detailed knowledge of the distribution of forces over the rudder.

The propeller rig is designed in such a way that the propeller position can be adjusted vertically, longitudinally, and at angle of attack to the flow if required. An in-line strain gauge dynamometer mounted close to the propeller is used to measure the delivered thrust and torque. Propellers up to 1000mm diameter rotating at up to 3,000 rpm can be accommodated.

3.2 Tests

All the tests to date have been carried out with a four-bladed propeller of diameter 800mm which was modelled on a Wageningen B4.40. Rudder spans have ranged from 1000mm up to 1300mm with a constant thickness ratio of 0.20. Six rudders of varying geometry have been employed together with various longitudinal (X), vertical (Z) and lateral (Y) positions of the propeller relative to the rudder. Propeller revolutions were adjusted such that J varied from 0.94 down to 0.35 with nominal K_T/J^2 values of 0.05 up to 2.30.

The rudder-propeller combinations tested to date are given in Table I and are shown diagrammatically in Fig. 2.

4.   THEORETICAL TECHNIQUES

4.1 General

Theoretical work carried out in support of the experimental investigation has entailed two complimentary approaches, one using lifting-line theory and the other lifting surface theory.

4.2 Lifting-Line Theory

This has entailed an extension of the modified lifting line approach, Ref. 2, with blade element momentum theory (along the lines of Ref. 8) used to predict the propeller induced velocities. The results of this approach are promising although dependent on experimental data to provide suitable empirical modifications.

4.3 Lifting Surface Theory

This has involved implementing Morino's perturbation potential method, Refs. 9, 10 and 11, with constant strength quadrilateral panels distributed on the actual body surface. Based on the findings of Ref. 12 the rudder and propeller lifting surfaces are modelled in isolation. The interaction between the two is accounted for by the use of a three-dimensional inflow velocity field. For the propeller this inflow is the radially averaged velocity field upstream of the rudder lifting surface and similarly for the rudder the circumferentially

TABLE I   Alternative Rudder-Propeller Arrangements Tested.

Rudder No.	2						3	4	5	6
S mm	1000						1200	1300	1000	1000
c mm	667						667	667	800	556
AR	3.0						3.6	3.9	2.5	3.6
TR	1.0						1.0	1.0	1.0	1.0
X_1/c	0.30	0.30	0.30	0.30	0.30	0.54	0.30	0.30	0.30	0.30
X/D	0.39	0.30 0.52	0.39	0.39	0.39	0.39	0.30 0.39 0.52	0.39	0.39	0.39
Z/D	0.75	0.75	1.125	0.75	0.75	0.75	0.75	1.125	0.75	0.75
Y/D	0	0	0	+0.25 -0.25	0	0	0	0	0	0
λ	1.0	1.0	0.625	0.866	1.0	1.0	1.0	0.0	1.0	1.0
ξ	0.8	0.8	0.500	0.693	0.8	0.8	0.667	0.615	0.8	0.8
P/D	0.95	0.95	0.95	0.95	0.69 1.34	0.95	0.95	0.95	0.95	0.95

* Rudder No. 2: base condition
In all tests, propeller diameter = 800 mm
In all cases, K_T/J^2 values tested = 0.05, 0.88 and 2.30

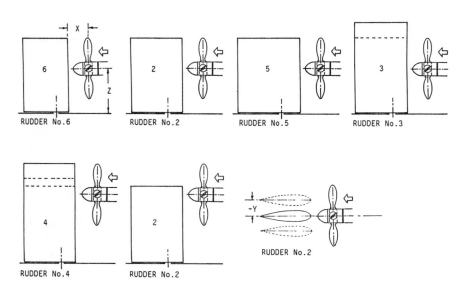

Fig. 2 Alternative Rudder-Propeller Arrangements Tested.

averaged velocity field downstream of the propeller. An iterative approach is used to converge to the final solution.

5. DATA PRESENTATION

An example of the influence of the propeller advance ratio and rudder incidence on rudder performance is shown in Fig 3. These results are for the base geometry configuration for Rudder No. 2 detailed in Table I. In Fig. 3 the rudder lift and drag and position of the spanwise and chordwise centre of pressure are plotted to a base of rudder incidence between -40° and +40°. The lift and drag coefficients used in this work are defined as

$$C_L = L / (0.5\rho V^2 A) \quad \text{and} \quad C_D = d / (0.5\rho V^2 A)$$

where lift (L) and drag (d) are defined normal and parallel to the free-stream flow respectively and noting that V is the free-stream velocity. The chordwise and spanwise centre of pressure are defined as

$$CP_c = ((M_z/N) - X_1) \times (100/c) \quad \text{and} \quad CP_s = (M_N/N) \times (100/S)$$

where M_z is the torque about the rudder stock, M_N the moment about the rudder root chord and N the rudder normal force. Also,

$$N = L \cos(\alpha) + d \sin(\alpha)$$

In these experiments the propeller rotated anti-clockwise when viewed from aft. The direction of positive incidence and propeller rotation is shown in Fig. 1.

Results are shown in Fig. 3 for three advance ratios of J=0.94, 0.51 and 0.35 with a free-stream velocity V of 10m/s. It can be seen that with decrease in advance ratio J (increase in propeller thrust K_T) the lift-curve slope increases. As for the free-stream, the lift varies almost linearly with incidence until stall is approached for all three advance ratios. For the high advance ratio the lift-curve slope is almost identical to that for the free-stream. However, there is a significant delay in stall compared with the free-stream and the magnitude of this delay increases with decreasing advance ratio. The stall angle is no longer the same for positive and negative incidence. Stall occurs later for positive incidence. Therefore, this gives rise to a greater value of maximum sideforce at positive incidence.

The rudder drag coefficient C_D for all three advance ratios is similar between -10° and +10°. As rudder incidence increased, the drag component due to lift increases rapidly for the lower advance ratios.

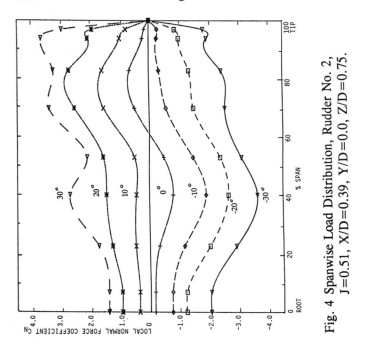

Fig. 4 Spanwise Load Distribution, Rudder No. 2,
J=0.51, X/D=0.39, Y/D=0.0, Z/D=0.75.

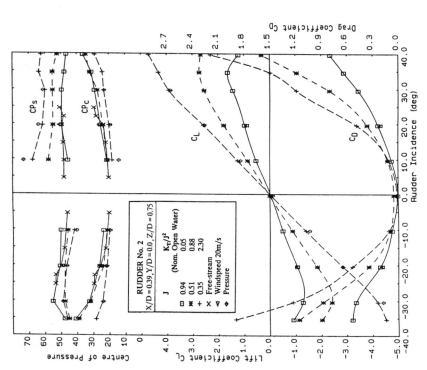

Fig. 3 Lift, Drag and Centre of Pressure Characteristics.

Centre of pressure chordwise, CP_c, generally moves forward with increasing thrust loading. CP_c in the presence of the propeller tends to be at or slightly further forward than the free-stream case, particularly at the higher thrust loading.

Centre of pressure spanwise, CP_s, increases with thrust loading at positive rudder angles, whilst for negative rudder angles decreases with increase in thrust loading. These characteristics result from the rotational nature of the rudder inflow.

The effect of the rotational nature of the inflow to the rudder is seen more clearly in Fig. 4. This shows plots of local normal force coefficient C_n against spanwise position for a range of incidence between $+30°$ and $-30°$ for an advance ratio $J = 0.51$. The local normal force coefficients were obtained by numerically integrating the measured chordwise rudder surface pressure distribution. These asymmetric load distributions explain the movement of CP_s for negative and positive rudder incidence. The asymmetry results from the angular flow change induced by the propeller. An estimate of velocity distribution induced by the propeller can be found directly by examining the local lift-curve at each spanwise position.

Refs. 3 and 4 give all the experimental data obtained in the parametric study using the same form of presentation. In addition, the actual surface pressure distributions are given. The principal features obtained in the study are described in the following section.

6.   DISCUSSION OF THE PARAMETRIC EXPERIMENTAL INVESTIGATION

6.1 General

The overall shape of the rudder lift and drag curves varied little for the parameters tested. For rudder sideforce, the features which changed were the lift-curve slope, rudder incidence for zero lift, and the positive and negative stall angle. The quadratic shape of the drag curve was maintained although the position of minimum drag altered away from zero incidence and both above and below the free-stream drag at zero incidence.

The effect of Reynolds Number on the results obtained was not investigated in detail. However, a limited number of cases were tested to confirm that no significant scaling problems exist between model tests and full-scale. The most sensitive feature for manoeuvring purposes is the stall angle. It is expected that the model tests will give conservative results, that is full scale stall angle for a given J will be greater.

The variation of rudder stock position did not give any appreciable change in rudder characteristics. With the change in rudder stock position the rudder stock torque increased but this was due to the increase in moment arm, the position of the chordwise centre of pressure remaining the same.

6.2 Propeller Pitch Ratio setting (P/D)

For a given advance ratio, changing the propeller pitch ratio setting alters the thrust coefficient (K_T) of the propeller. In these tests, the advance ratio was varied to maintain the same open-water thrust loading (K_T/J^2) to allow direct comparison of the rudder characteristic between the three pitch ratio settings tested. It was found for all the thrust loadings (0.05, 0.88, and 2.30) that there was little change in lift characteristic and position of the centre of pressure. This confirms that it is principally the propeller thrust loading which controls the rudder's performance. However, variations were observed in the drag characteristics which suggests a dependence on the flow structure within the propeller race.

6.3 Rudder Aspect Ratio (AR)

The comparison of three rudders with constant coverage $\xi = 0.80$, and at the same longitudinal separation showed for all three advance ratios an increase of lift-curve slope with increase in aspect ratio. This reproduces the effect of aspect ratio observed in the free-stream. The drag and centre of pressure follow the trends with change in aspect ratio. Again, at low rudder incidence the drag appears sensitive to the structure of the propeller race. Also with decrease in J, the effect of aspect ratio is greater than that for a free-stream rudder.

6.4 Longitudinal Separation (X/D)

At all advance ratios for the three separations tested for Rudder No.'s 2 and 3 there were only small changes in the rudder lift characteristics. The lift-curve slope did increase a small amount with separation, especially at low J. It should be noted that although the performance of a rudder aft of a propeller is of principal interest, the rudder both blocks and diverts the flow arriving at the propeller. This acts to reduce the effective propeller inflow velocity and hence increase propeller thrust for a given advance ratio. For the minimum separation this effect is greater and this may explain the small change in lift-curve slope with longitudinal separation. The effect of the induced change in K_T on the slipstream will work in the opposite sense to the acceleration within the slipstream for fixed K_T. Taken overall the results suggest that the two effects broadly cancel each other for a fixed value of J.

6.5 Lateral Separation (Y/D)

In Fig. 5, the effect of lateral separation on the performance characteristics of Rudder No. 2 is shown for an advance ratio J =0.51. The principal effect with lateral separation is the shift in the rudder incidence for zero lift. For Y/D=-0.25 zero lift occurs at +3.5° and for Y/D=+0.25 at an incidence of

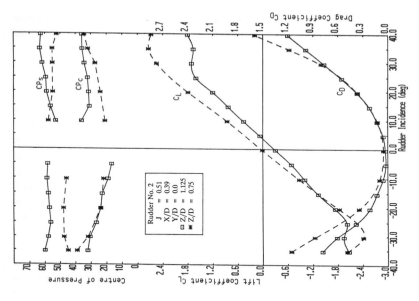

Fig. 6 Lift, Drag and Centre of Pressure Characteristics
Effect of Vertical Separation.

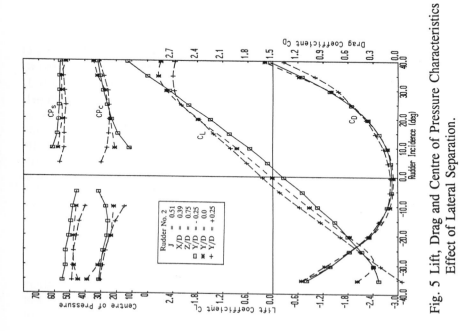

Fig. 5 Lift, Drag and Centre of Pressure Characteristics
Effect of Lateral Separation.

-3.5°. Corresponding to this is an increase in maximum lift in one direction and a decrease for the other. Likewise for the point of action of the sideforce as the rudder is moved from Y/D=-0.25 to Y/D=+0.25 the chordwise position moves forward. The spanwise position moves towards the root for negative incidence and towards the tip for positive incidence.

The lift-curve slope is no longer symmetric about the origin and for positive incidence its value decreases as Y/D changes from - 0.25 to +0.25 and with the opposite shift for negative incidence.

6.6 Vertical Separation (Z/D)

For Rudder No. 2, moving the propeller axis height from 600mm to 900mm changed Z/D from 0.75 to 1.125 and reduced the fraction of the propeller race in way of the rudder span (λ) from 1.0 to 0.625 leading to a coverage factor (ξ) of 0.50. The effect on the rudder characteristics, as shown in Fig. 6, is similar to that of a lateral movement. The lift characteristic is shifted so that a positive rudder incidence is required for zero lift. The positive stall angle is decreased as is the negative stall angle. The lift-curve slope decreases which is to be expected as the coverage decreased.

6.7 Coverage (ξ)

Two rudders with constant chord but spans of 1000mm and 1300mm (Rudders 2 and 4, Fig. 2), were used to investigate the effect of coverage. For these tests the rudder was in way of all the propeller race so $\lambda = 1.0$. The effect of tip flow was the same for both rudders. From the results for aspect ratio it would be expected that with increase in span the lift-curve slope would increase. This is indeed observed at high J, but as J is decreased the lift-curve slope for the high aspect ratio rudder becomes progressively less than the other rudder. Also, the stall angle is slightly reduced. Chordwise centre of pressure is the same for both rudders for all J values. However, there is a significant shift outboard of the spanwise centre of pressure for Rudder No.4, especially at low J.

7. PARAMETRIC RELATIONSHIPS FOR SHIP MANOEUVRING

7.1 General

The axial velocity at the rudder induced by the propeller is commonly taken to be a function of that predicted by simple momentum theory, and then used to scale the forces developed in the free-stream. This results in a prediction of the form

$$(V_R/V)^2 = (\ 1\ +\ (8/\pi)(K_T/J^2)\ )$$

where V_R is the axial velocity at the rudder.

It is generally accepted that in practice the term ($1 + (8/\pi)(K_T/J^2)$) needs attenuation, a suitable amount normally being applied empirically. The method also takes no account of the influence of propeller induced rotational velocities on rudder forces. Typical applications of this approach, cited here simply as examples, are seen in Refs. 13, 14, 15.

The aim of the current work has been to understand the physics of the flow controlling the rudder performance and hence to produce relationships which are physically realistic and which reflect interaction effects within the propeller-rudder combination.

In this section relationships are given for sideforce, drag and stall. Expressions for centre of pressure have not been finalised to date. Investigations indicate that an approach similar to that for sideforce will produce relationships for rudder stock torque and root bending moment. These will then allow CP_c and CP_s to be found.

The proposed relationships for sideforce, drag and stall, based on the work to date, are good working fits to the experimental data and are intentionally kept as simple as possible for practical applications. For this reason the relationships are given in terms of the nominal open-water propeller thrust loading rather than that actually generated by the propeller due to the blocking effect of the rudder.

It is envisaged, at this stage, that corrections to velocity due to hull wake effects would be incorporated in the normal way as corrections to K_T/J^2 and that oblique flow corrections would be applied as an incidence correction to that part of the rudder not in way of the propeller race.

7.2 Side force

The overall shape of the rudder lift (side force) characteristic in way of a propeller is similar to that of its free-stream performance. Fig. 3 illustrates the characteristic shape of the lift curve between positive and negative stall angle. If a linear relationship is assumed the lift coefficient at a given incidence α becomes:

$$C_L = (\alpha - \alpha_o) \, dC_L/d\,\alpha$$

where α_o is the rudder incidence for zero lift and α has not exceeded the stall angle.

To determine the relevant lift-curve slope to use for a given rudder-propeller geometry the coverage ξ of the rudder by the propeller race should be considered. The fraction of rudder not in way of the propeller ($1 - \xi$) can be considered as working with the free-stream lift characteristic $(dC_L/d\,\alpha)_V$.

The actual lift-curve slope may then be expressed as follows:

$$dC_L/d\alpha = (dC_L/d\,\alpha)_v\,[\,(\,1 - \xi\,).\,1 + \xi\,.\,k_o\,]$$

where k_o is a function of the propeller thrust loading and is equivalent to the ratio $(V_R/V)^2$ where V_R is the effective velocity over the rudder in way of the propeller.

Assuming that when K_T/J^2 is zero k_o is unity, a quadratic in K_T/J^2 provides a good fit to the data and can be expressed as:

$$k_o = 1.0 + 1.16(K_T/J^2).(\,1 - 0.12.(K_T/J^2))$$

Substituting and rearranging gives the final expression for C_L as

$$C_L = (\,\alpha - \alpha_o\,)\,.(dC_L/d\,\alpha)_v\,.\,[\,1.0 + \xi\,1.16(K_T/J^2)(\,1 - 0.12.(K_T/J^2)\,)]$$

The free-stream lift-curve slope $(dC_L/d\,\alpha)_v$ of the rudder may be found from the following empirical expression which corresponds satisfactorily with the free-stream results of the present work and with other free-stream published data:

$$(dC_L/d\,\alpha)_v = 1.9\,\pi\,/\,[\,(57.3\,(\,1 + 3/AR\,)]$$

For lateral or vertical displacement of the propeller where $\lambda < 1$ the zero-lift incidence can be expressed empirically as a quadratic function of thrust loading:

$$\alpha_o = 9.0\,[\,1 - 2\,ABS\,(\lambda - 0.5)\,]^{0.3}\,\xi\,(K_T/J^2)\,(\,1 - 0.18\,(K_T/J^2)\,)$$

The multiplication factor in terms of λ has a maximum when $\lambda = 0.5$ which corresponds to the maximum value of α_o and is zero when $\lambda = 0.0$ or 1.0.

For zero lateral separation and when the fraction of the propeller race arriving at the rudder (λ) is unity the zero lift incidence α_o is zero. The value of λ is unity if the rudder is in way of all the propeller race. However, if the vertical displacement of the propeller axis (Z) results in some of the propeller being clear of the rudder, λ can be found as follows:

$$\lambda = 0.5 + ((\,S - Z\,)/D)$$

Using the properties of a circle a lateral separation $Y < > 0.0$ can also be expressed as an equivalent λ as follows:

$$\lambda = [\,1 - 4\,(Y/D)^2\,]^{0.5}$$

The proposed expressions model the variation in rudder performance with rudder aspect ratio, coverage, and lateral and vertical separation. The effect of longitudinal separation was small and has not been included. Also, the difference from the mean lift-curve slope for positive and negative incidence with lateral separation has not been included, but can be found by inspection of Fig 5 and is of the order of 10% of k_o.

It should be noted that the sign of α_o depends on the direction of rotation of the propeller.

7.3 Stall Angle

The periodic nature of the propeller race delays stall on the rudder. Even for high J ($K_T \rightarrow 0$) the stall can occur at up to $+35°$ and $-28°$ compared with about $20°$ in the free-stream. The actual stall angle measured is sensitive to free-stream Reynolds number but only by a small amount ($+3°$ to $+4°$ for instance when Rn increases from 1×10^6 to 3×10^6 and very little thereafter). By estimating the stall angle from the shape of the lift curve an approximate relationship for stall was developed with a form similar to that for lift. That is:

$$+\alpha_{stall} = (10 + 30/AR) [1 + \xi (0.84 + 0.33 (K_T/J^2)(1 - 0.1 (K_T/J^2))]$$

$$-\alpha_{stall} = - (10 + 30/AR) [1 + \xi (0.26 + 0.69 (K_T/J^2)(1 - 0.2 (K_T/J^2))]$$

It should be emphasised that the above are approximate relationships, but they reflect the nature of the asymmetry of rudder stall in way of the propeller and its dependence on thrust loading.

7.4 Drag

In the manoeuvring situation rudder drag will be a significant component of resistance at larger rudder angles. Many manoeuvring models make simplified assumptions for this component, such as assuming it to be the longitudinal component of the rudder normal force. The level of the detailed measurements in the current work allows a more accurate assessment of rudder drag to be made for change in rudder incidence (hence C_L) and propeller thrust loading K_T/J^2.

Assuming total drag to be made up in the usual way,

$$C_D = C_{Do} + C_{Di}$$

C_{Do} is assumed to remain constant for different angles of attack and, for given AR, $C_{Di} = f(C_L^2)$ hence

$$C_D = C_{Do} + k_1.C_L^2$$

Although there is considerable movement of C_{D_0} at zero incidence the available data indicate that in the presence of the propeller for all cases investigated, an average practical value for C_{D_0} and a working fit for k_1 may be assumed as follows:

$$C_{D_0} = 0.05$$

$$k_1 = 0.105 \ (\ 2.0 - (K_T/J^2)^{0.35} \ )$$

noting that k_1 decreases as K_T/J^2 increases.

Inspection of the results for the various rudder and propeller configurations indicates that, in the presence of the propeller, AR has a small influence on the factor k_1 (AR in the range 2.5-3.9) and, similarly, coverage ξ has only a small influence on k_1. In both cases the change in C_L has adequately reflected the geometric changes in rudder properties.

Overall this expression models C_D well except in the case of $\lambda < 1$ for vertical separation and to a lesser extent lateral separation. In these cases the C_D curve is displaced with incidence (eg. see Figs 5 and 6).

8. CONCLUSIONS

8.1 A review has been made of investigations carried out into isolated rudder-propeller interaction. The discussion of the results provides a deeper insight into the dependence of the interaction effects on the various geometrical properties of the rudder and propeller and their relative position.

8.2 It is found that rudder sideforce and drag have a non-linear dependence on propeller thrust loading. Stall angle is increased significantly in the presence of the propeller with different values for positive and negative incidence.

8.3 Practical relationships are proposed for the forces developed by the rudder in the presence of the propeller. These are based on the investigations described which have provided data of a much more detailed nature than those available up to now.

8.4 The work reported on forms part of an overall approach which entails identifying the influence of the propeller on the rudder, the rudder on the propeller, and the rudder-propeller combination on the hull. The work to date has only considered the isolated rudder-propeller combination in straight flow. However, a programme of research is currently underway to help identify the effect of a hull form and obliquity on the performance of the rudder-propeller combination.

9. ACKNOWLEDGEMENTS

The work described in this paper covers part of a research project funded by the S.E.R.C./M.o.D. through the Marine Technology Directorate Ltd.

NOMENCLATURE

A   Rudder Area (S x c).
AR   Effective Aspect Ratio $(2S^2/A)$.
c   Rudder Chord.
CP_c Centre of pressure chordwise, %c, measured from leading edge.
CP_s Centre of pressure spanwise, %S, measured from root.
C_D Drag Coefficient.
C_L Lift Coefficient.
C_N Normal force coefficient, normal to rudder.
d   Rudder drag force, in direction of free-stream air flow.
D   Propeller Diameter.
J   Advance ratio (V/nD).
K_T Propeller thrust coefficient $(T/\rho n^2 D^4)$.
L   Rudder lift force, normal to free-stream air flow.
n   Propeller rate of revolution, revs. per sec.
N   Normal force, normal to centreline of rudder.
P   Propeller pitch.
Rn   Reynolds Number $(\rho Vc/\mu)$
S   Rudder span.
t   Rudder section thickness.
V   Wind speed (free-stream).
V_R Effective axial velocity at the rudder.
X   Longitudinal distance, propeller plane to rudder leading edge.
X_1 Distance of rudder stock from leading edge.
Y   Lateral distance between propeller axis and rudder stock.
Z   Vertical distance between rudder root and propeller axis.
α Rudder incidence.
α_o Rudder incidence for zero lift.
ρ Density
μ Dynamic viscosity
ξ Coverage, proportion of rudder span covered by propeller race $(\lambda D/S)$.
λ Proportion of propeller race diameter impinging on rudder.
γ Yaw angle.

REFERENCES

1.   Goodrich G.J., and Molland, A.F., *Wind Tunnel Investigation of Ship Skeg-Rudders*. Trans. RINA, Vol. 121, 1979.
2.   Molland, A.F., *A method for determining the free-stream characteristics of ship skeg-rudders*. International Shipbuilding Progress, Vol. 32, June 1985.

3. Molland, A.F., and Turnock, S.R., *Wind tunnel investigation of the influence of propeller loading on ship rudder performance*. University of Southampton, Ship Science Report No. 46, 1991.

4. Molland, A.F., and Turnock, S.R., *Further wind tunnel tests on the influence of propeller loading on ship rudder performance*. University of Southampton, Ship Science Report No. 52, 1992.

5. Turnock, S.R., *Validation of a lifting-surface method for modelling rudder-propeller interaction*. University of Southampton, Ship Science Report No. 53, 1992.

6. Molland, A.F., *The prediction of rudder-propeller interactions using blade element-momentum propeller theory and modified rudder lifting line theory*. University of Southampton, Ship Science Report No. 54, 1992.

7. Molland, A.F., and Turnock, S.R., *Wind tunnel investigation of the influence of propeller loading on ship rudder performance*. RINA (Written Discussion) 1992.

8. Eckhard, M.K. and Morgan, W.G., *A propeller design method*. Trans. SNAME, Vol. 63, 1955.

9. Morino, L., and Kuo, C.C., *Subsonic potential aerodynamics for complex configurations: a general theory*. AIAA Journal, Vol. 12, No. 2, 1974.

10. Kerwin, J.E., Kinnas, S.A., Lee, J-T., and Shih, W-Z., *A surface panel method for the hydrodynamic analysis of ducted propellers*. Trans. SNAME, Vol. 95, 1987.

11. Maitre, T.A., and Rowe, A.R., *Modelling of flow around a marine propeller using a potential based method*. Journal of Ship Research, Vol. 35, No. 2, 1991.

12. Cho. J., and Williams, M., *Propeller-wing interactions using a frequency domain panel method*. Journal of Aircraft, Vol. 27, No. 3, 1990.

13. Kose, D, *On a new mathematical model of manoeuvring motions of a ship and its applications*. International Shipbuilding Progress, Vol. 29, 1982.

14. Matsumoto, N., and Suemitsu, K., *Interference effects between the hull, propeller and rudder of a hydrodynamic mathematical model in manoeuvring motion*. Naval Architecture and Ocean Engineering, The Society of Naval Architects of Japan, Vol. 22, 1984.

15. Norrbin, N.H., *Ship turning circles and manoeuvring criteria. 14th STAR symposium*. SNAME, 1989.

New Method to Obtain Manoeuvring Coefficients by Means of Towing Tank Tests

J.M. Montero (*), A. García (**), J.R. Iribarren (*)

(*) CEPYC-CEDEX, Antonio López, 81, 28029 Madrid, Spain

(**) CONTROL DYNAMICS S.L. Dulcinea, 47, 28020 Madrid, Spain

INTRODUCTION

Under the title "New method to obtain manoeuvring coefficients by means of towing tank tests", the aim is to provide a new tool to understand the characteristics of ship manoeuvrability at the design stage.

The main aim of this study is to develop a new method concerning tests and data analysis, in order to get all the hydrodynamic derivatives or coefficients of the current mathematical models of ship manoeuvrability.

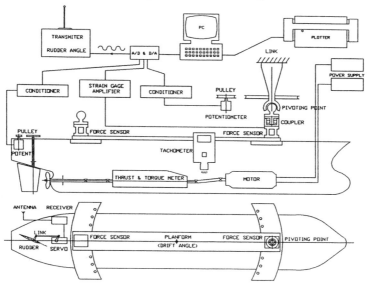

Figure 1. General layout of the data acquisition system

Therefore the techniques developed can serve as a basis for a proper understanding of ship manoeuvrability problems, and opens up a possibility for the ship designer to create a vessel with the desired manoeuvrability on a numerical basis resorting to previous model testing.

The present study shows the main results obtained from the doctoral thesis titled "Modelling and simulation of ship behaviour in calm water with applications to harbour manoeuvrability studies" by J.M.Montero made in the E.T.S. of Naval Architecture of "Universidad Politécnica de Madrid" (Spain).

MATHEMATICAL MODEL

In the normal ship-fixed axes used in manoeuvrability studies, the equations of motion of the ship are:

$$m \cdot (u - v \cdot r) = X_H + X_P + X_R$$

$$m \cdot (v + u \cdot r) = Y_H + Y_P + Y_R$$

$$I_{zz} \cdot r = N_H + N_P + N_R$$

Where the indexes H, P y R represent hull, propeller and rudder respectively.

HULL FORCES AND MOMENTS

Longitudinal force

$$X_H = - m_x \cdot u - m_y \cdot v \cdot r + X_{uu} \cdot u^2 + R^*(u) +$$
$$+ X_{vv} \cdot v^2 + X_{vr} \cdot v \cdot r + X_{rr} \cdot r^2$$

Transverse force

$$Y_H = - m_y \cdot v - m_x \cdot u \cdot r + Y_{uv} \cdot u \cdot v + Y_v \cdot v + Y_r \cdot r$$
$$+ Y_{vv} \cdot v \cdot |v| + Y_{vr} \cdot v \cdot |r| + Y_{rr} \cdot r \cdot |r|$$

Moments

$$N_H = - J_{zz} \cdot r - N_v \cdot v - N_r \cdot r - N_{uv} \cdot u \cdot |v| -$$
$$- N_{vv} \cdot v \cdot |v| - N_{vr} \cdot v \cdot |r| - N_{rr} \cdot r \cdot |r|$$

PROPELLER FORCES AND MOMENTS

Longitudinal force

$$X_P = (1-t_{PO}) \cdot \mu \cdot n^2 \cdot D^4 \cdot K_T(J_P)$$

Transverse force

$$Y_P = Y_{nn} \cdot n^2$$

Moment

$$N_P = N_{nn} \cdot n^2 \cdot x_P$$

RUDDER FORCES AND MOMENTS

The normal force on the rudder is:

$$F_N = 1/2 \cdot \mu \cdot S \cdot \frac{6.13 \cdot AR}{AR + 2.25} \cdot V_R^2 \cdot sen\alpha_R$$

Longitudinal force

$$X_R = - F_N \cdot sen\delta$$

Transverse force

$$Y_R = - (1 + a_H) \cdot F_N \cdot cos\delta$$

Moment

$$N_R = - (1 + a_H) \cdot x_R \cdot F_N \cdot cos\delta$$

NEW MODEL TESTING METHODS

In order to obtain all the coefficients of the mathematical model, some series of tests have been carried out using techniques based on captive model tests.

A ship model of 1850mm length, 323mm beam, 115mm draught and 0.811 block coefficient was towed in a towing tank of 100m length, 4m width and 2.20m depth.

1.- SELF PROPULSION TEST AND OPEN WATER TEST FOR THE PROPELLER

Specific thrust $K_T(J)$ and specific torque $K_Q(J)$ of the propeller were obtained from the open water test for the propeller. Combining self propulsion test and open water test for the propeller, w_{PO} and t_{PO} coefficients on straight-line condition can be obtained.

2.- TOWING SHIP MODEL AT DIFFERENT SPEEDS AND DIFFERENT DRIFT ANGLES (WITHOUT PROPELLER)

Ship model without propeller was towed at different speeds and different drift angles:

drift angle β (degrees): 0   5   10   15   20   25

ship model speed (m/s): 0.1 0.2 0.3 0.4 0.5 0.6 0.7

Measuring longitudinal and transverse hull forces, the following coefficients: X_{uu}, $R^*(u)$, Y_v, N_v, Y_{uv}, N_{uv} were obtained in static conditions.

3.-   MEASURE OF RUDDER FORCES AL DIFFERENT RUDDER ANGLES AND
       DIFFERENT PROPELLER REVOLUTIONS

    In this case, the ship model was fixed with zero speed,
the propeller was working at different revolutions and the rudder
angle also varied:

    Propeller revolutions n (r.p.m.): 850   1150   1500

    Rudder angle δ (degrees): 0 ±5 ±10 ±15 ±20 ±25 ±30

    Measuring rudder forces and taking into account the kind
of rudder belonging to NACA 0018 series with a particular aspect
ratio, the velocities induced by the propeller on the rudder were
obtained. These velocities are independent of rudder angle and
are proportional to propeller revolutions.

    Based on the previous measurements, the stall rudder
angle, the equivalent aspect ratio AR and the asymmetry effect
in water flow induced by propeller action δ_o, were obtained.

4.-   TOWING SHIP MODEL AT DIFFERENT SPEEDS AND DIFFERENT RUDDER
       ANGLES (WITH PROPELLER)

    The ship model was towed at different speeds and different
rudder angles δ for several propeller revolutions:

    Ship model speed (m/s): 0.1 0.2 0.3 0.4 0.5 0.6 0.7

    Rudder angle δ (degrees): 0 ±5 ±10 ±15 ±20 ±25 ±30

    Propeller revolutions n (r.p.m.): 1000   1500

    Measuring transverse hull forces, input rudder velocities
were obtained and the effect of asymmetry of propeller action δ_o
was confirmed.

5.-   TOWING SHIP MODEL AT DIFFERENT SPEEDS, DIFFERENT RUDDER
       ANGLES δ AND DIFFERENT DRIFT ANGLES ß

    The ship model was towed at different speeds and constant
propeller revolutions (1500 r.p.m.), varying rudder and drift
angles:

    Ship model speed (m/s): 0.1 0.2 0.3 0.4 0.5 0.6 0.7

    Rudder angle δ (degrees): 0 ±5 ±10 ±15 ±20 ±25 ±30

    Drift angle ß (degrees): 5   10

    Measuring transverse hull forces and using some model
experimental results from Hirano and Yumuro (References 1, 23 and
24), input velocity of rudder and interaction coefficients a_H, Γ,
w_P and w_R were obtained.

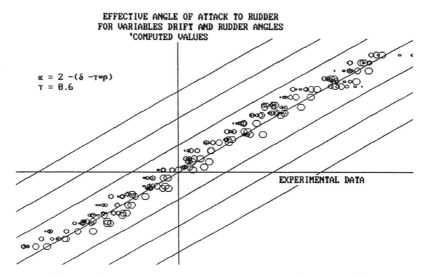

Figure 2. Comparison of computed and measured α_R

6.-   OSCILLATION TESTS

    Finally a special test using oscillation techniques was
carried out, fixing the pivoting point and forcing ship's motions
by harmonic oscillations of rudder with variable frequencies from
0.015 to 0.200 Hz, constant speed 0.5m/s and constant propeller
revolutions 1500 r.p.m.

    Frequency (Hz): 0.015   0.025   0.05   0.10   0.15   0.20

    Maximum amplitude of rudder angle: ±35 degrees

    The tests were carried out for two different locations of
the pivoting point, 1.011m and 0.481m ahead of midships.

    Measuring transverse hull forces and taking into account
the results of previous tests, dynamic hull coefficients: m_y, Y_v,
Y_r, Y_{vv}, Y_{vr}, Y_{rr}, J_{zz}, N_v, N_r, N_{vv}, N_{vr}, N_{rr} were obtained.

CONCLUSIONS

    The measurement of rudder forces at zero ship speed with
the propeller working confirms that the propeller actuates in an
imaginary cylinder with the same diameter as that of the
propeller and the velocities induced in the rudder are
proportional to propeller revolutions, independent of rudder
angle. For this reason the rudder works with an equivalent aspect
ratio and not with the geometric aspect ratio.

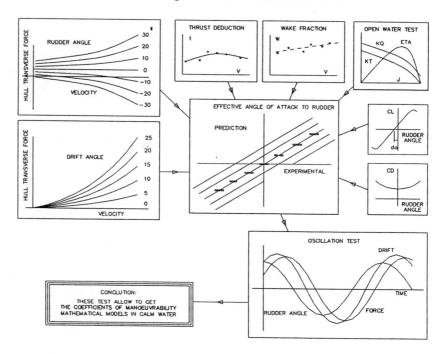

Figure 3. Description of the experimental method

The open water test for the propeller, the self propulsion test and the measurement of transverse hull forces at several ship model speeds and several rudder angles with and without propeller action allows to obtain input velocities in the rudder.

The influence of drift angle on the input velocity of the rudder can be analyzed by means of test number 5, where interaction coefficients can be obtained.

Finally, once the input rudder velocities are known, the dynamic coefficients can be obtained using tests based on oscillation techniques, fitting the results of the measured transverse forces in the hull.

The tests proposed in the present study allow to obtain the coefficients of current mathematical models for ship manoeuvrability in calm water. These tests can be carried out in a standard towing tank without using special techniques based on PMM devices.

REFERENCES

[1]   Hirano, M.
        "A practical calculation method of ship manoeuvring motion
        at initial design stage"
        The Society of Naval Architects of Japan. vol. 19. 1981.
        pp 68-80. Tokyo

[2]   Kose, K.; Hinata, H.; Hashizume, Y.; Futagawa, E.
        "On a new mathematical model for manoeuvring motions of
        ships in low speed"
        The Society of Naval Architects of Japan. vol. 23. 1985.
        pp 15-24. Tokyo

[3]   Norrbin, N. H.
        "Some   notes   on   the   rudder   derivatives   and   the
        representation of the control force in the prediction of
        ship manoeuvering capabilities"
        Conference of Ship Manoeuvrability. Paper 14. 1987. London

[4]   Akudinov, V.; Miller, E.; Alman, P.; Jacobsen, B.
        "Ship manoeuvrability assessment in ship design simulation
        concept"
        Conference of Ship Manoeuvrability. Paper 19. 1987. London

[5]   Fujino, M.; Fukasawa, T.; Ishiguro, T.; Watanabe, K.
        "Rudder force and manoeuvring motions in shallow water"
        Conference of Ship Manoeuvrability. Paper 22. 1987. London

[6]   Hirano, M.; Takashina, J.; Moriya, S.
        "A practical prediction method of ship manoeuvring motion
        and its application"
        Conference of Ship Manoeuvrability. Paper 17. 1987. London

[7]   Dand, I. W.
        "On modular manoeuvring models"
        Conference of Ship Manoeuvrability. Paper 8. 1987. London

[8]   Kobayashi, E.; Asai, S.
        "A simulation study on ship manoeuvrability at low speeds"
        Conference of Ship Manoeuvrability. Paper 10. 1987. London

[9]   Khattab, O.
        "Ship handling in harbours using real time simulation"
        Conference of Ship Manoeuvrability. Paper 11. 1987. London

[10]   Asinovsky, J.
        "Ship manoeuvrability analysis using the differential
        approach"
        Conference of Ship Manoeuvrability. Paper 9. 1987. London

[11]   Bogdanov, P; Milanov, E.
        "Computerized estimation of ship manoeuvrability at design
        stage"
        Conference of Ship Manoeuvrability. Paper 16. 1987. London

[12]   Jerzy, W Doerffer.
       "Devices improving manoeuvring characteristics of ships"
       Conference of Ship Manoeuvrability. Paper 16. 1987. London

[13]   Eda, H.
       "Effect of rudder rate on manoeuvring performance of a
       large tanker"
       The Society of Naval Architects and Marine Engineers.
       Technical and Research Report R-22.
       February 1976. New York

[14]   Hooft, J. P.
       "Computer simulation of the ship's manoeuvrability"
       Maritime Research Institute Netherlands, Wageningen.
       August 1987. The Netherlands

[15]   Hooft, J. P.; Pieffers, J. M. B.
       "Manoeuvrability of frigates in waves"
       Maritime Research Institute Netherlands, Wageningen.
       August 1987. The Netherlands

[16]   Norrbin, N. H.
       "Theory and observations on the use of mathematical model
       for ship manoeuvring in deep and confined waters"
       SSPA Report 68. 1971. Goteborg

[17]   Inoue, S.
       "A practical calculation method of ship manoeuvring
       motion"
       International Shipbuilding Progress. Vol 28, 325. 1981

[18]   Clarke, D.
       "The application of manoeuvring criteria in hull design
       using linear theory"
       Spring Meeting RINA. 1982

[19]   Glandsdorp, C. C.
       "Ship type modelling for a training simulator"
       Proceedings Fourth Ship Control System Symposium.
       1975. The Hague

[20]   Ogawa, A.; Kasai, H.
       "On the mathematical model of manoeuvring motion of ships"
       International Shipbuilding Progress. Vol 25, 292. 1978

[21]   Inoue, S.; Hirano, M.; Kijima, K.
       "Hydrodynamic derivatives on ship manoeuvring"
       International Shipbuilding Progress. Vol 28, 321. 1981

[22]   Soding, H.
       "Forces on rudders behind a manoeuvring ship"
       3rd Symposium of Numerical Ship Hydrodynamics. 1980. Paris

[23]   Matsumoto, N.; Suemitsu, K.
       "Interference effects between the hull propeller and
       rudder of a hydrodynamic mathematical model in manoeuvring
       motion"
       JSNA Kansai, 190. 1983

[24]   Yumuro, A.
        "Some experiments on flow straightening effect on a
        propeller in oblique flows"
        NAOE. Vol 18. 1'980

[25]   Nakatake, K.
        "On hydrodynamic force acting on rudder"
        Trans. SNAWJ, 56. 1978

[26]   Leeuwen, G. van; Journee, J. M. J.
        "Prediction of ship manoeuvrability"
        Netherlands Ship Research Centre. Report 158 S. 1972

[27]   Crane, C. L.
        "Studies of ship manoeuvring response to propeller and
        rudder actions"
        Stevens Institute of Technology. Report AD706571.
        1977. Hoboken, New York

[28]   ITTC Manoeuvring Committee
        "Report of the Manoeuvring Committee"
        ITTC Conference. 1990. Madrid

[29]   Abkowitz, M. A.
        "A manoeuvring simulation model for large angles of attack
        and backing propellers"
        ITTC Conference. PS -4.7. 1990. Madrid

[30]   Hooft, J. P.
        "Introduction of Group Discussion on Manoeuvring
        Simulation"
        ITTC Conference. GD - 3.1. 1990. Madrid

[31]   Oltmann, P.
        "Prediction of ship's manoeuvrability by simulation
        compared to model tests"
        ITTC Conference. GD - 3.2. 1990. Madrid

[32]   Kijima, K.; Tanaka, S.; Nakiri, Y.; Furukawa, Y.
        "On a numerical simulation for predicting on ship
        manoeuvring performance"
        ITTC Conference. GD - 3.3. 1990. Madrid

[33]   Hasegawa, K.
        "Ship manoeuvring simulation including navigator's model"
        ITTC Conference. GD - 3.5. 1990. Madrid

[34]   García Ferrández, A.
        "Estudio de las fuerzas laterales producidas en carenas
        asimétricas con grandes apéndices"
        Tesis Doctoral. E.T.S.I.N.. 1987. Madrid

[35]   Abad Arroyo, R.
        "Estudio de los movimientos del buque y su amortiguación
        por estabilizadores activos"
        Tesis Doctoral. E.T.S.I.N.. 1988. Madrid

[36]   Lincoln, C.; Eda, H.; Landsburg, A. C.
       "Principles of Naval Architecture"
       SNAME. Vol 3. Cap 9. 1989. New York

[37]   Saunders, H. E.
       "Hydrodynamics in ship design"
       SNAME. Vol 3. 1965. New York

Design of Control Surfaces with Rotating Cylinders

S. Cordier

Bassin D'Essais des Carènes, Chaussée du Vexin, Val de Reuil, 27100, France

ABSTRACT

The object of this paper is the developement of practical, compact and efficient high lift control surfaces for ship motion control at low speeds. A method is presented to determine the surface, aspect-ratio and lift coefficient of a control surface for a given lift, span and ship speed. Various methods of boundary layer control employing moving surfaces to achieve high lift are reviewed. Several configurations are selected. A numerical study of fins with a rotating leading edge cylinder (RLEC) yields an optimum cylinder diameter. The concept of fins with a rotating trailing edge cylinder (RTEC) is also studied numerically. An analytical model of the lift of this type of hydrofoil section is presented. Experimental results for different fins of aspect-ratio 1.0 and Magnus cylinders of different aspect-ratios in a water tunnel are presented. The results demonstrate the effectiveness of these devices. The power coefficient derived to scale the power lost to the fluid through friction is presented.

INTRODUCTION

The lift (L) developed by a control surface is related to its surface (S) and speed of advance (V) by the definition of the lift coefficient (C_L):

$$C_L = \frac{L}{\frac{1}{2} \rho\, S\, V^2}$$

Hence, for a control surface to maintain its lift at lower ship speeds, its surface and its lift coefficient have to be increased. The number and the size of the control surfaces being limited by physical constraints such as internal space, the draft or the breadth of the ship, there is a need for high lift coefficient control surfaces. For a *given lift and ship speed* the product $C_L.S$ is a constant which characterizes the lifting surface. To achieve this product at low speeds (8 knots or less) with control surfaces of reasonable size, an effort has been made to increase the lift coefficient of the fin.

HIGH-LIFT CONTROL SURFACES

Estimated characteristics

For a fixed span (b) the required product CL.S can be translated in the form of a fixed fin loading CL/A_g where A_g is the geometrical aspect-ratio ($A_g=b^2/S$). This ratio is simply a lift coefficient where the reference area is b^2. In the present study a lift force of 190KN is sought at 8 knots for a span of 3 m which yields a value of $CL/A_g=2.5$.

Lift From elementary wing theory, the lift curve slope $a_{3D}=(\delta CL/\delta\alpha)_{\alpha=0°}$ of a 3D wing is function of the 2D section lift curve slope a_{2D} and effective aspect-ratio (A_e). The maximum lift coefficient which can be reached by a fin of a given aspect-ratio can be calculated by a formula such as Helmbold's [1] :

$$CL_{max} = a_{3D} = a_{2D} \cdot \cfrac{A_e}{\dfrac{a_{2D}}{\pi} + \sqrt{A_e^2 + \left[\dfrac{a_{2D}}{\pi}\right]^2}} \qquad \text{where } A_e = 2 \cdot A_g$$

Using this formula a maximum aspect-ratio can be estimated as a function of the fin loading CL/A_g and a_{2D}. This relation is shown on figure 1. One can identify a maximum loading slightly above $CL/A_g=3$. For $CL/A_g<1.5$, there is no problem in meeting the desired loading. For a profile of thickness (t) small compared to the chord (c), $a_{2D}=1.8\pi$ can be used up to t/c=25%. For a very thick profile (t/c>60%) with boundary-layer control, this value may be doubled. In the present study ($CL/A_g=2.5$) the corresponding maximum geometrical aspect-ratios of the thin and the thick profiles are 1.0 and 2.0 with lift coefficients of 2.5 and 5.0 respectively.

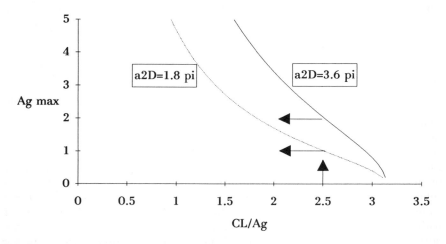

Figure 1: Maximum aspect-ratio of high-lift fins as a function of lift loading

<u>Drag</u> The drag of the fin at maximum lift is mainly caused by induced drag which can be estimated using Prandtl's induced drag formula:

$$CD_i = \frac{CL^2}{\pi \cdot A_e}$$

Hence, the lift to drag ratio CL/CD_i is inversely proportional to the fin loading (in the present case $CL/CD_i = 2.5$):

$$CL/CD_i = \frac{2 \cdot \pi}{CL/A_g}$$

<u>Power</u> The power ($\mathcal{P}$) necessary to overcome friction forces on a rotating cylinder with diameter d, can be estimated as the product of a friction torque and angular velocity. If the average shear velocity is taken to be the tangential velocity (Vt) and an average friction coefficient (Cf) is estimated, a power coefficient (Ca) can be written as follows:

$$Ca = \frac{\mathcal{P}}{\frac{1}{2} \rho \, \pi \, b^2 \, V^3 \, Cf} = \frac{d}{b} \cdot K^3 \qquad \text{where } K = \frac{Vt}{V}$$

<u>Boundary-Layer Control</u>
The viscosity in the fluid creates a boundary-layer on the profile which causes the fluid to separate at some point along the chord. At small angles of attack (AA) trailing edge separation reduces the lift curve slope. At high angles of attack the flow separates over the suction side: stall. To take full advantage of the theoretical lift potential of lifting surfaces, it is necessary to avoid separation through boundary-layer control in regions of negative pressure gradients (pressure recovery): leading edge, flap knee, and blunt trailing edge.

The low momentum fluid in the boundary-layer which causes the fluid to separate can either be accelerated or removed. These approaches require the use of physical devices. A very good overview of high-lift devices is contained in a document compiled by Wilson [4] at DTRC. As part of the present research effort, slot blowing, slot suction and moving surface boundary-layer control have been investigated. The work on moving surface boundary-layer control is presented here.

<u>Control Surfaces with Rotating Cylinders</u>
There are several embodiments of the concept of a movable surface on a profile, most of them come from the field of aeronautics. From a literature survey various concepts were identified: a rotating band on the suction side [5], a rotating leading edge cylinder (RLEC) [6,7,8,9,10,11], a rotating cylinder on the suction side [11], a rotating cylinder at the knee of a flap [12], a rotating trailing edge cylinder (RTEC) [13,14] and rotating cylinders at the leading and trailing edges [14,15]. A German company manufactures rudders with a rotating leading edge and with a flap at the trailing edge. To the author's knowledge, the hydrodynamic performance of this device has not been published. The Magnus rotating cylinder [16,17,18] is the limiting case of these configurations: the entire foil surface is in movement. It has been

suggested for various marine applications [19] and has had a few practical implementations.

Based on the reported performance and on the practicality of these configurations four were selected for analysis and test: a RLEC profile with symmetrical trailing edge (RLEC-SYM), a RLEC profile with a flap (RLEC-FLAP), several RLEC+RTEC profiles (RL&TEC), and several Magnus rotating cylinders (RC). A fifth configuration which is believed to be novel is one where the chord of the Magnus cylinder is augmented by a small trailing edge flap (RC-FLAP).

THEORETICAL ANALYSIS

An analysis of the profiles was performed using a 2D potential flow code written by Eppler [20]. It was used in the direct mode: the pressure distributions are calculated from a known geometry. The desired lift coefficient in these calculations was set at 2.5 which corresponds to the average sectional lift coefficient for a fin with A_g=1.0.

Analysis of the Rotating Leading Edge Cylinder
A parametric study of profiles with a circular leading edge was performed assuming that no separation occurred until the trailing edge where the Kutta condition is met. Under these conditions viscous effects can be neglected. The model ignores any circulation which may be induced by the rotation of the cylinder. It is considered that it is the trailing edge Kutta condition which determines the lift and that the rotation of the cylinder controls only the boundary-layer. Efforts to include this circulation have shown that it has no effect on lift [21].

The goal for better boundary-layer control is to reduce the adverse pressure gradient present at the leading edge at high angles of attack and to maximize the extent of the pressure recovery effected by the surface of the cylinder. Profiles of 25% thickness ratio with a circular leading edge of varying radii were generated. The pressure distributions calculated around the leading edge of the profiles are presented in figure 2. The chordwise position of the profile/cylinder tangency point is marked by an arrow. It can be seen that increasing the leading edge radius has three favorable consequences on the pressure distribution:
o Reducing the leading edge suction peak, lowering the tangential velocity of the cylinder
o Reducing the pressure gradient in the pressure recovery area, reducing the risks of separation
o Increasing the portion of the pressure recovery covered by the cylinder, providing a more extensive area of boundary-layer control.

Since a convex section aft of the cylinder will cause separation when the cylinder is not turning, profiles where the maximum thickness equals the diameter of the cylinder were selected as being optimum. The results of an experimental investigation by Youhua [9] confirm this hypothesis. To minimize the drag at higher speeds, the thickness of the profile is limited to a relative thickness of 25%. A configuration with a flap provides a more uniform pressure distribution on the suction side up to the flap knee where separation is likely to occur.

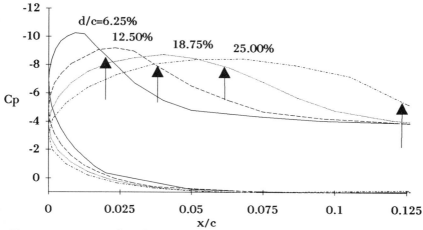

Figure 2: Pressure distributions on sections with circular leading edges
(C_L=2.5, α=19°, t/c=25%)

<u>Analysis of the Rotating Trailing Edge Cylinder</u>

The presence of a rotating cylinder at the trailing edge of a profile was investigated using the same code. The rotation of the cylinder is modeled by setting the trailing edge separation point arbitrarily at an angular position δ. The results of a parametric numerical study show that the position of the separation point can be modeled as a camber which is a function of the RTEC diameter d/c and of the angle δ. A regression on the calculated data yields the following relationship for an induced camber β.

$$\beta = (d/c)^{0.30} \cdot \delta$$

This camber can be added to the angle between the freestream velocity and the chord line (geometrical angle of attack: α) to calculate the lift coefficient. This relation is illustrated in figure 3:

$$C_L = 2 \cdot \pi \, (1+t/c) \sin (\alpha + \beta)$$

For the Magnus cylinder (d/c=1.0) this expression is reduced to the classic potential flow result of the flow around a concentric doublet and vortex in a uniform stream :

$$C_{L_{Mag}} = 4 \cdot \pi \sin \delta$$

The lift of a RTEC profile at zero angle of attack can be compared to the performance of the rotating cylinder alone by defining a lift augmentation ratio (R) which is given by the following expression.

$$R = \frac{L_{Profile}}{L_{Mag}} = \frac{CL_{\alpha=0°}}{CL_{Mag}} \cdot \frac{c}{d} = 0.5 \cdot (1 + c/d) \cdot (d/c)^{0.30}$$

This result is illustrated in figure 4 and shows an augmentation of lift due to the presence of a profile ahead of the rotating cylinder for a given angle δ (R=1.64 for d/c=0.25). Of course, angle of attack contributions can be added to this result at the expense of a more complicated and fragile configuration.

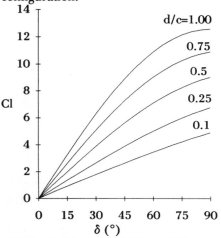

Figure 3: Theoretical lift coefficient for a profile with a circular trailing edge ($\alpha=0°$)

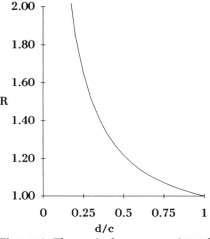

Figure 4: Theoretical augmentation of the lift of a cylinder behind a profile ($\alpha=0°$)

MODELS

Based on the preceding analysis, the fin model selected for testing was a 25% thickness RLEC fin 150x150 mm². The fin is modular with 4 different trailing edges. An end plate mounted at the tip of the fin houses a belt which drives the RTEC from a pulley at the top of the RLEC. These models were fabricated on numerical control machines out of stainless steel and anodised aluminum. Provisions were made for die injection from 3 hypodermic needles bent ahead of the RLEC for the purpose of flow visualisation. The characteristics of the sections tested are described in Table I and are shown on figure 5. The RL&TEC2 fin is identical to the RL&TEC1 fin, with the trailing and leading edges inverted in the tunnel. The rotating cylinder (RC) models are described in Table II using the following notation:

$$d_{LE} = \frac{d_{cyl}}{c} \qquad d_b = \frac{d_{bas}}{d_{cyl}} \qquad d_t = \frac{d_{tip}}{d_{cyl}}$$

For all the cylinders tested, the gap between the fin or flap and the cylinders was reduced to the minimum mechanically possible and in most cases a sliding contact was achieved. Based on the gap Reynolds number identified by Johnson et al [22], the present gap size is hydrodynamically null.

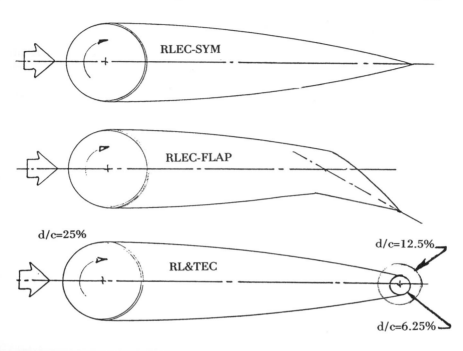

d/c=25%

RLEC-SYM

RLEC-FLAP

d/c=12.5%

RL&TEC

d/c=6.25%

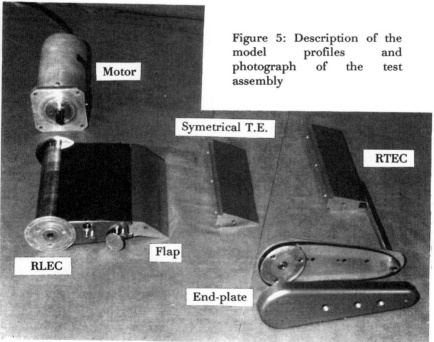

Figure 5: Description of the model profiles and photograph of the test assembly

RLEC Models	Trailing edge	d_{LE} (%)	d_{TE} (%)	Comments
RLEC-SYM	symmetrical	25	0	
RLEC-FLAP	flap	25	0	15% chord, 30° flap angle
RL&TEC1	cylinder	25	6.25	$K_{TE}=K_{LE}$
RL&TEC2	cylinder	6.25	25	$K_{TE}=K_{LE}$
RL&TEC3	cylinder	25	12.5	$K_{TE}= 2\ K_{LE}$

Table I: Characteristics of the RLEC models

RC Models	Aspect-Ratio	Span	Diameter	Disks		Flap
		(mm)	(mm)	d_b	d_t	
RC1	4.0	150	37.5	1.50	1.50	
RC2a	2.5	150	60	1.00	1.25	
RC2b	"	"	"	1.25	1.25	
RC2c	"	"	"	1.25	1.50	
RC2d	2.0	"	"	1.25	1.50	15 mm
RC3	2.0	150	75	1.50	1.50	
RC4	1.0	60	60	1.25	1.50	

Table II: Characteristics of the RC models

EXPERIMENTAL SET-UP

The tests were performed in the small hydrodynamic tunnel (PTH) of the Bassin d'Essais des Carènes which is located in Val de Reuil. This tunnel has a section of 0.6x0.45 m^2 with a range of speeds from 2 to 12 m/s. The models were mounted on a 5 component dynamometer installed on a vertical side of the test section. The test section was configured without a free surface and could be split in two by a vertical plexiglass plate which formed a two-dimensional test section for the models 150 mm in span.

The effect of wall interference was investigated by taking advantage of the asymmetrical position of the fin or cylinder in the test section. Tests were performed with the lift towards the top and bottom. Two-dimensional computations for this geometry show an increase in lift when the suction side is closest to the wall and a decrease in lift when the pressure side is closest to the wall. The lift coefficients and angle of attack at which these trends appeared were noted. In the 3D configuration wall effects appeared around 40° angle of attack and the tests were performed in the configuration where the smaller values of lift were measured. No wall corrections were applied.

The tunnel pressure was kept at atmospheric level except for high Reynolds number tests where it was increased to delay the appearance of cavitation. The tunnel speed was typically about 5m/s which allowed testing within the limits of the dynamometer (1 KN and 0.3 KN in lift and drag respectively). At that speed the chord Reynolds number is about 7.10^5 for the fin and between 2.10^5 and 5.10^5 for the rotating cylinders.

The angle of attack of the fin was controlled by the data acquisition system on a range of 60° centered about any desired mean position from 0 to 360°. A watertight 700 W DC motor was used to rotate the cylinders up to speeds of 10000 rpm for the RC and RLEC and 24000 rpm for the RTEC.

The base of the models was immersed in the tunnel wall boundary-layer which is 30 mm thick at 5 m/s. A tunnel wall blowing system was developed to eliminate the wall boundary-layer effects. The results presented here were obtained without wall blowing.

EXPERIMENTAL RESULTS

<u>Profiles with rotating cylinders</u>
The three dimensional results for the different profiles are shown on figure 6 for K=2, 3 and 4 for a range of angle of attack (AA) from -15 to 55°. The validity of the parameter K (K=Vt/V) was verified by tests at tunnel speeds of 3 and 6 m/s for the RLEC and RL&TEC fins. No significant Re effect was observed.

<u>K=2</u> The lift of the RLEC-SYM fin levels off at 40° AA. The RLEC-FLAP fin does not stall because of the more favorable pressure distribution created by the flap. The flow over the flap was always separated. At this small cylinder tangential velocity the lift of the the RL&TEC1 fin is lower than that of the sharp edged RLEC-SYM fin. The RL&TEC2 fin stalls at about 20° AA. In this case the suction peak is quite high and the small RLEC is not sufficient to control the flow. Still, at 0° AA this fin reaches $C_L=1.0$. The RL&TEC3 fin stalls abrupltly at 38° AA because the K value of the RLEC is only 1.0. However, before stall its lift is already larger than that of the RLEC-FLAP fin.

<u>K=3</u> At this speed the RLEC-SYM fin does not stall up to the maximum AA tested. The lift of RLEC-FLAP fin does not increase from the K=2 values. The lift of the RL&TEC1 fin becomes slightly greater than that of the RLEC-FLAP fin. The RL&TEC2 fin increases its lift at 0° AA to 1.8. However it stalls at about 10° AA. The RL&TEC3 fin stalls at 45° AA ($K_{LE}=1.5$). It reaches $C_L=2$ at 20° AA. The strange behavior of its lift slope at small AA is due to the blunt TE formed by the 12.5% RTEC.

<u>K=4</u> There is no change in the lift of the RLEC-SYM and RLEC-FLAP fins compared to the K=3 values. Only the fins with RTECs show an increase in lift. The RL&TEC1 fin reaches a lift coefficient of 2.5 at 40° AA. The lift of the RL&TEC2 fin is limited by the ineffective flow control at its LE (small d_{LE}). The RL&TEC3 fin reaches a maximum lift coefficient close to 3.0.

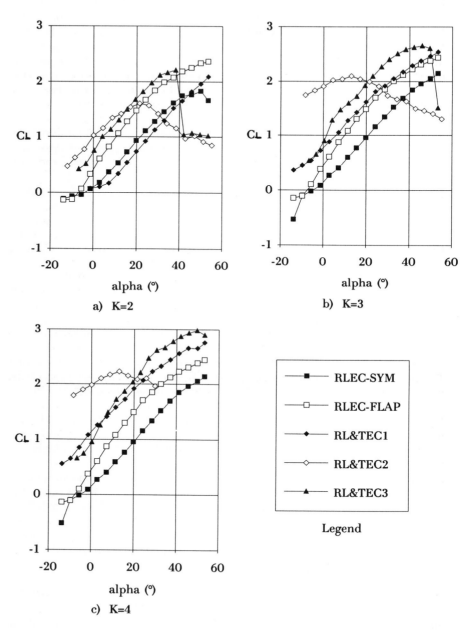

Figure 6: Comparison of the experimental lift of the different RLEC fins tested as a function of angle of attack for K=2, 3 and 4 (A_g=1.0, Re=5 10^5)

Rotating Cylinders

Reynolds Number The effect of Reynolds number (Re=V.d_{cyl}/ν) on the lift of RC fins was studied on the RC1 fin (37.5 mm diameter) by increasing the tunnel velocity from 2 to 8 m/s to a maximum Re of 3.10^5. At the higher Re, the values of K are limited by the lift generated which has to stay within the capacity of the dynamometer. These results are shown on figure 7. For K less than 2.0 dramatic changes in CL are observed as Re increased. In this range, the lift tends towards a linear relashionship: δCL/δK=2.2. The same tests were performed on the RC3 cylinder where the range of Re increased by a factor of 2. No changes in CL were found above Re=$3.5.10^5$. This value was taken as a minimum required for this type of test.

Aspect-ratio The results for cylinders of aspect-ratio 4.0, 2.5, 2.0 and 1.0 are presented on figure 8. The disks of the cylinders only differ for models RC2c and RC4 where the base disk is smaller (Table II). At high Reynolds number, for K<2.0, the lift of cylinders of aspect-ratio 2.0 and above are identical. For K>2.0, the lift of RC1 appears to be increasing with the same slope while the smaller aspect-ratio cylinders approach a limit. The lift of RC4 shows a dramatic reduction in δCL/δK due to its small aspect-ratio.

End Disks A small parametric study was performed on the influence of end disks on the perfomance of RC2. Configurations with a smaller tip disk (RC2b) and no base disk (RC2a) were tested. The results are presented in figure 9. The reduction of tip disk reduces the slope δCL/δK for K>1.5, while the removal of the base disk causes a reduction in this slope from the origin. The reduction in lift for the RC2a and RC2b models as compared to the RC2c model (with larger disks) is of 12% and 30% respectively at K=2.5.

Flap The influence of a small trailing edge flap on the lift of the RC2c model was investigated. The results on figure 10 show that a significant increase in lift can be obtained for a given value of K for some positions of the flap. The lift at flap angles of 30° and 40° are shown. In this specific instance the lift coefficient is based upon the *cylinder diameter* and not the total chord of the foil. For a given flap angle there is an optimum value of flap angle when the augmentation of lift is maximum (23% for K=1.0 at 30°, 20% for K=1.5 for 40°). Other tests have shown that the flap is very effective in reducing the fluctuations in lift.

ANALYSIS OF THE EXPERIMENTAL RESULTS

Power The results for both RLEC fins and Magnus cylinders have been compared on the basis of absorbed power and fin lift to drag ratio. This comparison is presented as a function of fin loading following the hypothesis of a span limited design. The results are shown on figure 11. In terms of required power, the RLEC-FLAP configuration is most economical (Ca=2.0) if

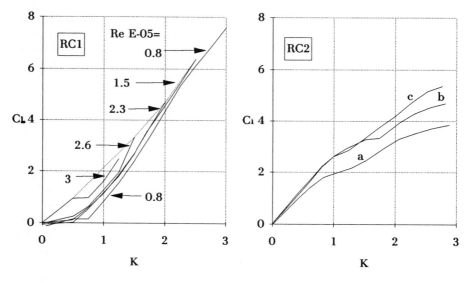

Figure 7: Effect of Re on RC lift

Figure 9: Effect of disks on RC lift

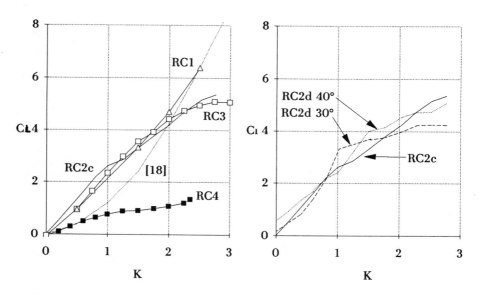

Figure 8: Comparison of the lift
different RC models

Figure 10: Effect of flap on RC lift

a loading of 2.3 is sufficient. At a loading of 2.5 the Magnus cylinder RC3 and the RL&TEC1 fins are available (Ca of about 10). A fin with a RLEC tangential velocity half that of the RTEC saves a significant amount of power (RL&TEC3). In this case, the larger RTEC allows this fin to reach a loading of 3.0 with Ca=10. The optimum combination of diameter and speed of the RTEC for a desired lift has to be further explored.

Drag In terms of drag, there is a relatively small spread between the different configurations in the high loading range where induced drag is predominant. The RL&TEC1 fin has a drag equal to that of the RC3 cylinder and slightly lower than that of the RLEC-FLAP (separation). Again, the RL&TEC3 fin has superior characteristics despite its non-streamlined blunt trailing edge. At lower loadings a more detailed comparison would have to be done.

Published Data The present experimental results for the classical RLEC-SYM fin (C_L=2.2 at 54° AA with K=3) with A_g=1.0 compare favorably to those published in the literature. The maximum lift coefficient obtained in [7] for a similar fin (A_g=1.267) was 1.46 at 50° AA for K=3. The 2-D results obtained are compared to the data of [10] for both a RLEC-SYM fin and a RL&TEC fin in figure 12. As in the 3D data, the larger RLEC (25% vs 13%) prevent separation up to angles of attack three times higher for the same value of K (54° vs 18°). The characterisics of the fins are summarized in Table III.

Fin	RLEC-SYM		RL&TEC	
Source	present	[11]	present	[11]
t/c (%)	25	19	25	19
d_{LE} (%)	25	13	25	13
d_{TE} (%)	0	0	6.25	7
K	2	2	3	3

Table III: Characteristics of fins in figure 12

Theory The experimental results show that the 25% RLEC with K=2.0 controls the flow at angles of attack in excess of 60°. Increases in K above this value do not increase the lift. In the case of the RTEC fin, the lift increases monotonically with K and the slope $\delta C_L/\delta K$ increases with the RTEC diameter. From the experimental data at 0° AA, it is possible to obtain an approximate expression for the lift contribution due to the RTEC:

$$C_{L_{RTEC}} = K \cdot \sqrt{d_{TE}}$$

Within the limits of the experimental data gathered (A_g>2.0 , K<2.0) , the lift coefficient of the circular cylinder can be taken as $C_{L_{Mag}}$=2.2 K. Hence the following experimental lift augmentation ratio:

$$R_{Exp} = \frac{0.45}{\sqrt{d_{TE}}}$$

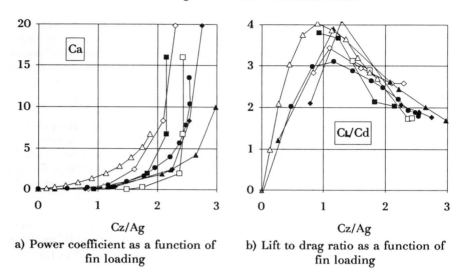

a) Power coefficient as a function of
fin loading

b) Lift to drag ratio as a function of
fin loading

Figure 11 : Synthesis of the lift
provided and power absorbed for the
various fins tested (legend below)

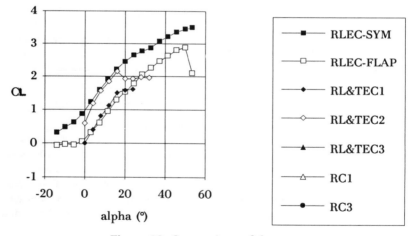

Figure 12: Comparison of the present
results to those of Modi et al [10]
(legend below)

This ratio becomes less than one (no gain) for $d_{TE}>25\%$. Compared to the theoretical model developed in the preceding section there is an important loss of lift which can be attributed to viscous effects. From the experimental data a value of d_{TE} of about 10% to 15% might be desirable.

CONCLUSIONS

Some theoretical considerations were advanced to define the overall characteristics of a span limited high-lift fin using the parameter of fin loading. A theoretical analysis led to some conclusions regarding the optimum design of RLEC and RTEC cylinders. An extensive experimental study showed that high levels of lift could be achieved by low aspect-ratio fins. Depending on the fin loading, different configurations have been identified which require a minimum amount of power. A maximum fin loading of 3.0 has been achieved by an RL&TEC fin with $A_g=1.0$ and a small end-plate. The minimum value of K required at the leading edge is around 2.0. Further work is required to identify the optimum diameter and K value for a cylinder at the trailing edge to achieve a desired lift. The augmentation of lift provided by a fin at 0° AA ahead of a rotating cylinder was demonstrated experimentally. This paper presents an original data base of the performance of different configurations of RLEC fins and Magnus cylinders at high Re. The importance of using high Re data and end disks for the design of Magnus cylinders is stressed.

ACKNOWLEDGEMENTS

This work has been sponsored by the Direction Technique des Constructions Navales and the Direction des Recherches Etudes et Techniques, which the author acknowledge.

REFERENCES

1. Thwaites, B. *Incompressible Aerodynamics* Dover Publications Inc., New-York, 1960
2. Abbott, I. and Von Doenhoff, A. *Theory of Wings Sections* Dover Publications Inc. New-York, 1959
3. Mc Cormick, B. *Aerodynamics, Aeronautics, and Flight Mechanics* John Wiley and Sons New York, 1979
4. Wilson, M. and Von Kerczek, C. 'An Inventory of Force Producers for Use in Marine Vehicle Control' David Taylor Research Center Report 79/097, 1975
5. Favre, M. 'Un Nouveau Procédé Hypersustentateur: l'Aile à Paroi d'Extrados Mobile' *Mécanique Expérimentale des Fluides, Comptes Rendus*, pp. 634, 1934
6. Steele, B. and Harding, M. 'The application of Rotating Cylinders to Ship Manoeuvering' *National Physical Laboratory,* Ship Report 148, December 1970

7. McGeough, F. and Millward, A. 'The Effect of Cavitation on the Rotating Cylinder Rudder' *International Shipbuilding Progress*, Vol. 28, No. 317, pp. 2-9, 1981
8. Edwards, P., Wakeling, B. and Millward, A. 'The Rotating Cylinder Rudder: The Effect of Cylinder Roughness and Cylinder Gap' *International Shipbuilding Progress*, Vol. 31, No. 361, pp. 226-230, 1984
9. Youhua, L. and Hanzhen, X. 'Further Experiments on the Rotating Cylinder Rudder' *International Shipbuilding Progress*, Vol. 34, No. 397, pp. 170-176, 1987
10. Modi, V., Mokhtarian F., Fernando M. and Yokomizo, T. 'Moving Surface Boundary-layer Control as Applied to Two-Dimensional Airfoils' in 27th Aerospace Science Meeting, Reno Nevada USA, 1989 (AIAA 89-0296)
11. Modi, V., Mokhtarian F. and Yokomizo, T. 'Effect of Moving Surfaces on the Airfoil Boundary-Layer Control' *Journal of Aircraft*, Vol. 27, No.1, pp. 42-50, 1990
12. Calderon, A. 'Rotating Cylinder flaps for V/STOL Aircraft' *Aircraft Engineering*, pp. 304-310, 1964
13. Modi, V., Sun, J., Akutsu, T., Lake, P., McMillan, K., Swinton, P. and Mullins, D. 'Moving Surface Boundary-Layer Control for Aircraft Operation at High Incidence' *Journal of Aircraft*, Vol.18, No.11, pp. 963-968, 1981
14. Brooks, J. 'Effect of Rotating Cylinder at the Leading and Trailing Edges of a Hydrofoil' U.S. Ordonance Naval Test Station, Dept of the Navy, NAVWEPS Rept. 8042, 1963
15. Kudrevatyi, V., Khudin and V., Zakharov, B. 'A Shipboard Aerodynamic propulsive Device of Higher Efficiency' *Sudostoeie*, No.2, pp. 14-18, 1983
16. Von G. Magnus 'Ueber des Entstchen von Theer aus Olbidendem Gase' *Annalen der Physik und Chemic*, No.9, 1853
17. Prandtl, L. 'Magniseffekt und Windkraftschiff' *Die Natur Wissenschaften*, p. 93,1925. English translation: NACA TM 367, 1926
18. Charrier, B. 'Etude Théorique et Expérimentale de l'Effet Magnus Destinée à la Propulsion Eolienne des Navires' Doctoral Thesis, Paris VI University, 1979
19. Morisseau, K. 'Marine Applications of Magnus Effect Devices', *Naval Engineers Journal,* Vol.97, No.1, pp.51-57, 1985.
20. Eppler, R., and Somers, D. 'A Computer program for the Design and Analysis of Low-Speed Airfoils' NASA TM-80210, 1980
21. El-Dandoush, S. and Puls, D. 'Hydrodynamical Investigations of the Flow as Well as the Forces and Moments on Profiles and Rudders with Rotors' *International Shipbuilding Progress*, Vol. 30,No. 351, pp. 249-257, 1983
22. Johnson, W., Tennant, J.and Stamps, R. 'Leading-Edge Rotating Cylinder for Boundary-Layer Control on Lifting Surfaces' *Journal of Hydronautics*, Vol.9, No. 2, pp 76-78, 1975

Experiments to Investigate Vortex Separation on an Appended Body of Revolution

B. Ward (*), P.A. Wilson (**)

(*) Ship and Submarine Dynamics Section, DRA Haslar, Gosport, Hampshire, UK

(**) Department of Ship Science, University of Southampton, Highfield, Southampton SO9 5NH, UK

ABSTRACT

A knowledge of hydrodynamic forces is necessary to determine the manoeuvring characteristics of a submarine design. Computer models have been used for this purpose using derivative data from model experiments. A computer model has been developed at DRA Haslar over the last decade which requires no input derivative data and hence avoids the need to carry out model experiments for each design in the early stages.

Recent validations have shown the prediction of submarine manoeuvring characteristics such as turning circle, speed loss and yaw rate in the turn, and vertical pulse manoeuvres to be good. However, predictions of depth change during turns are unsatisfactory. This is certainly due to the estimation of the out-of-plane forces which are related to the circulation around the hull.

Experiments were conducted to examine vortex separation and the pressure distribution around a submerged body of revolution with and without an appendage.

INTRODUCTION

If a body is at a moderate angle of incidence and turn rate, the boundary layer on the leeward surface separates as shown in Figure 1. Vorticity shed from the boundary layer is convected away and coalesces to form a diffuse pair of vortices with cores almost parallel to the body axis. The strength of the vortices increases towards the tail of the body as more vorticity is added.

Determination of the point of separation on bodies of revolution has been a problem in fluid dynamics for sometime. The use of an empirical estimate from experimental results has tended to be the more common solution. Lloyd[1,2] described a mathematical model, SUBSIM, which predicts the manoeuvring characteristics of submarines. The model uses a combination of classical theory and empirical equations. The empirical equations are derived from model experiments as described in Ward[3].

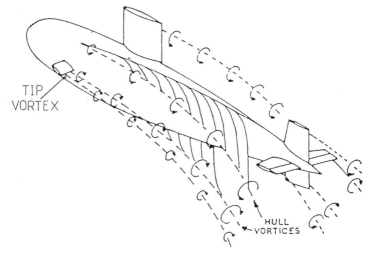

Figure 1 : A typical pattern of vortices on a manoeuvring submarine

PREVIOUS EXPERIMENTS TO INVESTIGATE VORTEX FLOW

Lloyd [4,5] described experiments to measure vortex strengths and positions. The aim was to acquire data from which empirical estimates of vorticity could be derived. The author became involved in the subsequent analysis of experiments which measured body vortices in curved flow.

The experiments were conducted on the rotating arm facility in the manoeuvring tank at DRA Haslar (formerly ARE Haslar). They were performed by the Wolfson Unit for Marine Technology and Industrial Aerodynamics (University of Southampton) working under contract.

A 5 metre body of revolution was used with fineness ratio L/D of 8.5. A Freestone[6] probe was used to measure vorticity. The probe was mounted on a stayed circular strut which could be positioned at one of three locations along the length of the model (x'=0.7, 0.85, 0.925). The probes radial and angular location could be adjusted.

EXPERIMENTAL PROCEDURE AND RESULTS

Runs were conducted over a range of angles of incidence and turn rates at the three stations.

A typical faired traverse is shown in Figure 2.

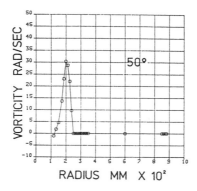

Figure 2 : A typical vorticity traverse

Measurements were taken at 10 degree angular intervals (taking 0 degrees with the strut parallel to the surface of the tank on the leeward side of the model and 90 degrees with the probe vertical above the model) at 25 mm radial steps from the body surface.

The local circulation density is

$$\Gamma_\theta = \int_0^\infty \zeta r\, dr \qquad (1)$$

A graph of circulation density against angle was plotted for each experiment condition and an example is shown in Figure 3. An empirical curve was derived from all results. Other equations were derived to determine positions of vortices and core radii. Figure 4 shows a representation of the flow as two symmetrical sets of vortices.

VALIDATION

The equations were incorporated into the SUBSIM computer program. The modified program was then validated by comparing predictions of submarine manoeuvres with full-scale trials results. Figure 5 is typical of a turning circle prediction where control deflections have been replicated exactly as on the trial. It can be seen that the trajectory in the lateral plane, heading and speed loss in the turn simulations are all very good. However, there are problems in predicting depth change during turns.

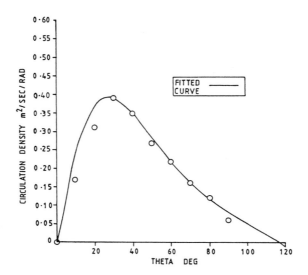

Figure 3 : Circulation density against strut angle
(x'=0.925, r'=0.4, α=5 degrees)

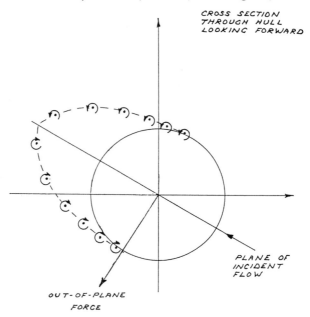

Figure 4 : Location of body vortices and out-of-plane force

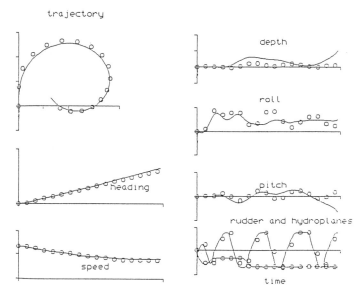

Figure 5 : Typical submarine turning circle

The reason for poor prediction of depth change in the turn is almost certainly due to unsatisfactory estimation of the out-of-plane force (Figure 4). This force is related to body vortices and as noted earlier the vortices are modelled as symmetrical pairs. This modelling would be correct in dealing with an unappended body of revolution as was the case in the experiments described above. In reality, if a change in separation point occurred on one side of the body then an asymmetry would occur in the force. This phenomenon occurs in the presence of an appendage. On a submarine the most forward appendages are the bow hydroplanes and the bridge fin. The bow hydroplanes are relatively small in relation to the submarine hull but bridge fins are usually substantial. This has caused some problems in the prediction of submarine manoeuvres.

MEASUREMENTS OF VORTICITY AND PRESSURE DISTRIBUTIONS

It was decided to conduct experiments on a body of revolution with an appendage and examine the vortical flow and pressure distribution at various cross-sections. The Freestone probe was again used to measure vorticity as in the rotating arm experiments.

MODEL HULL DESIGN

The model hull was a 1 metre body of revolution made of glass-reinforced plastic and had a fineness ratio L/D of 8.

Figure 6 : Model and traverse rig

Metal rings were positioned at four stations flush with the surface of the hull with 36 pressure tappings drilled accurately at 10 degree intervals. The model had a detachable NACA 0020 wing with chord length 0.1125 metres and span 0.09 metres.

EXPERIMENTAL PROCEDURE

The experiments were conducted in the Circulating Water Channel (Figure 6) at DRA Haslar in two stages during 1990 and 1991. The model hull was tested at various conditions to explore the relationship between the vortex characteristics, angle of incidence and pressure distribution at particular cross-sections along the body. All angles of incidence were measured with the model's nose to starboard. Speed was constant at 2.5 m/s.

A traverse rig was specially designed for these experiments and was used to position the Freestone probe. For the second stage of the experiment the rig was controlled by stepper motors that gave 0.5mm positional accuracy. A single computer program was also used during the second stage to control the rig, acquire data and perform the arithmetic operations to calculate vorticity.

RESULTS

1990 RESULTS
The rig was traversed in the horizontal direction taking readings at 10mm intervals. If a fine peak was suspected say in the case of the appendage vortex a more refined mapping at 1mm intervals was carried out over the area of maximum vorticity. Horizontal traverses were made at 10mm intervals in the vertical direction. Searches at shorter step sizes were conducted in order to find the peak values for appendage vortices.

The horizontal traverses were integrated using a simple trapezoidal rule to give the circulation density. The circulation density values were then integrated (Equation 2) in the vertical direction to give the total circulation in that area of the body.

$$\Gamma = \int_{-\infty}^{\infty} \int_{-\infty}^{\infty} \zeta_x \, dy \, dz \tag{2}$$

The results are presented in Table 1.

Table 1

x'	Body α	Fin α	Γ_D	Γ_K	Γ_D/UD	Γ_K/UD
0.575	10	0	0.001	-0.034	0.005	-0.11
0.75	10	0	0.004	-0.034	0.013	-0.11
0.925	10	0	0.009	-0.072	0.029	-0.25

Figure 7 shows a body vortex contour plot at x'=0.925. This plot is of vorticity values measured with body incidence of 10 degrees and the appendage at 0 degrees to the body.

1991 RESULTS
Vorticity was measured at x'= 0.575 (with appendage) and x'= 0.925 (with and without appendage) with body incidence 5, 10 and 15 degrees.

Pressure meassurements were taken at x'=0.4, 0.575, 0.75 and 0.925 with and without an appendage. The body was yawed up to an angle of 17.5 degrees. A Scanivalve was used to scan round the 36 pressure tappings at each station.

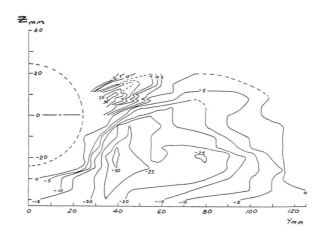

Figure 7 : Body vortex contours, ζ_x , rad/sec
body 10 degrees, appendage 0 degrees, x'=0.925

The probe used in the 1990 experiments was damaged during the rigging of the 1991 experiments and a new probe had to be manufactured. It became apparent that there were considerable offsets in the 1991 results compared with 1990. Attempts were made to correct for discrepancies but in the end no reliable method could be achieved and therefore no circulation values could be calculated. The offsets are certainly due to imperfection in the production of the new probe. On reflection it was felt that the contour plots of the 1991 results do give a qualitative feel for the circulation around the body under particular conditions. An example is given in Figure 8.

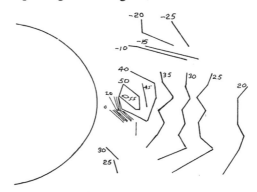

Figure 8 : Body vortex contours, ζ_x , rad/sec
body 10 degrees, appendage 0 degrees, x'=0.575

Pressure coefficients were calculated from the pressure measurements.

Figure 9 shows plots of pressure coefficients for unappended and appended bodies. Note the suction on the top of the body for the unappended case at high angles; this does not occur with the presence of the appendage.

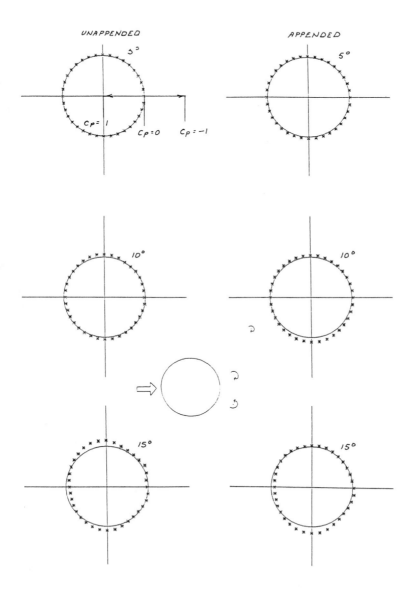

Figure 9 : Pressure coefficients, x' = 0.575

Pressure coefficients were integrated to give force per unit length in both the Y and Z plane as given in equations 3 and 4.

$$F_Y' = -\frac{2\pi R}{36}\sum C_P \sin\theta_P \qquad (3)$$

$$F_Z' = \frac{2\pi R}{36}\sum C_P \cos\theta_P \qquad (4)$$

Integrated values (Figure 10) show that the distribution of side force along the body changes with the presence of an appendage.

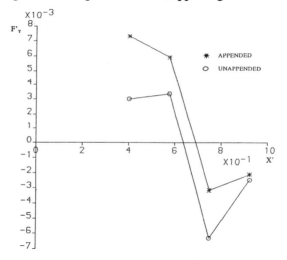

Figure 10 : Side force distribution at 15 degrees yaw

Figure 11 shows Z force distribution for the appended case. There is a significant downward force on the model which gets higher as the model is yawed to higher angles.

The body was held fixed at zero incidence with the appendage at an angle. The force on the body due to the isolated vortex was then examined. These values were small but variations did exist between station and angle. There is less significant effect on the body due to an isolated vortex compared with the change in pressure distribution for a body yawed at a high incidence. However, the presence of the appendage does change the pressure distribution around the body when the body is yawed.

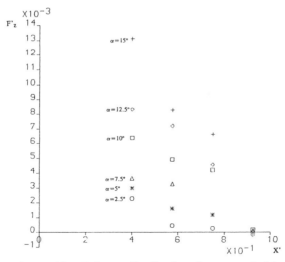

Figure 11 : Z force distribution for appended body

DISCUSSION OF VORTEX RESULTS

From the vorticity contour plots an asymmetry between the deck and the keel vortices is apparent, ie the keel vortex covers a much larger area. The values for circulation in Table 1 confirm this. Vorticity contours for x'=0.575 show there appears to be a single vortex certainly shed from the keel side of the body. For x'=0.925 there is evidence of two distinct vortices.

Table 1 shows at x'=0.575 Γ_D=0.001 which builds up to 0.009 at x'=0.925. Hence there is evidence of a deck vortex at x'=0.575.

The SUBSIM model at present assumes no separation until x'=0.65 and then two identical sets of vortices are created which as mentioned earlier is not the case in reality.

The change in circulation around the aft end of the body is not caused by the vortex from the tip of the fin but the presence of the fin itself. The fin acts as a spoiler and delays the longitudinal point of separation hence the reduced strength of the upper body vortex (Figure 12).

With the fin at 0 degrees aligned to the body and the body yawed at 10 degrees, the circulation from the fin was found to be Γ_F=0.07 which makes the total circulation approximately zero, as predicted by Stokes' theorem. Perhaps this factor could point the way to modelling the reduced strength of the upper body vortex. Taking the whole body as one closed system the circulation will add up to zero as shown in Figure 12.

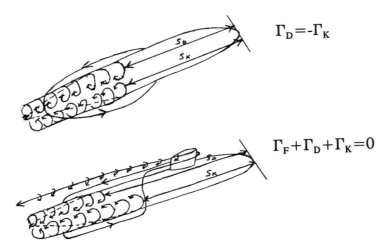

$$\Gamma_D = -\Gamma_K$$

$$\Gamma_F + \Gamma_D + \Gamma_K = 0$$

Figure 12 : Separation point and distribution of circulation

CONCLUSIONS

This paper has described experiments to examine the flow around an appended body of revolution. The model was tested over a range of angles with and without an appendage. The effects of the appendage on circulation around the body and pressure around the hull are evident from the results.

The findings of these experiments suggest that the method of calculating the out-of-plane forces in SUBSIM is unsatisfactory. At present the method only accounts for appendage vortices and the interaction between appendage vortices and body vortices. No account is taken of body vortices since they are modelled as symmetrical pairs and it has been assumed that they do not contribute to the out-of-plane force. However, it is necessary to model the body vortices correctly to account for the change the appendage makes to the circulation around the body. It may be sufficient to calculate the force on the body due to these modified body vortices alone. Further work is required to acquire more accurate data, perhaps in a towing tank with a larger model.

ACKNOWLEDGEMENT

This work has been carried out with the support of the Procurement Executive of the Ministry of Defence.

REFERENCES

1. Lloyd A R J M. Progress Towards a Rational Method of Predicting Submarine Manoeuvres. RINA Symposium on Naval Submarines. London 1983.
2. Lloyd A R J M. Developments in the Prediction of Submarine Manoeuvres. Undersea Defence Technology. 1988.
3. Ward B. Experiments to Improve the Predictions of Submarine Manoeuvres. MCMC Conference. University of Southampton. July 1992.
4. Lloyd A R J M, Campbell I F. Experiments to Investigate Vortices Shed from a Submarine-like Body of Revolution. 59th Meeting of the AGARD Fluid Dynamics Panel Symposium, Monterey, California, USA. Aerodynamics and Related Hydrodynamic Studies Using Water Facilities. AGARD-CCP 413. October 1986.
5. Lloyd A R J M. Experiments to Investigate the Vorticity Shed by a Body of Revolution in Curved Flow. Advances in Underwater Technology, Ocean Science and Offshore Engineering. Volume 15: Technology Common to Aero and Marine Engineering. 1988.
6. Freestone M M. Vorticity Measurements by a Pressure Probe. The Aeronautical Journal of the Royal Aeronautical Society. January 1988.

Notation

C_P	Pressure coefficient ; $P/0.5\rho U^2 L$	
D	Diameter of hull	m
F'_Y	Side force per unit length$/0.5\rho U^2 L$: positive to starboard	
F'_Z	Downward force per unit length$/0.5\rho U^2 L$: positive down	
K	Calibration factor for Freestone probe	
L	Length of hull	m
P	Pressure	Nm^{-2}
r	Radius from body axis to position of probe	m
r'	Non-dimensional rate of turn or turn parameter ; L/S	
R	Radius of model at cross-section	m
S	Arm radius ; radius of turn	m
S_D	Longitudinal point of separation - deck side of body	m
S_K	Longitudinal point of separation - keel side of body	m
U	Flow velocity	m/s
x	Longitudinal distance from nose of body : positive aft	m
x'	Non-dimensional distance from nose to body ; x/L	
y	Lateral distance from body centre : positive starboard	mm
z	Vertical distance from body centre	mm
Γ	Circulation	m^2/s
Γ_θ	Circulation density at a given angle	$m^2/s/rad$

Γ_D	Circulation from body - deck side : positive clockwise looking forward	m²/s
Γ_F	Circulation from fin : positive clockwise looking forward	m²/s
Γ_K	Circulation from body - keel side : positive clockwise looking forward	m²/s
α	Angle of incidence	deg
ζ	Vorticity	rad/s
ρ	Mass density of fresh water	tonnes/m³
θ	Angle of strut	deg
θ_P	Angular location of pressure tapping 0 degrees pointing up, positive clockwise looking forward	deg

Broaching - A Dynamic Analysis of Yaw Behaviour of a Vessel in a Following Sea

N. Umeda (*)*, M.R. Renilson (**)

(*) National Research Institute of Fisheries Engineering, Ebidai, Hasaki, Ibaraki, 314-04, Japan

(**) Australian Maritime College, Newnham Drive, Launceston, Tasmania, 7250, Australia

*Currently visiting Research Fellow, Australian Maritime College

ABSTRACT

The surge, sway and yaw motions of a ship in quartering seas are analyzed as a nonlinear dynamical system. Using this method, critical conditions of broaching are obtained from calculated trajectories in phase space. These calculated results are validated by the results from free running model experiments by Fuwa et al. [1].

INTRODUCTION

Small high speed craft, such as fishing vessels, travelling in following seas are in danger of suddenly yawing from the desired course despite application of maximum opposite rudder. This is known as broaching-to and has been feared by seafarers for many years as it can lead to loss of control in critical situations, and even a capsize.

Motora et al.[2] and Renilson[3] carried out simulations in the time domain which enabled them to conclude that broaching is caused when the large wave induced yaw moment exceeds the moment available from the rudder for sufficient time to allow the large yaw velocity to develop. This occurs when the vessel is forced to travel at wave speed, which is known as 'surf-riding'.

Because, like any other nonlinear phenomena, broaching is very sensitive to initial conditions, time domain simulations are limited in their ability to be used for a global investigation of the phenomenon.

Makov & Ananyev[4], Umeda[5] and Kan[6] carried out global investigations of surf-riding using phase plane analysis which allowed them to obtain the critical conditions of surf-riding, including dependence on initial conditions. Since their studies ignored sway and yaw motions, they could not determine whether surf-riding will lead to a broach.

The present study makes use of the earlier work on lateral motions to extend the phase plane technique to investigate the global structure of broaching-to.

MATHEMATICAL MODEL

As can be seen in Figure 1, two coordinate systems are used: wave fixed with origin at a wave trough, ξ axis in the direction of wave travel; and body fixed with origin at the centre of gravity, the x axis pointing towards the bow, the y axis to starboard and the z axis downwards. The symbols follow the usual notation and are defined in the nomenclature.

For a given wave condition, propeller revolutions and rudder angle, the state vector of this system is defined as follows:

$$x = \{ \, \xi_G/\lambda \, , u, v, \chi \, , r \, \}^T \qquad\qquad (1)$$

The dynamical system can be represented by the following state equation:

$$\dot{x} = F\,(\,x\,) = \{ \, f_1(x), f_2(x), \text{---}, f_5(x) \, \}^T \qquad\qquad (2)$$

where

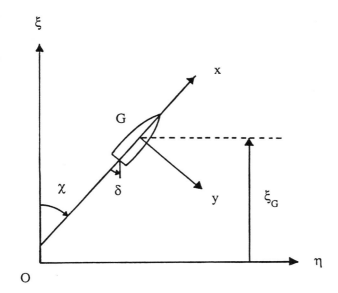

Figure 1: Coordinate systems

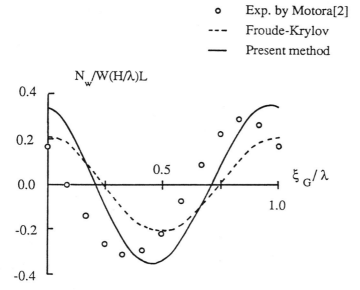

Figure 2: Wave induced yaw moment (λ/L=1.6, χ =30 deg.)

$$f_1(x) = \{ \, u\cos\chi + v\sin\chi - c \, \} / \lambda$$

$$f_2(x) = \{ \, T(u) - R(u) + X_w(\xi_G / \lambda) \} / (m + m_x)$$

$$f_3(x) = \{ -(m+m_x)ur + Y_v(u)v + Y_r(u)r + Y_\delta(\xi_G/, u, \chi)\delta$$

$$+ Y_w(\xi_G/, u, \chi) \} / (m + m_y)$$

$$f_4(x) = r$$

$$f_5(x) = \{ \, N_v(u)v + N_r(u)r + N_\delta(\xi_G/\lambda, u, \chi)\delta$$

$$+ N_w(\xi_G/\lambda, u, \chi) \} / (I_{zz} + J_{zz}) \tag{3}$$

The wave induced surge force can be predicted using the Froude-Krylov component of the force only as examined by Renilson [3] and by Umeda [5], however to accurately obtain the sway force and yaw moment, diffraction forces must also be taken into account, Umeda and Renilson [7]. Results using this method are compared with those from captive model experiments, by Motora et al. [1], in Figure 2.

The rudder derivatives are calculated using the inflow velocity modified to take into account the orbital velocity due to the wave, together with the change in the propeller race due to the longitudinal force from the wave, Renilson [3]. Other coefficients are assumed to be independent of waves, since their effects are not significant for broaching, Renilson [3].

DYNAMICAL SYSTEM ANALYSIS

Broaching-to occurs in a quartering sea when, despite maximum application of full opposite rudder, the vessel's yaw rate increases in an uncontrolled manner.

As can be seen in Figure 3 the behaviour of the vessel can be broken into two stages: varying rudder angle under the control of the auto pilot or helmsman; and fixed rudder angle at the maximum angle possible.

Since the aim of this work is to determine whether the vessel will broach, it concentrates on the second stage with the rudder fixed at its maximum angle. If, as in the case in Figure 3, the rudder rate is high this can occur at a low heading angle.

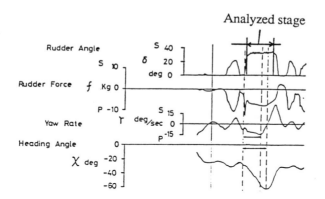

Figure 3: Analyzed stage in time series of broaching [1]

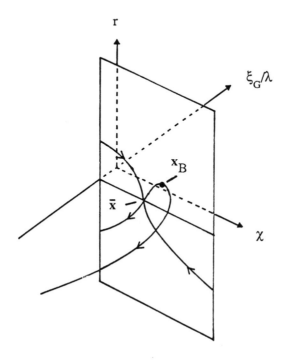

Figure 4: Sketch of stable and unstable manifolds

First, the static equilibrium points, $\bar{\mathbf{x}}$, are obtained by solving the following equation:

$$\mathbf{F}(\bar{\mathbf{x}}) = 0 \tag{4}$$

If a solution exists, the vessel will be in an equilibrium position surf-riding on the wave with a drift angle and heading angle. $\mathbf{F}(\mathbf{x})$ is linearlized at $\bar{\mathbf{x}}$, putting $\mathbf{x}=\bar{\mathbf{x}}+\mathbf{y}$ to obtain the following equation:

$$\dot{\mathbf{y}} = DF(\bar{\mathbf{x}}) \, \mathbf{y} \tag{5}$$

where

$$DF(\mathbf{x}) = \partial \ / \partial x_j \, (f_i(\mathbf{x}) \qquad 1 < i,j < 5 \tag{6}$$

If the eigenvalues of $DF(\bar{\mathbf{x}})$ have nonzero real parts, the solution of Equation (5) not only yields local asymptotic behaviour, but, by Hartman's theorem and the Stable manifold theorem, also provides the local topological structure of the system by Equation (2) [8].

That is, there exist local stable and unstable manifolds $W^s_{loc}(\bar{\mathbf{x}})$, $W^u_{loc}(\bar{\mathbf{x}})$ tangent to eigen spaces, spanned by eigen vectors of $DF(\mathbf{x})$, at $\bar{\mathbf{x}}=0$. Then the global stable and unstable manifold W^s, W^u are obtained by letting points in W^s_{loc} flow backwards in time and those in W^u_{loc} flow forwards. These indicate the topological structure of the system under $\delta = -35$ degrees.

A sketch of $W^s(\bar{\mathbf{x}})$ and $W^u(\bar{\mathbf{x}})$ on a phase space spanned by ξ_G/λ, χ ,r is shown in Figure 4. The trajectories near the equilibrium point $\bar{\mathbf{x}}=(\bar{\xi}_G/\lambda, \bar{\chi}$,r) in wave trough are forced to be near the $\xi_G/\lambda = \bar{\xi}_G/\lambda$ plane, since the motion near the wave trough is strongly stable in the ξ_G/λ direction as indicated in the surf-riding problem, Umeda [5].

Thus, the behaviour projected on a χ - r plane becomes significant. Within a zone, surrounded by $W^s(r>0)$ and $W^u(r<0)$, all trajectories stay near $\bar{\xi}_G/\lambda$ and do not exceed $\bar{\chi}$. This results in stable surf-riding without a rapid increase in yaw. When the yaw rate, r, is greater than $W^s(r>0)$ at $0< \chi < \overline{\chi}$, on the other hand, the yaw angle will increase, resulting in a broach.

The trajectory $W^u(r>0)$ indicates an increase in yaw rate reaching a maximum at x_B where $x_B=((\xi_G/\lambda)_B, \chi_B, r_B)$. Thus, if an initial condition exists with $\overline{\chi} < \chi < \chi_B$, the yaw angle increases despite the maximum opposite rudder. If the resulting uncontrolled yaw is violent enough then this is known as broaching-to.

After x_b there is a rapid decrease in ξ_G/λ from $\overline{\xi}_G/\lambda$ because the ship is overtaken since the larger heading angles which have developed reduce the component of ship velocity in the wave direction and hence surf-riding does not continue.

Finally, the critical conditions for broaching can be summarised as follows. If $\overline{x}$ exists and the initial heading angle is smaller than $\overline{\chi}$, stable surf-riding occurs with a small initial yaw rate and broaching occurs with a large initial yaw rate. If $\overline{x}$ exists and the initial heading angle is greater than $\overline{\chi}$ and smaller than χ_B, broaching may occur. If $\overline{x}$ does not exist, even surf-riding does not occur.

RESULTS AND DISCUSSION

In order to compare the proposed method with existing free running model experiments (Fuwa et al. [1]) it was applied to the small Japanese fishing vessel with principal particulars given in Table 1. The results from captive model experiments in calm water for this hull were also available. (Motora et al. [2])

For this application, the calm water manoeuvering derivatives were obtained from Motora et al. [2], the rudder derivatives were estimated from free running model experiments (Fuwa et al. [1]) together with data from a similar vessel, the added mass and propulsive coefficients were obtained empirically, and the wave forces were calculated using the method developed by the authors. (Umeda and Renilson [7].)

Figure 5 shows the critical conditions for broaching from the analysis of the dynamical system. The solid line corresponds to the value $\bar{\chi}$ of for $\bar{x}$ from Figure 2. Below this line the behaviour depends on the initial conditions. Broaching occurs if the initial yaw rate is large wheras if the yaw rate is small surf-riding will occur.

The dotted line corresponds to the value of χ_B from Figure 2. Between these two lines the vessel will experience an increase in yaw rate despite the maximum opposite rudder which, if severe enough, will be considered to be a broach.

Elsewhere, the vessel will experience periodic motion.

Overall, the prediction gives similar results to those observed in the free running model experiments. (Fuwa et al. [1])

CONCLUSION

The phase plane technique already developed to predict surf-riding behaviour has been extended to utilise phase space to predict the behaviour of a vessel in following seas.

Predictions of the conditions for broaching-to from this method compare reasonably well with the results from free running model experiments.

○   Periodic motion   (exp. by Fuwa[1])
■   Stable surf-riding (exp. by Fuwa[1])
●   Broaching   (exp. by Fuwa[1])

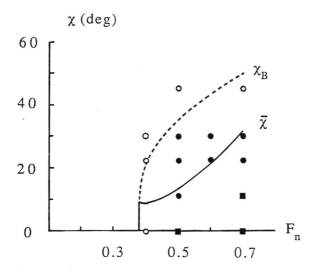

Figure 5: Critical conditions of broaching-to
(H/λ =1/20, λ/L=2.0)

NOMENCLATURE

c = wave celerity
F_n = nominal Froude number
H = wave height
I_{zz} = moment of inertia in yaw
J_{zz} = added moment of inertia in yaw
m = mass of ship
m_x = added mass of ship in surge
m_y = added mass of ship in sway
R = resistance
r = yaw rate
N_w = wave induced yaw moment
T = propeller thrust
u = component of ship speed in x-axis direction
v = component of ship speed in y-axis direction
X_w = wave induced surge force
Y_w = wave induced sway force
δ = rudder angle
λ = wave length
χ = heading angle

ACKNOWLEDGEMENTS

The work described in this paper was carried out at the Australian Maritime College during the first author's stay there as a research fellow. This was supported by the Asia Pacific Maritime Centre Research Award of this college.

REFERENCES

1. Fuwa,T., Sugai,K. Yoshino,T., Yamamoto,T. 'An Experimental Study on Broaching of a Small High speed Craft', *Papers of Ship Research Institute*, No.66, pp.1-40, 1982.
2. Motora,S., Fujino,M. and Fuwa,T. 'On the Mechanism of Broaching-to Phenomena' *Pro. 2nd Int. Conf. on Stability of Ships and Ocean Vehicles*, Tokyo, Vol.4, pp.1-15, 1982.

3. Renilson,M.R. 'An Investigation into the Factors Affecting the Likelihood of Broaching-to in Following Seas' *Pro. 2nd Int. Conf. on Stability of Ships and Ocean Vehicles*, Tokyo, pp.17-28, 1982.

4. The USSR Delegation 'Stability of a Fishing Vessel in a Seaway' IMCO, PFV X/8/1, pp.1-28, 1970.

5. Umeda,N. 'Probabilistic Study on Surf-riding of a Ship in irregular Following Seas' *Pro. 4th Int. Conf. on Stability of Ships and Ocean Vehicles*, Naples, Vol.1, pp.336-343, 1990.

6. Kan,M. 'A Guideline to Avoid the Dangerous Surf-riding' *Pro. 4th Int. Conf. on Stability of Ships and Ocean Vehicles*, Naples, Vol.1, pp.90-97, 1990.

7. Umeda,N. and Renilson,M.R. 'Simplified Method for Calculating Lateral Wave forces on a Ship Running in Quartering Seas with Very Low Encounter Frequency' Report of Ship Hydrodynamics Centre, Australian Maritime College, (to be submitted), 1992.

8. Guckenheimer,J. and Holmes,P. *Nonlinear Oscillations, Dynamical Systems, and Bifurcations of Vector Fields* Spring-Verlag, New York, pp.1-65, 1983.

Table 1 Principal particulars of the fishing vessel

Length	L	7.14	[m]
Breadth	B	1.87	[m]
Draft fore	d_f	0.260	[m]
Draft midship	d_m	0.3835	[m]
Draft aft	d_a	0.507	[m]
L.C.B.(aft)	l/L	0.0842	
Displacement	W	2413	[kg]
Gyro radius in yaw	κ_{zz}/L	0.2976	
Propeller Diameter	D_p	0.440	[m]
Rudder area ratio	A_R/Ld_m	1/27.18	

SECTION 9: SEA STATE PREDICTION

Techniques for Sea State Predictions

E.L. Morris (*), H.K. Zienkiewicz (*),
M.M.A. Pourzanjani (*), J.O. Flower (**),
M.R. Belmont (*)
*(*) School of Engineering, University of Exeter,
Exeter EX4 4QF, UK*
*(**) Department of Engineering, University of
Warwick, Coventry, UK*

INTRODUCTION

It is well known that seas with large wave amplitudes possess a relatively narrow band spectrum, and that such a spectrum would result in a narrow autocorrelation function. This shows the presence of some statistical dependence in aspects of the sea surface behaviour and suggests, at least in principle, the possibility of short term forecasting, (Belmont *et al*[1]). This result is purely based on single point data and treats such information as a single stochastic variable. Consequently, it represents the most pessimistic view of the situation and one could hope, in view of the energy requirements necessary to change the dynamics of the sea, that greater determinism would be found. Considering only the fluid dynamics of the problem, there is no reason to expect that the sea is other than totally deterministic; it is only the complexity of the problem that precludes a complete evaluation of the sea surface.

This paper is concerned with the mathematical background required to develop a practical sea-surface estimator, which could be of great benefit to ship operators in situations where it would be useful to forecast or control the motion of the ship. It is assumed that it is possible to measure the present state of the surface of the sea (Belmont *et al*[2]). These measurements will be used to generate a prediction of the sea state at some time into the future.

PROPAGATION OF A TRAIN OF LINEAR DISPERSIVE WAVES

Consider a train of small amplitude one-dimensional dispersive waves satisfying the linear wave equation. The wave frequencies in the train range over a finite interval $f_l \leq f \leq f_h$, and the phase velocity c is a known function of f. The waves are travelling in one direction *only* (either the positive or the negative x-direction). It is useful to illustrate the paths of propagation of the individual component waves as lines in the $(x - t)$-plane, the slope of a line, dx/dt, being equal to the phase velocity $c(f)$ of a particular component.

Suppose now that the wave amplitude is measured *at fixed* x, say $x = 0$, over a time interval $0 \leq t \leq T$ (shown as the line AB in Fig. 1); denote this temporal wave-form by $z_0(t)$. The paths of propagation of the lowest and highest frequency waves which have passed the point A at time $t = 0$ are represented by the lines labelled f_{la} and f_{ha}, respectively; similarly for the point B at time $t = T$.

Within the triangular region ABC bounded by the lines AB, f_{ha} and f_{lb}, shown cross-hatched in Fig. 1, the only waves present are those which have passed the location $x = 0$ during the time interval AB. Therefore, it follows that the history of the waves along AB, represented by the time-series $z_0(t)$, completely determines wave propagation in this region; provided, of course, that no events affecting the existing wave system occur for $x > 0$ within ABC. It is important to note that it is immaterial whether the wave-train $z_0(t)$ was generated by a deterministic or a stochastic process: its existence ensures determinacy within the region ABC regardless of the nature of its origins.

As is obvious, the extent of the region ABC decreases with increasing band-width, $(f_h - f_l)$, of $z_0(t)$, and would diminish to insignificant size for a wide spectrum. However, for narrow enough spectra, it should be possible to make accurate predictions over significant intervals of either spatial wave-forms, e.g. along the line BD in Fig. 1, or, more usefully, of temporal wave-forms, such as that along the line DE, *for times greater than* T.

Along a line such as EG in the region CBH, bounded by the lines f_{lb} and f_{hb}, wave propagation is progressively more and more affected by the waves which have passed the station $x = 0$ at $t > T$, beginning with the fastest (lowest frequency) components. Similarly, along the line DF in the region CAI, conditions are first affected by the slowest (highest frequency) components which have passed the station $x = 0$ at $t < 0$. In principle, predictability of wave-forms in these regions *does* depend on the nature of the wave-train at $x = 0$.

Suppose, first, that the wave train is fully deterministic. Then, if it were possible to determine its *actual* spectrum from $z_0(t)$ observed during $0 \leq t \leq T$, wave propagation would be predictable anywhere at any time. By contrast, for a stochastic wave train, the wave spectra for $t < 0$ and $t > T$ at $x = 0$ might be correlated only weakly, if at all, with the spectrum of $z_0(t)$. However, in practice, the spectrum has to be obtained by carrying out a Discrete Fourier Transform (DFT) of $z_0(t)$. This would yield the true spectrum only if the wave train at $x = 0$ were periodic, with period T. As this is not so for either kind of wave train, we should expect similar practical constraints on the predictability of wave propagation outside the region ABC in both cases.

Unless the time interval T is much larger than the longest period in the wave train, the Fourier spectrum will be necessarily broader than the actual spectrum. The presence of spurious component waves in the Fourier spectrum outside the actual spectrum of $z_0(t)$, especially on the high frequency side, will have two consequences. First, there will be *a reduction in the extent of the region ABC*, and second, some inaccuracies will arise when the inverse DFT is used to reconstruct wave-forms even within the region ABC. As will be seen later, the importance of these effects depends largely on the magnitude of the difference between wave amplitudes at the end points A and B (and, to a lesser extent, on the difference between wave slopes there); the accuracy of predictions can be substantially enhanced by a judicious choice of the time origin for $z_0(t)$, so as to minimize the differences between wave amplitudes and slopes at A and B.

Similar arguments apply, *mutatis mutandis*, when the initial wave-train is observed at *fixed time*, say $t = 0$, as a function of distance, $z_0(x)$, for $0 \leq x \leq L$. The corresponding $(x - t)$-diagram is shown in Fig. 2.

In this case, the most useful prediction would be that of variation with time at $x = 0$, *i.e.* along ADE in Fig. 2. It is interesting to note that here the broadening of the Fourier spectrum on the high frequency side should not contaminate the region ABC with spurious wave components.

APPLICATION TO SWELL WAVES

An analysis of measurements of the sea displacement was carried out to verify the form of the spectrum (Belmont *et al*[1]). The measurements were obtained from two deep water sites; one off the Isles of Scilly, the other off South Uist. The results verify that swell waves have a narrow frequency spectrum with a dominant frequency of about $0.1Hz$. Since the corresponding wave-length is about $150m$, waves as high as $10m$ might be regarded as of sufficiently small amplitude for the linearized theory to provide a reasonable approximation to their propagation in deep water, at least over time intervals no longer than a few multiples of the dominant period of $10s$. It has long been recognised, (Pierson *et al*[3], Nonweiler *et al*[4], Kinsman[5]), that models of the power density spectrum of the sea contain strongly dependent parameters. This aspect was explored (Belmont *et al*[1]]) in the case of the Isles of Scilly and South Uist data, where it was found that there was a strong relationship between the width of the spectrum, and the amplitude of the main component. This would suggest that as the waves get larger and the need to predict the sea surface grows, the ability to make accurate predictions might also grow.

Sea Model

To test the proposed methods on real sea waves would require data on spatial and temporal propagation of such waves, or, at least, time-histories at two stations separated by a few hundred metres. As we have not been able to find access to such data, we have tested our methods on a simple model proposed by (Nonweiler et al[4]). This model (Equation 1) consists of five component waves with specified frequencies and amplitudes, as shown in Table 1.

$$z(x,t) = \sum_{i=1}^{5} a_i cos(\omega_i t - q_i x) \qquad (1)$$

where $q_i = \omega_i/c_i$ and $c_i = g/\omega_i$.

Note that the frequencies do not form a harmonic series for either the narrow or the wide spectrum but belong to the more general class of Almost Periodic Functions (Bohr[6]). However, the spatial frequencies, q, for the narrow spectrum are almost harmonic. The phase velocities, c, are assumed to have the deep water values of $g/2\pi f$. The phases are picked at random from the uniform distribution in the interval $(0-2\pi)$, or the starting time is randomly chosen to obtain the equivalent effect. Also shown in the Table are the angular frequencies, ω, the spatial frequencies, $q = 2\pi/\lambda$, the wavelengths, λ, and the periods, τ; the scale of the amplitudes is arbitrary. Note that the RMS value of the amplitude of the waves generated with these models is 0.707.

Table 1. Model-Sea Parameters

NARROW SPECTRUM

f, Hz	ω, s^{-1}	c, m/s	q, m^{-1}	λ, m	τ, s	a
0.059	0.37	26.4	0.014	448	16.9	0.34
0.080	0.50	19.5	0.026	244	12.5	0.49
0.099	0.62	15.8	0.039	159	10.1	0.53
0.116	0.73	13.4	0.054	116	8.6	0.49
0.131	0.82	11.9	0.069	91	7.6	0.34

WIDE SPECTRUM

f, Hz	ω, s^{-1}	c, m/s	q, m^{-1}	λ, m	τ, s	a
0.050	0.31	31.2	0.010	624	20.0	0.34
0.076	0.48	20.5	0.023	270	13.2	0.49
0.099	0.62	15.8	0.039	159	10.1	0.53
0.119	0.75	13.1	0.057	110	8.4	0.49
0.136	0.85	11.5	0.074	84	7.4	0.34

This simple deterministic model appears to present the obvious features of a one-dimensional swell and we consider it adequate, at this stage, for the purpose of testing the proposed methods.

Use of *FFT* to obtain spatial spectrum of sea

Tests were made to determine an appropriate number of sample points and their spatial separation to ensure an adequate Fast Fourier Transform (Cooley and Tukey[7]) model of the one-dimensional sea surface. The inverse Discrete Fourier Transform was computed from the *FFT* model and compared with the surface generated from the Nonweiler model, (Nonweiler *et al*[4]), to test the 'goodness' of the *FFT* model.

Actual and predicted sea wave elevations at a large number of points (1024) were computed using the narrow spectrum model for the sea, and the root-mean-squared difference was calculated. This was repeated, at differing values of time, to obtain average amplitudes independent of the initial wave shape. Three curves are shown (Fig. 3) for different numbers of *FFT* samples used (64, 128, 256), and are plotted as a function of the total scanned distance. The curves are fairly constant in value, except that a pronounced minimum is demonstrated at 460 meters, which corresponds roughly to the wavelength of the longest component of the original sea model. As would be expected, the errors decrease with increasing values of N.

The spectra were computed for a selection of values for N (64, 128, 256) and a total scan distance of 460.8 meters. The amplitude only was computed, and averaged over 50 sets of measurements, made at randomly selected times. The first 32 spectral components were plotted, and as can be seen from Fig. 4, were effectively independent of the order of the *FFT* model. Double the magnitude is plotted, to make comparison with the original sea model easier. The values computed are almost exactly those used in the original sea model. This was unexpected, as the frequencies of the components of the original sea model are not equally spaced, although the spatial frequencies turn out to be almost harmonic.

As this might have an effect on the accuracy of the *FFT* model, the tests were repeated using the wide spectrum sea model. It was found that the plot of error versus scan distance showed no pronounced minimum at the wavelength of the longest component, but that errors gradually decreased with increased scan distance. The spectra were found to be more as expected, and comparable with the spectra obtained at a fixed point (Fig. 5).

FIXED TIME METHOD

Using either sea model at $t = 0$ and scanning along the x-axis from $x = 0$ to some maximum value, the FFT algorithm was used to compute a spectral representation of the sea. This model could then be used through the equation

$$z(x,t) = \frac{1}{\sqrt{N}}(A_0 + 2 \sum_{i=1}^{\frac{N}{2}-1} \left(A_i cos(\frac{2\pi i x}{L} + \omega_i t) \right) \tag{2}$$

$$- B_i sin(\frac{2\pi i x}{L} + \omega_i t)) + A_{\frac{N}{2}} e^{j\frac{\pi N x}{L}})$$

where $\omega_i = \sqrt{\frac{2\pi g i}{L}}$ and t is the time after the FFT was evaluated.

This equation may be evaluated for any values of x and t. Note that the last term in $A_{\frac{N}{2}}$ must be assumed to be 0, otherwise there will be an imaginary component produced, which is impossible. In fact the coefficient is always very small. As a first trial, z is evaluated for $x = 0$ and $t = 20$. Since the original model is known, the accuracy of the prediction may be determined. A series of 50 tests with different starting times was made and the RMS error is shown in Fig. 6 for the wide spectrum model. This shows a monotonic decrease in prediction errors with increasing scan distance, levelling off at distances approaching the maximum wavelength of the original model. All subsequent tests were carried out with $N = 128$ and a scan distance approximately equal to the maximum wavelength.

The second set of tests consisted of comparing the predictions based on equation 2 with the original model for both the wide and narrow spectrum sea models. The RMS error at the each sample point was calculated as a function of time. Inevitably, at $t = 0$, the errors are zero everywhere, but as the time is increased, it is plain that the errors at points remote from the origin grow, while errors at points close to the origin remain small. The region of large errors moves towards the origin, as waves from outside the region of measurement propagate towards the origin. These results are displayed in two sets of curves (Fig. 7a, b), the first showing the errors as a function of distance from the origin, while the second show the errors as a function of time, at fixed positions.

Note that the errors for the wide spectrum model are significantly larger than those for the narrow spectrum, although the prediction times are longer, as one would expect from the increased scan distance involved. In both cases the prediction times at $x = 0$ exceed 30 seconds. The errors are of the order of 5 to 10 percent (Fig. 8a, b). It was observed that the spectra obtained for the wide band model had significant high and low frequency components. As these were not present in the original sea model, attempts were made to eliminate them. Inevitably, with the *FFT* applied as in these calculations, the lack of periodicity in the sea waves produces errors in the spectra computed. Increasing the scan distance to include multiples of the longest wavelength might improve the accuracy of the results but is likely to prove impossible in practice. The high frequency components found are caused by the assumed discontinuities at the ends of the scan. Attempts were made, therefore, to choose end points for the scan that eliminated these discontinuities. Points were selected that had zero offset from the mean, and whose slopes at these points were approximately equal. Interpolation was used to find 128 intermediate points, which were used for the *FFT* algorithm. This meant that the total scan distance varied from test to test, but as the prediction error was insensitive to the scan distance for the wide band model, this was not important. Although the high frequency components were eliminated from the spectra obtained, the errors were not significantly reduced.

FIXED POINT METHOD

If measurements were to be made at a point some distance from the position where the prediction was required, and the sea waves were propagating towards that position from the direction of the point chosen, then it would be possible to predict the sea surface at the required position. One advantage of this technique over the scan method is that measurements could be made over several periods with no increase in complexity, and thus the accuracy of the results should be increased.

Model wave-trains, $z_0(t)$, were computed at $x = 0$ for time intervals, T, of 64 seconds, with randomized phases in each case. Spectra of these wave-trains were found by applying a Fast Fourier Transform with $N = 128$. Predictions were then made of spatial wave-trains for $0 \leq x \leq 800\, m$ at $t = 64\, s$, and of temporal wave-trains for $64 \leq t \leq 128\, s$ at various values of $x = x_1$; this was done using inverse *DFT* with each component of the spectrum propagating at the deep-water phase velocity. As a check, $z_0(t)$ were reconstructed and were found to coincide, as they should, with the original wave-trains at the sampling points of the *FFT*. Fig. 1 is drawn to scale for T of 64 s and x_1 of 400 m.

Comparisons were then made with the corresponding wave-trains calculated for the actual sea model. The quality of predictions was found to depend significantly on the magnitude of the difference, Δz_{ab}, between the wave elevations at the points A and B (in Fig. 1), and to a lesser extent on the difference between the wave slopes there, Δs_{ab}.

When these differences were small enough, good agreement was found for distances up to $400\,m$ or more at $t = 64\,s$, and times exceeding some $100\,s$ (*i.e.* for about $40\,s$ "into the future") at $x_1 = 400\,m$. A typical result is illustrated in Fig. 9; in this case Δz_{ab} is 0.21 and Δs_{ab} is $0.19s^{-1}$. The sampled and reconstructed waveform is shown in Fig. 9a. The Fourier spectrum of $z_0(t)$, shown in Fig. 9b, differs in detail from the model spectrum of Table 1, but is only marginally broader. Figs. 9c and 9d show the actual and predicted waveforms in both the space and time domains.

When wave elevation and slope differences at points A and B increase, the accuracy of prediction deteriorates. No systematic quantitative investigation of the resulting errors has yet been made, but visual observation of a number of examples has suggested that the errors become unduly large when $|\Delta z_{ab}|$ and $|\Delta s_{ab}|$ exceed about 1 and $1s^{-1}$, respectively; an illustration is shown in Fig. 10 in which the 'raw' predictions were based on $z_0(t)$ with $|\Delta z_{ab}|$ of 1.34 and $|\Delta s_{ab}|$ of $1.30/s$. The 'raw' Fourier spectrum is now considerably broader.

An obvious way of mitigating such errors is to minimize these differences of wave elevation and slope at A and B by an appropriate shift of the starting point A. For the present purposes this was done by searching the wave-train $z_0(t)$, beginning at $t = 0$, until the following conditions were satisfied:

(i) $|\Delta z_{ab}| < 0.6$;

(ii) $|\Delta s_{ab}| < 0.6s^{-1}$;

(iii) $t \leq 12.8\,s$ (the purpose of this restriction is to prevent an undue reduction of the length of $z_0(t)$);

(iv) FFT with $N = 128$ can be carried out without interpolation of $z_0(t)$.

When this procedure was applied to the example of Fig. 10, the differences in wave elevations and slopes at A and B were reduced to 0.60 and $0.16s^{-1}$, respectively. This resulted in a notably 'cleaner' Fourier spectrum, Fig. 11a, and much improved predictions shown in Fig. 11b and c. It is worth noting that the changes in the Fourier spectrum involve not only a virtual disappearance of the high frequency tail, which could have been achieved by the simple expedient of filtering, but also in a significant improvement of the low frequency side; it is the latter effect which, we believe, is mainly responsible for the improvement in predictions.

Fig. 12 illustrates the case of the original difference in wave elevations, but *not* in wave slopes, exceeding its threshold, with $|\Delta z_{ab}| = 2.74$ and $|\Delta s_{ab}| = 0.07s^{-1}$. For the new time-origin, $|\Delta z_{ab}|$ was reduced to 0.47 at the expense of an insignificant increase of $|\Delta s_{ab}|$ to $0.32s^{-1}$. In this case, the 'raw' Fourier spectrum, Fig. 12b, was very broad, as a consequence of the large original difference in wave elevations. Fig. 13 shows the improved spectrum and predictions.

The converse case of excessive difference of $1.46s^{-1}$ in wave slopes, with a moderate difference of 0.57 in wave elevations is shown in Figs. 14 and 15; the initial differences were reduced to $0.10s^{-1}$ and 0.12 by the shift of the time origin. This situation does not appear to be very common, as observations suggest that large differences in wave slopes are usually associated with large differences in wave elevations.

The search procedure for a new time origin for the *FFT* of the wave-train at $x = 0$ can be improved by interpolation between data values, thus allowing even closer fits between the wave elevations and slopes at the end points. Furthermore, if the proposed method were implemented in practice, time-variation at $x = 0$ would be monitored continuously and search for the new time origin could be more usefully extended backwards in time.

Qualitatively similar results have been obtained for values of x_1 other than $400\ m$, but no quantitative evaluation of errors, corresponding to that described in the preceding section for the *Fixed-Time Method*, has yet been made.

Increasing the length of the time interval, T, over which $z_0(t)$ is observed has a number of important effects. First, there is an obvious increase in the extent of the region ABC within which predictions can be made. Second, more accurate Fourier spectra can be obtained since the frequency resolution varies as $1/T$. Third, there is reduced sensitivity of the 'raw' spectra, and hence of predictions, to the differences in wave elevations and slopes at $t = 0$ and $t = T$. Thus, it would be of advantage to have T as large as possible, subject, of course, to overriding considerations such as a possible occurrence of extraneous events during this time interval, which might invalidate subsequent predictions.

CONCLUSIONS

It has been shown that it is possible to predict the form of a one-dimensional sea surface at a given point for some $30s$ into the future. Further investigations are necessary to establish whether this information can be used to improve the operational conditions of ships at sea.

The fixed time method has inherent mensuration difficulties that do not entirely apply to the fixed distance method. Even so, there are substantial difficulties in making reliable, continuous measurements of the sea surface some distance from the point where the prediction is to be made. Many of these difficulties have been discussed elsewhere (Belmont et al[2]). It is clear that some form of intelligent interpolator and estimator will be required to provide data when individual measurements are missing from the series.

However, should it prove possible to make reliable measurements of the sea surface at a distance from the observation point, then it has been shown that it is possible to predict the future surface of a long-crested sea for periods of up to $30s$ with a useful degree of accuracy.

REFERENCES

1.   Belmont M.R., Zienkiewicz H.K., Morris E.L., Pourzanjani M.M.A. and Flower J.O. 'The Correlation between Width and Maximum Power for North Atlantic Wave Spectra' *Proc. 2nd Int Conf. on Manœuvring and Control of Marine Craft*, Southampton, U.K., 1992.
2.   Belmont M.R., Zienkiewicz H.K., Morris E.L., Pourzanjani M.M.A. and Flower J.O. 'Sea Surface Predictor' *Report on S.E.R.C. Contract No. GR/F 32165 (SHP54)* 1991.
3.   Pierson W.J., Jr, Neumann E. and James R.W. 'Practical Methods of Observing and Forecasting Ocean Waves by Means of Wave Spectra and Statistics.' *U. S. Navy Hydrographic Office Pub. No. 603*, 1955.
4.   Nonweiler T.R.F., Tanner P.H. and Wilkinson P. 'Moving-weight Ship Stabilizers' *Third Ship Control Systems Symposium*, Bath, U.K., 1972.
5.   Kinsman B. *Wind Waves* Dover Inc, 1984.
6.   Bohr H. *Almost Periodic Functions* Chelsea Publ. Co., N. Y., 1951.
7.   Cooley W.J. and Tukey J.W. 'An Algorithm for the Machine Calculation of Complex Fourier Series' *Math. of Comput.*, Vol. 9, No. 90, pp 297-301, 1965.

ACKNOWLEDGEMENTS

The work reported here was done in the course of research supported by a grant from the Marine Technology Directorate and the Ministry of Defence.

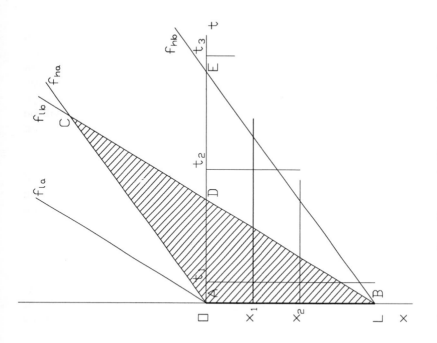

Figure 2. Fixed Time Method

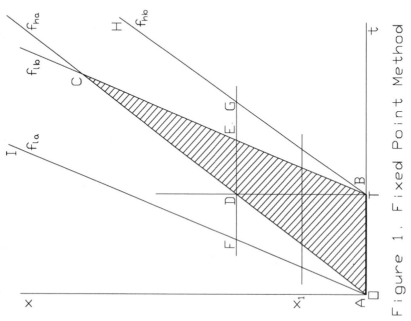

Figure 1. Fixed Point Method

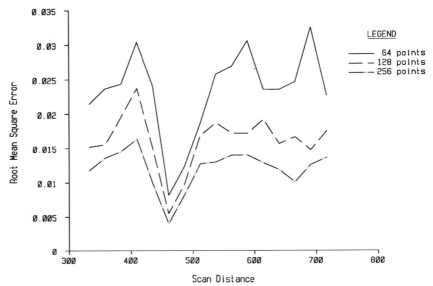

Fig. 3. FFT Model Errors

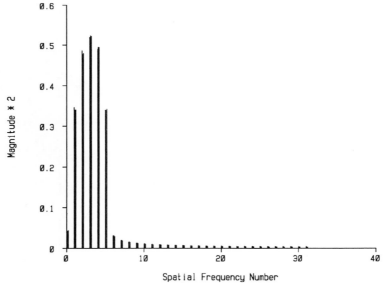

Fig. 4. FFT Spectral Magnitudes

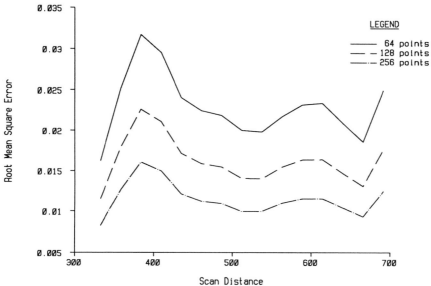

Fig. 5a. FFT Model Errors - Wide Spectrum

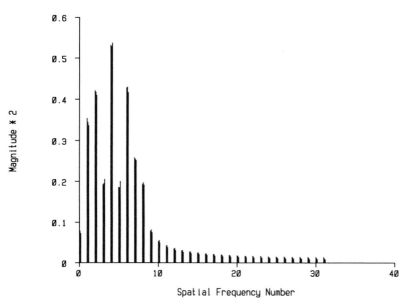

Fig. 5b. FFT Spectral Magnitudes - Wide Spectrum

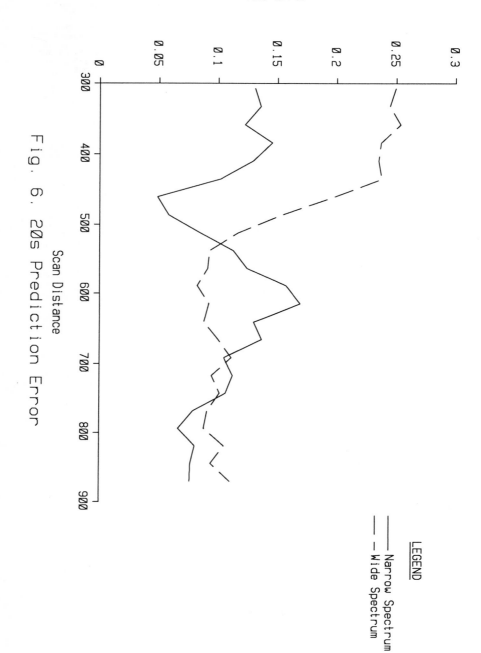

Fig. 6. 20s Prediction Error

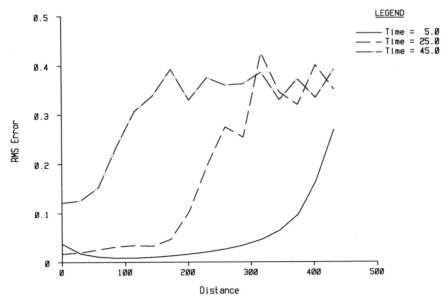

Fig. 7a. Prediction Errors vs Distance

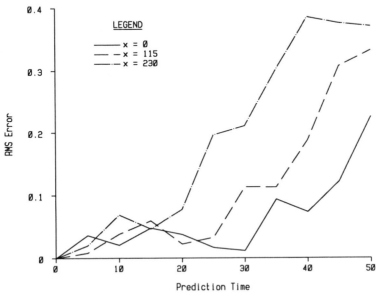

Fig. 7b. Prediction Errors vs Time

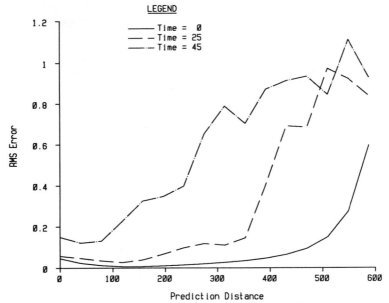

Fig. 8a. Prediction Error vs Distance

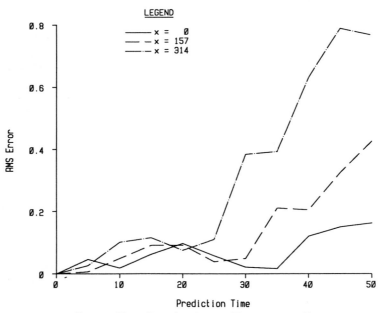

Fig. 8b. Prediction Error vs Time

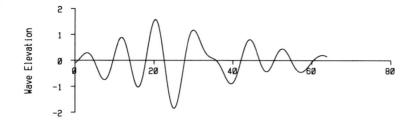

Fig. 9a. Variation with Time at x = 0

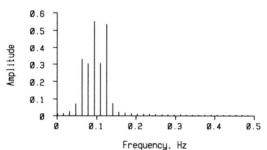

Fig. 9b. FFT Spectral Magnitudes

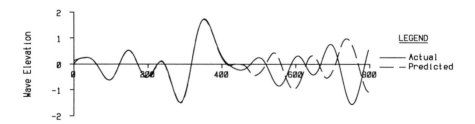

Fig. 9c. Variation with Distance at t = 64s

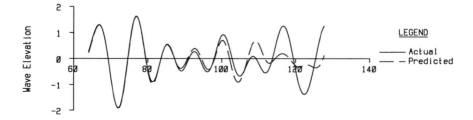

Fig 9d. Variation with Time at x = 400m

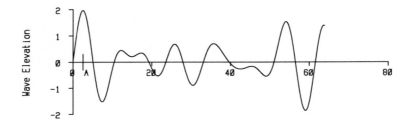

Fig. 10a. Variation with Time at x = 0
A marks the new origin.

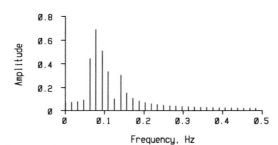

Fig. 10b. 'Raw' Fourier Spectrum

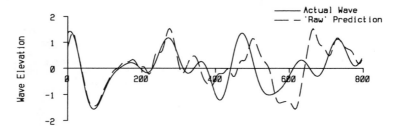

Fig. 10c. Variation with Distance at t = 64s

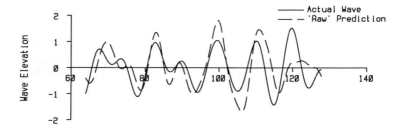

Fig. 10d. Variation with Time at x = 400m

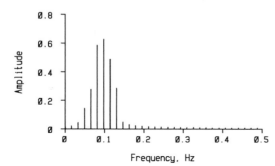

Fig. 11a. 'Improved' Fourier Spectrum

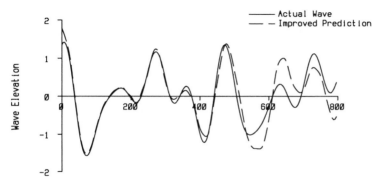

Fig. 11b. Variation with Distance at t = 64s

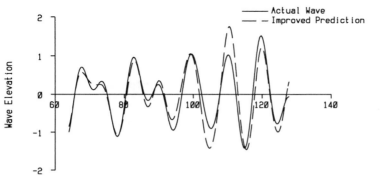

Fig 11c. Variation with Time at x = 400m

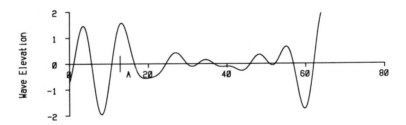

Time, s
Fig. 12a. Variation with Time at x = 0
A marks the new origin.

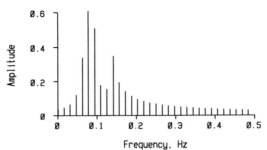

Frequency, Hz
Fig. 12b. 'Raw' Fourier Spectrum

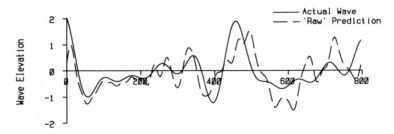

Distance, m
Fig. 12c. Variation with Distance at t = 64s

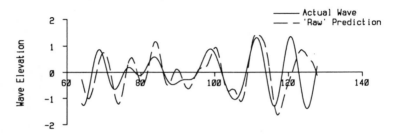

Time, s
Fig. 12d. Variation with Time at x = 400m

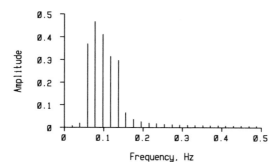

Fig. 13a. 'Improved' Fourier Spectrum

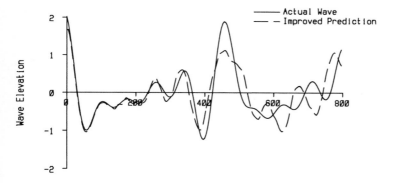

Fig. 13b. Variation with Distance at t = 64s

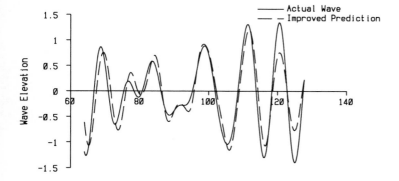

Fig 13c. Variation with Time at x = 400m

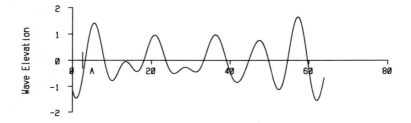

Fig. 14a. Variation with Time at x = 0
A marks the new origin.

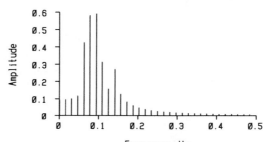

Fig. 14b. 'Raw' Fourier Spectrum

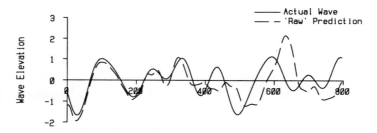

Fig. 14c. Variation with Distance at t = 64s

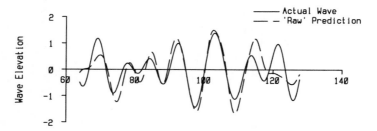

Fig. 14d. Variation with Time at x = 400m

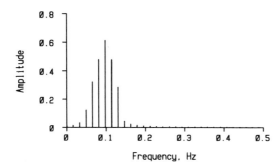

Fig. 15a. 'Improved' Fourier Spectrum

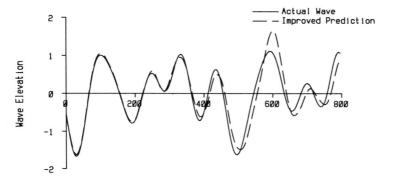

Distance, m

Fig. 15b. Variation with Distance at t = 64s

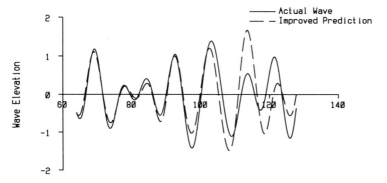

Time, s

Fig 15c. Variation with Time at x = 400m

The Correlation Between Width and Maximum Power for North Atlantic Wave Spectra

M.R. Belmont (*), H.K. Zienkiewicz (*),
E.L. Morris (*), M.M.A. Pourzanjani (*),
J.O. Flower (**)
(*) School of Engineering, University of Exeter, Exeter EX4 4QF, UK
(**) Department of Engineering, University of Warwick, Coventry, UK

ABSTRACT

Examination of discrete spectra of some records of sea waves at two widely separated deep-water sites off the eastern seaboard of the North Atlantic reveals the presence of a good correlation between the widths of time-averaged spectra and the power of their largest harmonics. The spectral width decreases with increasing sea state, but at large wave amplitudes may be regarded as approximately constant.

INTRODUCTION

The authors [1] have shown that given the initial knowledge of a relatively short segment of a train of one-dimensional dispersive waves satisfying the linear wave equation, it is possible to make accurate predictions of spatial or temporal wave-forms, provided that the spectrum of the initial wave-train is narrow enough.

To the extent that a linearized mathematical model can be used to represent reasonably accurately, at least over limited distances and periods of time, long-crested surface waves on deep water, our results should be of use in the development of a practical sea-surface predictor.

With the above observations in mind, the purpose of the work, reported here, was to investigate how the widths of spectra of actual sea-waves vary with the sea state, using data from two deep-water sites in the North Atlantic.

THE SEA DATA USED

Data were generously provided by the British Oceanographic Data Centre. The records examined had been collected at two deep-water sites: South Uist during January to March 1981, and the Isles of Scilly during November and December 1981. The records consisted of sea surface elevations sampled by buoys at intervals of 0.5 second for a period of 2048 seconds at Scillies and 1024 seconds at South Uist. The consecutive recording periods were normally separated by intervals of three hours, except when some records were invalidated because of failing to satisfy a number of checks, Gleason [2], designed to guard against malfunction of equipment or instrumentation. Such spurious records were deleted before spectral analysis was performed.

DATA PROCESSING

The spectra were obtained by determining 128-point Discrete Fourier Transforms over 16 consecutive sets of 128 data-points covering a period of 1024 seconds. The transforms were then averaged over each set; thus each frequency point is the average of 16 individual determinations.

Transforms of the Isles of Scilly data were also determined over 32 consecutive sets of 128 data-points covering the longer period of 2048 seconds.

To check whether the sea state changed significantly over periods of up to 1024 seconds, we have used the Isles of Scilly data to calculate typical running averages, over this period, of the wave elevation and the corresponding root-mean-square values. The means of wave elevation are judged to have remained constant within the accuracy of the data. Typical variations of the RMS values are shown in Figure 1. Some sea states, such as (a) and (d) show a relatively slow rise or fall; others vary remarkably little. Thus we believe that, for our purposes, we may regard such seas to behave as (weakly) stationary processes on these time-scales and that the averaged spectra should lead to reasonably unbiased estimates.

As a measure of spectral width we have adopted the standard deviation $sd(f)$ of each average of 16 individual 128-point spectra, with $sd(f)$ given by

$$sd(f) = \left[\frac{m_2}{m_0} - \left(\frac{m_1}{m_0} \right)^2 \right]^{1/2} \tag{1}$$

where m_n is the n-th moment of the spectrum:

$$m_n = \sum_{i=0}^{N/2-1} f_i^n P(f_i) \quad . \tag{2}$$

RESULTS AND DISCUSSION

Figures 2 and 3 show records of sea state and averaged spectra of illustrative sea conditions. These range from large maximum amplitudes of some ±6 m to slight seas of less than ±0.5 m. For the sake of direct comparability, the Isles of Scilly spectra shown in these figures are the averages over 16 sets.

In order to explore how the spectral width varies with the sea state, we have plotted $sd(f)$ against $P(max)$, the power of the largest harmonic of each spectrum average. Figures 4 and 5 for the two sites show the 523 points for South Uist and 1000 points for the Isles of Scilly.

The general behaviour at the two sites, some 500 miles apart, is very similar. This is despite the fact that the results presented were obtained at different times and were not produced by the same weather systems. The basic features of the spectra were as expected, e.g. a reduction in spectral width with increasing wave height.

The data were correlated by a simple least-squares regression of $log[sd(f)]$ on $log[P(max)]$. The resulting regression fits are also shown in Figures 4 and 5. Figure 6 shows the regression functions superimposed for the two sites to emphasize their similarity. The functional forms were $sd(f) = 0.0596/P(max)^{0.159}$ for South Uist and $sd(f) = 0.0567/P(max)^{0.166}$ for the Isles of Scilly. The corresponding values of the coefficient of determination, R^2, were 77% and 73%, respectively, this coefficient being defined as the square of the Pearson product moment correlation coefficient:

$$R^2(x,y) = \frac{\left[\sum (x - \bar{x})(y - \bar{y})\right]^2}{\sum (x - \bar{x})^2 \sum (y - \bar{y})^2} \quad ,$$

with bars denoting mean values.

The Figures 4 and 5 show that for large seas the standard deviation $sd(f)$ changes very little and is effectively constant at about 0.05 to 0.06 hertz.

For the Isles of Scilly data, it is possible to average the spectra over 32 rather than 16 consecutive sets of 128 data points, thus reducing standard errors by the factor of $\sqrt{2}$. The resulting variation of $sd(f)$ with $P(max)$ is shown in Figure 7. The corresponding regression fit, $sd(f) = 0.0567/P(max)^{0.164}$, is not significantly different from that for the averages of 16 sets, but has a slightly higher R^2 of 75% which reflects the smaller scatter in Figure 7 as compared with that of Figure 5.

Evaluating the form of the peak power density versus spectral width relationship from idealized *continuous* spectra of the form $S(f) = A\,exp(-B/f^p)/f^n$ gives $sd(f)$ proportional to $1/S_{max}^{1/n}$. This suggests that if one were to represent such seas as we have examined by spectra of this form, the value of n should be 6, as in the Neumann spectrum, rather than 5, as in the Pierson-Moskowitz or Bretschneider spectra, (e.g. Lewis [3]). This would avoid the disadvantage of the fourth moment of $S(f)$ becoming infinite, as it does for $n = 5$.

CONCLUSIONS

The results show that the spectral width of deep-water sea waves can be well correlated with the power of the largest harmonics of spectra when the data are averaged over 16 or more consecutive sets of time-series data taken at intervals of 0.5 s. This width, defined as the standard deviation of the averaged spectrum, decreases with increasing sea state, but at large wave amplitudes may be regarded to have an approximately constant value. For winter conditions at the eastern seaboard of the North Atlantic, where the two sites were located, this value is about 0.05 to 0.06 Hz.

ACKNOWLEDGEMENTS

The work reported here was done in the course of research supported by a grant from the Marine Technology Directorate and the Ministry of Defence. The authors would also like to thank the British Oceanographic Data Centre for providing the sea data.

REFERENCES

1. Morris, E.L., Zienkiewicz, H.K., Pourzanjani, M.M.A., Flower, J.O. and Belmont, M.R. 'Techniques for Sea State Predictions' *Proc. 2nd Int Conf. on Manœuvring and Control of Marine Craft*, Southampton, U.K., 1992.

2. Gleason, R. 'A User Guide to IOS Digital Wave Data Time Series'. *Institute of Oceanographic Sciences, Internal Document No. 154*, 1982.

3. Lewis, E.V. (Ed). 'Principles of Naval Architecture.' Chapter VIII, *Motion in Waves*, vol.III, SNAME, 1989.

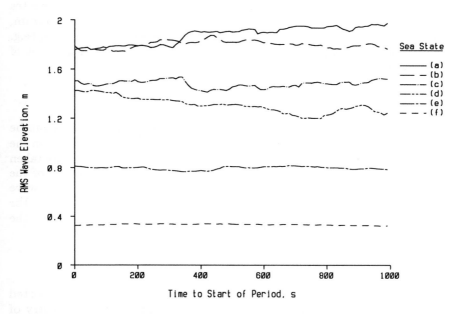

Figure 1. RMS Wave Elevation (over a period of 1024s): Evolution with Time

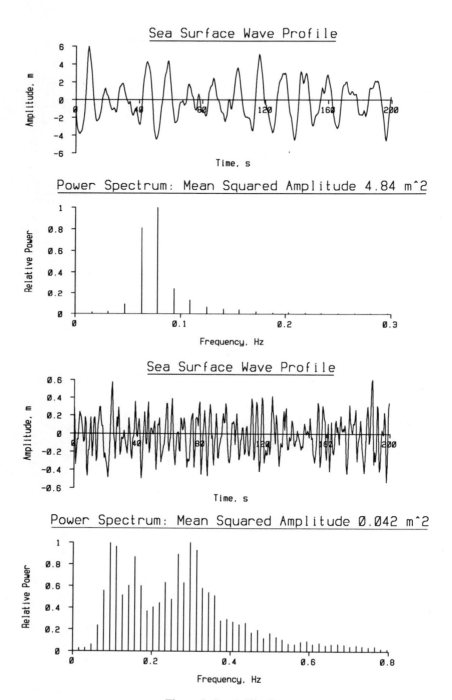

Figure 2. South Uist Data

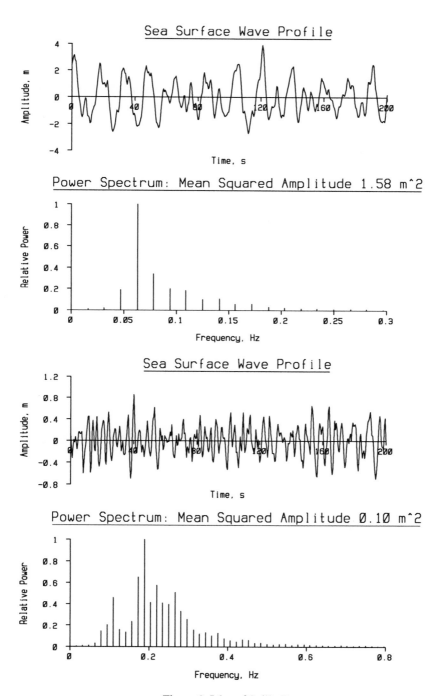

Figure 3. Isles of Scilly Data

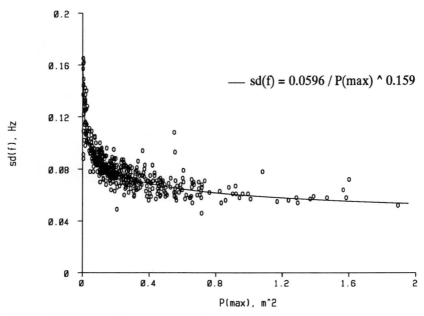

Figure 4. Spectrum Standard Deviation vs. Maximum Power: South Uist Data
Averages of 16 spectra with N = 128

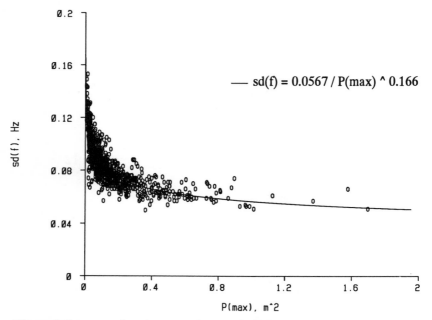

Figure 5. Spectrum Standard Deviation vs. Maximum Power: Isles of Scilly Data
Averages of 16 spectra with N = 128

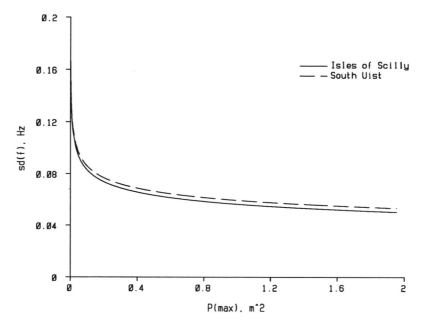

Figure 6. Comparison of Regression Fits

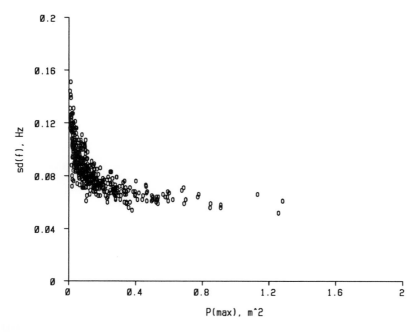

Figure 7. Isles of Scilly Data: Averages of 32 spectra with N = 128

Application of a Sea Surface Estimator in Predictive Ship Control

M.M.A. Pourzanjani (*), M.R. Belmont (**),
E.L. Morris (**), H.K. Zienkiewicz (**)
*(*) Maritime Division, Southampton Institute,
Warsash Campus, Warsash, Southampton
SO3 9ZL, UK*
*(**) School of Engineering, University of Exeter,
Exeter EX4 4QF, UK*

ABSTRACT

The state of the art in controlling the behaviour of a ship in a seaway, appears to be in using the current state of a vessel and using one of the well established control strategies (this could be based on Fuzzy logic, Neural network, Sliding Mode etc.) to get optimum settings for control surfaces.

This approach, however, indicates that the vessel has been disturbed from the desired set position and requires some action in order to correct it. The way forward in this field is to aim for achieving the ability to predict the ship response in advance (i.e. before the error occurs) and set the control surfaces at some estimated settings to counteract the effect of disturbance before it has happened. Hence the controller is constantly working against the future events rather than trying to counteract what has already happened.

This paper reviews the exiting techniques in ship motion control looking at their shortcomings. It is also concerned with a qualitative description of the requirements of a predictive ship motion control system and strategy if it was to be adopted, and also how a sea surface estimator can be used in achieving this goal.

INTRODUCTION

Autopilots have been in service on board merchant ships for decades. The

main purpose for these since they were invented was to maintain a steady
heading (see Sperry[12]), or course keeping in order to reduce the manning
requirements of merchant ships. This is obviously an important area and
requires a great deal of attention, since on long crossings, ships tend to
spend most of their time on straight line headings. More recently some
interest has also been shown in the controllers ability to cope with
course changing situations, although this is not considered as important
as course keeping.

The traditional approach has been to use a three term controller (i.e.
proportional, integral and derivative). Although a great deal of research
has been going on in this area to develop more efficient autopilots, the
reality is that most autopilots being installed on board merchant ships are
still based on this traditional (PID) approach. The major difficulty in this
approach is that the control action is based on the error caused as a result
of a disturbance. This would mean the control action is being enforced
after the effect. Hence in the presence of disturbances the system would
tend to oscillate as the control action takes its effect.

Many studies have been conducted in this area (for a comprehensive
bibliography see Vahedipour[13]), however, all of these studies are based
on the current state of the vessel and deviation from a desired heading.
The way forward in this field and to produce a more satisfactory motion
control system for ships seems to be in employment of predictive ship
control. The controller will still be based on the three term PID controller
but now linked with an intelligent or semi-intelligent system, with the
difference that the action taken by the controller will be in advance of
the disturbance, hence reducing the required control action and deviation
from the desired settings.

Control of other modes of motion (e.g. Roll and Pitch) have also
received some attention although the activities in these areas has been
much less than the attention given to yaw control. Both passive and active
devices have been examined with again a variety of control strategies. Roll
control is of interest to passenger and military craft, and is usually achieved
by a pair of fins to the astern of amidships. Rudder roll stabilisation is
also an area which has received some attention, with the Dutch Navy
implementing it on a full size vessel and a Fuzzy Logic approach currently
being the subject of research at the Royal Naval Engineering College in
Manadon. A combined Roll and Pitch control system using two fins at
the bow and two fins towards stern has also been examined by Burns[4].
This study, however, gives no consideration to the size of forces involved,
in particular in pitch, requiring very large control surfaces to achieve the
combined pitch and roll control. These studies again suffer from the same
problem that they are based only on the current state and the induced
error.

The Predictive control can make significant improvements in these areas similar to course keeping control as discussed earlier.

TRADITIONAL APPROACH TO SHIP MOTION CONTROL

A rather simplistic diagram of the elements involved in directional ship control as a whole system is shown in figure 1.

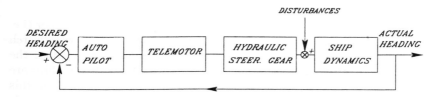

Figure 1. Whole ship block diagram

The origins of Ship Motion Control as recorded in the open literature goes back to the work carried out by Sperry[12], where the main objective was to produce a system which can satisfactorily control the straight ahead motion of a ship in a sea-way.

The next excitement in this area was the work carried out by Nomoto et al[10] where a three degrees of freedom equation of motion for the ship dynamics was rearranged into two and then one equation. The three equations for a three degrees of freedom in the horizontal plane (surge, sway, and yaw only) assuming a body fixed coordinate system are:

$$\sum X = m\dot{u} - mvr - mx_g r^2$$
$$\sum Y = m\dot{v} + mur + mx_g \dot{r}$$
$$\sum N = I\dot{r} + mx_g \dot{v} + mx_g ur \qquad (1)$$

Assuming a constant forward speed and only small deviations from a set heading, and also taking into account the symmetry of the vessel about various planes, the above equations are then reduced to a single equation describing the dynamics of the vessel.

$$T_1 T_2 \ddot{r} + (T_1 + T_2)\dot{r} + r = K(\delta + T_3 \dot{\delta}) \qquad (2)$$

The above second order differential equation relates the rate of change of heading ($\dot{r}$) with the rudder setting (δ). The coefficients T_1, T_2, and T_3 relate to the rate of change of heading and the rudder angle. As it stands it ignores the most important non-linear and cross coupling effects which exists in ship dynamic behaviour between different modes of motion (see Lloyd[8]). The main advantage of this model being the very few parameters required for system developments. However work by many researchers has shown that similar values for these coefficients are identified for vessels with totally different dynamic characteristics. Equation 2 can be further simplified to a first order equation but to include some of the non-linearities absent in equation 2, as discussed by Beck[1]

$$T\dot{r} + K(\alpha + \beta r^2)r = K\delta \qquad (3)$$

where the inherent non-linearities are lumped together and included in the term β. It should be noted that, strictly speaking, the above equations only apply to calm deep water conditions for a directionally stable vessel for small deviations of heading. In most autopilot studies white noise has been used to simulate the effect of external disturbances, this however does not take into account the cross coupling and interaction between various modes of motion. These inefficiencies have been highlighted by Katebi and Grimble[6], and Clark[5], suggesting that a more realistic mathematical model for ship manœuvring should be used.

A study was carried out at Exeter University by Vahedipour[13] to assess the suitability of this type of mathematical modelling and approach for autopilot design. The study included a comparison between the linearised model and a more realistic and more detailed model of the same ship. This report also concluded that more comprehensive mathematical models should be used in autopilot design.

The autopilot algorithm would have three terms with three coefficients relating to the three terms i.e. proportional, integral and derivative terms. Evaluation of these coefficients are usually based on some cost function relating to the requirements of the study (e.g. minimum overshoot, fast settling time etc.).

PREDICTIVE CONTROL

Predictive control has been used in other industrial applications in particular in systems with large time delays (e.g. Pearce et al[11]). This control strategy is usually linked with an expert system or rule based system that the controller can make predictive control decisions based on the simulation results of the system.

Predictive Ship Control

One of the shortcomings in the traditional approach to autopilot design is that the nature of the disturbance is always assumed to be random and hence unpredictable. The traditional approach mentioned here encompasses all control strategies employed in ship control to date, including Fuzzy logic, Pseudo Derivative Feedback, Sliding mode, Linear Quadratic Gaussian controller (LQG), Neural Net, H^∞, etc. Most of these methods are fairly complex in their nature and in many respects, are still under development. Nevertheless, the information provided to the controller is always based on the current state of the vessel and related to the error caused by the disturbance, or the error induced by the dynamics of the vessel. Most of these studies have indicated only little improvement on a simple PID controller is gained.

One other problem is that the mathematical model used to describe the dynamics of the vessel is a very simplistic and in most cases unrealistic because of the fact that the simplified mathematical model only relates the rudder action with the change of heading and totally ignores the course error caused due to other modes of motion e.g., heave and pitch.

The concept of 'Predictive Ship Control' is based on the fact that the dynamics of the ship and the disturbances present at the time can be predicted and modelled realistically in advance of the event. This will then provide the required information to an intelligent controller to decide on the corrective action in advance of the event. Hence the ship and the control systems are constantly adjusting themselves to accommodate the future events. Figure 2 shows the block diagram of the elements involved in a predictive ship controller when used for directional control. It is also claimed by some researchers that it is possible to predict the ship response for short periods of time from the time history of the ship motion. This however assumes a periodic sea state which is clearly not the case for sea waves.

The main areas of applications for a sea surface estimator in ship dynamics control are:

* Improved heading control as mentioned above which is applicable almost to all ships.

* Station keeping for various marine activities such as loading and discharging of heavy lifts in the open sea environment such as those experienced by offshore supply vessels in the North sea.

* Increasing the operational window for smaller vessels and passenger craft. Advantages are both economical and in terms of passenger comfort.

* Towing situations.

★ Military application.

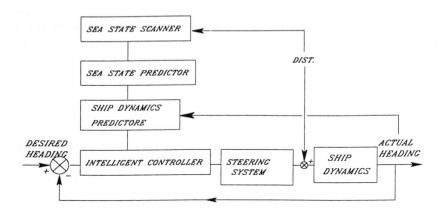

Figure 2. Block diagram of Predictive Ship Control

Sea State Scanner

This is a general purpose device which can be installed on a fixed or floating
platform. The device is directionally set and points to the direction of
interest and not necessarily straight ahead. It scans at a very high rate a
selected area of the sea (say about $500m \times 500m$), and returns values of
interest (wave height, wave slope etc.) regarding the patch of the sea under
consideration. A feasibility study of the hardware requirements have
been carried out and is included in the end of project report as reported
by Belmont et al[2], also indicating the difficulties in development and operation
of such a device.

Sea Surface Estimator

The major forces involved in disturbing a vessel from a straight line course
are those induced from sea and swell. The Exeter Marine Dynamics Group
have, for some years, been involved with research projects funded by Marine Technology Directorate and MOD to develop a system in order to
predict the sea conditions in a deterministic manner as reported in final project report, Belmont et al[2]. This study included two different
approaches to this problem and comparison with real sea data collected in
deep water for two different locations around the United Kingdom. The results from this study indicates that sea waves, although random by nature
(strictly speaking this is not correct since given enough computing power
and knowledge of all the required parameters the equations governing the
evolution of sea waves can be solved), can be deterministically predicted

over a short period of time as discussed by Morris et al[9] and Belmont et al[3].

The concept is based on a software element which continuously receives directional information of sea surface parameters, analysing the provided picture and predicting the evolution of the sea state for a short period of time (seconds).

Ship Dynamics Predictor

To ensure that the system developed here covers all possible applications, a six degrees of freedom mathematical model of ship dynamics is required. The work in this area is well under way following the methods suggested by Lloyd[8] and Lewis[7]. The mathematical model is based on the two dimensional strip theory, although some of the coefficients are developed using the three dimensional theory. An on-line solution of the three dimensional equations of motion is unsuitable due to the required time.

As it is expected that the system developed will be used on craft of different sizes, it is important to ensure suitability for use for small craft as well as large ships. One important application is the offshore supply vessels working in the North Sea, which due to their size are very responsive to environmental disturbances. The prediction time is a crucial issue particularly when dealing with more sluggish vessels which would take some time to respond to a rudder action.

Referring to figure 2, the ship dynamic predictor gets information regarding the disturbance about to happen in the near future from the sea state predictor, and the actual state of the vessel is also fed back to this module. The motion of the vessel is then simulated in advance with this information being fed into the intelligent controller.

One of the requirements is that the initial conditions have to be worked out from the current state of the vessel and after a short transient the system will stabilise returning predictions of ship's motion based on the predictions of the sea state.

Intelligent Controller

The intelligent controller comprises computing facilities (hardware and software) capable of making decisions based on the information provided from the ship dynamics predictor the desired state of the vessel and actual state of the vessel. A variational optimisation technique as set out below will be used in this module for predictive ship control.

The core problem of predictive ship control is to close the time dependence of a set of controller functions over an interval $t_1 \rightarrow t_2$ which optimises some cost function. Such a cost is most likely to be an averaged measure of the departure of the ships dynamical variables from some ideal form. A simple example might be a weighted combination of the squared departure of the six ship motions $\Phi_i(t)$ from the ideal values $\Phi_{i,0}(t)$:

$$C = \int_{t_1}^{t_2} \left(W_1 \left[\Phi_1(t) - \Phi_{1,0}(t) \right]^2 \ldots\ldots W_6 \left[\Phi_6(t) - \Phi_{6,0}(t) \right]^2 \right) dt \qquad (4)$$

Here C is the overall cost function, the integration provides the averaging and the $W_1, \ldots, W_6$ are weight denoting the relative importance of the different motion variables. The $W's$ may also be functions of time or even the ships motion themselves indicating for example that a given variable only becomes important if it exceeds given ranges.

The general form of the cost function should allow for all types of choices, not merely the squared distance measure mentioned above. It should also explicitly denote the role of the ship controller functions $r_1(t), \ldots\ldots, r_n(t)$ which physically would correspond to the states of rudders, fins, thrusters etc. Thus a general cost function will be written as:

$$C = \int_{t_1}^{t_2} f \left\{ \Phi_1(t)\ldots\ldots\Phi_6(t), \Phi_{1,0}(t)\ldots\ldots\Phi_{6,0}(t), r_1(t)\ldots\ldots\ldots r_n(t), t \right\} dt \qquad (5)$$

Now in the absence of any further constraints the procedure would be to determine the n functions $r_1(t), \ldots\ldots, r_n(t)$ which minimise C using the associated set of Euler Lagrange equations. This problem is highly constrained because the $\Phi_1(t)\ldots\ldots\Phi_6(t)$ must satisfy the dynamical equations of motion.

The ship motion equations will be written as:

$$L_i \left(\Phi(t)\ldots\ldots\Phi_6(t), w(t), r_1(t)\ldots\ldots r_n(t), t \right) = 0 \qquad (6)$$

There are six of these equations which in general are non-linear integro-differential equations. As usual explicit spatial coordinates are not present in equation (6).

The constrain system defined by (6) is incorporated into the variational scheme by first defining an extended form F of the integrand of f of the cost cost function in (5) i.e.

$$F = f + \sum_{i=1}^{6} v_i(t) Li \tag{7}$$

which by the nature of the constraint forms of (6) is still numerically equivalent to f but allows the introduction of six arbitrary functions $v_i(t)$.

It is then possible to show that the choice of $r_1(t)........r_n(t)$ which minimises the cost function (5) also satisfies the following system of n equations:

$$\frac{\partial F}{\partial r_i(t)} - \frac{d}{dt}\left(\frac{\partial F}{\partial \dot{r}_i(t)}\right) = 0 \tag{8}$$

where $\dot{r}_i(t)$ denotes $\frac{d}{dt} r_i(t)$

The system of n equations in (8) taken with the six constraint equations allow the $n + 6$ unknown functions $r_1(t)......r_n(t), v_1(t)......v_6(t)$ to be determined.

Equation (8) is a set of Euler Lagrange equations and the type of problem is termed an Isoperimetric problem. There is much literature on the algorithmic approach to determining the $r_i(t), v_i(t)$ set and with the present day computing potential of even modest machines it should be entirely realistic to employ this method for predictive ship control.

FINAL REMARKS

The basic elements involved in predictive ship control have been discussed in a qualitative manner with some notes on a variational optimiser to be used in the intelligent controller. The next phase of this project involves further development of the intelligent module followed by a series of computer simulation, model scale and then full scale implementation of a prototype.

ACKNOWLEDGEMENTS

This work has been conducted under a research grant awarded by the Marine Technology Directorate and the Ministry of Defence.

REFERENCES

1- Beck M I, "*Some Aspects of the Stability of Automatic Course Control of Ships*", Journal of Mechanical Engineering Science, Vol 14, No 7, Special supplement, 1972.

2- Belmont M R, Zienkiewicz H K, Morris E L, Pourzanjani M M, and Flower J O, "*Report on SERC Contract No GR/F 32165 (SHP 54)*', 1991.

3- Belmont M R, Zienkiewicz H K, Morris E L, Pourzanjani M M, Flower J O, "*The Correlation between Width and Maximum Power for North Atlantic Wave Spectra*", Proceedings of the 2nd MCMC conference, Southampton, July 1992.

4- Burns R S, "*A new Approach to Optimising Fuel Economy for Ships in a Seaway*", Proceedings of the first international conference on modelling and control of marine craft, Exeter, 1990.

5- Clark D., "*Do Autopilots Save Money*", Trans IMarE, Vol 94, 1982.

6- Katebi M R, and Grimble M J, "*LQG Control Design for Ship Autopilots*", To be published.

7- Lewis E V (Editor), "*Principals of Naval Architecture*", SNAME publication, 1989.

8- Lloyd A R J M, "*Seakeeping, Ship Behaviour in Rough Weather*", Ellis Horwood Series in Marine Technology, 1989.

9- Morris E L, Zienkiewicz H K, Pourzanjani M M, Flower J O, "*Techniques for Sea State Predictions*", Proceedings of the 2nd MCMC conference, Southampton, July 1992.

10- Nomoto K., Taguchi T., Honda K., and Hirano S., "*On the Steering Qualities of Ships*", International Shipbuilding Progress, Vol 4, No 35, 1957.

11- Pearce, D F, Self A W, Tong K C., "*Simulation of Hardboard Mill Expert Control*", Proceedings of the 1990 UKSC Conference on Computer Simulation, Brighton, United Kingdom, 1990.

12- Sperry, E., "*Automatic Steering*", Transactions of SNAME, 1922.

13- Vahedipour A, '*A Pseudo Derivative Feedback Controller for Autopilot Design*', PhD Thesis, School of Engineering, University of Exeter, 1991.

Aspects of Design and Evaluation of Control Systems for SWATH Ships

J.C. Byrne, J. Howell, A.C. Fairlie-Clarke,
R.C. McGregor
*Marine Technology Centre, University of Glasgow,
Glasgow, UK*

ABSTRACT

A stabilization system has been fitted to a 4 tonne SWATH vessel to evaluate various forms of motion controller. Motion control, where the objective is to minimise heave, pitch and roll, has been examined. All controllers considered have been based on a control strategy which requires the same pre-compensator to square the system matrix. This pre-compensator calculates those angles of attack which would achieve the desired heave, pitch and roll stabilising forces or moments whilst minimising fin movement. The various control algorithms are outlined and results obtained during calm and open water trials are given.

INTRODUCTION

The SWATH concept has been explored in some depth over the past 20 years [1-3] with a number of researchers focusing on motion control [4-6]. A number of vessels have been built, particularly in the USA and Japan but it is only recently [7,8] that practical field implementations have been made available to the UK research community. One such implementation is that of a 4 tonne vessel, named SAMHACH which has been built by Yarrows Shipbuilders Ltd as a tenth scale model of a 2400 tonne naval design. The authors have previously described [7] the stabilization system that they have designed, built and fitted to SAMHACH with the purpose of evaluating various forms of motion controller. After a brief resume of SWATH motion control, this paper describes the instrumentation and computer system developed to implement the various motion controllers, outlines the control algorithms considered and reports on the results obtained during calm and open water trials.

To date, control studies have concentrated on that mode of motion control, known as platforming, where the objective is to minimise heave, pitch and roll. All controllers have made use of the same pre-compensator (known as the fin allocation algorithm) to square the system matrix. This pre-compensator is central to the control strategy and is therefore described in detail.

SWATH SHIP MOTION CONTROL

The vertical motion control requirement of SWATH vessels can be summarised as

1)   to ensure pitch stability under all operating conditions,
2)   to control pitch and heave so as to reduce wave slamming forces and propeller emergence in bad weather,
3)   to control trim so as to optimise propulsive efficiency,
4)   to reduce the magnitude of roll, pitch and heave motions.

These motion requirements must be met while at the same time satisfying two major constraints.

1)   Fault modes of the motion control system must not compromise the safety of the vessel and should have a minimum impact on ship operation.
2)   Life cycle cost of the control must be minimised.

The small waterplane area and submerged hull configuration, which result in the SWATHs small induced dynamic motions, produce other important dynamic characteristics resulting in particular control requirements.

This leads to the following control rationale.

Pitch Stability: A destabilising bow down pitch moment, which varies with ship speed, is generated by hydrodyanmic forces on the pontoons and this is counteracted by the restoring moment due to the waterplane area. The restoring moment does not increase with ship speed and a pitch instability can therefore occur at higher speeds with the basic SWATH configuration. This must be corrected in order for the vessel to attain design speeds above the critical value. To do this an additional pitch restoring moment can be introduced by a pair of horizontal fins at the aft end of the pontoons.

Pitch Control: In severe seas, a SWATH vessel may encounter waves of such a height that the deck structure may slam into the oncoming wave crests. Fins can be fitted to the forward end of the pontoons that will control the attitude of the vessel so as to follow (contour) the profile of the large waves. To generate a large lift force with a small area the whole fin should tilt dynamically.

Motion Reduction: The requirements stated so far result in a four rotatable fin system with two forward and two aft. By varying the amount of lift generated by each fin it is possible to improve the already excellent seakeeping characteristics by providing active motion reduction in three degrees of freedom, vis heave, pitch and roll. Two operating regions exist: platforming where minimum heave, pitch and roll are sought and contouring to avoid wet deck impacts in the higher waves. This paper reports work focused on platforming and a follow on programme has been proposed to examine contouring.

SAMHACH IMPLEMENTATION

One of our main objectives has been to produce a flexible research facility where

1.   fins of alternative design can be readily fitted,
2.   alternative control strategies can be implemented, quickly,
3.   the effect of placing various sensors at alternative locations on SAMHACH can be easily investigated,
4.   alternative sensors can be easily tested,
5.   trials data can be readily collected and analysed.

The stabilisation system installed on SAMHACH is outlined in Figure 1 and described more fully in ref [7]. It consists of four projecting fins situated inboard fore and aft on each pontoon. The fins can be moved within a limited arc to produce an angle of incidence to the flow of water which in turn produces a vertical lift force. The angle of attack of each fin is controlled through a shaft connected to electric motors inside the ship by a control unit which senses the motions of the vessel (pitch, heave and roll) and drives the motors to produce a stabilising response.

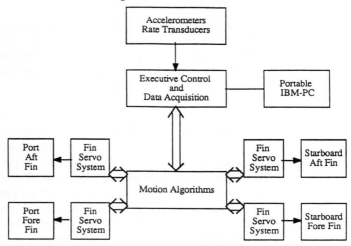

Figure 1: SAMHACH Stabilisation System

Central to this system is the control system hardware which has been chosen to meet both flexibility and cost requirements. It is based on 2 DEC T11 microprocessors, 4 LM628 motor control integrated circuits and four analogue controllers. The overall system operates under SWEPSPEED, again chosen because of its cost, flexibility and user friendly interface. The desired angle of attack of each fin is updated, at between 0.1 and 0.2 second intervals, on the basis of a user programmable control algorithm which aggregates information from various sensors (e.g. accelerometers and rate gyros). The actual angle of attack of each fin is then set by counting the number or part of revolutions of the corresponding motor using an incremental encoder and comparing this count with a setpoint value. This error forms a velocity demand which is input to the local analogue velocity controller for each motor.

MOTION CONTROL STRATEGY

The control problem is therefore to design an algorithm which can translate measurements of the ships motion into fin angle demands such that the pitch, heave and roll motions are minimised. The design of such an algorithm is complicated by the inherent coupling between vessel motions and by the fact that the stabilisation system must operate over a range of ship speeds in an environment where both the ship's dynamics and external disturbances vary with ship speed. The stabiliser fins are by design forms of hydrodynamic foils and as such depend for their effective control force upon the relative motion of the water over their surface. As the ship speed increases the relationship which describes their effect on the relevant ship motions changes. The external disturbances as well as being dependent upon the ship speed are also functions of the environmental state and the wave encounter angle. The combined effect of these stochastic phenomena influence the frequency dependent shape of the disturbance spectra. Thus the control system must be able to adapt to the ever changing environment.

There are three outputs to be controlled: pitch, heave and roll, and four inputs: the angle of attack of each of the four stabiliser fins. Therefore the system will be underdefined unless an actuator fails. Each fin can produce a lift force, dependent on its angle of attack, which can be resolved to give an effective heave stabilising moment, a pitch stabilising moment and a roll stabilising moment. The system can therefore be simplified by introducing a pre-compensator (Figure 2) which calculates those angles of attack which would achieve the desired heave stabilising force, the desired pitch stabilising moment and the desired roll stabilising moment whilst minimising fin movement. This will result in the system to be controlled having three outputs and three inputs, a so-called 'square system' thus enabling conventional multivariable frequency domain techniques to be applied.

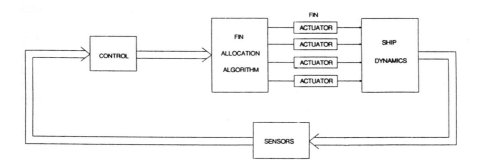

Figure 2: Control Strategy

There are then 2 design issues: design of the pre-compensator (known as the fin allocation algorithm) and design of the 3*3 compensator.

FIN ALLOCATION ALGORITHM

From slender wing theory the lift force produced by an aerofoil passing through a fluid is given by:

$$L = \tfrac{1}{2}\rho \, A \, U^2 \, C_{L\alpha} \, r \, \alpha$$

where ρ is the density of the fluid
A is the area of the aerofoil
U is the speed of the fluid over the aerofoil
$C_{L\alpha}$ is the lift coefficient of the aerofoil per unit angle of incidence
r is a correction coefficient to allow for fixed portions of the fins
and α is the angle of attack (radians)

It can be observed that if the lift coefficient is assumed to be a constant for different fin angle deflections then at a fixed speed the lift force produced is directly proportional to the angle of attack, α. It can also be observed that the lift force is proportional to the square of the speed. This observation demonstrates the need for a gain scheduling scheme to keep the overall system gain constant at all ship speeds.

The pitch moment produced by this force is

$$M = Lx$$

where x is the distance from the $\frac{1}{4}$ chord point of the fin to the vessel's L.C.G. and, by convention, is +ve forward.

The roll moment produced by this force is given by

$$K = Ly$$

where y is the distance between midspan of the fin and the centreline of the vessel and, by convention, y is +ve to starboard.

Assigning an x and y co-ordinate to each fin: since the fins are normally situated symmetrically along the hull, the forward fins have an identical x co-ordinate, which can be denoted by x_{for}. Similarly the aft fins have a similar x co-ordinate, which can be denoted by x_{aft}. The forward fins also have a similar y co-ordinate although the sign is opposite and similarly for the aft fins.

If it is further assumed that the forward fins are identical and that the aft fins are identical, the lift force produced by a forward fin can be denoted by

$$Z_1 = L_{for}\, \alpha_1$$
and
$$Z_2 = L_{for}\, \alpha_2$$

and the lift force produced by the aft fins can be denoted by

$$Z_3 = L_{aft}\, \alpha_3$$
$$Z_4 = L_{aft}\, \alpha_4$$

The total heave force produced is then the sum of the heave force generated by each fin

$$Z_T = L_{for}\, \alpha_1 + L_{for}\, \alpha_2 + L_{aft}\, \alpha_3 + L_{aft}\, \alpha_4$$

The total pitch moment is given by

$$M_T = L_{for}\, x_{for}\, \alpha_1 + L_{for}\, x_{for}\, \alpha_2 - L_{aft}\, x_{aft}\, \alpha_3 - L_{aft}\, x_{aft}\, \alpha_4$$

and the roll moment is given by

$$K_T = -L_{for}\, y_{for}\, \alpha_1 + L_{for}\, y_{for}\, \alpha_2 - L_{aft}\, y_{aft}\, \alpha_3 + L_{aft}\, y_{aft}\, \alpha_4$$

The fin allocation problem is therefore one of computing fin angle demands $\alpha_1, \alpha_2, \alpha_3$, and α_4 to obtain the desired heave force, Z_T, desired pitch moment M_T and desired roll moment K_T. There are 3 equations with 4 unknowns. Since these demands must be met whilst minimising the fin activity it seems natural to employ static optimization techniques to compute the angles.

Consider the following cost function

$$J = \frac{\alpha_1^2}{Q_1} + \frac{\alpha_2^2}{Q_2} + \frac{\alpha_3^2}{Q_3} + \frac{\alpha_4^2}{Q_4}$$

where Q_1, Q_2, Q_3 and Q_4 are scalar weighting terms.

and form the Lagrangian

$$L = \frac{\alpha_1^2}{Q_1} + \frac{\alpha_2^2}{Q_2} + \frac{\alpha_3^2}{Q_3} + \frac{\alpha_4^2}{Q_4}$$

$$+ \lambda(L_{for}\,(\alpha_1 + \alpha_2) + L_{aft}\,(\alpha_3 + \alpha_4) - Z_T)$$

$$+ \beta\,(L_{for}\,x_{for}\,(\alpha_1 + \alpha_2) - L_{aft}\,x_{aft}\,(\alpha_3 + \alpha_4) - M_T)$$

$$+ \gamma\,(\,L_{for}\,y_{for}\,(\alpha_2 - \alpha_1) + L_{aft}\,y_{aft}\,(\alpha_4 - \alpha_3) - K_T)$$

The necessary conditions for the existence of a local optimum are

$$\frac{\partial L}{\partial \alpha_1} = \frac{2\alpha_1}{Q_1} + \lambda L_{for} + \beta L_{for}\,x_{for} - \gamma\,L_{for}\,y_{for} = 0$$

$$\frac{\partial L}{\partial \alpha_2} = \frac{2\alpha_2}{Q_2} + \lambda L_{for} + \beta L_{for}\,x_{for} + \gamma\,L_{for}\,y_{for} = 0$$

$$\frac{\partial L}{\partial \alpha_3} = \frac{2\alpha_3}{Q_3} + \lambda L_{aft} - \beta L_{aft}\,x_{aft} - \gamma\,L_{aft}\,y_{aft} = 0$$

$$\frac{\partial L}{\partial \alpha_4} = \frac{2\alpha_4}{Q_4} + \lambda L_{aft} - \beta L_{aft}\,x_{aft} + \gamma\,L_{aft}\,y_{aft} = 0$$

If $Q_1 = Q_2 = Q_3 = Q_4 = 1$, the above leads to

$$L_{for}\,\alpha_1 = \tfrac{1}{2}\left\{\left(\frac{x_{aft}}{x_{for} + x_{aft}}\right)Z_T + \frac{1}{(x_{for} + x_{aft})}\,M_T + \left(\frac{L^2_{for}\,y^2_{for}}{S_s}\right)\frac{1}{y_{for}}\,K_T\right\}$$

$$L_{for}\,\alpha_2 = \tfrac{1}{2}\left\{\left(\frac{x_{aft}}{x_{for} + x_{aft}}\right)Z_T + \frac{1}{(x_{for} + x_{aft})}\,M_T - \left(\frac{L^2_{for}\,y^2_{for}}{S_s}\right)\frac{1}{y_{for}}\,K_T\right\}$$

$$L_{aft}\,\alpha_3 = \tfrac{1}{2}\left\{\left(\frac{x_{for}}{x_{for} + x_{aft}}\right)Z_T - \frac{1}{(x_{for} + x_{aft})}\,M_T + \left(\frac{L^2_{aft}\,y^2_{aft}}{S_s}\right)\frac{1}{y_{aft}}\,K_T\right\}$$

$$L_{aft}\, \alpha_4 = \tfrac{1}{2}\left\{\left(\frac{x_{for}}{x_{for} + x_{aft}}\right)Z_T - \frac{1}{(x_{for} + x_{aft})} M_T - \left(\frac{L^2_{aft}\, y^2_{aft}}{S_5}\right)\frac{1}{y_{aft}} K_T\right\}$$

where $S_5 = -L^2_{for}\, y^2_{for} - L^2_{aft}\, y^2_{aft}$

This result has a number of important features. The coefficients on the right hand sides are all speed independent because identical speed components will exist on both the numerator and denominator of the K_T coefficients and will therefore cancel. Thus these coefficients need only be established once. Only 3 parameters, x_{aft}, L_{for} and L_{aft} need be identified because $(x_{for} + x_{aft})$, y_{for} and y_{aft} can be obtained from the geometry of the ship. The terms on the left hand sides represent the actual lift required of each fin; the actual angles of attack are therefore 'scaled' by a variable which is proportional to speed squared.

Although the minimisation approach attempts to avoid saturation implicitly, there is no explicit guarantee that simultaneous demands for a roll stabilising moment, heave stabilising force and pitch stabilising moment will not result in a solution (i.e. set of fin angles) that are outside the operating range of the fins. The most straightforward approach to ameliorating this possibility appears to be to weigh, preferentially, the 3 demands. That is, to provide a facility which reduces the signals input to the pre-compensator. This would be equivalent to reducing the controller gains if 3 separate roll, pitch and heave controllers were to be installed.

COMPENSATOR DESIGN

The approach to designing a suitable control algorithm largely depends on the relative significance of the various off-diagonal terms of the transfer function matrix which relates

$$\begin{bmatrix} \text{demanded heave stabilising force} \\ \text{demanded pitch stabilising force} \\ \text{demanded roll stabilising force} \end{bmatrix}$$

to a vector which describes the relevant motions of a ship

$$\text{ie} \quad \begin{bmatrix} \text{heave} \\ \text{pitch} \\ \text{roll} \end{bmatrix} .$$

Considerable uncertainty surrounds these elements so the approach has been to cater for all possibilities. In addition, factors like the need to suppress dc gain (trim being handled seperately), the need to compensate for gyro drift, noise filtering and fin saturation all affect performance and must therefore be taken into account. There is therefore considerable merit in drawing on the experience that exists in the design of single degree of freedom (in particular, roll) stabilisation systems [9,10].

All Off-Diagonal Terms Relatively Insignificant

In this case, all 3 loops can be designed independently enabling the application of well-established single degree of freedom techniques.

One Degree Of Freedom Not Coupled To The Other Two

From basic modelling assumptions, the roll motion is usually considered to be completely decoupled from the pitch/heave motions. Again this enables standard techniques to be applied, at least to the attenuation of roll. Persuing this possibility further.

Either Pitch-into-Heave or Heave-into-Pitch Also Insignificant It can be easily shown that, in this case, the 2 loops can be viewed as uncoupled when examining stability but coupled when considering disturbance rejection. Thus the loop with the insignificant transfer function can be designed separately whilst the design procedure for the other loop will need to account for disturbances originating from the former. Two approaches appear sensible.

Ignore the problem It is likely that the 2 resonant frequencies ω_1 and ω_2 will be so close together that the frequency response of the cross coupled disturbance should be sufficiently similar to that of the uncoupled disturbance to enable it to be easily rejected. That is, a control filter designed to attenuate the uncoupled disturbance should also be able to attenuate the coupled one.

Pseudo-diagonalization A cross-coupling term may be introduced into the controller to cancel the effect of the cross-disturbance. Thus, if the transfer function matrix, relating heave and pitch demands to their measured values, can be represented as two coupled second order systems ie

$$G(s) = \begin{bmatrix} \dfrac{\alpha_{11}\omega^2 n_1}{s^2+2\xi_1\omega n_1 s+\omega^2 n_1} & \dfrac{\alpha_{12}\,\omega^2 n_1\,\omega^2 n_2\,g_{12}(s)}{[s^2+2\xi_1\omega n_1 s+\omega^2 n_1][s^2+2\xi_2\omega n_2 s+\omega^2 n_2]} \\[4ex] \dfrac{\alpha_{21}\,\omega^2 n_1\,\omega^2 n_2\,g_{21}(s)}{[s^2+2\xi_1\omega n_1 s+\omega^2 n_1][s^2+2\xi_2\omega n_2 s+\omega^2 n_2]} & \dfrac{\alpha_{22}\omega^2 n_2}{s^2+2\xi_2\omega n_2 s+\omega^2 n_2} \end{bmatrix}$$

and heave were affecting pitch

$$k_{12} = 0$$

and $k_{21} = -\left(\dfrac{\alpha_{21}}{\alpha_{22}}\right) \cdot \dfrac{\omega n_1 s}{s^2 + 2\xi_1\omega n_1 s + \omega^2 n_1} \cdot g_{21}(s)$

would lead to a significant decoupling or diagonalization. It is unlikely that this theoretically desirable result would be attainable because of uncertainty surrounding the model. Pseudo-diagonalization where k_{21} is approximated by say,

$$k_{21} = -\left(\frac{\alpha_{21}}{\alpha_{22}}\right) \cdot \left(\frac{1}{2\xi_1}\right) \left| g_{21}(j\omega n_1) \right|$$

might be more practicable. Single degree of freedom techniques can then be applied.

<u>Both Pitch-into-Heave and Heave-into-Pitch Significant.</u> Three methods have been considered for designing control algorithms in this situation.

<u>Pseudo-diagonalization</u>. A similar approach to that above can be adopted to produce 2 non-zero terms k_{12} and k_{21}. Stability can be assessed by examining their characteristic loci.

<u>Diagonalization</u>. A number of techniques have been proposed to choose pre- and post-compensators which result in a diagonal forward path. Probably the INA method [11] is best known. They require detailed knowledge of the transfer function matrix G(s). A suitable design package (MATLAB) was available to the Project for when such a model became available.

Reverse-frame compensation. Caldeira-Saraiva and Clarke [4] have proposed this technique as being suitable for motion control of SWATHs. A reverse-frame compensator can be constructed based on the eigenframes and singular values of the transfer function matrix G(s). Again a design procedure has been developed in MATLAB which enabled us to generate such a compensator when a suitable model was obtained.

Coupled-Motions

This is simply an extension of the above.

TRIALS

Two sets of trials were performed on SAMHACH: in calm waters, up river on the Clyde and further down river in more open waters.

Calm Waters

Speed trials were first carried out to ascertain the maximum speed available. A maximum speed of about 5 knots was obtained which was well below the design speed of 8 knots and was such that only about 40% of the design fin lift could ever be generated. This was deemed to be a minimum thus restricting trials to a single speed and preventing us from confirming that the fin allocation matrix was, indeed, speed independent.

Various fin orientations were tried to trim the boat at 5 knots. Orientations of 5° down on the forward fins, 5° up on the aft fins were needed to achieve the horizontal. Various combinations of the 4 fins were then excited sinusoidally, at a relatively low frequency, to examine their static lift capabilities and to determine x_{for}. All coefficients of the fin allocation algorithm were determined from the results obtained and it was demonstrated that SAMHACH could be made to heave, pitch and roll independently.

SAMHACH was now made to heave, then pitch, then roll, sinusoidally over a discrete range of frequencies to identify the dynamics of the vessel. The gain and phase were measured at each frequency and Bode plots produced. The natural frequency and damping factor was also estimated from the decay observed once the sinusoidal excitations ceased. These values were corroborated by comparing them with the Bode plots. A damping factor of 0.23 was determined for heave, 0.4 for pitch and 0.33 for roll. Little cross-coupling was observed.

Open Waters

The only really good rough water conditions were experienced during the first day's trials when the controller was not set up. In a series of trials at various headings to the waves, SAMHACH showed exceptional seakeeping qualities. The waves were of the order of 0.8 to 1.0 metre which was about twice the design value but in spite of this SAMHACH rode them extremely well and its helmsperson was undoubtedly the most comfortable, warmest and driest person in the trials team. The SWATH motions were low (Figure 3) and deckwetness insignificant. This behaviour under the action of passive fins confirmed the large contribution to the damping that fitting the fins made.

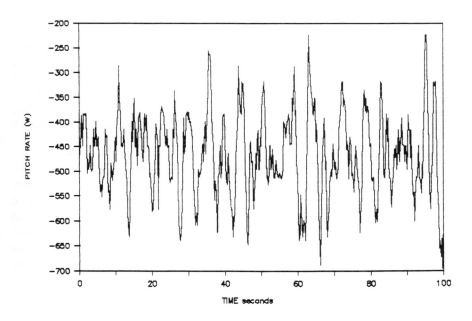

Figure 3: Typical SAMHACH pitch rates - unscaled (by 0.0125 deg/sec) and not backed-off.

For the rest of the trials period, although there were some waves, they were generally too short for the effects of the controller to be clearly seen. An enhanced roll trial was conducted (Figure 4) which shows the effectiveness of the controller in ordering the fins to resist roll.

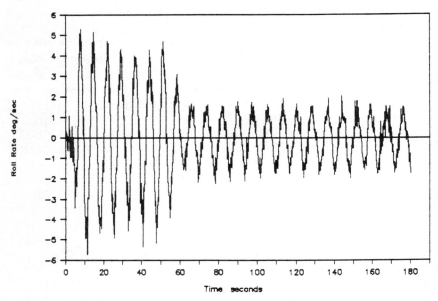

Figure 4: Improvement in roll rate obtained by switching on roll stabiliser after 60 seconds

Overall, SAMHACH was rather heavily damped by the passive fins. This along with the lack of long wave components in the seas during the trials due to the coastal location (necessary because of the demonstrator nature of SAMHACH) did not allow the controllers properties to be adequately validated. The performance achieved however did indicate that the controller and the fins did enhance the already good SWATH performance.

CONCLUSIONS

A control strategy has been proposed which is both practicable and flexible. Composed of 2 parts: a fin allocation algorithm and a compensator, an optimum design for the latter can only be obtained once cross-coupling terms in the ship dynamics have been identified. Thus a suite of options must be made available to the commissioning engineer. On the other hand based on 3 physically identifiable parameters, the fin allocation algorithm is both easy to obtain and implement.

ACKNOWLEDGEMENTS

The work described in this report is funded by the Marine Technology Directorate Ltd. together with active participation and support from Yarrows Shipbuilders Ltd. and Brown Brothers & Co. Ltd.

REFERENCES

1.   Smith, D.L., Cuthbertson, W., MacGregor, J.R. and McGregor, R.C. 'SWATH Design - A Shipbuilder's View and a Practical Example', Second International SWATH and Multihull Conference, RINA, Nov. 1988.
2.   Chun, H.H., Djatmiko, E.G. and McGregor, R.C. 'A Wide Ranging Study on the Motions of SWATH Ships With and Without Forward Speeds', Proceedings of the Ninth Int. OMAE Conference, Paper No. OMAE-90-576, Houston, Feb. 1990.
3.   Betts, C.V. 'A Review of Developments in SWATH Technology', Second Int. SWATH and Multihull Conference, RINA, Nov. 1988.
4.   Caldeira-Saraiva, F. and Clarke, D., "The Active Control of SWATH Motions", 8th Ship Control Symposium, The Hague, Oct. 1987.
5.   McGregor, R.C., Wu, J-Y and Drysdale, L.H. 'SWATH Behaviour in the Presence of Control Fins', Eighth Ship Control Symposium, The Hague, Oct. 1987.
6.   Ware, J.R. and Kim, R.R., "A Simple Method of Compensating for Control Delays in SWATH Vehicles", 8th Ship Control Systems Symposium, The Hague, October 1987.
7.   Fairlie-Clarke, A.C., Howell J., McGregor, R.C. and Smith, D. 'On The Design and Evaluation of a Control System for a SWATH Ship.' *Modelling and Control of Marine Craft* ed. Pourzanjani, M.M.A., Roberts, G.N., pp. 52-74, Elsevier Publications Ltd, Barking, Essex, 1991.
8.   Miller, A.F. and McGregor, R.C. 'Development of SWATHMAN, a Manoeuvring Simulation Tool for Small Waterplane Area Twin Hull Ships', Second Int. Conference on Manoeuvring and Control of Marine Craft, Southampton, July 1992.
9.   Lloyd, A.R.J.M. 'SEAKEEPING: Ship Behaviour in Rough Weather', Ellis Harwood Series in Marine Technology, 1989.
10.   Byrne, J.C. 'Polynomial Systems Control Design with Marine Applications', PhD Thesis, University of Strathclyde, 1989.
11..   Rosenbrock, H.H., "Computer Aided Control System Design", Academic Press, New York, 1974.

Some Hydrodynamic Aspects of Ship Manoeuvring: An Introduction to the UK Managed Research Programme

G.E. Hearn (*), D. Clarke (*),
M. Staunton-Lambert (**)

(*) Hydromechanics Research Group, Department of Marine Technology, University of Newcastle upon Tyne, UK

(**) Marine Technology Directorate (MTD) Ltd., 19 Buckingham Street, London, UK

ABSTRACT

The hydrodynamics of a manoeuvring ship are not trivial. This paper suggests that fundamental research is a necessary prerequisite to the development of design-for-manoeuvring orientated computer programs, sufficient to permit assessment of the satisfaction of any internationally adopted manoeuvrability standards. The shortcomings of simulation packages in the context of design are discussed, together with the need for experimental hydrodynamic data of quality, the limitations of current hydrodynamic predictive capability, identification of short and long term research objectives and the role of a new UK managed research programme.

INTRODUCTION

The catalyst for the managed research programme, funded by the Science and Engineering Research Council (SERC) through MTD Ltd., has been the increased level of discussion concerned with the form and detailing of possible manoeuvring standards, to be imposed on all new ship designs of length greater than 100m, or vessels carrying dangerous cargoes, irrespective of their length. Such discussions have taken place within the Sub-Committee on Ship Design and Equipment at the International Maritime Organisation (IMO). However, the final form of the 'manoeuvrability standards' adopted will represent a compromise based on some politically limited recognition of the problems of manoeuvrability, and the political acceptability of their perceived impact upon the shipbuilding and shipowning communities of the different member countries of IMO.

Having recognised this situation, it is the responsibility of the research community to look beyond the national or international politics of the acceptability of any particular set of rules and to assess the implications of the existence of a set of 'manoeuvrability standards'. The possibility of the existence of a set of manoeuvrability standards immediately prompts some simple, but searching technical questions:

- Can current design procedures encompass the technical implications of introducing manoeuvrability standards, whether they be those under discussion or others?

- Can the current state-of-knowledge supplement the current state-of-the-art regarding the introduction of manoeuvrability standards?

- If research were to be undertaken, in what areas should research effort be expended and why?

The level of appreciation or seriousness attached to such questions, outside the research community, tends to rest with the belief, or disbelief, in statements [1] such as

'There are still considerable examples of casualties such as collision, ramming and grounding caused directly and indirectly by inadequate ship manoeuvrability',

in the acceptability, or otherwise, of such observations as [1],

'Ships' fullness has been remarkably increased . . . and recent trends in ship design are together apt to make ships' directional stability poor',

and the perceived relevance, or otherwise, of such guidance [1] as,

'The measures to be used for the manoeuvrability standards have to express well the manoeuvring performance closely related to the manoeuvring safety. To get such measures, . . . examine what performance is directly related to the safety . . . employ the measures or indices which can express and rate the performance clearly'.

This paper will attempt to address a number of important issues related to the problems of accepting or rejecting statements like those quoted above. To do this a number of fundamental issues, related to the hydrodynamic aspects of the basic technical questions already put, will be discussed in a simple and non-mathematical manner. In particular, the remaining sections will consider ship manoeuvring simulation in the context of ship design, the importance of quality in the measurement of hydrodynamic derivatives, the prediction of hydrodynamic forces and moments, the short-term and long-term research objectives, and the role of the recently instigated MTD Ltd. managed programme on Manoeuvrability of Ships and Estimation Schemes (MOSES). Each topic will be discussed in a manner which recognises that the results of research should ultimately become the subject of technology transfer to the industry we strive to serve.

SHIP MANOEUVRING SIMULATION AND SHIP DESIGN

The simplest conceptual way of dealing with manoeuvring standards in the context of ship design would be to use a simulation program [2,3] to provide estimates of the behaviour of the proposed ship 'design', and then to establish the degree of satisfaction of the manoeuvrability standards. However, such an approach makes a number of very basic assumptions regarding the aspirations of the designers, the infallibility of the available simulation packages, and the 'drivers' of the simulations, namely

- the new design is relatively 'conventional', in the sense that the characteristics of the hull form proposed, and hence the hydrodynamic and control characteristics, are unquestionably in keeping with the force and moment generation process built into the simulation program.

- the simulation packages are capable of dealing with all ship types, in all required situations.

- there is sufficient understanding and know-how to modify a design which fails to meet any aspect of a set of manoeuvrability standards, through the process of design iteration.

The first point highlights the conflict of providing novel designs from the extrapolation of historical databases, when there is likely to be insufficient analysis capability to validate the earlier decisions of the conceptual design stage.

Whereas Newton's second law of motion may be readily applied to generate the equations of motion, with respect to any number of different reference systems, its application is dependent upon provision of the forces and moments responsible for the dynamic responses. For a manoeuvring ship the generation of the required hydrodynamic loads must include the effects due to the hull forces, the resistance forces, the rudder forces, the propeller forces, the wind forces and if appropriate the thruster forces. Here 'force' is used in a collective sense to mean force or moment. The expressions used to predict each of the six distinct sources of fluid loading can be based on: regressing available experimental data [4-9], fitting a simplified hydrodynamic model of the hull forces to experimentally measured forces using simple force characterisation coefficients [10], or using slender-body theory directly to predict particular linear hull force derivatives [11].

The need to address the problem of hull form modification, in the case of a ship failing to meet a particular manoeuvrability standard, is not trivial. In the context of seakeeping [12,13], the problem of modifying an initial design to provide preferred motion characteristics has been investigated using both 'design charts' and 'inverse analysis' methods. Design charts provide a graphical indication of the expected variations in seakeeping characteristics, relative to the initial design, as a result of changing different selected hull form descriptors. Thereafter, the designer may modify the initial hull form, using the design charts, so that a balance of improved seakeeping, acceptable resistance and satisfaction of IMO stability regulations is achieved. The inverse analysis technique automates the design chart approach and requires:

- Identification of the more important hull form parameters responsible for significant changes in seakeeping characteristics.

- A method of automatically modifying the hull form so that any selected parameter, of a set of relevant hull form parameters, can be changed at will, whilst all others remain fixed so that cause-and-effect understanding is achievable, irrespective of the hull type under investigation.

- A quick, robust and reliable method of generating hull force related hydrodynamic quantities in a manner which is sensitive to both minor and major changes in hullform.

- Strategies and associated search techniques for improving designer selected hydrodynamic characteristics, subject to satisfaction of other equally important hydrostatic and hydrodynamic constraints.

The last point ensures that sub-optimisation does not take place. However, the whole process assumes that the required hydrodynamic prediction tools exist in a form which allows easy application at the conceptual design stage.

Transference of these 'seakeeping-for-design' developed procedures to an equivalent 'manoeuvring-for-design' system would be limited on at least two counts:

- The existing 'fitted' equations for predicting the required manoeuvring hydrodynamic forces are usually based on global hull form parameters such as L, B, T, and C_B, and not on actual subtle changes in hull form shape introduced by varying parameters such as C_{WP}, LCB and LCF.

- The hydrodynamic predictive capability in manoeuvring is not developed to the same level of sophistication as the corresponding seakeeping related hydrodynamic analyses.

Thus verifiable, let alone contractual, satisfaction of 'manoeuvrability standards' at the design stage through the use of ship manoeuvring simulation is not a particularly soft option when considering novel designs.

DERIVATIVE MEASUREMENTS AND THE PROPOSED IMO STANDARDS

The assessment of the manoeuvring behaviour of a new ship design would be relatively straightforward, if a proven estimation method was available. However, for that to be the case, a mathematical model describing the hydrodynamic forces and moments acting on the hull would need to exist. Then, using a physical model, experiments would have to be performed to justify the mathematical model.

Now we already know that at present a satisfactory mathematical model does not exist, but suppose at some time during the MOSES research programme we are able to provide an appropriate mathematical model. We might then wish to test it against experimental evidence. A reasonable approach would be to calculate the forces and moments, or the associated force and moment derivatives, using the mathematical model which had been developed, and then to compare the predicted results with captive model tests designed to give experimental values of the same force and moment derivatives. The degree of success of the mathematical model would be judged by the level of agreement between the force and moment derivatives produced by the mathematical and physical models.

This process too has a fundamental problem, in that the physical model results could be unwittingly taken as an absolute base line for agreement. In reality, account must be taken of experimental error, which must be known for each particular set of test data.

However, the problem is even wider than that just described. Several years ago, the Manoeuvrability Committee of the International Towing Tank Conference (ITTC) carried out a collaborative study, involving model tanks throughout the world, where they all measured the force and moment derivatives for the same hull form. The model was a *Mariner* hull form and was chosen because an excellent set of full-scale trials data existed for one Mariner class ship the *U.S.S. Compass Island* [14].

The results of the model tests were reported in 1969 at the 12th ITTC [15], and were submitted by fourteen member organisations. The disappointing feature of this exercise was the spread of the measured derivative data, varying from $\pm 10\%$ to as much as $\pm 40\%$ in the case of certain derivatives. The measurements summarised in Table 1 are the extreme values produced in the ITTC collaborative exercise, together with a further set of derivatives given by Hydronautics [16] from a later independent set of experiments.

Reference [16] specifies both the linear and non-linear hydrodynamic derivatives and the equations of motion used in an associated simulation study. A computer program based on this Hydronautics form of the equations of motion and hydrodynamic forces has been written for a Sharp PC 1600 pocket computer and used to study Kempf zig-zag manoeuvres of the ITTC specified Mariner hull form. Using the Hydronautics data, the initial turning ability, as well as the first and second overshoot angles, has been calculated for three distinct cases.

In the first case the derivative data as given by Hydronautics [16] has been used. In the second and third case the value of each linear derivative has been adjusted up or down, by the same percentages as found in the spread of the ITTC data [15]. Table 2 shows the percentage variations used for cases 2 and 3, where the decision to move the value up or down was taken to produce the smallest and the largest overshoot angles respectively.

Table 1
Derivative Variations from ITTC
Collaborative Mariner Tests [15]

Derivative x 10^5	ITTC 15 knots max min	ITTC All Speeds max min	Hydronautics [16]
Y_v'	- 970 - 1513	- 720 - 1690	- 857
Y_r'	372 190	372 190	202
N_v'	- 291 - 399	- 291 - 447	- 296
N_r'	- 191 - 290	- 191 - 290	- 142
Y_δ'	294 232	399 232	198
N_δ'	- 110 - 137	- 110 - 149	- 96

Table 2
Percentage Variation of Derivatives

Derivative	Case 1	Case 2	Case 3
Y_v'	0	+ 25%	- 25%
Y_r'	0	+ 40%	- 40%
N_v'	0	- 17.5%	+ 17.5%
N_r'	0	+ 22.5%	- 22.5%
Y_δ'	0	- 12.5%	- 12.5%
N_δ'	0	- 12.5%	- 12.5%

Table 3 shows the intial turning ability and the overshoot angles for the three cases, as well as the limiting values now proposed by IMO [17]. It can be seen that for the mean values of the derivatives used in case 1, the initial turning and overshoot angles are satisfactory. In case 2 the initial turning ability is worse but still less than 2.5 ship lengths, but in case 3, the first and second overshoot angles exceed the IMO proposed values.

Table 3
10/10 degree Zig-Zag Manoeuvre

Case	Initial Turning (ship lengths)	First Overshoot (deg)	Second Overshoot (deg)
1	1.55	8.8	7.5
2	1.91	3.7	3.1
3	1.48	17.3	20.4
IMO rules	2.5	15.4*	20.0

* Determined from interpolation for $L/U = 20.8$ ($L_{pp} = 528$ ft, $U = 15$ knots) using Figure 1, Reference [17].

The case 1 predictions of Table 3 show good agreement with the full-scale results [14] and lie approximately in the mid range of the predictions based on the ITTC data [15]. The Hydronautics derivative data [16] can therefore be taken to be more likely to represent the real derivative values.

The consequence of the uncertainty in the linear derivative values, is that forecasting the ship behaviour, in order to ensure satisfaction of the proposed IMO rules, would not appear to be possible, unless the model experiments can be performed to a higher degree of accuracy. Clearly using such model test results cannot lead to any reliable verification of a mathematical model either.

The variation in the experimental values of the ITTC derivatives measurement study of Table 1 is thought to have come about in a number of ways:

- Model size selected, giving rise to viscous scale effects.

- Tank size in relation to model size, giving rise to blockage effects.

- Different experimental techniques used to measure derivatives:

  - Rotating Arm.

- Planar Motion Mechanism.

- Model tested with or without propeller.

- Different force measuring techniques.

The level of experimental uncertainty associated with the ITTC Mariner data would render verification of a mathematical model impossible. We shall revert to this point later when describing the proposed experimental research programme associated with MOSES.

HYDRODYNAMIC FORCE AND MOMENT PREDICTION

The section on Ship Manoeuvring Simulation and Ship Design concluded that simulation of the manoeuvring behaviour of novel hull forms would necessitate the development and use of appropriate hydrodynamic force prediction procedures, whereas the previous section demonstrated the necessity for ensuring that the experimental data used in any simulation (or simulation related database) should represent force or derivative measurements of quality. Experimental measurements of quality are also required to validate any theoretical prediction techniques. Therefore, prior to discussing any proposed theoretical developments it is obviously necessary to assess the current state-of-the-art in the prediction of manoeuvring hydrodynamic forces and moments. First we consider the different aspects that may be included in such analyses.

Most theoretical hydrodynamic analyses of a manoeuvring ship neglect the viscous stresses in the fluid, and the wave effects on the free-surface. However, viscosity is important in manoeuvring in the context of separated flow, and the associated 'cross-flow drag' force on the hull, to the extent that viscosity affects propeller-hull interactions [18]. The free-surface effect is considered less important for ships manoeuvring in the horizontal plane, due to the longer characteristic time-scales associated with the rigid-body motions because of the physical limitations of the control systems involved, although free-surface effects are important in other fields of ship hydrodynamics, namely wave-resistance and seakeeping. Since the inertia effects are dominated by gravity on the free-surface, an equivalent 'double-body' analysis can be formulated without any further consideration of this particular boundary. Fluid-structure interaction models in the context of a double-body formulation will recur throughout this section.

Shallow-water effects are very important for lateral ship manoeuvres, with the importance of this effect increasing with decreasing clearance beneath ship keel and sea-bed. A rational analysis of 'squat' based on slender-body theory has been shown to compare favourably with experimental measurements of trim and sinkage [19]. However, increases in ship size have now made some waterways, once considered unbounded, comparatively shallow and/or narrow waterways. Whereas the 'method of images' can be used to determine the hydrodynamic forces and moments if the seabed is flat and horizontal, the 'grounding effect method' is more realistic for irregular bottom shapes. Three-dimensional effects are important in shallow water as there is a tendency for the fluid to flow around the body ends, rather than under the body. Recently a 3D boundary element method was used to investigate the shallow-water lifting potential about a three-dimensional ship [20]. A separated vortex sheet was assumed to be shed from the bilge keel and both the image and the grounding effect based fluid-structure interaction analyses were considered.

Restricted-water effects are important when navigating in a canal or channel, and among islands or similar obstructions [21]. The simplest theoretical problem is that corresponding to steady-motion parallel to a vertical canal bank or wall. An analogy also exists between this situation and the problem of ship-to-ship interactions. Two-dimensional and three-dimensional studies of specific 'added mass' coefficients in restricted water have been undertaken using the finite-element approach [22,23]. Comparison of alternative three-dimensional numerical methods for specific acceleration derivatives [24] demonstrate consistency of prediction. Experimental studies in the case of a vertical channel bank tend to show a constant dependance between sway force and yaw moment with Froude number. For sloping and submerged banks the relationship is less straightforward [25].

For deep open water the classical approach to the derivation of the hydrodynamic derivatives of a manoeuvring ship was provided by Lamb [26]. In particular, using a Kirchoff velocity potential expansion and Lagrange's equations explicit expressions for the associated hydrodynamic forces and moments may be determined as linear functions of acceleration and quadratic functions of velocity. The coefficients of acceleration and velocity dependent terms can be described in terms of sectional 'added-mass' coefficients. The expressions for the moment related derivatives include the effects known as Munk moments [27]. This approach coupled with the assumptions of slender-body theory and 'low-frequency', means that the derived integral expressions over the wetted-surface of the vessel can be reduced to longitudinal integrals of different functions of sectional added mass coefficients, which may be evaluated using the 'double-body' approach.

The earlier identified restricted analysis techniques [22-24], only provide those 'added mass' terms purely dependent upon wetted-surface integrals, that is the acceleration added mass terms associated with pure surge, sway and yaw. The other velocity dependent terms involve explicit definition of the sectional added mass at the stern, because 'lifting' effects must be accounted for, in even the simplest relevant model [18]. The nature of the ship's 'trailing edge' is therefore of paramount importance. If the rudder and deadwood are regarded as an abrupt vertical trailing edge, of semi-span equal to the draught, and the ship hull is assumed to be an elongated slender body, expressions can be derived for the sway force and moment [27]. That is, the steady movement of the ship through the fluid at a small angle of attack, the 'drift angle', is modelled by a suitable inviscid model, irrotational except for a thin sheet of shed vorticity trailing downstream from the stern. However, this is not the case for modern pram stern hull types, where the manner in which the vorticity is shed from the hull is not at all clear.

Comparison of slender-body theory predicted and rotating arm measured sectional forces indicate an incomplete model within the existing hydrodynamic theory. The measured and predicted forces compare well over the forward part of the hull, but they progressively diverge over the after part of the hull. The presence and strength of vortices is thought to be an important omission from current prediction capability. Furthermore the zero frequency limits of pure surge, sway and yaw added mass coefficients derived from 2D or 3D seakeeping analyses represents an incomplete prediction tool. Whereas global measurements of hydrodynamic forces and moments are more generally available, studies using sectional models are very rare [28-31]. The effects of free-surface, boundary-layer existence and asymmetry effects due to heeling of a ship in a turn, are other influences which might be examined. Having discussed the problem of predicting hydrodynamic derivatives, it is also necessary to recognise that control derivatives are equally complex and require considerable insight and understanding if they too are to be predicted.

SHORT TERM AND LONG TERM RESEARCH OBJECTIVES

It is not possible to study all aspects of the manoeuvring problem in a single managed research programme of two years duration. The politically sensitive tasks are best left to discussion within IMO. Within universities, fundamental research and development should be pursued. The specific tasks undertaken depend upon matching available resources, in terms of the available financial support and research skills, to the higher ranked technical problems consistent with the introduction of some set of manoeuvrability standards. Ranking of the many technical problem areas indentified by the academics was undertaken, in this case, by a mix of industrial researchers and practitioners concerned with manoeuvring. Thereafter detailing of the possible solution strategies was provided by academic researchers and the proposals peer reviewed.

One particular identified aim for this research programme was the improvement of the theoretical method of calculating the hydrodynamic manoeuvring and control derivatives. In the previous section the existing methods of hydrodynamic derivative estimation were briefly described and their shortcomings highlighted. Thus before any consideration of enhanced simulation programs can be envisaged, improvement in the estimation of the derivatives must be accomplished first. This must not be achieved under very restrictive conditions. That is, the primary task must be to improve the estimation technique to give unambiguous results for a wide range of hull forms.

The objectives of the research programme may be divided into a number of short term and long term objectives as follows:

Short Term Objectives

- Improve hydrodynamic derivative prediction capability.

- Understand fluid flow phenomena associated with vortex formations and subsequent shedding downstream.

- Understand mechanism of hull and propeller-rudder interactions and its effect on the control derivatives.

- Extend the slender-body method to include vortex effects.

- Include free-surface and forward-speed effects.

- Investigate influence of boundary layer growth, along the hull, on manoeuvring derivatives.

- Ensure that the prediction method deals satisfactorily with changes in stern shape and skeg size.

Long Term Objectives

- Produce versatile simulation programs, which access experimentally derived hydrodynamic forces and moments, or predict the necessary terms directly from a knowledge of the hull form particulars.

- Understand the sensitivities of the predicted derivatives to local rather than global hull form changes.

- Develop 'manoeuvring-for-design' software, capable of modifying a ship hull form design, which gives rise to manoeuvring behaviour which satisfies prevailing manoeuvrability standards.

- Investigate the effectiveness of using closed loop control systems to synthetically improve the manual handling properties of the ship, in a similar way to aircraft 'fly-by-wire' systems.

THE ROLE OF THE *MOSES* MANAGED RESEARCH PROGRAMME

The content of the MOSES research programme is a consequence of iteration of the individual project proposals, a balancing of overall programme objectives and available financial resources, together with industrial assessment, evaluation and ranking of the rich and wide ranging set of proposals made available throughout the programme development. All these factors led to some changes in the emphasis and content of the programme now underway. Initially different aspects of control were included for two reasons. Firstly, it is an important topic in its own right. Secondly, where ship owner design specifications severely restrict modification of the hull form shape, so that hydrodynamic changes sufficient to provide motion stability and satisfaction of manoeuvrability standards are impermissible or impossible, a total systems approach might achieve the required behavioural characteristics through enhancement of the ship control system. However, since assessment of any proposed control strategy is dependent upon the quality of the ship motions predictor, control aspects of the manoeuvrability problem have generally been postponed to an anticipated Phase II managed programme. Consequently the current (Phase I) managed programme is biased towards hydrodynamic aspects of ship manoeuvring. The particular objectives of the tasks to be undertaken are now summarised, without presenting any of the details of the associated mathematical theory.

As already indicated in the section on Derivative Measurements and the Proposed IMO Standards, verification of any developed mathematical model is dependent upon quality experimental data to make comparison sensible. Equally important is the use of experimentation to provide insight regarding the physical nature of the hydrodynamic phenomena associated with a manoeuvring ship. Therefore the research objectives of the joint Newcastle-Glasgow Universities programme is to:

- Reanalyse original experimental data for the 'Mariner' and 'British Bombardier' hull forms investigated at ARE Haslar from 1969 through to 1971.

- Develop through mathematical and physical models a deeper understanding of the relevant aspects of the fluid flow which effects the behaviour of a manoeuvring ship.

- Identify appropriate enhancements to available hydrodynamic theory, to reduce differences between measured and predicted longitudinal distribution of hydrodynamic derivatives.

- Assess capability of the method(s) developed to provide improved predictions of the lateral hydrodynamic forces and moments acting on a bare hull due to drift angle and yaw rate.

As an adjunct to the theoretical investigations an experimental captive model programme is to be undertaken to provide measurements, on a number of different models, of:

- Sway forces and yaw moments for different drift angles and forward speeds.

- Pressure distributions at different stations for each drift angle and forward speed.

- Sufficient vorticity measurements to determine equi-vorticity contours for each yaw angle and forward speed, at selected stations along the hull.

Underwater filming of fluid flow will be undertaken simultaneously. The findings of the experimental programme will be used to specify the number, the location and strength of the vortex elements in several transverse planes along the hull.

The theoretical study will endeavour to enhance an earlier slender-body study [28] by including the influence of vortices of assumed strengths. In particular the effects of the expected differential in vortex strengths between the port and starboard sides due the drift angle will be studied. The theory will be used to reduce differences between the Haslar experimental data and earlier predictions [28], and be used with the new experimental data assuming the measured values of vortex strength. If necessary, more generalised fluid potential methods [32], developed to improve low-frequency motions of moored structures, will be used to reflect any important forward-speed and free-surface effects. Earlier work in Japan provides insight regarding the nature and position of five different kinds of vortex generation from a ship under manoeuvre [33,34].

Closely associated with the Newcastle-Glasgow tasks are the proposed studies of the first of two projects from the University of Southampton. In particular the first project research objectives are to:

- Extend a basic inviscid slender-body procedure to incorporate the effect of vortex sheets being convected (so as to 'wrap up' into concentrated vortices) downstream of bilge corners and lifting appendages.

- Extend the theory to simulate an asymmetric boundary layer at the after end of a ship.

- Undertake a comparison of different ship manoeuvring simulation programs and to assess the influence of the effect of new force and moment predictions derived from the fundamental hydrodynamic studies of the research programme.

- Employ the Southampton Horizontal Planar Motion Mechanism (HPMM) to provide global force and moment information for defined manoeuvres, including the fixed drift angle cases of the Newcastle-Glasgow study, and to measure force and moment sensitivities not being monitored elsewhere, for instance the effects of trim and draught changes.

The theoretical analysis requires the extension of the earlier two-dimensional analysis [35], to incorporate transverse cuts through external vortex sheets [36] with numerical instability avoided using an appropriate sub-vortex technique [37]. Boundary layer displacement effects will be incorporated using either an approximate method [38] or by considering an Oseen flow model [39]. The free-surface condition will also reflect Froude number effects.

Within the MOSES experimental research programme uncertainty in experimental measurements will be reduced by constructing at Glasgow University all the models to be used by the Newcastle-Glasgow, University College London (UCL) and Southampton researchers. Thus for each hull form of a selected model scale, the same mould, materials and method of construction will be undertaken by the same model maker. Test and measurement programmes have also been agreed in advance between the collaborating establishments to ensure comparability of the measured results. Similarly larger scale models will be used at Glasgow to study Reynolds number effects. Blockage effects are not considered a problem in either the Glasgow University or the Southampton Institute of Higher Education (SIHE) tanks because of the common agreed model scales.

The experimental programme described so far assumes a bare hull form. To complement this work a second University of Southampton project will investigate the influence of the hull and propeller on the development of rudder forces, together with the influence of rudder action on the propeller and hull in the larger University of Southampton wind tunnel. In particular, information will be sought on the effects of oblique flow and upstream hull form on a representative propeller-rudder combination and the forces developed on the hull.

This particular study represents an extension of earlier research based on propeller-rudder combinations examined in isolation [40,41]. Supporting theoretical work initially required extension of a modified lifting line approach [42] with a blade element-momentum propeller theory [43] to predict propeller induced velocities. Current work involves modifications to achieve better correlation and the blockage and upwash effects of the rudder on the propeller. The additional experimental data provided by the new experimental programme should allow extensions of the theory to include oblique flow effects with and without the hull form present. A simple four-quadrant model might be developed from low-speed experimental studies in the ahead condition.

In an officially affiliated UCL project, computer simulation and experimental testing at Haslar are being combined to develop new techniques for determining the control characteristics of a vessel, sufficient to allow simulation of different manoeuvres. Based on a vessel being towed, using a tow-line, a simple and inexpensive alternative procedure to HPMM testing or free-running model testing is sought, based on significant displacements rather than small forces [44,45]. The experimental derivative determination procedure under development allows the models to exhibit coupled motions. Once the technique is proven it will be used with the same models tested by the Newcastle-Glasgow and Southampton researchers at Glasgow University. Hence comparisons can also be made with the Haslar measurements. The precise work content of the new UCL project will be comfirmed once the current affiliated project is nearer to completion.

FINAL COMMENTS AND CONCLUSIONS

Space shortage has meant that the descriptions of the proposed managed research programme tasks have been exceedingly terse. The authors extend their apologies to their collaborators. However, the foregoing discussions should have convinced many readers of the complexity of the ship manoeuvring problems and the difficulty of the task of providing manoeuvring-for-design related software, to assess satisfaction of manoeuvrability standards adopted in the future. The physics of the various fluid-structure interactions identified are very complex and the general lack of detailed information on the development of the different forces generated means that a considerable amount of fundamental hydrodynamic research is still necessary. The quality of the simulation of a manoeuvring ship is totally dependent upon the quality of the hydrodynamic data utilised. At the present time consideration of the proposed IMO Resolution on manoeuvrability standards is taking place in earnest in the USA, Norway and Japan, but in comparison, little is being undertaken in Europe or the United Kingdom. However, some very positive responses to invitations to participate in the reported managed research programme have been received from such companies as Burness Corlett and Partners, YARD (now BAe SEMA), Lloyds Register of Shipping, Vosper Thorneycroft Ltd. and Swan Hunter International Ltd.

ACKNOWLEDGEMENTS

The programme outlined stems from humble beginnings. One of the authors, Grant Hearn, as an individual researcher, but now the Programme Manager, initially sought funding of a single Newcastle University based project. Therefore Mr. Don Lennard, Chief Executive and Managing Director of MTD Ltd., is thanked for his foresight and the encouragement of the principal author to develop the managed programme. Similarly, Emeritus Professor John B. Caldwell is thanked for his encouragement and assistance. However, the programme also exists because of the mutual enthusiasm of other academic colleagues, namely Dr. Atilla Incecik and Dr. Kamlesh Varyani (Glasgow University), Mr. Philip Wilson, Dr. John Wellicome and Dr. Tony Molland (Southampton University), Professor Roy Burcher (UCL), Dr. Malek Pourzanjani (Exeter University, now SIHE), Professor Mike Dove (Polytechnic South West, now SIHE), Dr. Geoffrey Roberts (RNEC, Manadon), Mr. John Chudley (Polytechnic South West) and Dr. Dracos Vassalos (Strathclyde University). Mr. Ian Brown of MTD Ltd., is also thanked for his helpfulness and general willingness to discuss all aspects of the programme development. SERC is duly thanked for the financial support provided, £350,000 of new research funding and £170,000 of affiliated research. The panel of industrial specialists, who helped to shape the research programme, are thanked for their many helpful comments and suggestions. Helen Clough is thanked for her assistance with the preparation of this paper. Finally responsibility for the statements and views expressed in this paper rest with the authors.

REFERENCES

1. 'Manoeuvrability of Ship and Manoeuvring Standards', *International Maritime Organisation* (IMO), DE 33/INF. 11, submitted by Japan, March 1990.

2. Wilson, P.A. and Lewis, W. 'Predicting Surface Ship Manoeuvring Characteristics for the Preliminary Design using a Desktop Computer', *J.N.S.*, Vol. 14., No. 1, pp. 51-58.

3. Khattab, O.M. 'Ship Handling in Harbours Using Real Time Simulation', *RINA International Conference on Ship Manoeuvrability*, Paper 11, London, May 1987.

4. Clarke, D., Gedling, P. and Hine, G. 'The Application of Manoeuvring Criteria in Hull Design using Linear Theory', *Trans. RINA.* Vol. 125, pp. 45-68, 1983.

5. Inoue, S., Hirano, M., Kijima, K. and Takashina, J. 'A Practical

Calculation Method of Ship Manoeuvring Motion'. *International Shipbuilding Progress*, Vol. 28, No. 325, pp. 207-222, Sept. 1981.

6. Lewis, G.D.W. 'A Computer Program to Predict Ship Manoeuvring in the Horizontal Plane', *Undergraduate Report SS201*, Department of Ship Science, University of Southampton, 1985.

7. Ankudinov, V.R., Miller, E.R., Alman, P.R., Jacobsen, B.K. and Conrad, R.E. 'Ship Manoeuvrability Assessment in Ship Design - Simulation Concept', *RINA International Conference on Ship Manoeuvrability*, Paper 19, London, May 1987.

8. Isherwood, R.M. 'Wind Resistance of Merchant Ships', *Trans. RINA*, Vol. 115, pp. 327-338, 1973.

9. English, J.W. 'The Design and Performance of Lateral Thruster Units for Ships', *Trans. RINA*, Vol. 105, pp. 251-278, 1963.

10. Pourzanjani, M.M.A., Zienkiewicz, H.K. and Flower, J.O. 'A Hybrid Method of Estimating Hydrodynamically Generated Forces for Use in Manoeuvring Simulation', *International Shipbuilding Progress*, Vol. 34, No. 399, pp. 207-216, 1987.

11. Clarke, D. 'The Effect of Skegs and Stern Shape on the Dynamic Stability of Ships', *Second International Conference on Manoeuvring and Control of Marine Craft*, University of Southampton, July 1992.

12. Hearn, G.E., Hills, W. and Sarıöz, K. 'Practical Seakeeping for Design: A Ship Shape Approach', *RINA Spring Meeting*, Paper No. 2, April 1991.

13. Sarıöz K., Hearn, G.E. and Hills, W. 'Practical Seakeeping for Design: An Optimise Approach', *PRADS 92*, University of Newcastle upon Tyne, May 1992.

14. Morse, R.V. and Price, D. 'Manoeuvring Characteristics of the Mariner Type Ship *U.S.S. Compass Island* in Calm Seas', *Sperry Gyroscope Company Publication No. GJ-2233-1019*, USA, December 1961.

15. Gertler, M. 'Final Analysis of First Phase of ITTC Standard Captive Model Test Programme', *Proceedings of 12th ITTC*, pp. 609-626, Rome, 1969.

16. Goodman, A., Gertler, M. and Kohl, R. 'Experimental Techniques and Methods of Analysis used at Hydronautics for Surface Ship Manoeuvring Predictions', *Proceedings of 11th ONR Symposium on Naval Hydrodynamics*, pp. 55-114, London, April 1976.

17. 'Report of the Ad-hoc Working Group on Manoeuvrability of Ships and Manoeuvring Standards', *International Maritime Organisation* (IMO), DE 35/WP.4, 25th March 1992.

18. Newman, J.N. 'Theoretical Methods in Ship Manoeuvring', *Proceedings of the International Symposium on Advances in Marine Technology*, Vol. 1, pp. 335-359, University of Trondheim, June 1979.

19. Tuck, E.O. 'Shallow-Water Flows Past Slender Bodies', *Journal of Fluid Mechanics*, Vol. 26, Part I, pp. 89-95, 1966.

20. Caitu, Z., Xiedong, Z., Xinheng W. and Guoping, Z., 'A Study on Ship Hydrodynamic Forces in Restricted Water', *Proceedings of International Conferences on Marine Simulation (MARSIM) & Ship Manoeuvrability (ICSM)*, pp. 477-484, Japan, June 1990.

21. Fujino, M. 'Manoeuvrability in Restricted Waters: State of the Art', *Department of Naval Architecture and Marine Engineering Report*, University of Michigan, No. 184, 1976.

22. Mikelis, N.E. and Price, W.G., 'Two Dimensional and Sway Added Mass Coefficients for Vessels Manoeuvring in Restricted Waters', *RINA Supplementary Papers*, Vol. 121, pp. 145-150, July 1979.

23. Mikelis, N.E. and Price, W.G., 'Calculational of Hydrodynamic Coefficients for a Body Manoeuvring in Restricted Waters Using a Three Dimensional Method', *RINA Supplementary Papers*, pp. 209-216, July 1981.

24. Inglis, R.B., Mikelis, N.E., Price, W.G. and Waite, J.B., 'Comparison of Restricted Open Water Ship Manoeuvring Acceleration Derivatives Evaluated by Finite Elements and Boundary Integral Methods', *International Shipbuilding Progress*, Vol. 28, No. 320, pp. 90-93, April 1981.

25. Renilson, M.R. and Ch'ng, P.W., 'The Effect of Bank Slope and Water Depth on the Forces on a Ship in Restricted Water', *Proceedings of International Conference on Marine Simulation (MARSIM) & Ship Manoeuvrability (ICSM)*, pp. 485-491, Japan, June 1990.

26. Lamb, Sir H. 'Hydrodynamics', 6th Edition, *Cambridge University Press*, London, 1932, In particular see Articles 124 and 126.

27. Munk, M.M., 'The Aerodynamic Forces on Airship Hulls', *National Advisory Committee for Aeronautics*, Report No. 184, Washington D.C., 1924.

28. Clarke, D., 'A Two-Dimensional Strip Method for Surface Ship Hull Derivatives: Comparison of Theory with Experiments', *Journal of Mechanical Engineering Science*, Vol. 14, No. 7, Paper 8, Supplementary Issue, 1972.

29. Burcher, R.K., 'Developments in Ship Manoeuvrability', *Trans. RINA*, Vol. 114, pp. 1-32, 1972.

30. Burcher, R.K., 'Captive Model Tests with a Segmented Mariner Hull Form', *Proceedings 13th ITTC*, Berlin-Hamburg, pp. 107-120, 1972.

31. Beukelman, W. and Gerritsma, J., 'The Longitudinal Distributions of Low Frequency Hydrodynamic Derivatives for Lateral Motions in Shallow Water', *Ship Hydromechanics Laboratory Report*, No. 562A, Delft University of Technology, September 1983.

32. Hearn, G.E., Tong, K.C. and Lau, S.M., 'Sensitivity of Wave Drift Damping Coefficient Predictions to the Hydrodynamic Analysis Models used in the Added Resistance Gradient Method', *Journal of Offshore Mechanics and Arctic Engineering*, Vol. 11, No. 4, pp. 337-348, November 1988.

33. Tanaka, H., Kawakami, I., Ueda, T. and Takahashi, K., 'Experimental Studies on Trailing Vortices of a Ship', *Proceedings 2nd International Symposium on Practical Design in Shipbuilding (PRADS)*, pp. 295-302, Tokyo & Seoul, 1983.

34. Nonaka, K., Fuwa, T. and Nimura, T., 'Measurements of Wake Flow and Hydrodynamic Force Distribution on a Ship Model with Drift Angle', *Trans. West-Japan Society of Naval Architects*, 1st Report, No. 71, pp. 29, October 1983, 2nd Report, No. 72, pp. 197-212, August 1986.

35. Wellicome, J.F. and Mirza, S., 'Evaluation of Forces and Moments on a Manoeuvring Ship Using Slender Body Theory', *Proceedings RINA International Conference on Ship Manoeuvrability - Prediction and Achievement*, Vol. I, Paper 27, April/May 1987.

36. Newman, J.N. and Wu, T.Y., 'A Generalised Slender-Body Theory for Fish-Like Forms', *Journal of Fluid Mechanics*, Vol. 57, Part 4, pp. 673-693, 1973.

37. Maskew, B., 'Subvortex Technique for the Close Approach to a Discretised Vortex Sheet', *Journal of Aircraft*, Vol. 14, No. 2, pp. 188-193, 1977.

38. Gadd, G.E., 'The Approximate Calculation of Turbulent Boundary Layer Development on Ship Hulls', *Trans. RINA*, Vol. 13, pp. 59-71, 1971.

39. Price, W.G. and Tan, M., 'The Calculations of Fluid Actions on Arbitrary Shaped Submerged Bodies Using Viscous Boundary Elements', *Proceedings of 8th Symposium on Naval Hydrodynamics*, pp. 801-814, University of Michigan, USA, 1990.

40. Molland, A.F. and Turnock, S.R., 'The Design, Construction and Calibration of a Thrust and Torque Dynamometer for a Wind Tunnel Propeller Model', *Ship Science Report*, No. 43, University of Southampton, December 1990.

41. Molland, A.F. and Turnock, S.R., 'The Prediction of Ship Rudder Performance Characteristics in the Presence of a Propeller', *Second International Conference on Manoeuvring and Control of Marine Craft*, University of Southampton, July 1992.

42.   Molland, A.F., 'A Method for Determining the Free-Stream Charac-
      teristics of Ship Skeg-Rudders', *International Shipbuiding Progress*,
      Vol. 32, pp. 138-150, June 1985.

43.   Eckhard, M.K. and Morgan, W.G., 'A Propeller Design Method',
      Trans. SNAME, Vol. 63, pp. 325-374, 1955.

44.   Zhang, H., 'Control Characteristics of a Floating Vehicle from Towed
      Model Tests', *SERC/MoD Progress Report*, Department of Mechan-
      ical Engineering, University College London, May 1991.

45.   Zhang, H., 'Manoeuvring of Ships', *SERC/MoD Progress Report*,
      Department of Mechanical Engineering, University College London,
      April 1992.

Development of An Adaptive Track Keeping Module Controlled by 16 bit Single Chip Computer

J.-H. Jiang, J. Lu, X.-R. Lu

Department of Marine Electrical Engineering, Dalian Maritime University, Dalian 116024, P.R. China

ABSTRACT

This paper presents the development and the implementation of an adaptive track keeping module controlled by a 16-bit single-chip computer. In the track keeping loop, the self-tuning strategy is considered while in the heading control loop a fuzzy controller is designed. The developed adaptive track keeping module was implemented in the laboratory and tested on a real ship. The test result shows that the cross error of track is less than 100 meters.

INTRODUCTION

At present more and more ships are equipped with adaptive autopilots. It is a foregone conclusion that the conventional PID autopilots are being alternated by adaptive autopilots. Although this replacement is quite recent, some new categories such as fuzzy autopilots have been developed [1] ~ [3]. In this paper the hybrid scheme of adaptive and fuzzy control is presented. The autopilot system has three control loops. The inner loop is the conventional feedback control loop of rudder angle. The intermediate loop contains the fuzzy controller of heading. The outer loop is the track keeping loop which contains a robust self-tuning controller and a calculator of ship position. The block diagram of the hybrid control system for marine autopilots is shown in Figure 1. The main design considerations of this scheme are as follows:

(1) The parameters of dynamics of ship-motion during track keeping are varied due to changing of rudder angle, ship speed, draught and load. There are random disturbances (such as wave and wind) and certainty disturbance (such as current) applied to the ship, the random disturbances are nonzero

mean noises generally.   Obviously the parameters of dynamics of ship motion and the disturbances applied to the ship are indeterminate.   In order to obtain good control behaviour under such conditions, a robust and adaptive control is necessary for track keeping loop.

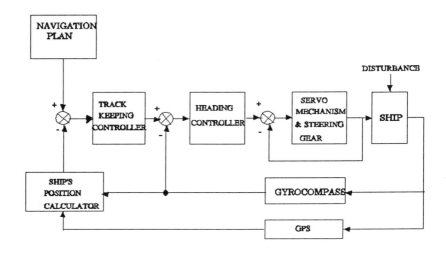

Figure 1: The block diagram of the hybrid control system for marine autopilots

(2) There are various approaches for adaptive autopilot design [4]~[9]. However, at present most of the control strategies of adaptive autopilot in market are self-tuning control (STC) and model reference adaptive control (MRAS).   MRAS method is the rapid adaption to defined input signals but may cause problems for the adaptation under the condition of the presence of significant noise signal [10].   Thus it is suitable for track manoeuvring change (defined input signals) and worse performance in track keeping (presence of significant noise signal of waves, winds and current).   STC can achieve parameter identification and control according to the change of parameters of the ship dynamics and the disturbance model, obviously it is suitable for track keeping, but it is not as good as MRAS in track manoeuvring change.   To design the track keeping loop, we select the STC scheme.   The reason for the choice is that it is suitable for track keeping which is a major function of the autopilot.   In order to improve control behaviour in track change manoeuvring, it is critical to choose an appropriate performance criterion.   We choose the explicit quadratic

performance criterion with limitation on the output change rate for adaptive algorithm of STC which has been verified feasibly [9][11]. In addition, the modelling of the disturbances are considered so that the designed track keeping loop is robust and adaptive.

(3) The adaptive autopilots are designed based on the mathematical model of a ship. However the model of ship is complicated, nonlinear and of high order. In order to reduce the on-line solution time, the model is simplified frequently.   This may cause unmodelling and the reducing of control precision. To overcome this problem the fuzzy control may be used. In a fuzzy control system, human experience is transformed into executable rules. The more experience is obtained, the better rules can be applied. For the design of track keeping autopilot, the experience of heading (course) control of helmsman is much richer than that of track keeping control. Thus in this paper, the fuzzy control of heading control was considered rather than track keeping control.

THE FUZZY CONTROLLER OF HEADING

The block diagram of the fuzzy controller of heading is shown in Figure 2, where E is the heading error and C is the change in error between current and previous heading error (i.e. derivate of E). The values of e and c are the fuzzy values of E and C.

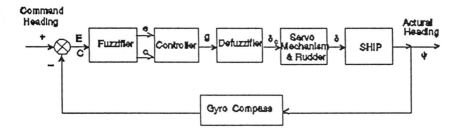

Figure 2: The block diagram of fuzzy controller of heading

The fuzzy controller is designed with revised factor α which changes between 0 and 1. The output of controller g is given by

$$g = \alpha e + (1-\alpha)c \qquad (1)$$

In equation (1) α is the linear function of parameter b_1 of ship dynamics. b_1 can be obtained by identifying the ship model, so that α is revised in accordance with b_1. Moreover the control rule of the controller is adjusted. After defuzzying the command rudder angle δ_c is input to servo mechanism and steering gear.

The rule-base or decision table, of which Table 1 is an example, is obtained in accordance with the membership function which is acquired from the experience of expert helmsmen. On the domains of definition of E, eight fuzzy sets: NL, NM, NS, NZ, PZ, PS, PM and PL are specified, while for C and δ_c are seven: NL, NM, NS, ZO, PS, PM and PL, where N, P, L, M, S, and Z(ZO) are negative, positive, large, medium, small and zero respectively.

Table 1: A typical decision table

\e g c|	-6	-5	-4	-3	-2	-1	-0	+0	1	2	3	4	5	6
-6	6	5	4	3	4	3	1	2	1	1	0	0	-1	-1
-5	4	4	3	3	3	2	1	1	1	0	0	0	0	0
-4	4	4	4	3	2	2	2	2	1	0	0	0	-2	-2
-3	3	3	3	3	2	2	2	1	1	0	0	-1	-2	-2
-2	4	3	4	3	2	1	1	1	0	0	0	-1	-2	-2
-1	4	3	2	2	1	1	1	0	0	0	-1	-1	-2	-3
0	4	3	2	2	1	0	0	0	-1	-1	-1	-2	-2	-3
1	4	3	1	1	0	0	0	-1	-1	-2	-2	-3	-4	-4
2	4	3	1	0	0	0	-1	-1	-1	-2	-2	-3	-4	-4
3	3	2	0	0	0	-1	-1	-1	-1	-2	-3	-3	-4	-4
4	4	2	0	0	0	-1	-1	-1	-1	-2	-3	-3	-4	-4
5	2	1	0	0	-1	-1	-1	-1	-2	-2	-2	-2	-3	-4
6	2	2	0	0	-1	-1	-2	-2	-2	-3	-3	-4	-5	-6

The universes of discourse of E, C, δ_c, e, c and g are:

E: [-3.6,3.6] degrees;

C: [-4.8,4.8] degrees;

δ_c: [-28,28] degrees;

e, c and g: [-n, -n+1,...., 0, 1,...., n]; n is selected as 6.

THE TRACK KEEPING LOOP

For the design of the track keeping loop it is important to select the model of the actual control process for track keeping containing the effect of both control and disturbances. Two different models were selected and all have good control performance according to the real ship tests. The one is based on the principle of cross track error [11] and the other is based on the principle of course revising of track-keeping (i.e. automatic follow-up mode) [3].

According to the principle of cross track error, the transfer function of ship model with output of cross track error d and inputs of command heading ψ and disturbances are [11]

$$G_{d\psi}(s) = \frac{d(s)}{\psi(s)} = \frac{V(1-\frac{K_\beta}{K}s)}{s} = \frac{K_1+K_2s}{s} \qquad (2)$$

$$G_{df}(s) = \frac{d(s)}{f(s)} = \frac{K_1'+K_2's}{s}f(s) \qquad (3)$$

$$\therefore d(s) = \frac{K_1+K_2s}{s}\psi(s) + \frac{K_1'+K_2's}{s}f(s) \qquad (4)$$

where V is the speed of ship with respect to sea water, K and K_β are the K index of first order Nomoto's model of yaw and drift.

The principle of course revising of track-keeping is shown in Figure 3, where TR_{wc} is the ship track angle in wind and current, ψ is the given heading, α_w is the leeway angle of wind, α_c is the leeway angle of current and α_{wc} is the resultant leeway angle of wind and current. If the actual heading is always ψ, the ship moves from point A to point B during the period of a sample. The leeway angle α, i.e. drift angle, appears. It causes the ship to move off the plan track. In order to reduce yawing, the course revising of track-keeping is adopted. It takes into account the influence of wind and current and calculates revisory amount of course as shown in

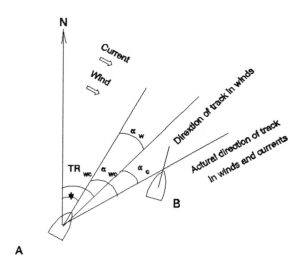

Figure 3: The actual moving trace of interfered ship

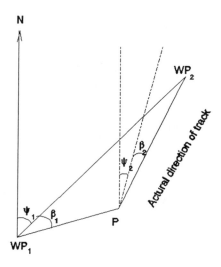

Figure 4: The principle of revising of track-keeping

Figure 4, where WP_1 is the departure point and WP_2 is the destination point
or waypoint. After a Δt time, the ship navigates with heading ψ to point
P due to the influence of drift angle β_1. Considering drift angle β_2, the
developed STC controller can identify the parameters of disturbance model
and gives the command heading ψ_2, not the bearing of the line between point
P and WP_2. Let drift angle β of the ship be output y, and the yaw rate of

the ship be input u, according to the following ship dynamics of equations (5) and (6) and simplifying the first order model of equation (7) can be obtained.

$$T_1 T_2 \frac{d^2\psi}{dt^2} + (T_1+T_2)\frac{d\psi}{dt} + \psi = K\delta + KT_3\frac{d\delta}{dt} \tag{5}$$

$$T_1 T_2 \frac{d^2\beta}{dt^2} + (T_1+T_2)\frac{d\beta}{dt} + \beta = K_\beta\delta + K_\beta T_3\beta\frac{d\beta}{dt} \tag{6}$$

$$G_{\beta\psi} = \frac{y(S)}{u(S)} = \frac{K_\beta'}{1+K_\beta' S} \tag{7}$$

Considering random disturbance f(S), the general dynamics model is

$$y(S) = \frac{K_\beta'}{1+T_\beta' S} u(S) + \frac{K_c}{1+K_\beta' S} f(S) \tag{8}$$

Equations (4) and (8) are two different models of the actual control process for track-keeping containing the effect of both control and disturbance based on two different principles of track-keeping. These two models were examined using the same self-tuning control strategy as real ship test, as shown in Figure 5 and 6. It was justified that these two models are feasible and the latter is better than the former. Thus equation (8) is adopted which is discretised in the form

$$y_t = a_1 y_{t-1} + \ldots + a_n y_{t-n} + b_1 u_{t-1} + \ldots + b_n u_{t-n} + \eta_t + c_1 \eta_{t-1} + \ldots + c_n \eta_{t-n} \tag{9}$$

where y_t is the output of the drift angle

u_t is the input of the heading

η_t is nonzero mean value because of the effect of the lateral continuous wind and current.

In order to obtain the unbiased estimation of the identification, equation (9) is modified into

$$y_t = a_1 y_{t-1} + \ldots + a_n y_{t-n} + b_1 u_{t-1} + \ldots + b_n u_{t-n} + \xi + c_1 \xi_{t-1} + \ldots + c_n \xi_{t-n} + w \tag{10}$$

where ξ_t is the independent random variable with zero mean value caused by

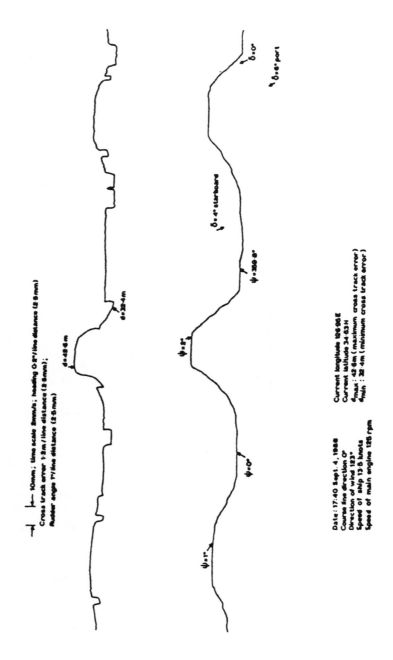

Figure 5: The cross track error and heading graph of real ship test based on the principle of cross track error

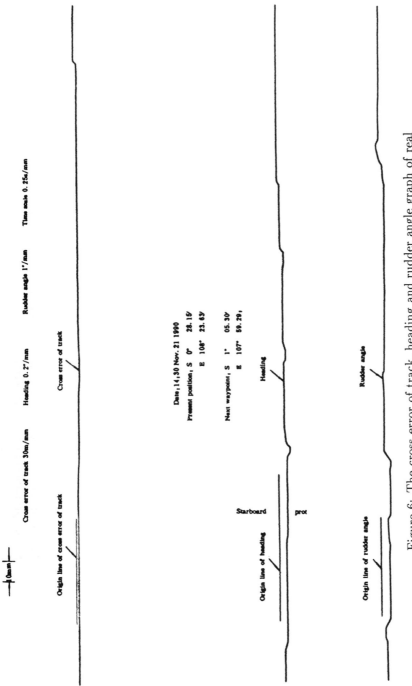

Figure 6: The cross error of track, heading and rudder angle graph of real ship test based on the principle of course revising

random wind, wave disturbances and observation error
w is the static random disturbances of the lateral continuous wind and
current.

The recursive extended least-square algorithm with forget factor for identifying the parameters of ship dynamics and the disturbances (such as a_i, b_i, c_i and w in equation (10) where $i=1, 2, ..., n$) is used as the on-line identification method.   In order to obtain good performance in track manoeuvring change, the following performance criterion has the explicit output rate limit

$$J = E\{(1-p_1)y_{t+1}^2 + p_1(y_{t+1}-y_t)^2 + ru_t^2 / Y_t, U_t\} \qquad (11)$$

where r is the weight parameter of control
   p_1 is the weight parameter of output rate limit, $0 \le p_1 \le 1$
   E is the mean expectation operator
   $Y_t = \{y_t, y_{t-1}, ...\}$
   $U_t = \{u_t, u_{t-1}, ...\}$.

The following control algorithm can be derived from equation (10) and (11)

$$u_t = -\frac{Z(PC-A)y_t + \lambda d}{ZB + QC} \qquad (12)$$

where $\lambda = 1 + Q(1)/B(1); P = 1 - p_1 Z^{-1}; Q = r/b_1; A = 1 - a_1 Z^{-1} - .... - a_n Z^{-n};$
   $B = b_1 Z^{-1} + ... + b_n Z^{-n}; C = 1 + c_1 Z^{-1} + ... + c_n Z^{-n}.$

IMPLEMENTATION OF THE ADAPTIVE TRACK KEEPING MODULE

The block diagram of the adaptive track keeping module is shown in Figure 7. It contains an Intel 8094BH 16-bit single-chip microcomputer, clock, RAM, EPROM, decoder, A/D converter, tristate buffer and extender, etc. Compared with an 8-bit chip 8031 [11], it has higher precision, higher computing speed and reliability.

The serial port of the 8094BH chip receives signals of the instantaneous longitude and latitude of ship from GPS or NNSS. The heading signal ψ is obtained from the repeater of gyrocompass.   Using the angle-digital transmitter the shaft angle code from the synchro of repeater can generate a group of state codes and analog signals which provide the digital heading

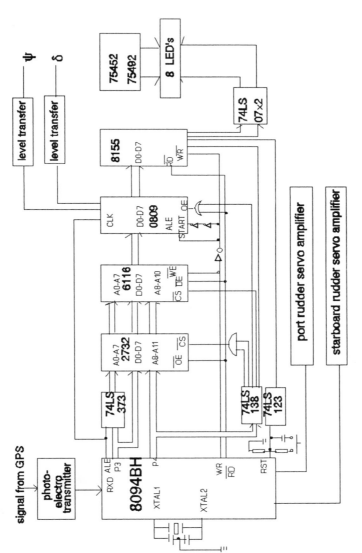

Figure 7: Diagram of the track keeping module

value to 8094BH chip after A/D conversion of 0809 chip. The rudder angle signal δ which is obtained from the potentiometer of rudder feedback is converted to 0 ~ 5 volts through level transmitter and then sent to A/D converter 0809 chip. The 2.5 volt is correspondent to zero rudder angle while 0 and 5 volts to -35 and +35 rudder angle respectively. 8094BH chip offers the switching output signals for port and starboard rudder servo amplifier using the method of pulse-width modulation (PWM) with constant period and 1/256 resolution. If the driving signal of rudder servo amplifier is not PWM signals, whereas the analogue output signals are necessary, the additional buffer and filter must be inserted as shown in Figure 8. The flow chart of software of the module is shown in Figure 9.

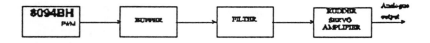

Figure 8: The block diagram of D/A conversion

CONCLUSIONS

This paper has considered a hybrid scheme of adaptive and fuzzy control of track keeping module controlled by 16-bit single-chip microcomputer. There are two improvements in this scheme than that described in [11]. For track keeping loop, the robust self-tuning controller was designed using the model of control process based on the principle of course revising of track-keeping instead of that of cross track error. For heading control loop, the fuzzy controller was adopted. Comparing the results of real ship tests of Figures (5) and (6), it is shown that this scheme provides better performance due to higher track-keeping accuracy and less heading change which means that the propulsion energy of the ship can be reduced and the speed of the ship can be increased.

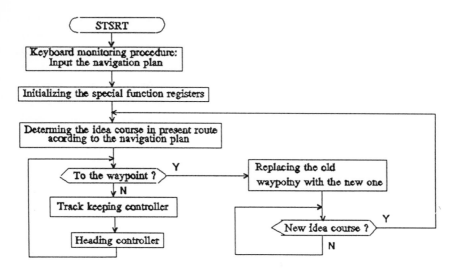

Figure 9: The flow chart of software of the module

REFERENCES

1. Sutton, R. and Towill, D.R. 'A Fuzzy Autopilot Model for Ship Control', in Colloquium on the use of Expert System in Control Engineering, *IEE Colloquium (Digest)* No. 27, pp 4/1 ~ 4/4, London, 1987.
2. Amerongen, J.van., Nauta Lemke, H.R. van and Veen, J.C.T. van der. 'An Autopilot for Ships Designed with Fuzzy Sets'. *Digital Computer Applications to process control,* ed. Van Nauta Lemke, pp. 479-488, IFAC and North-Holland Publishing Company, 1977.
3. Jiang, J.H. and Lu, X.R. 'Development of Adaptive Track-keeping module with the Course Loop of Fuzzy Control' in IMECE/91, pp.187 - 194, *Proceedings of the International Maritime Electrotechnical Conference & Exhibition,* Shanghai, China, 1991.
4. Ohtsu, K., Honigome, M. and Kitagama, G. 'A new ship's autopilot design through a stochastic model', *Automatica*, 15, pp255-268, 1979.
5. Källström, C.G., Åström, K.J. and Thoreu, N.E. 'Adaptive autopilots for tankers', *Automatica*, 15, pp 241-254, 1979.
6. Amerongen, J.V. and Udink ten Cate, A.J. 'Model reference adaptive autopilots for ships', *Automatica*, 11, pp 441-449, 1975.
7. Amerongen, J.V. 'Adaptive steering for ships—A model reference approach', *Automatica*, 20, pp 3-14, 1984.

8. Holzhüter, T. and Stranch, H. 'A commercial adaptive autopilot for ships: design and operational experiences', *Automatic Control World Congress, 1987, Selected Papers from the 10th Triennial World Congress of the IFAC*, Vol. VI, pp. 233-238, 1987.

9. Lu, X.R. and Zhang, B.S. 'An adaptive algorithm for ship's adaptive autopilot design', *Automatic Control World Congress, 1987, Selected papers from the 10th triennial world congress of the IFAC*, Vol VI, pp 239-247, 1987.

10. Isermann, R., Lachmann, K.-H. and Matko, D. *Adaptive Control Systems* Prentice Hall, New York ●London ●Torono ●Sydney ●Tokyo ●Singapore, 1992.

11. Lu, X.R., Jiang,J.H. and Huang, Y.X. 'Design of a self-tuning adaptive track-keeping control system for ships', in the First International Conference on Manoeuvring and Control of Marine Craft, Exeter, U.K./90 (Ed. Pourzanjani, M.M.A. and Roberts, G.N.), pp. 178 - 192, *Manoeuvring and Control of Marine Craft*, 1991.